HANDBOOK OF

MATHEMATICAL TABLES

AND FORMULAS

—

BURINGTON

HANDBOOK OF
MATHEMATICAL TABLES
AND FORMULAS

COMPILED BY

RICHARD STEVENS BURINGTON, Ph. D.

ASSISTANT PROFESSOR OF MATHEMATICS

CASE SCHOOL OF APPLIED SCIENCE

CLEVELAND

HANDBOOK PUBLISHERS, INC.

SANDUSKY, OHIO

This HANDBOOK OF MATHEMATICAL TABLES AND FORMU-
LAS *forms the appendix of* LANGE'S HANDBOOK OF CHEMISTRY—
*a reference volume of nearly 2000 pages of chemical and physical
data useful in laboratory work and manufacturing. Published
and for sale by* HANDBOOK PUBLISHERS, INC., SANDUSKY,
OHIO. U. S. A.

PRINTED IN THE UNITED STATES OF AMERICA

PREFACE

This book has been compiled to meet the needs of students in mathematics and other subjects requiring mathematical computations. At the same time the contents are sufficiently inclusive to supply the mathematical requirements of the worker in other fields of science, such as chemistry, physics and engineering.

In the first part of the book, a careful summary of the more important formulas and theorems of algebra, trigonometry, analytic geometry, calculus and vector analysis is given. A comprehensive table of series, derivatives and integrals is included.

In the second part, the usual logarithmic and trigonometric tables up to five places, both in degrees and radians, are given. Numerous short tables are presented including those of natural logarithms, exponential and hyperbolic functions, probability integrals, logarithms of Gamma functions, interest and annuities as well as those of squares, cubes and other numerical quantities. In the preparation of the tables, vertical lines separating the columns are largely eliminated, it being felt that their absence would enhance the legibility of the page. Ease and convenience in using the tables have been considered as desirable objects; and the material organized with that end in view.

To insure accuracy in the tabular material, proof of the entire book has been read against the final electro plates.

The author wishes to acknowledge his indebtedness to Professor C. C. MacDuffee of Ohio State University, to Professor F. B. Wiley of Denison University and to Dean T. M. Focke of Case School of Applied Science for their encouragement and helpful criticism. The writer is also indebted to various members of the faculty at Case School of Applied Science for their constructive suggestions, and to the publishers and printers who have cooperated in the preparation of the book.

R. S. B.

Cleveland, Ohio, January 9, 1933.

Greek Alphabet

A	α	Alpha	N	ν	Nu
B	β	Beta	Ξ	ξ	Xi
Γ	γ	Gamma	O	o	Omicron
Δ	δ	Delta	Π	π	Pi
E	ε	Epsilon	P	ρ	Rho
Z	ζ	Zeta	Σ	σ	Sigma
H	η	Eta	T	τ	Tau
Θ	θ	Theta	Y	υ	Upsilon
I	ι	Iota	Φ	φ	Phi
K	κ	Kappa	X	χ	Chi
Λ	λ	Lambda	Ψ	ψ	Psi
M	μ	Mu	Ω	ω	Omega

TABLE OF CONTENTS

Frontispiece. Mathematical Symbols and Abbreviations.

PART ONE. FORMULAS AND THEOREMS FROM ELEMENTARY

MATHEMATICS.

PART TWO. TABLES.

Index.

Mathematical Symbols and Abbreviations

Symbol	Meaning	Symbol	Meaning
$+$	Plus or Positive	sec	Secant
$-$	Minus or Negative	csc	Cosecant
$\pm$	Plus or minus / Positive or negative	vers	Versed sine
$\mp$	Minus or plus / Negative or positive	covers	Coversed sine
$\times$ or $\cdot$	Multiplied by	exsec	Exsecant
$\div$ or $:$	Divided by	$\sin^{-1} a$ or arc sin a	Anti-sine a / Angle whose sine is a / Inverse sine a
$=$ or $::$	Equals, as	sinh	Hyperbolic sine
$\neq$, $\neq$	Does not equal	cosh	Hyperbolic cosine
$\cong$	Equals approximately / Congruent	tanh	Hyperbolic tangent
$>$	Greater than	$\sinh^{-1} a$ or arc sinh a	Anti-hyperbolic sine a / Angle whose hyperbolic sine is a
$<$	Less than	$P(x,y)$	Rect. coörd. of point P
$\geq$	Greater than or equal to	$P(r, \theta)$	Polar coörd. of point P
$\leq$	Less than or equal to	$f(x), F(x)$ or $\Phi(x)$	Function of x
$\sim$	Similar to	Δy	Increment of y
$\therefore$	Therefore	$\doteq$ or $\rightarrow$	Approaches as a limit
$\sqrt{}$	Square root	Σ	Summation of
$\sqrt[n]{}$	nth root	∞	Infinity
a^n	nth power of a	dy	Differential of y
log or $\log_{10}$	Common logarithm / Briggsian "	$\dfrac{dy}{dx}$ or $f'(x)$	Derivative of $y=f(x)$ with respect to x
ln or $\log_e$ or log	Natural logarithm / Hyperbolic " / Napierian "	$\dfrac{d^2y}{dx^2}$ or $f''(x)$	Second deriv. of $y=f(x)$ with respect to x
e or ϵ	Base (2.718) of natural system of logarithms	$\dfrac{d^n y}{dx^n}$ or $f^{(n)}(x)$	nth deriv. of $y=f(x)$ with respect to x
π	Pi (3.1416)	$\dfrac{\partial z}{\partial x}$	Partial derivative of z with respect to x
$\angle$	Angle	$\dfrac{\partial^2 z}{\partial x\, \partial y}$	Second partial deriv. of z with respect to y and x
$\perp$	Perpendicular to		
$\parallel$	Parallel to	$\displaystyle\int$	Integral of
$a°$	a degrees (angle)	$\displaystyle\int_a^b$	Integral between the limits a and b
a'	a minutes (angle) / a prime		
a''	a seconds (angle) / a second / a double-prime	j or i	Imaginary quantity $(\sqrt{-1})$, $i^2 = -1$
a'''	a third / a triple-prime	$x = a + jb$	Symbolic vector notation
a_n	a sub n	$n! = 1\cdot 2\cdot 3 \cdots n$	
sin	Sine		
cos	Cosine		
tan	Tangent		
cot or ctn	Cotangent		

PART ONE

Formulas and Theorems from Elementary Mathematics

I. ALGEBRA

1. Fundamental Laws.

(**a**) Commutative law: $a + b = b + a$, $ab = ba$.

(**b**) Associative law: $a + (b + c) = (a + b) + c$, $a(bc) = (ab)c$.

(**c**) Distributive law: $a(b + c) = ab + ac$.

2. Laws of Exponents.

$$a^x \cdot a^y = a^{x+y}, \quad (ab)^x = a^x \cdot b^x, \quad (a^x)^y = a^{xy}.$$

$$a^0 = 1 \text{ if } a \neq 0, \quad a^{-x} = \frac{1}{a^x}, \quad \frac{a^x}{a^y} = a^{x-y}.$$

$$a^{\frac{x}{y}} = \sqrt[y]{a^x}, \quad a^{\frac{1}{y}} = \sqrt[y]{a}.$$

3. Operations with Zero.

$$a - a = 0, \quad a \cdot 0 = 0 \cdot a = 0.$$

If $a \neq 0$, $\dfrac{0}{a} = 0$, $0^a = 0$, $a^0 = 1$. (Division by zero undefined.)

4. Complex Numbers (a number of the form $a + bi$, where a and b are real).

$$i = \sqrt{-1}, \quad i^2 = -1, \quad i^3 = -i, \quad i^4 = 1, \quad i^5 = i, \text{ etc.}$$

$a + bi = c + di$, if and only if $a = c$, $b = d$.

$$(a + bi) + (c + di) = (a + c) + (b + d)i.$$

$$(a + bi)(c + di) = (ac - bd) + (ad + bc)i.$$

$$\frac{a+bi}{c+di} = \frac{(a+bi)(c-di)}{(c+di)(c-di)} = \frac{ac+bd}{c^2+d^2} + \frac{bc-ad}{c^2+d^2} i.$$

5. Laws of Logarithms (See explanation of Table 1).

If M, N, b are positive numbers and $b \neq 1$:

$$\log_b MN = \log_b M + \log_b N, \qquad \log_b \frac{M}{N} = \log_b M - \log_b N,$$

$$\log_b M^p = p \cdot \log_b M, \qquad \log_b \sqrt[q]{M} = \frac{1}{q} \cdot \log_b M,$$

$$\log_b \left(\frac{1}{M}\right) = -\log_b M, \qquad \log_b b = 1, \quad \log_b 1 = 0.$$

Change of base of Logarithms $(c \neq 1)$:

$$\log_b M = \log_c M \cdot \log_b c = \frac{\log_c M}{\log_c b}.$$

6. Binomial Theorem $(n$ a positive integer).

$$(a + b)^n = a^n + na^{n-1} b + \frac{n(n-1)}{2!} a^{n-2} b^2$$

$$+ \frac{n(n-1)(n-2)}{3!} a^{n-3} b^3 + \cdots + nab^{n-1} + b^n,$$

where

$$n! = \underline{|n} = 1 \cdot 2 \cdot 3 \cdots (n-1)n.$$

7. Expansions and Factors.

$$(a \pm b)^2 = a^2 \pm 2ab + b^2.$$

$$(a \pm b)^3 = a^3 \pm 3a^2 b + 3ab^2 \pm b^3.$$

$$(a + b + c)^2 = a^2 + b^2 + c^2 + 2ab + 2ac + 2bc.$$

$$a^2 - b^2 = (a - b)(a + b).$$

$$a^3 - b^3 = (a - b)(a^2 + ab + b^2).$$

$$a^3 + b^3 = (a + b)(a^2 - ab + b^2).$$

$$a^n - b^n = (a - b)(a^{n-1} + a^{n-2} b + \cdots + b^{n-1}).$$

$$a^n - b^n = (a + b)(a^{n-1} - a^{n-2} b + \cdots - b^{n-1}), \text{ for } n \text{ an}$$
even integer.

$$a^n + b^n = (a + b)(a^{n-1} - a^{n-2} b + \ldots + b^{n-1}), \text{ for } n \text{ an}$$
odd integer.

$$a^4 + a^2 b^2 + b^4 = (a^2 + ab + b^2)(a^2 - ab + b^2).$$

8. Ratio and Proportion.

If $a : b = c : d$ or $\dfrac{a}{b} = \dfrac{c}{d}$, then $ad = bc$, $\dfrac{a}{c} = \dfrac{b}{d}$.

If $\dfrac{a}{b} = \dfrac{c}{d} = \dfrac{e}{f} = \cdots = k$, then

$$k = \frac{a + c + e + \cdots}{b + d + f + \cdots} = \frac{pa + qc + re + \cdots}{pb + qd + rf + \cdots}.$$

9. Constant Factor of Proportionality (or Variation), k.

If y varies directly as x, or y is proportional to x,

$$y = kx.$$

If y varies inversely as x, or y is inversely proportional to x,

$$y = \frac{k}{x}.$$

If y varies jointly as x and z,

$$y = kxz.$$

If y varies directly as x and inversely as z,

$$y = \frac{kx}{z}.$$

10. Arithmetic Progression.

$$a, \quad a + d, \quad a + 2d, \quad a + 3d, \cdots.$$

If a is the first term, d the common difference, n the number of terms, l the last term and s the sum of n terms,

$$l = a + (n - 1) d, \quad s = \frac{n}{2} (a + l).$$

The *arithmetic mean* of a and b is $(a + b)/2$.

11. Geometric Progression.

$$a, ar, ar^2, ar^3, \cdots.$$

If a is the first term, r the common ratio, n the number of terms, l the last term, and S_n the sum of n terms,

$$l = ar^{n-1}, \quad S_n = a \left(\frac{r^n - 1}{r - 1} \right) = \frac{rl - a}{r - 1}.$$

If $r^2 < 1$, S_n approaches the limit S_∞ as n increases without limit,

$$S_\infty = \frac{a}{1 - r}.$$

The *geometric mean* of a and b is $\sqrt{ab}$.

12. Harmonic Progression.

A sequence of numbers whose reciprocals form an arithmetic progression is called an *harmonic* progression. Thus,

$$\frac{1}{a}, \quad \frac{1}{a+d}, \quad \frac{1}{a+2d}, \quad \cdots$$

The *harmonic mean* of a and b is $2ab/(a+b)$.

13. Permutations. Each different arrangement of all or a part of a set of things is called a *permutation*. The number of permutations of n things taken r at a time is

$$_nP_r = n(n-1)(n-2)\cdots(n-r+1) = \frac{n!}{(n-r)!},$$

where

$$n! = n(n-1)(n-2)\cdots(1).$$

14. Combinations. Each of the groups or relations which can be made by taking part or all of a set of things, without regard to the arrangement of the things in a group, is called a *combination*. The number of combinations of n things taken r at a time is

$$_nC_r = \binom{n}{r} = \frac{_nP_r}{r!} = \frac{n(n-1)\cdots(n-r+1)}{r(r-1)\cdots(1)} = \frac{n!}{r!(n-r)!}.$$

15. Probability. If an event may occur in p ways, and may fail in q ways, all ways being equally likely, the *probability* of its occurrence is $p/(p+q)$, and that of its failure to occur is $q/(p+q)$.

16. Remainder Theorem (See §30). If the polynomial $f(x)$ is divided by $(x-a)$, the remainder is $f(a)$. Hence, if a is a root of the equation $f(x) = 0$, then $f(x)$ is divisible by $(x-a)$.

17. Determinants. The determinant D of order n,

$$D = \begin{vmatrix} a_{11} & a_{12} & \cdot & \cdot & \cdot & a_{1n} \\ a_{21} & a_{22} & \cdot & \cdot & \cdot & a_{2n} \\ \vdots & \vdots & \vdots & \vdots & \vdots & \vdots \\ a_{n1} & a_{n2} & \cdot & \cdot & \cdot & a_{nn} \end{vmatrix},$$

is defined to be the sum

$$\Sigma \ (\pm) \ a_{1i} \ a_{2j} \ a_{3k} \cdots a_{nl}$$

of $n!$ terms, the sign in a given term being taken plus or minus according as the number of inversions (of the numbers $1, 2, 3, \cdots, n$) in the corresponding sequence $i, j, k, \cdots, l$, is even or odd.

The *cofactor* A_{ij} of the element a_{ij} is defined to be the product of $(-1)^{i+j}$ by the determinant obtained from D by deleting the ith row and the jth column.

The following theorems are true:

(*a*) If the corresponding rows and columns of D be interchanged, D is unchanged.

(*b*) If any two rows (or columns) of D be interchanged, D is changed to $-D$.

(*c*) If any two rows (or columns) are alike, then $D = 0$.

(*d*) If each element of a row (or column) of D be multiplied by m, the new determinant is equal to mD.

(*e*) If to each element of a row (or column) is added m times the corresponding element in another row (or column), D is unchanged.

(*f*) $D = a_{1j} A_{1j} + a_{2j} A_{2j} + \cdots + a_{nj} A_{nj}, \quad j = 1, 2, \cdots, n.$

(*g*) $0 = a_{1k} A_{1j} + a_{2k} A_{2j} + \cdots + a_{nk} A_{nj},$ if $j \neq k.$

(*h*) The solution of the system of equations

$$a_{i1} x_1 + a_{i2} x_2 + \cdots + a_{in} x_n = c_i, \quad i = 1, 2, \cdots, n,$$

is unique if $D \neq 0$. The solution is given by the equations

$$Dx_1 = C_1, \qquad Dx_2 = C_2, \cdots, \qquad Dx_n = C_n,$$

where C_k is what D becomes when the elements of its kth column are replaced by $c_1, c_2, \ldots, c_n$, respectively.

Example 1.

$$\begin{vmatrix} a_{11} & a_{12} & a_{13} \\ a_{21} & a_{22} & a_{23} \\ a_{31} & a_{32} & a_{33} \end{vmatrix} = a_{11} \begin{vmatrix} a_{22} & a_{23} \\ a_{32} & a_{33} \end{vmatrix} - a_{12} \begin{vmatrix} a_{21} & a_{23} \\ a_{31} & a_{33} \end{vmatrix} + a_{13} \begin{vmatrix} a_{21} & a_{22} \\ a_{31} & a_{32} \end{vmatrix}$$

$$= a_{11}(a_{22} a_{33} - a_{32} a_{23}) - a_{12}(a_{21} a_{33} - a_{31} a_{23}) + a_{13}(a_{21} a_{32} - a_{31} a_{22}).$$

Example 2.   Find the values of x_1, x_2, x_3, which satisfy the system

$$\begin{aligned} 2x_1 + x_2 - 2x_3 &= -6, \\ x_1 + x_2 + x_3 &= 2, \\ -x_1 - 2x_2 + 3x_3 &= 12. \end{aligned}$$

By 17 (*h*), we find

$$x_1 = \frac{\begin{vmatrix} -6 & 1 & -2 \\ 2 & 1 & 1 \\ 12 & -2 & 3 \end{vmatrix}}{\begin{vmatrix} 2 & 1 & -2 \\ 1 & 1 & 1 \\ -1 & -2 & 3 \end{vmatrix}} = \frac{8}{8} = 1; \quad x_2 = \frac{\begin{vmatrix} 2 & -6 & -2 \\ 1 & 2 & 1 \\ -1 & 12 & 3 \end{vmatrix}}{\begin{vmatrix} 2 & 1 & -2 \\ 1 & 1 & 1 \\ -1 & -2 & 3 \end{vmatrix}} = \frac{-16}{8} = -2; \quad x_3 = \frac{\begin{vmatrix} 2 & 1 & -6 \\ 1 & 1 & 2 \\ -1 & -2 & 12 \end{vmatrix}}{\begin{vmatrix} 2 & 1 & -2 \\ 1 & 1 & 1 \\ -1 & -2 & 3 \end{vmatrix}} = 3.$$

Interest, Annuities, Sinking Funds.

In this section, n is the number of years, and r the rate of interest expressed as a decimal.

18. Amount. The amount (A_n) of a principal (P) placed at a rate of interest (r) for n years is given as follows.

At simple interest: $\qquad\qquad\qquad A_n = P(1 + nr).$

At interest compounded annually:* $\qquad A_n = P(1 + r)^n.$

At interest compounded q times a year: $\quad A_n = P\left(1 + \dfrac{r}{q}\right)^{nq}.$

19. Nominal and Effective Rates. The rate of interest quoted in describing a given variety of compound interest is called the *nominal rate.* The rate per year at which principal grows under this investment is called the *effective rate.* The effective rate (i) corresponding to the rate (r), compounded q times a year on a principal of P dollars, is:

$$i = \left(1 + \frac{r}{q}\right)^q - 1.$$

20. Present Value. The present value (P) of an amount A_n due in n years at rate r.

At simple interest: $\qquad\qquad\qquad P = \dfrac{A_n}{1 + nr}.$

At interest compounded annually:† $\qquad P = \dfrac{A_n}{(1 + r)^n}.$

At interest compounded q times a year: $\quad P = \dfrac{A_n}{\left(1 + \dfrac{r}{q}\right)^{nq}}.$

21. True Discount. The true discount is:

$$D = A_n - P.$$

22. Annuity. A fixed sum of money paid at regular intervals is called an *annuity.*

23. Amount of an Annuity. ‡ The amount of an annuity (N) of P dollars per annum for n years, beginning one year hence, at rate r, compounded annually, is:

$$N = P \cdot \frac{(1 + r)^n - 1}{r}.$$

---

* See Table XIX. $\qquad$ † See Table **XX.** $\qquad$ ‡ See Table **XXI.**

24. Present Value of an Annuity.* The present value (P) of an annuity of N dollars payable annually for n years, beginning a year hence, drawing interest at rate (r), interest compounded annually is:

$$P = N \cdot \frac{(1 + r)^n - 1}{r(1 + r)^n}.$$

25. Amount of a Sinking Fund. The amount (S) of a sinking fund created by a fixed investment (N) placed annually at compound interest (r) for a term of n years, the first investment being made at end of first year, is:

$$S = N \cdot \frac{(1 + r)^n - 1}{r}.$$

26. Fixed Investment. The amount (N) that must be placed annually (end of the year) at compound interest (r) for a term of n years to create a sinking fund (S), is:

$$N = S \cdot \frac{r}{(1 + r)^n - 1}.$$

Algebraic Equations†

27. Quadratic Equations. If

$$ax^2 + bx + c = 0, \quad a \neq 0,$$

then

$$x = \frac{-b \pm \sqrt{b^2 - 4ac}}{2a}.$$

If a, b, c are real and

if $b^2 - 4ac > 0$, the roots are real and unequal.

if $b^2 - 4ac = 0$, the roots are real and equal.

if $b^2 - 4ac < 0$, the roots are imaginary.

28. Cubic Equations. The cubic equation

$$y^3 + py^2 + qy + r = 0,$$

may be reduced by the substitution

$$y = \left(x - \frac{p}{3} \right)$$

---

* See Table XXII.   † For linear equations, see § 17.

to the normal form

$$x^3 + ax + b = 0,$$

where

$$a = \frac{1}{3}(3q - p^2), \quad b = \frac{1}{27}(2p^3 - 9pq + 27r),$$

which has the solutions $x_1, \quad x_2, \quad x_3,$

$$x_1 = A + B, \quad x_2, \quad x_3 = -\frac{1}{2}(A + B) \pm \frac{i\sqrt{3}}{2}(A - B),$$

where

$$i^2 = -1, \quad A = \sqrt[3]{-\frac{b}{2} + \sqrt{\frac{b^2}{4} + \frac{a^3}{27}}}, \quad B = \sqrt[3]{-\frac{b}{2} - \sqrt{\frac{b^2}{4} + \frac{a^3}{27}}}.$$

If p, q, r are real, and

if $\dfrac{b^2}{4} + \dfrac{a^3}{27} > 0,$ there are one real root and two conjugate imaginary roots,

if $\dfrac{b^2}{4} + \dfrac{a^3}{27} = 0,$ there are three real roots of which two are equal,

if $\dfrac{b^2}{4} + \dfrac{a^3}{27} < 0,$ there are three real and unequal roots.

If

$$\frac{b^2}{4} + \frac{a^3}{27} < 0,$$

the above formulas are impractical. The real roots are,

$$x_k = \mp 2\sqrt{-\frac{a}{3}}\cos\left(\frac{\phi}{3} + 120°K\right), \quad K = 0, 1, 2.$$

where

$$\cos\phi = \sqrt{\frac{b^2}{4} \div \left(-\frac{a^3}{27}\right)},$$

and where the upper signs are to be used if b is positive and the lower signs if b is negative.

If

$$\frac{b^2}{4} + \frac{a^3}{27} > 0,$$

the real root is,

$$x = \pm 2\sqrt{\frac{a}{3}}\operatorname{ctn} 2\phi,$$

where ϕ and ψ are to be computed from

$$\operatorname{ctn} 2\,\psi = \sqrt{\frac{b^2}{4} \div \frac{a^3}{27}}, \quad \tan \phi = \sqrt[3]{\tan \psi},$$

and where the upper sign is to be used if b is positive and the lower sign if b is negative.

If

$$\frac{b^2}{4} + \frac{a^3}{27} = 0,$$

the roots are,

$$x = \mp 2 \sqrt{-\frac{a}{3}}, \quad \pm \sqrt{-\frac{a}{3}}, \quad \pm \sqrt{-\frac{a}{3}},$$

where the upper sign is to be used if b is positive, and the lower sign if b is negative.

29. Biquadratic (Quartic) Equation.

The quartic equation

$$y^4 + py^3 + qy^2 + ry + s = 0$$

may be reduced to the form

$$x^4 + ax^2 + bx + c = 0$$

by the substitution

$$y = \left(x - \frac{p}{4} \right).$$

Let l, m, and n, denote the roots of the resolvent cubic

$$t^3 + \left(\frac{a}{2} \right) t^2 + \left(\frac{a^2 - 4\,c}{16} \right) t - \frac{b^2}{64} = 0.$$

The required roots of the reduced quartic are,

$$x_1 = \pm(-\sqrt{l} - \sqrt{m} - \sqrt{n}); \quad x_2 = \pm(-\sqrt{l} + \sqrt{m} + \sqrt{n});$$

$$x_3 = \pm(\sqrt{l} - \sqrt{m} + \sqrt{n}); \quad x_4 = \pm(\sqrt{l} + \sqrt{m} - \sqrt{n});$$

where the upper signs are to be used if b is positive, and the lower signs if b is negative.

30. General Equations of the nth degree.

$$P \equiv a_0 x^n + a_1 x^{n-1} + a_2 x^{n-2} + \cdots + a_{n-1}\, x + a_n = 0.$$

If $n > 4$, there is no formula which gives the roots of this general equation. The following methods may be used to advantage:

(a) *Roots by factors.* By trial, find a number r such that $x = r$, satisfies the equation, that is, such that

$$a_0 r^n + a_1 r^{n-1} + a_2 r^{n-2} + \cdots + a_{n-1} r + a_n = 0.$$

Then $(x-r)$ is a factor of the left hand member P of the equation. Divide P by $(x-r)$ leaving an equation of degree one less than that of the original equation. Next, proceed in the same manner with the reduced equation. (All integer roots of $P = 0$ are divisors of a_n.)

(b) *Roots by Approximation.* If for $x = a$ and $x = b$, the left member, P, of the equation has opposite signs, then a root lies between a and b. By repeated application of this principle, real roots to any desired degree of accuracy may be obtained.

(c) *Descartes' Rule.* The number of positive real roots of an equation with real coefficients is either equal to the number of its variations of sign or is less than that number by a positive even integer. A root of multiplicity m is here counted as m roots.

31. The Equation $x^n = a$. The n roots of this equation are:

$$x = \sqrt[n]{a} \left(\cos \frac{2k\pi}{n} + \sqrt{-1} \sin \frac{2k\pi}{n} \right), \text{ if } a > 0,$$

$$x = \sqrt[n]{-a} \left(\cos \frac{(2k+1)\pi}{n} + \sqrt{-1} \sin \frac{(2k+1)\pi}{n} \right), \text{ if } a < 0,$$

where k takes successively the values $0, 1, 2, 3, \cdots, n-1$.

II. ELEMENTARY GEOMETRY

Let a, b, c, d, and s denote lengths, A denote areas, and V denote volumes.

32. Triangle (see §65).

$A = bh/2$, where b denotes the base and h the altitude.

33. Rectangle.

$A = ab$, where a and b denote the lengths of the sides.

34. Parallelogram (opposite sides parallel).

$A = ah = ab \sin \theta$, where a and b denote the sides, h the altitude and θ the angle between the sides.

35. Trapezoid (four sides, two parallel).

$A = \frac{1}{2}h(a + b)$, where a and b are the sides and h the altitude.

36. Regular Polygon of n Sides (Fig. 1., See §37).

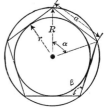

Fig. 1

$A = \dfrac{1}{4} n \cdot a^2 \operatorname{ctn} \dfrac{180°}{n}$, where a is length of side.

$R = \dfrac{a}{2} \cdot \csc \dfrac{180°}{n}$, where R is radius of circumscribed circle.

$r = \dfrac{a}{2} \cdot \operatorname{ctn} \dfrac{180°}{n}$, where r is radius of inscribed circle.

$\alpha = \dfrac{360°}{n} = \dfrac{2\pi}{n}$ radians,

$\beta = \left(\dfrac{n-2}{n}\right) \cdot 180° = \left(\dfrac{n-2}{n}\right)\pi$ radians where α and β are the angles indicated in Fig. 1.

$a = 2r \cdot \tan \dfrac{\alpha}{2} = 2R \cdot \sin \dfrac{\alpha}{2}$.

37. Circle (Fig. 2).

Let C = circumference, S = length of arc subtended by θ.
     R = radius, l = chord subtended by arc S,
     D = diameter, h = rise,
     A = area, θ = central angle in radians.

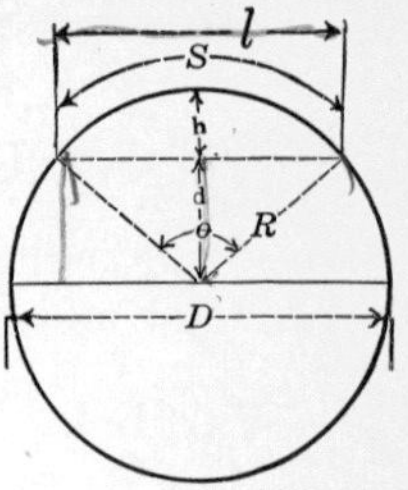

$$C = 2\pi R = \pi D, \quad \pi = 3.14159 \cdots.$$

$$S = R\theta = \tfrac{1}{2}D\theta = D \cos^{-1} \frac{d}{R}.$$

$$l = 2\sqrt{R^2 - d^2} = 2R \sin \frac{\theta}{2} = 2d \tan \frac{\theta}{2}.$$

$$d = \tfrac{1}{2} \sqrt{4R^2 - l^2} = R \cos \frac{\theta}{2} = \tfrac{1}{2} l \operatorname{ctn} \frac{\theta}{2}.$$

$$h = R - d.$$

$$\theta = \frac{S}{R} = \frac{2S}{D} = 2 \cos^{-1} \frac{d}{R} = 2 \tan^{-1} \frac{l}{2d} = 2 \sin^{-1} \frac{l}{D}.$$

Fig. 2

$$A \text{ (circle)} = \pi R^2 = \tfrac{1}{4}\pi D^2.$$

$$A \text{ (sector)} = \tfrac{1}{2} Rs = \tfrac{1}{2} R^2\theta.$$

$$A \text{ (segment)} = A \text{ (sector)} - A \text{ (triangle)} = \tfrac{1}{2} R^2 (\theta - \sin \theta)$$

$$= R^2 \cos^{-1} \frac{(R-h)}{R} - (R-h) \sqrt{2Rh - h^2}.$$

Perimeter of a n-side regular polygon inscribed in a circle

$$= 2n R \sin \frac{\pi}{n}.$$

Area of inscribed polygon $= \tfrac{1}{2}nR^2 \sin \frac{2\pi}{n}.$

Perimeter of a n-side regular polygon circumscribed about a circle

$$= 2nR \tan \frac{\pi}{n}.$$

Area of circumscribed polygon $= nR^2 \tan \frac{\pi}{n}.$

Radius of circle inscribed in a triangle of sides a, b, and c is

$$r = \sqrt{\frac{(s-a)(s-b)(s-c)}{s}}, \quad s = \tfrac{1}{2} (a+b+c).$$

Radius of circle circumscribed about a triangle is

$$R = \frac{abc}{4\sqrt{s(s-a)(s-b)(s-c)}}.$$

38. Ellipse   (See §84).

Perimeter $= \pi(a+b)\left[1 + \frac{1}{4}\left(\frac{a-b}{a+b}\right)^2 + \frac{1}{64}\left(\frac{a-b}{a+b}\right)^4 + \cdots\right].$

$A = \pi ab$, where a and b are lengths of semi-major and semi-minor axes respectively.

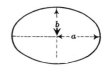

39. Parabola   (See §83).

$$A = 2ld/3.$$

Fig. 3

Height of $d_1 = \frac{d}{l^2}(l^2 - l_1^2).$

Width of $l_1 = l\sqrt{\frac{d-d_1}{d}}$

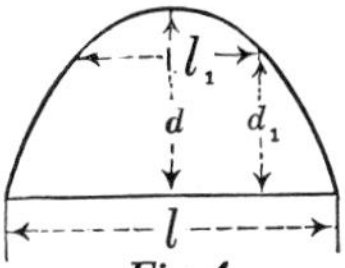

Length of arc $= l\left[1 + \frac{2}{3}\left(\frac{2d}{l}\right)^2 - \frac{2}{5}\left(\frac{2d}{l}\right)^4 + \cdots\right].$

Fig. 4

40. Catenary, Cycloid, etc.   (See §91 to §101).

41. Area by Approximation.   If y_0, y_1, y_2, $\cdots$, y_n be the lengths of a series of equally spaced parallel chords, and if h be their distant apart, the area enclosed by boundary is given approximately by any one of the following formulae:

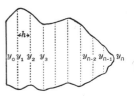

Fig. 5

$A_T = h\left[\frac{1}{2}(y_0 + y_n) + y_1 + y_2 + \cdots + y_{n-1}\right].$ (Trapezoidal Rule.)

$A_D = h\left[0.4(y_0 + y_n) + 1\cdot1(y_1 + y_{n-1}) + y_2 + y_3 + \cdots + y_{n-2}\right].$
(Durand's Rule.)

$A_S = \frac{1}{3}h\left[(y_0 + y_n) + 4(y_1 + y_3 + \cdots + y_{n-1})\right.$
$\left. + 2(y_2 + y_4 + \cdots + y_{n-2})\right].$ (n even, Simpson's Rule.)

In general, A_S gives the most accurate approximation.

The greater the value of n, the greater the accuracy of approximation.

42. Cube.

$V = a^3$; $d = a\sqrt{3}$;   total surface area $= 6a^2$, where a is length of side and d is length of diagonal.

43. Rectangular Parallelopiped.

$V = abc$; $d = \sqrt{a^2 + b^2 + c^2}$; total surface area $= 2(ab + bc + ca)$, where a, b, and c are the lengths of the sides and d is length of diagonal.

44. Prism or Cylinder.

$V =$ (area of base) $\cdot$ (altitude).

Lateral area $=$ (perimeter of right section) $\cdot$ (lateral edge).

45. Pyramid or Cone.

$V = \frac{1}{3}$ (area of base) $\cdot$ (altitude).

Lateral area of regular pyramid
$$= \tfrac{1}{2} \text{ (perimeter of base)} \cdot \text{(slant height)}.$$

46. Frustum of Pyramid or Cone.

$V = \frac{1}{3}(A_1 + A_2 + \sqrt{A_1 \cdot A_2})\, h$, where h is the altitude and A_1 and A_2 are the areas of the bases.

Lateral area of a regular figure
$$= \tfrac{1}{2} \text{ (sum of perimeters of base)} \cdot \text{(slant height)}.$$

47. Area of Surface and Volume of Regular Polyhedra of edge l.

Name	Type of Surface	Area of Surface	Volume
Tetrahedron	4 equilateral triangles	$1.73205l^2$	$0.11785l^3$
Hexahedron (cube)	6 squares	$6.00000l^2$	$1.00000l^3$
Octahedron	8 equilateral triangles	$3.46410l^2$	$0.47140l^3$
Dodecahedron	12 pentagons	$20.64578l^2$	$7.66312l^3$
Icosahedron	20 equilateral triangles	$8.66025l^2$	$2.18170l^3$

48. Sphere.

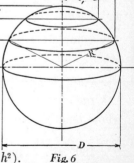

A (sphere) $\quad = 4\pi R^2 = \pi D^2.$

A (zone) $\quad = 2\pi Rh = \pi Dh.$

V (sphere) $\quad = \frac{4}{3}\pi R^3 = \frac{1}{6}\pi D^3.$

V (spherical sector) $\quad = \frac{2}{3}\pi R^2 h = \frac{1}{6}\pi D^2 h.$

V (spherical segment
of one base) $= \frac{1}{6}\pi h_1 (3r_1^2 + h_1^2).$

V (spherical segment
of two bases) $= \frac{1}{6}\pi h(3r_1^2 + 3r_2^2 + h^2).$ *Fig. 6*

49. Solid Angle (ψ). The solid angle (ψ) at any point P subtended by a surface S is equal to the area (A) of the portion of the surface of a sphere of unit radius, center at P, which is cut out by a conical surface with vertex at P and the perimeter of S for a base.

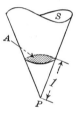

Fig. 7

The unit solid angle (ψ) is called the *steradian*.

The total solid angle about a point is 4π *steradians*.

50. Ellipsoid.

$V = \frac{4}{3}\pi abc$, where a, b, and c are the lengths of the semi-axes.

51. Torus.

$V = 2\pi^2 R r^2$,

Area of surface $= (S) = 4\pi^2 R r$.

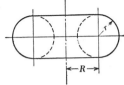

Fig. 8

III.   TRIGONOMETRY

52.   Angle. If two lines intersect, one line may be rotated about their point of intersection through the *angle* which they form until it coincides with the other line.

The angle is said to be *positive* if the rotation is counterclockwise, and *negative*, if clockwise.

A complete revolution of a line is a rotation through an angle of 360°. Thus,

A *degree* is 1/360 of the plane angle about a point.

A *radian* is the angle subtended at the center of a circle by an arc whose length is equal to that of the radius.

$$180° = \pi \text{ radians}; \quad 1° = \frac{\pi}{180} \text{ radians}; \quad 1 \text{ rad.} = \frac{180}{\pi} \text{ degrees}.$$

53. Trigonometric Functions of an Angle α.

Let α be any angle whose initial side lies
on the positive x-axis and whose vertex
is at the origin, and (x, y) be any point on
the terminal side of the angle. (x is positive
if measured along OX to the right, from the
y-axis; and negative, if measured along OX'
to the left from the y-axis. Likewise, y is
positive if measured parallel to OY, and

Fig. 9

negative if measured parallel to OY'.) Let r be the positive distance
from the origin to the point. The trigonometric functions of an
angle are defined as follows:

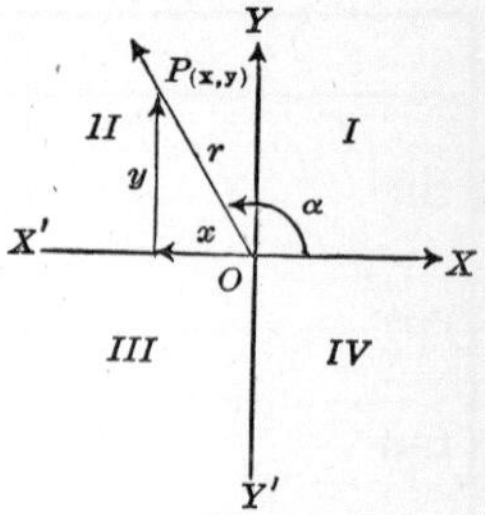

sine α	=	sin α	=	$\dfrac{y}{r}$.
cosine α	=	cos α	=	$\dfrac{x}{r}$.
tangent α	=	tan α	=	$\dfrac{y}{x}$.
cotangent α	=	ctn α = cot α	=	$\dfrac{x}{y}$.
secant α	=	sec α	=	$\dfrac{r}{x}$.
cosecant α	=	csc α	=	$\dfrac{r}{y}$.
exsecant α	=	exsec α	=	sec α -1 .
versine α	=	vers α	=	$1 - \cos α$.
coversine α	=	covers α	=	$1 - \sin α$.
haversine α	=	hav α	=	$\frac{1}{2}$ vers α .

54. Signs of the Functions.

Quadrant	sin	cos	tan	ctn	sec	csc
I	+	+	+	+	+	+
II	+	−	−	−	−	+
III	−	−	+	+	−	−
IV	−	+	−	−	+	−

55. Functions of 0°, 30°, 45°, 60°, 90°, 180°, 270°, 360°.

	0°	30°	45°	60°	90°	180°	270°	360°
sin	0	$\dfrac{1}{2}$	$\dfrac{\sqrt{2}}{2}$	$\dfrac{\sqrt{3}}{2}$	1	0	-1	0
cos	1	$\dfrac{\sqrt{3}}{2}$	$\dfrac{\sqrt{2}}{2}$	$\dfrac{1}{2}$	0	-1	0	1
tan	0	$\dfrac{\sqrt{3}}{3}$	1	$\sqrt{3}$	∞	0	∞	0
ctn	∞	$\sqrt{3}$	1	$\dfrac{\sqrt{3}}{3}$	0	∞	0	∞
sec	1	$\dfrac{2\sqrt{3}}{3}$	$\sqrt{2}$	2	∞	-1	∞	1
csc	∞	2	$\sqrt{2}$	$\dfrac{2\sqrt{3}}{3}$	1	∞	-1	∞

56. Variations of the Functions.

Quadrant	sin	cos	tan	ctn	sec	csc
I	$0\rightarrow+1$	$+1\rightarrow0$	$0\rightarrow+\infty$	$+\infty\rightarrow0$	$+1\rightarrow+\infty$	$+\infty\rightarrow+1$
II	$+1\rightarrow0$	$0\rightarrow-1$	$-\infty\rightarrow0$	$0\rightarrow-\infty$	$-\infty\rightarrow-1$	$+1\rightarrow+\infty$
III . . .	$0\rightarrow-1$	$-1\rightarrow0$	$0\rightarrow+\infty$	$+\infty\rightarrow0$	$-1\rightarrow-\infty$	$-\infty\rightarrow-1$
IV	$-1\rightarrow0$	$0\rightarrow+1$	$-\infty\rightarrow0$	$0\rightarrow-\infty$	$+\infty\rightarrow+1$	$-1\rightarrow-\infty$

57. Functions of Angles in any Quadrant in Terms of Angles in First Quadrant.

	$-\alpha$	$90°\pm\alpha$	$180°\pm\alpha$	$270°\pm\alpha$	$n(360)°\pm\alpha$
sin	$-\sin\alpha$	$+\cos\alpha$	$\mp\sin\alpha$	$-\cos\alpha$	$\pm\sin\alpha$
cos	$+\cos\alpha$	$\mp\sin\alpha$	$-\cos\alpha$	$\pm\sin\alpha$	$+\cos\alpha$
tan	$-\tan\alpha$	$\mp\ctn\alpha$	$\pm\tan\alpha$	$\mp\ctn\alpha$	$\pm\tan\alpha$
ctn	$-\ctn\alpha$	$\mp\tan\alpha$	$\pm\ctn\alpha$	$\mp\tan\alpha$	$\pm\ctn\alpha$
sec	$+\sec\alpha$	$\mp\csc\alpha$	$-\sec\alpha$	$\pm\csc\alpha$	$+\sec\alpha$
csc	$-\csc\alpha$	$+\sec\alpha$	$\mp\csc\alpha$	$-\sec\alpha$	$\pm\csc\alpha$

n denotes any integer.

For example: $\tan(270° + \alpha) = -\ctn\alpha$.

58. Fundamental Identities.

$$\sin \alpha = \frac{1}{\csc \alpha}; \quad \cos \alpha = \frac{1}{\sec \alpha}; \quad \tan \alpha = \frac{1}{\operatorname{ctn} \alpha} = \frac{\sin \alpha}{\cos \alpha}.$$

$$\csc \alpha = \frac{1}{\sin \alpha}; \quad \sec \alpha = \frac{1}{\cos \alpha}; \quad \operatorname{ctn} \alpha = \frac{1}{\tan \alpha} = \frac{\cos \alpha}{\sin \alpha}.$$

$$\sin^2 \alpha + \cos^2 \alpha = 1; \quad 1 + \tan^2 \alpha = \sec^2 \alpha; \quad 1 + \operatorname{ctn}^2 \alpha = \csc^2 \alpha.$$

$$\sin 2 \alpha = 2 \sin \alpha \cos \alpha,$$

$$\cos 2 \alpha = 2 \cos^2 \alpha - 1 = 1 - 2 \sin^2 \alpha = \cos^2 \alpha - \sin^2 \alpha,$$

$$\tan 2 \alpha = \frac{2 \tan \alpha}{1 - \tan^2 \alpha},$$

$$\sin 3 \alpha = 3 \sin \alpha - 4 \sin^3 \alpha,$$

$$\cos 3 \alpha = 4 \cos^3 \alpha - 3 \cos \alpha,$$

$$\sin n \alpha = 2 \sin (n - 1)\alpha \cdot \cos \alpha - \sin (n - 2)\alpha,$$

$$\cos n \alpha = 2 \cos (n - 1)\alpha \cdot \cos \alpha - \cos (n - 2)\alpha,$$

$$\sin (\alpha \pm \beta) = \sin \alpha \cos \beta \pm \cos \alpha \sin \beta,$$

$$\cos (\alpha \pm \beta) = \cos \alpha \cos \beta \mp \sin \alpha \sin \beta,$$

$$\tan (\alpha \pm \beta) = \frac{\tan \alpha \pm \tan \beta}{1 \mp \tan \alpha \tan \beta}.$$

$$\sin \alpha + \sin \beta = 2 \sin \tfrac{1}{2}(\alpha + \beta) \cdot \cos \tfrac{1}{2}(\alpha - \beta),$$

$$\sin \alpha - \sin \beta = 2 \cos \tfrac{1}{2}(\alpha + \beta) \cdot \sin \tfrac{1}{2}(\alpha - \beta),$$

$$\cos \alpha + \cos \beta = 2 \cos \tfrac{1}{2}(\alpha + \beta) \cdot \cos \tfrac{1}{2}(\alpha - \beta),$$

$$\cos \alpha - \cos \beta = - 2 \sin \tfrac{1}{2}(\alpha + \beta) \cdot \sin \tfrac{1}{2}(\alpha - \beta).$$

$$\sin \frac{\alpha}{2} = \pm \sqrt{\frac{1 - \cos \alpha}{2}}, \quad$$ positive if $\frac{\alpha}{2}$ in I or II quadrants, negative otherwise.

$$\cos \frac{\alpha}{2} = \pm \sqrt{\frac{1 + \cos \alpha}{2}}, \quad$$ positive if $\frac{\alpha}{2}$ in I or IV, negative otherwise.

$$\tan \frac{\alpha}{2} = \frac{1 - \cos \alpha}{\sin \alpha} = \frac{\sin \alpha}{1 + \cos \alpha} = \pm \sqrt{\frac{1 - \cos \alpha}{1 + \cos \alpha}}$$ positive if $\frac{\alpha}{2}$ in I or III, negative otherwise.

$$\sin^2 \alpha = \tfrac{1}{2}(1 - \cos 2 \alpha); \qquad \cos^2 \alpha = \tfrac{1}{2}(1 + \cos 2 \alpha).$$

$$\sin^3 \alpha = \tfrac{1}{4}(3 \sin \alpha - \sin 3 \alpha); \quad \cos^3 \alpha = \tfrac{1}{4}(\cos 3 \alpha + 3 \cos \alpha).$$

$$\sin \alpha \sin \beta = \tfrac{1}{2} \cos (\alpha - \beta) - \tfrac{1}{2} \cos (\alpha + \beta),$$

$$\cos \alpha \cos \beta = \tfrac{1}{2} \cos (\alpha - \beta) + \tfrac{1}{2} \cos (\alpha + \beta),$$

$$\sin \alpha \cos \beta = \tfrac{1}{2} \sin (\alpha + \beta) + \tfrac{1}{2} \sin (\alpha - \beta).$$

59. Equivalent Expressions for sin α, cos α, tan α, etc.

Function	Sin α	Cos α	Tan α	Ctn α	Sec α	Csc α
Sin α	$\sin \alpha$	$\pm \sqrt{1-\cos^2 \alpha}$	$\dfrac{\tan \alpha}{\pm \sqrt{1+\tan^2 \alpha}}$	$\dfrac{1}{\pm \sqrt{1+\operatorname{ctn}^2 \alpha}}$	$\dfrac{\pm \sqrt{\sec^2 \alpha -1}}{\sec \alpha}$	$\dfrac{1}{\csc \alpha}$
Cos α	$\pm \sqrt{1-\sin^2 \alpha}$	$\cos \alpha$	$\dfrac{1}{\pm \sqrt{1+\tan^2 \alpha}}$	$\dfrac{\operatorname{ctn} \alpha}{\pm \sqrt{1+\operatorname{ctn}^2 \alpha}}$	$\dfrac{1}{\sec \alpha}$	$\dfrac{\pm \sqrt{\csc^2 \alpha -1}}{\csc \alpha}$
Tan α	$\dfrac{\sin \alpha}{\pm \sqrt{1-\sin^2 \alpha}}$	$\dfrac{\pm \sqrt{1-\cos^2 \alpha}}{\cos \alpha}$	$\tan \alpha$	$\dfrac{1}{\operatorname{ctn} \alpha}$	$\pm \sqrt{\sec^2 \alpha -1}$	$\dfrac{1}{\pm \sqrt{\csc^2 \alpha -1}}$
Ctn α	$\dfrac{\pm \sqrt{1-\sin^2 \alpha}}{\sin \alpha}$	$\dfrac{\cos \alpha}{\pm \sqrt{1-\cos^2 \alpha}}$	$\dfrac{1}{\tan \alpha}$	$\operatorname{ctn} \alpha$	$\dfrac{1}{\pm \sqrt{\sec^2 \alpha -1}}$	$\pm \sqrt{\csc^2 \alpha -1}$
Sec α	$\dfrac{1}{\pm \sqrt{1-\sin^2 \alpha}}$	$\dfrac{1}{\cos \alpha}$	$\pm \sqrt{1+\tan^2 \alpha}$	$\dfrac{\pm \sqrt{1+\operatorname{ctn}^2 \alpha}}{\operatorname{ctn} \alpha}$	$\sec \alpha$	$\dfrac{\csc \alpha}{\pm \sqrt{\csc^2 \alpha -1}}$
Csc α	$\dfrac{1}{\sin \alpha}$	$\dfrac{1}{\pm \sqrt{1-\cos^2 \alpha}}$	$\dfrac{\pm \sqrt{1+\tan^2 \alpha}}{\tan \alpha}$	$\pm \sqrt{1+\operatorname{ctn}^2 \alpha}$	$\dfrac{\sec \alpha}{\pm \sqrt{\sec^2 \alpha -1}}$	$\csc \alpha$

Note: The quadrant in which α terminates determines the sign to be used. See previous table of signs.

60. Inverse or Anti-trigonometric Functions. The complete solution of the equation $x = \sin y$ is

$$y = (-1)^n \sin^{-1} x + n(180°), \quad -\pi/2 \leqq \sin^{-1} x \leqq \pi/2,$$

where $\sin^{-1} x$ is the principal value of the angle whose sine is x.

Likewise, if $x = \cos y$,

$$y = \pm \cos^{-1} x + n(360°), \quad 0 \leqq \cos^{-1} x \leqq \pi.$$

If $x = \tan y$,

$$y = \tan^{-1} x + n(180°), \quad -\pi/2 \leqq \tan^{-1} x \leqq \pi/2.$$

Similar relations hold for $x = \operatorname{ctn} y$, $x = \sec y$, $x = \csc y$.

61. Certain Relations Among Inverse Functions. If the inverse functions are restricted as in §60, the following formulae hold:

$$\sin^{-1} a = \cos^{-1} \sqrt{1-a^2} = \tan^{-1} \frac{a}{\sqrt{1-a^2}} = \operatorname{ctn}^{-1} \frac{\sqrt{1-a^2}}{a}$$

$$= \sec^{-1} \frac{1}{\sqrt{1-a^2}} = \csc^{-1} \frac{1}{a}.$$

$$\cos^{-1} a = \sin^{-1} \sqrt{1-a^2} = \tan^{-1} \frac{\sqrt{1-a^2}}{a} = \operatorname{ctn}^{-1} \frac{a}{\sqrt{1-a^2}}$$

$$= \sec^{-1} \frac{1}{a} = \csc^{-1} \frac{1}{\sqrt{1-a^2}}.$$

$$\tan^{-1} a = \sin^{-1} \frac{a}{\sqrt{1+a^2}} = \cos^{-1} \frac{1}{\sqrt{1+a^2}} = \operatorname{ctn}^{-1} \frac{1}{a}$$

$$= \sec^{-1} \sqrt{1+a^2} = \csc^{-1} \frac{\sqrt{1+a^2}}{a}.$$

$$\operatorname{ctn}^{-1} a = \tan^{-1} \frac{1}{a}; \quad \sec^{-1} a = \cos^{-1} \frac{1}{a}; \quad \csc^{-1} a = \sin^{-1} \frac{1}{a}.$$

62. Solution of Trigonometric Equations. To solve a trigonometric equation, reduce the given equation, by means of the relations expressed in §58 to §60 inclusive, to an equation containing only a single function of a single angle. Solve the resulting equation by algebraic methods (§30) for the remaining function, and from this find the values of the angle, by §57 and Table V. All these values should then be tested in the original equation, discarding those which do not satisfy it.

63. Relations Between Sides and Angles of Plane Triangles. Let a, b, c, denote the sides and α, β, γ, the corresponding opposite angles with

$2s = a + b + c;$ $\qquad\qquad$ $r =$ radius of inscribed circle;

$A =$ area; $\qquad\qquad\qquad$ $R =$ radius of circumscribed circle;

$h_b =$ altitude on side b.

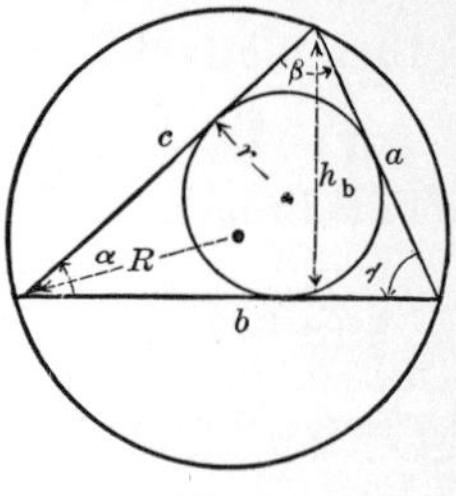

$\alpha + \beta + \gamma = 180°$.

$$\frac{a}{\sin \alpha} = \frac{b}{\sin \beta} = \frac{c}{\sin \gamma}.$$ (Law of Sines).

$$\frac{a + b}{a - b} = \frac{\tan \frac{1}{2}(\alpha + \beta)}{\tan \frac{1}{2}(\alpha - \beta)}.$$ (Law of Tangents).*

$$a^2 = b^2 + c^2 - 2\,bc \cos \alpha.$$ (Law of Cosines).*

Fig. 10

$a = b \cos \gamma + c \cos \beta.$*

$$\cos \alpha = \frac{b^2 + c^2 - a^2}{2\,bc},* \quad \sin \alpha = \frac{2}{bc} \sqrt{s(s-a)(s-b)(s-c)}.*$$

$$\sin \frac{\alpha}{2} = \sqrt{\frac{(s-b)(s-c)}{bc}}, *\cos \frac{\alpha}{2} = \sqrt{\frac{s(s-a)}{bc}};*$$

$$\tan \frac{\alpha}{2} = \sqrt{\frac{(s-b)(s-c)}{s(s-a)}} = \frac{r}{s-a}, * \text{ where } r = \sqrt{\frac{(s-a)(s-b)(s-c)}{s}}.$$

$$A = \tfrac{1}{2} bh_b* = \tfrac{1}{2} ab \sin \gamma * = \frac{a^2 \sin \beta \sin \gamma}{2 \sin \alpha}*$$

$$= \sqrt{s(s-a)(s-b)(s-c)} = rs.$$

$$R = \frac{a}{2 \sin \alpha}* = \frac{abc}{4A}. \qquad h_b = c \sin \alpha * = a \sin \gamma* = \frac{2\,rs}{b}$$

---

*Two more formulas may be obtained by replacing a by b, b by c, c by a, α by β, β by γ, γ by α.

64. Solution of a Right Triangle. Given one side and any acute angle α, or any two sides, to find the remaining parts.

$$a = \sqrt{(c+b)(c-b)} = c \sin \alpha = b \tan \alpha.$$

$$b = \sqrt{(c+a)(c-a)} = c \cos \alpha = \frac{a}{\tan \alpha}.$$

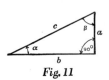

Fig. 11

$$\sin \alpha = \frac{a}{c}, \quad \cos \alpha = \frac{b}{c}, \quad \tan \alpha = \frac{a}{b}, \quad \beta = 90° - \alpha.$$

$$c = \frac{a}{\sin \alpha} = \frac{b}{\cos \alpha} = \sqrt{a^2 + b^2}.$$

$$A = \tfrac{1}{2} ab = \frac{a^2}{2 \tan \alpha} = \frac{b^2 \tan \alpha}{2} = \frac{c^2 \sin 2\alpha}{4}.$$

65. Solution of Oblique Triangles **(Fig. 12).** The formulas of the preceding section §63 will suffice to solve any oblique triangle. Use the trigonometric tables for numerical work. We give one method. Solutions should be checked by some other method.

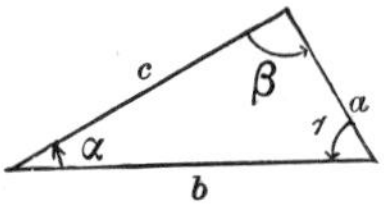

(*a*) Given any two sides b and c and included angle α.

Fig. 12

$$\tfrac{1}{2}(\beta + \gamma) = 90° - \tfrac{1}{2}\alpha; \quad \tan \tfrac{1}{2}(\beta - \gamma) = \frac{b-c}{b+c} \tan \tfrac{1}{2}(\beta + \gamma);$$

$$\beta = \tfrac{1}{2}(\beta + \gamma) + \tfrac{1}{2}(\beta - \gamma); \quad \gamma = \tfrac{1}{2}(\beta + \gamma) - \tfrac{1}{2}(\beta - \gamma); \quad a = \frac{b \sin \alpha}{\sin \beta}.$$

(*b*) Given any two angles α and β, and any side c.

$$\gamma = 180° - (\alpha + \beta); \quad a = \frac{c \sin \alpha}{\sin \gamma}; \quad b = \frac{c \sin \beta}{\sin \gamma}.$$

(*c*) Given any two sides a and c, and an angle opposite one of these, say α.

$$\sin \gamma = \frac{c \sin \alpha}{a}, \quad \beta = 180° - (\alpha + \gamma), \quad b = \frac{a \sin \beta}{\sin \alpha}.$$

This case may have two sets of solutions, for γ may have two values, $\gamma_1 < 90°$ and $\gamma_2 = 180° - \gamma_1 > 90°$. If $\alpha + \gamma_2 > 180°$, use only γ_1.

(*d*) Given the three sides a, b, and c.

$$s = \tfrac{1}{2}(a + b + c), \quad r = \sqrt{\frac{(s-a)(s-b)(s-c)}{s}}.$$

$$\tan \tfrac{1}{2}\alpha = \frac{r}{s-a}, \quad \tan \tfrac{1}{2}\beta = \frac{r}{s-b}, \quad \tan \tfrac{1}{2}\gamma = \frac{r}{s-c}$$

Spherical Trigonometry

66. The Right Spherical Triangle.

Let O be the center of sphere and a, b, c the sides of a right triangle with opposite angles $\alpha, \beta,$ and $\gamma = 90°$, respectively, the sides being measured by the angle subtended at the center of the sphere.

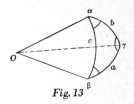

Fig. 13

$$\sin a = \sin \alpha \cdot \sin c, \qquad \sin b = \sin \beta \cdot \sin c.$$
$$\sin a = \tan b \cdot \operatorname{ctn} \beta, \qquad \sin b = \tan a \cdot \operatorname{ctn} \alpha.$$
$$\cos \alpha = \cos a \cdot \sin \beta, \qquad \cos \beta = \cos b \cdot \sin \alpha.$$
$$\cos \alpha = \tan b \cdot \operatorname{ctn} c, \qquad \cos \beta = \tan a \cdot \operatorname{ctn} c.$$
$$\cos c = \operatorname{ctn} \alpha \cdot \operatorname{ctn} \beta, \qquad \cos c = \cos a \cdot \cos b.$$

67. Napier's Rules of Circular Parts (See Fig. 14).

Let the five quantities a, b, co–α (complement of α), co–c, co–β, be arranged in order as indicated in the figure. If we denote any one of these quantities a *middle* part, then two of the other parts are *adjacent* to it, and the other two parts are *opposite* to it. The above formulas may be remembered by means of the following rules:

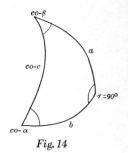

Fig. 14

(**a**) *The sine of a middle part is equal to the product of the tangents of the adjacent parts.*

(**b**) *The sine of a middle part is equal to the product of the cosines of the opposite parts.*

68. The Oblique Spherical Triangle.

Let a, b, c denote the sides and α, β, γ the corresponding opposite angles of the spherical triangle, Δ its area, E its spherical excess, R the radius of the sphere upon which the triangle lies, and α', β', γ', a, b, c the corresponding parts of the polar triangle.

$$0° < a + b + c < 360°, \qquad 180° < \alpha + \beta + \gamma < 540°.$$
$$\alpha = 180° - a', \qquad \beta = 180° - b', \qquad \gamma = 180° - c',$$
$$a = 180° - \alpha', \qquad b = 180° - \beta', \qquad c = 180° - \gamma'.$$

$$\frac{\sin \alpha}{\sin a} = \frac{\sin \beta}{\sin b} = \frac{\sin \gamma}{\sin c}. \quad \text{(Law of Sines).}$$

$$\cos a = \cos b \cdot \cos c + \sin b \cdot \sin c \cdot \cos \alpha.$$
$$\cos \alpha = -\cos \beta \cdot \cos \gamma + \sin \beta \cdot \sin \gamma \cdot \cos a. \quad \text{(Law of Cosines).}$$

$$\tan \frac{\alpha}{2} = \sqrt{\frac{\sin (s-b) \cdot \sin (s-c)}{\sin s \cdot \sin (s-a)}}, \text{ where } s = \tfrac{1}{2}(a + b + c).$$

$$\tan \frac{a}{2} = \sqrt{\frac{-\cos \sigma \cdot \cos (\sigma-\alpha)}{\cos (\sigma-\beta) \cdot \cos (\sigma-\gamma)}}, \text{ where } \sigma = \tfrac{1}{2}(\alpha + \beta + \gamma).$$

$$\frac{\sin \tfrac{1}{2}(\alpha + \beta)}{\sin \tfrac{1}{2}(\alpha - \beta)} = \frac{\tan \tfrac{1}{2}c}{\tan \tfrac{1}{2}(a - b)}, \quad \frac{\cos \tfrac{1}{2}(\alpha + \beta)}{\cos \tfrac{1}{2}(\alpha - \beta)}, = \frac{\tan \tfrac{1}{2}c}{\tan \tfrac{1}{2}(a + b)}.$$

$$\frac{\sin \tfrac{1}{2}(a + b)}{\sin \tfrac{1}{2}(a - b)} = \frac{\text{ctn} \tfrac{1}{2}\gamma}{\tan \tfrac{1}{2}(\alpha - \beta)}, \quad \frac{\cos \tfrac{1}{2}(a + b)}{\cos \tfrac{1}{2}(a - b)}, = \frac{\text{ctn} \tfrac{1}{2}\gamma}{\tan \tfrac{1}{2}(\alpha + \beta)}.$$

$$\tan \frac{E}{4} = \sqrt{\tan \tfrac{1}{2}s \cdot \tan \tfrac{1}{2}(s-a) \cdot \tan \tfrac{1}{2}(s-b) \cdot \tan \tfrac{1}{2}(s-c)}$$

$$\Delta = \frac{\pi R^2 \cdot E}{180} \qquad\qquad \alpha + \beta + \gamma - 180° = E.$$

*Hyperbolic Functions**

69. Definitions (For definition of e see §108).

Hyperbolic sine of $\quad x \quad = \sinh x = \tfrac{1}{2}(e^x - e^{-x})$;

Hyperbolic cosine of $x \quad = \cosh x = \tfrac{1}{2}(e^x + e^{-x})$;

Hyperbolic tangent of $x = \tanh x = \dfrac{e^x - e^{-x}}{e^x + e^{-x}}$;

$$\text{csch } x = \frac{1}{\sinh x} \; ; \qquad \text{sech } x = \frac{1}{\cosh x} \; ; \qquad \text{ctnh } x = \frac{1}{\tanh x}.$$

*For derivatives and integrals of Hyperbolic functions see §108 and §121.

70. Inverse or Anti-Hyperbolic Functions (See §60).

If $x = \sinh y$, then y is the *inverse hyperbolic sine* of x, written $y = \sinh^{-1} x$ or arc sinh x.

$$\sinh^{-1} x = \log_e(x + \sqrt{x^2 + 1}), \quad \cosh^{-1} x = \log_e(x + \sqrt{x^2 - 1}),$$

$$\tanh^{-1} x = \tfrac{1}{2} \log_e \left(\frac{1 + x}{1 - x} \right), \quad \operatorname{ctnh}^{-1} x = \tfrac{1}{2} \log_e \left(\frac{x + 1}{x - 1} \right),$$

$$\operatorname{sech}^{-1} x = \log_e \left(\frac{1 + \sqrt{1 - x^2}}{x} \right), \quad \operatorname{csch}^{-1} x = \log_e \left(\frac{1 + \sqrt{1 + x^2}}{x} \right).$$

71. Certain Relations among Hyperbolic Functions.

$$\sinh(-x) = -\sinh x, \qquad \cosh^2 x - \sinh^2 x = 1,$$
$$\cosh(-x) = \cosh x, \qquad \operatorname{sech}^2 x + \tanh^2 x = 1,$$
$$\tanh(-x) = -\tanh x, \qquad \operatorname{csch}^2 x - \operatorname{ctnh}^2 x = -1.$$

$$\tanh(x) = \frac{\sinh x}{\cosh x}$$

$$\sinh(x \pm y) = \sinh x \cosh y \pm \cosh x \sinh y.$$
$$\cosh(x \pm y) = \cosh x \cosh y \pm \sinh x \sinh y.$$
$$\sinh 2x = 2 \sinh x \cdot \cosh x, \qquad \cosh 2x = \cosh^2 x + \sinh^2 x.$$

$$2 \sinh^2 \frac{x}{2} = \cosh x - 1, \qquad 2 \cosh^2 \frac{x}{2} = \cosh x + 1.$$

72. Hyperbolic Functions of Complex Quantities, Connection with Circular Functions.

$$\sin x = -\tfrac{1}{2}i(e^{ix} - e^{-ix}) = -i \sinh ix, \quad i^2 = -1.$$
$$\cos x = \tfrac{1}{2}(e^{ix} + e^{-ix}) = \cosh ix.$$
$$\sinh iy = i \sin y, \quad \cosh iy = \cos y, \quad \tanh iy = i \tan y.$$
$$\sinh(x \pm iy) = \sinh x \cdot \cos y \pm i \cosh x \sin y.$$
$$\cosh(x \pm iy) = \cosh x \cdot \cos y \pm i \sinh x \cdot \sin y.$$
$$\sinh(x + 2 i\pi) = \sinh x, \qquad \cosh(x + 2 i\pi) = \cosh x.$$
$$\sinh(x + i\pi) = -\sinh x, \quad \cosh(x + i\pi) = -\cosh x.$$
$$\sinh(x + \tfrac{1}{2}i\pi) = i \cosh x, \quad \cosh(x + \tfrac{1}{2}i\pi) = i \sinh x.$$

$$\log_e(x \pm iy) = \tfrac{1}{2} \log_e(x^2 + y^2) \pm i \arctan \frac{y}{x}.$$

IV. ANALYTIC GEOMETRY

73. Rectangular Coördinates. Let $X'X$ (x-axis) and $Y'Y$ (y-axis) be two perpendicular lines meeting in the point O called the origin. The point P (x, y) in the plane of the x and y axes is fixed by the distances x (abscissa) and y (ordinate) from $Y'Y$ and $X'X$, respectively, to P. x is positive to the right and negative to the left of the y-axis, and y is positive above and negative below the x-axis.

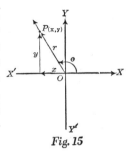

Fig. 15

74. Polar Coördinates. Let OX (initial line) be a fixed line in the plane and O (pole or origin) a point on this line. The position of any point P (r, θ) in the plane is determined by the distance r (radius vector) from O to the point together with the angle (vectorial angle) measured from OX to OP. θ is positive if measured counter-clockwise, negative if measured clockwise, r is positive if measured along the terminal side of θ and negative if measured along the terminal side of θ produced through the pole.

75. Relations between Rectangular and Polar Coördinates (See §113).

$$\begin{cases} x = r \cos \theta, \\ y = r \sin \theta, \end{cases} \quad \begin{cases} r = \sqrt{x^2 + y^2}, \\ \theta = \tan^{-1} \dfrac{y}{x}, \end{cases} \quad \begin{cases} \sin \theta = \dfrac{y}{\sqrt{x^2 + y^2}}, \\ \cos \theta = \dfrac{x}{\sqrt{x^2 + y^2}}, \end{cases}$$

76. Points and Slopes.

Let $P_1(x_1, y_1)$ and $P_2(x_2, y_2)$ be any two points, and α_1 be the angle measured counter-clockwise from OX to P_1P_2:

Distance between P_1 and $P_2 = P_1P_2$

$$= d = \sqrt{(x_2 - x_1)^2 + (y_2 - y_1)^2}.$$

Slope of $P_1P_2 = \tan \alpha_1 = m = \dfrac{y_2 - y_1}{x_2 - x_1}.$

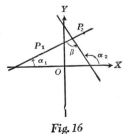

Fig. 16

Point dividing P_1P_2 in the ratio $m_1 : m_2$ is $\left(\dfrac{m_1x_2 + m_2x_1}{m_1 + m_2}, \dfrac{m_1y_2 + m_2y_1}{m_1 + m_2} \right)$.

Mid-point of P_1P_2 is $\left(\dfrac{x_1 + x_2}{2}, \dfrac{y_1 + y_2}{2} \right)$.

The angle β between lines of slopes m_1 and m_2, respectively, is given by
$$\tan \beta = \frac{m_2 - m_1}{1 + m_1m_2}.$$

Two lines of slopes m_1 and m_2 are perpendicular if $m_2 = -\dfrac{1}{m_1}$, and parallel if $m_1 = m_2$.

77. Area of Triangle. If the vertices are the points (x_1, y_1), (x_2, y_2), (x_3, y_3), then the area is equal to the numerical value of

$$\frac{1}{2} \begin{vmatrix} x_1 \ y_1 \ 1 \\ x_2 \ y_2 \ 1 \\ x_3 \ y_3 \ 1 \end{vmatrix} = \frac{1}{2}(x_1y_2 - x_1y_3 + x_2y_3 - x_2y_1 + x_3y_1 - x_3y_2).$$

78. Locus and Equation. The set of all points which satisfy a given condition is called the *locus* of that condition. An *equation* is called the equation of the locus if it is satisfied by the coördinates of every point on the locus and by no other points. There are three common representations of the locus by means of equations:

(*a*) *Rectangular equation* which involves the rectangular coördinates (x, y).

(*b*) *Polar equation* which involves the polar coördinates (r, θ).

(*c*) *Parametric equations* which expresses x and y or r and θ in terms of a third independent variable called a parameter.

79. Transformation of Coördinates. To transform an equation or a curve from one system of coördinates in x, y, to another such system in x', y', substitute for each variable its value in terms of variables of the new system.

(*a*) *Rectangular System. Old axes parallel to new axes.*

The coördinates of new origin in terms of old system are (h, k).

$$\begin{cases} x = x' + h, \\ y = y' + k. \end{cases}$$

(*b*) *Rectangular System.* *Old origin coincident with new origin and the x'-axis making an angle θ with the x-axis.*

$$\begin{cases} x = x' \cdot \cos \theta - y' \cdot \sin \theta, \\ y = x' \cdot \sin \theta + y' \cdot \cos \theta. \end{cases}$$

(*c*) *Rectangular System.* *Old axes not parallel with new.* *New origin at (h, k) in old system.*

$$\begin{cases} x = x' \cdot \cos \theta - y' \cdot \sin \theta + h, \\ y = x' \cdot \sin \theta + y' \cdot \cos \theta + k. \end{cases}$$

80. Straight Line. The equations of the straight line may assume the following forms:

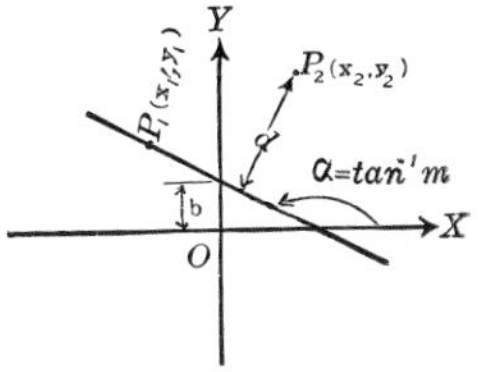

Fig. 17

(*a*) $y = mx + b$. (m = slope, b = intercept on y-axis.)

(*b*) $y - y_1 = m(x - x_1)$. [m = slope, line passes through point (x_1, y_1).]

(*c*) $\dfrac{y - y_1}{x - x_1} = \dfrac{y_2 - y_1}{x_2 - x_1}$. [line passes thru points (x_1, y_1) and (x_2, y_2).]

(*d*) $\dfrac{x}{a} + \dfrac{y}{b} = 1$. (a and b are the intercepts on x and y-axes, respectively.)

(*e*) $x \cos\alpha + y \sin \alpha = p$. (normal form. p is distance from origin to the line, α is angle which normal to the line makes with x-axis.)

(*f*) $Ax + By + C = 0$. (general form. slope $= -A \div B$).

To reduce $Ax + By + C = 0$ to normal form (*e*), divide by $\pm \sqrt{A^2 + B^2}$, where the sign of the radical is taken opposite to that of C when $C \neq 0$.

The distance from the line $Ax + By + C = 0$ to the point $P_2(x_2, y_2)$ is:

$$d = \frac{Ax_2 + By_2 + C}{\pm \sqrt{A^2 + B^2}}.$$

81. Circle (See §37). General equation of circle with radius R and center at (h, k) is:

$$(x - h)^2 + (y - k)^2 = R^2.$$

82. Conic. The locus of a point (P) which moves so that its distance from a fixed point (focus) bears a constant ratio e (eccentricity) to its distance from a fixed straight line (directrix) is a conic.

If d is the distance from focus to directrix,

$$x^2 + y^2 = e^2 (d + x)^2.$$

$$r = \frac{de}{1 - e \cos \theta}.$$

If $e = 1$, the conic is a *parabola*; if $e > 1$, a *hyperbola*; and if $e < 1$, an *ellipse*.

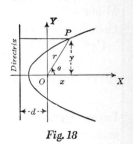

Fig. 18

83. Parabola (See §39). $e = 1$.

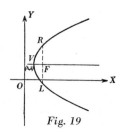

Fig. 19

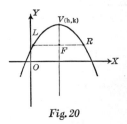

Fig. 20

(a) $(y - k)^2 = 4a(x - h)$. Vertex at (h, k), axis $\parallel OX$. (*Fig.* 19.)

(b) $(x - h)^2 = 4a(y - k)$. Vertex at (h, k), axis $\parallel OY$. (*Fig.* 20.)

Distance from vertex to focus $= VF = a.$

Latus rectum $= LR = 4a.$

84. Ellipse (See §38). $e < 1$.

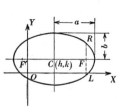

Fig. 21

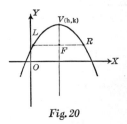

Fig. 22

$$\frac{(x - h)^2}{a^2} + \frac{(y - k)^2}{b^2} = 1.$$ Center at (h, k), axes $\parallel OX, OY$.

	$a > b$, (Fig. 21)	$a < b$, (Fig. 22)
Major axis	$2a$	$2b$
Minor axis	$2b$	$2a$
Distance from center to either focus	$\sqrt{a^2 - b^2}$	$\sqrt{b^2 - a^2}$
Eccentricity, e	$\dfrac{\sqrt{a^2 - b^2}}{a}$	$\dfrac{\sqrt{b^2 - a^2}}{b}$
Latus rectum	$\dfrac{2b^2}{a}$	$\dfrac{2a^2}{b}$
Sum of distances from any point P on ellipse to the foci, $PF' + PF$	$2a$	$2b$

85. Hyperbola. $e > 1$.

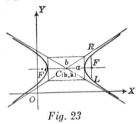

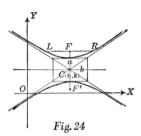

Fig. 23   Fig. 24

(a) $\dfrac{(x - h)^2}{a^2} - \dfrac{(y - k)^2}{b^2} = 1$. Center at (h, k), transverse axis $\| OX$.

Slopes of asymptotes $= \pm b/a$. (Fig. 23.)

(b) $\dfrac{(y - k)^2}{a^2} - \dfrac{(x - h)^2}{b^2} = 1$. Center at (h, k), transverse axis $\| OY$.

Slopes of asymptotes $= \pm a/b$. (Fig. 24.)

Transverse axis $= 2a$.   Conjugate axis $= 2b$.

Distance from center to either focus $= \sqrt{a^2 + b^2}$.

Difference of distances of any point on hyperbola from the foci $= 2a$.

Eccentricity $= e = \dfrac{\sqrt{a^2 + b^2}}{a}$.

Latus Rectum $= 2b^2/a$.

86. Sine Wave.

$y = a \sin(bx + c)$.

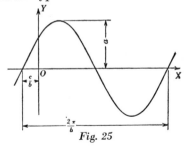

Fig. 25

$$y = a \cos (bx + c') = a \sin (bx + c), \text{ where } c = c' + \frac{\pi}{2}.$$

$$y = p \sin bx + q \cos bx = a \sin (bx + c),$$

$$\text{where } c = \tan^{-1} \left(\frac{q}{p}\right), \quad a = \sqrt{p^2 + q^2}.$$

a = amplitude = maximum height of wave.

$\frac{2\pi}{b}$ = wave length = distance from any point on wave to the corresponding point on the next wave.

$x = -\frac{c}{b}$ = phase, indicates a point on x-axis from which the positive half of the wave starts.

87. Trigonometric Curves.

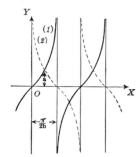

Fig. 26

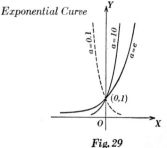

Fig. 27

(1) $y = a \tan bx$ or $x = \frac{1}{b} \tan^{-1}\left(\frac{y}{a}\right)$. (1) $y = a \sec bx$ or $x = \frac{1}{b}\sec^{-1}\left(\frac{y}{a}\right)$.

(2) $y = a \operatorname{ctn} bx$ or $x = \frac{1}{b} \operatorname{ctn}^{-1}\left(\frac{y}{a}\right)$. (2) $y = a \csc bx$ or $x = \frac{1}{b}\csc^{-1}\left(\frac{y}{a}\right)$.

88. Logarithmic and Exponential Curves.

Logarithmic Curve

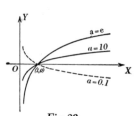

Fig. 28

$y = \log_a x$ or $x = a^y$.

Exponential Curve

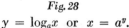

Fig. 29

$y = a^x$ or $x = \log_a y$.

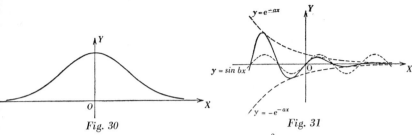

Fig. 30　　　　　　　　　　　　　　　Fig. 31

89.　Probability Curve (Fig. 30).　$y = e^{-x^2}$

90.　Oscillatory Wave of Decreasing Amplitude (Fig. 31).

$$y = e^{-ax} \sin bx.$$

91.　Catenary (Fig. 32).

$$y = \frac{a}{2}\left(e^{\frac{x}{a}} + e^{-\frac{x}{a}}\right).$$

A curve made by a cord of uniform weight suspended freely between two points at the same level.　(See §69.)

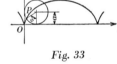

Fig. 32

Length of arc $= s = l\left[1 + \frac{2}{3}\left(\frac{2d}{l}\right)^2\right]$

approximately, if d is small in comparison with l.

92.　Cycloid (Fig. 33).　$\begin{cases} x = a(\phi - \sin\phi). \\ y = a(1 - \cos\phi). \end{cases}$

A curve described by a point on the circumference of circle which rolls along a fixed straight line.

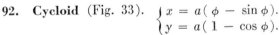

Fig. 33

Area one arch　　　　　　　$= 3\pi a^2.$

Length of arc of one arch　$= 8a.$

93.　Prolate and Curtate Cycloid.　$\begin{cases} x = a\phi - b\sin\phi, \\ y = a - b\cos\phi. \end{cases}$

A curve described by a point on a circle at a distance b from the center of the circle of radius a which rolls along a fixed straight line.

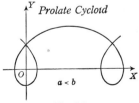

Fig. 34

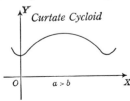

Fig. 35

94. Epicycloid (Fig. 36).

$$\begin{cases} x = (a + b) \cos \phi - a \cos \left(\dfrac{a + b}{a} \phi \right), \\ y = (a + b) \sin \phi - a \sin \left(\dfrac{a + b}{a} \phi \right). \end{cases}$$

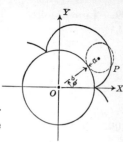

A curve described by a point on the circumference of a circle which rolls along the outside of a fixed circle.

Fig. 36

95. Cardioid (Fig. 37).

$$r = a(1 + \cos \theta).$$

An epicycloid in which both circles have same radii is called a cardioid.

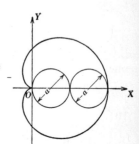

Fig. 37

96. Hypocycloid.

$$\begin{cases} x = (a - b) \cos \phi + b \cos \left(\dfrac{a - b}{b} \phi \right), \\ y = (a - b) \sin \phi - b \sin \left(\dfrac{a - b}{b} \phi \right). \end{cases}$$

A curve described by a point on the circumference of a circle which rolls along the inside of a fixed circle.

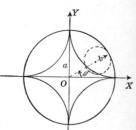

97. Hypocycloid of four cusps (Fig. 38).

$x^{\frac{2}{3}} + y^{\frac{2}{3}} = a^{\frac{2}{3}}.$

$x = a \cos^3 \phi, \quad y = a \sin^3 \phi.$

Fig. 38

The radius of fixed circle is four times the radius of rolling circle.

98. Involute of the Circle (Fig. 39).

$$\begin{cases} x = a \cos \phi + a \phi \sin \phi, \\ y = a \sin \phi - a \phi \cos \phi. \end{cases}$$

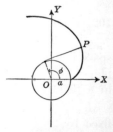

A curve generated by the end of a string which is kept taut while being unwound from a circle.

Fig. 39

99. Lemniscate (Fig. 40).

$$r^2 = 2\,a^2 \cos 2\,\theta.$$

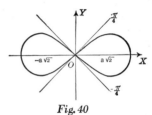

Fig. 40

100. N-Leaved Rose (Fig. 41).

(1) $r = a \sin n\theta$

(2) $r = a \cos n\theta.$

If n is an odd integer there are n leaves, and if n is even, $2n$ leaves, of which the figure shows one.

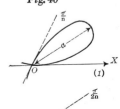

Fig. 41

101. Spirals.

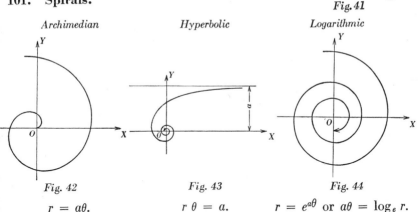

Archimedian	*Hyperbolic*	*Logarithmic*
Fig. 42	*Fig. 43*	*Fig. 44*
$r = a\theta.$	$r\,\theta = a.$	$r = e^{a\theta}$ or $a\theta = \log_e r.$

Solid Analytic Geometry

102. Coördinates (Fig. 45).

(**a**) *Rectangular system.* The position of a point $P\ (x, y, z)$ in space is fixed by its three distances x, y, and z from three coördinate planes XOY, XOZ, ZOY, which are mutually perpendicular and meet in a point O (origin).

(**b**) *Cylindrical system.* The position of any point $P\ (r, \theta, z)$ is fixed by (r, θ), the polar coördinates of the projection of P in the XOY plane, and by z, its distance from the XOY plane.

(*c*) *Spherical* (*or polar or geographical*) *system.* The position of any point $P(\rho, \theta, \phi)$ is fixed by the distance $\rho = \overline{OP}$, the angle $\theta = \angle XOM$, and the angle $\phi = \angle ZOP$. θ is called the *longitude* and ϕ the *co-latitude*.

The following relations exist between the three coördinates systems:

$$\begin{cases} x = \rho \sin \phi \cos \theta, \\ y = \rho \sin \phi \sin \theta, \\ z = \rho \cos \phi. \end{cases} \qquad \begin{cases} r = \rho \sin \phi, \\ z = \rho \cos \phi. \end{cases} \qquad \begin{cases} \rho = \sqrt{r^2 + z^2}, \\ \cos \phi = \dfrac{z}{\sqrt{r^2 + z^2}}. \end{cases}$$

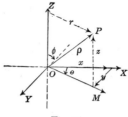

Fig. 45

103. Points, Lines, and Planes. Distance between two points $P_1(x_1, y_1, z_1)$ and $P_2(x_2, y_2, z_2)$, is

$$d = \sqrt{(x_2 - x_1)^2 + (y_2 - y_1)^2 + (z_2 - z_1)^2}.$$

Direction cosines of a line are the cosines of the angles α, β, γ which the line or any parallel line makes with the coördinate axes.

The direction cosines of the line segment $P_1(x_1, y_1, z_1)$ to $P_2(x_2, y_2, z_2)$ are:

$$\cos \alpha = \frac{x_2 - x_1}{d}, \quad \cos \beta = \frac{y_2 - y_1}{d}, \quad \cos \gamma = \frac{z_2 - z_1}{d}.$$

If $\cos \alpha : \cos \beta : \cos \gamma = a : b : c$, then

$$\cos \alpha = \frac{a}{\sqrt{a^2 + b^2 + c^2}}, \cos \beta = \frac{b}{\sqrt{a^2 + b^2 + c^2}}, \cos \gamma = \frac{c}{\sqrt{a^2 + b^2 + c^2}}.$$

$$\cos^2 \alpha + \cos^2 \beta + \cos^2 \gamma = 1.$$

Angle θ between two lines, whose direction angles are α_1, β_1, γ_1, and α_2, β_2, γ_2, is given by

$$\cos \theta = \cos \alpha_1 \cos \alpha_2 + \cos \beta_1 \cos \beta_2 + \cos \gamma_1 \cos \gamma_2.$$

Equation of a plane is

$$Ax + By + Cz + D = 0,$$

where A, B, C are proportional to the direction cosines of a normal (a line perpendicular to the plane) to the plane.

Angle between two planes is the angle between their normals.

Equation of a straight line through the point P_1 (x_1, y_1, z_1) is

$$\frac{x - x_1}{a} = \frac{y - y_1}{b} = \frac{z - z_1}{c},$$

where a, b, c are proportional to direction cosines of line.

104. Figures in Three Dimensions.

Plane*

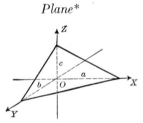

Fig. 46

$$\frac{x}{a} + \frac{y}{b} + \frac{z}{c} = 1.$$

Elliptic Cylinder*

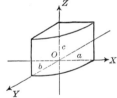

Fig. 47

$$\frac{x^2}{a^2} + \frac{y^2}{b^2} = 1.$$

Sphere*

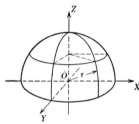

Fig. 48

$$x^2 + y^2 + z^2 = r^2.$$

Ellipsoid

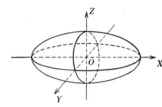

Fig. 49

$$\frac{x^2}{a^2} + \frac{y^2}{b^2} + \frac{z^2}{c^2} = 1.$$

*Only a portion of the figure is shown.

Elliptic Paraboloid

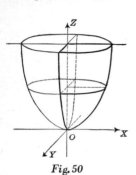

Fig. 50

$$\frac{x^2}{a^2} + \frac{y^2}{b^2} = cz.$$

Portion of Cone

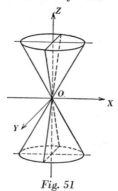

Fig. 51

$$\frac{x^2}{a^2} + \frac{y^2}{b^2} - \frac{z^2}{c^2} = 0.$$

Hyperboloid of One Sheet

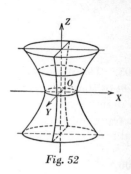

Fig. 52

$$\frac{x^2}{a^2} + \frac{y^2}{b^2} - \frac{z^2}{c^2} = 1.$$

Hyperboloid of Two Sheets

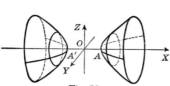

Fig. 53

$$\frac{x^2}{a^2} - \frac{y^2}{b^2} - \frac{z^2}{c^2} = 1.$$

Hyperbolic Paraboloid

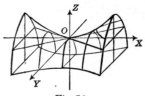

Fig. 54

$$\frac{x^2}{a^2} - \frac{y^2}{b^2} = cz.$$

V. DIFFERENTIAL CALCULUS

105. Definition of Function. A variable y is said to be a *function* of the variable x, if, for every x, (taken at will on its range), y is determined. The symbols $f(x)$, $F(x)$, $g(x)$, $\phi(x)$, etc., are used to represent various functions of x. The symbol $f(a)$ represents the value of $f(x)$ when $x = a$.

106. Definition of Derivative and Notation. Let $y = f(x)$ be a single-valued (continuous) function of x. Let Δx be any increment (increase or decrease) given to x, and let Δy be the corresponding increment in y. The *derivative* of y with respect to x is the limit, (if it exists), of the ratio of Δy to Δx as Δx approaches zero in any manner whatsoever; that is,

$$\frac{dy}{dx} = \lim_{\Delta x \to 0} \frac{\Delta y}{\Delta x} = \lim_{\Delta x \to 0} \frac{f(x + \Delta x) - f(x)}{\Delta x} = f'(x) = D_x y = y'.$$

Higher derivatives are defined as follows:

$$\frac{d^2y}{dx^2} = \frac{d}{dx}\left(\frac{dy}{dx}\right) = \frac{d}{dx} f'(x) = f''(x). \qquad \text{(2nd derivative.)}$$

$$\frac{d^3y}{dx^3} = \frac{d}{dx}\left(\frac{d^2y}{dx^2}\right) = \frac{d}{dx} f''(x) = f'''(x). \qquad \text{(3rd derivative.)}$$

$$\frac{d^ny}{dx^n} = \frac{d}{dx}\left(\frac{d^{n-1}y}{dx^{n-1}}\right) = \frac{d}{dx} f^{(n-1)}(x) = f^{(n)}(x). \qquad \text{(nth derivative.)}$$

The symbol $f^{(n)}(a)$ represents the value of $f^{(n)}(x)$ when $x = a$.

107. Certain Relations among Derivatives.

If $x = f(y)$, then $\dfrac{dy}{dx} = 1 \div \dfrac{dx}{dy}$.

If $y = f(u)$, and $u = F(x)$, then $\dfrac{dy}{dx} = \dfrac{dy}{du} \cdot \dfrac{du}{dx}$.

If $x = f(\alpha)$, $y = \phi(\alpha)$, then

$$\frac{dy}{dx} = \frac{\phi'(\alpha)}{f'(\alpha)}, \qquad \frac{d^2y}{dx^2} = \frac{f'(\alpha) \cdot \phi''(\alpha) \cdot -\phi'(\alpha) \cdot f''(\alpha)}{[f'(\alpha)]^3}.$$

108. Table of Derivatives. In this table, u and v represent functions of x; a, n, e represent constants ($e = 2.7183 \cdots$), and all angles are measured in radians.

$$\frac{d}{dx}(x) = 1. \qquad\qquad \frac{d}{dx}(a) = 0.$$

$$\frac{d}{dx}(u \pm v \pm \cdots) = \frac{du}{dx} \pm \frac{dv}{dx} \pm \cdots.$$

$$\frac{d}{dx}(au) = a\frac{du}{dx}. \qquad\qquad \frac{d}{dx}(uv) = u\frac{dv}{dx} + v\frac{du}{dx}.$$

$$\frac{d}{dx}\left(\frac{u}{v}\right) = \frac{v\dfrac{du}{dx} - u\dfrac{dv}{dx}}{v^2}. \qquad \frac{d}{dx}\sin u = \cos u \frac{du}{dx}.$$

$$\frac{d}{dx}(u^n) = nu^{n-1}\frac{du}{dx}. \qquad \frac{d}{dx}\cos u = -\sin u \frac{du}{dx}.$$

$$\frac{d}{dx}\log_a u = \frac{\log_a e}{u}\frac{du}{dx}. \qquad \frac{d}{dx}\tan u = \sec^2 u \frac{du}{dx}.$$

$$\frac{d}{dx}\log_e u = \frac{1}{u}\frac{du}{dx}. \qquad \frac{d}{dx}\operatorname{ctn} u = -\csc^2 u \frac{du}{dx}.$$

$$\frac{d}{dx}a^u = a^u \cdot \log_e a \cdot \frac{du}{dx}. \qquad \frac{d}{dx}\sec u = \sec u \tan u \frac{du}{dx}.$$

$$\frac{d}{dx}e^u = e^u \frac{du}{dx}. \qquad \frac{d}{dx}\csc u = -\csc u \operatorname{ctn} u \frac{du}{dx}.$$

$$\frac{d}{dx}u^v = vu^{v-1}\frac{du}{dx} + u^v \log_e u \frac{dv}{dx}. \qquad \frac{d}{dx}\operatorname{vers} u = \sin u \frac{du}{dx}.$$

$$\lim_{x \to 0}\frac{\sin x}{x} = 1,\ \lim_{x \to 0}(1+x)^{1/x} = e = 2.71828\cdots = 1 + 1 + \frac{1}{2!} + \frac{1}{3!} + \cdots.$$

$$\frac{d}{dx}\sin^{-1} u = \frac{1}{\sqrt{1-u^2}}\frac{du}{dx}, \qquad \frac{-\pi}{2} \leqq \sin^{-1} u \leqq \frac{\pi}{2}.$$

$$\frac{d}{dx}\cos^{-1} u = -\frac{1}{\sqrt{1-u^2}}\frac{du}{dx}, \qquad 0 \leqq \cos^{-1} u \leqq \pi.$$

$$\frac{d}{dx}\tan^{-1} u = \frac{1}{1+u^2}\frac{du}{dx}. \qquad \frac{d}{dx}\operatorname{ctn}^{-1} u = -\frac{1}{1+u^2}\frac{du}{dx}.$$

$$\frac{d}{dx}\sec^{-1} u = \frac{1}{u\sqrt{u^2-1}}\frac{du}{dx},\ -\pi \leqq \sec^{-1} u < -\frac{\pi}{2},\ 0 \leqq \sec^{-1} u < \frac{\pi}{2}.$$

$$\frac{d}{dx}\csc^{-1} u = -\frac{1}{u\sqrt{u^2-1}}\frac{du}{dx}, \quad -\pi < \csc^{-1} u \leqq -\frac{\pi}{2}, \, 0 < \csc^{-1} u \leqq \frac{\pi}{2}.$$

$$\frac{d}{dx}\text{vers}^{-1} u = \frac{1}{\sqrt{2u-u^2}}\frac{du}{dx}, \quad 0 \leqq \text{vers}^{-1} u \leqq \pi.$$

$$\frac{d}{dx}\sinh u = \cosh u \frac{du}{dx}. \qquad \frac{d}{dx}\cosh u = \sinh u \frac{du}{dx}.$$

$$\frac{d}{dx}\tanh u = \text{sech}^2 u \frac{du}{dx}. \qquad \frac{d}{dx}\text{ctnh } u = -\text{csch}^2 u \frac{du}{dx}.$$

$$\frac{d}{dx}\text{sech } u = -\text{sech } u \tanh u \frac{du}{dx}. \qquad \frac{d}{dx}\text{csch } u = -\text{csch } u \text{ ctnh } u \frac{du}{dx}.$$

$$\frac{d}{dx}\sinh^{-1} u = \frac{1}{\sqrt{u^2+1}}\frac{du}{dx}. \qquad \frac{d}{dx}\cosh^{-1} u = \frac{1}{\sqrt{u^2-1}}\frac{du}{dx}, u>1.$$

$$\frac{d}{dx}\tanh^{-1} u = \frac{1}{1-u^2}\frac{du}{dx}. \qquad \frac{d}{dx}\text{ctnh}^{-1} u = -\frac{1}{u^2-1}\frac{du}{dx}.$$

$$\frac{d}{dx}\text{sech}^{-1} u = -\frac{1}{u\sqrt{1-u^2}}\frac{du}{dx}, u>0. \, \frac{d}{dx}\text{csch}^{-1} u = -\frac{1}{u\sqrt{u^2+1}}\frac{du}{dx}.$$

109. Slope of a Curve. Equation of Tangent and Normal (Rectangular Coördinates). The slope of the curve $y = f(x)$ at the point $P(x, y)$ is defined as the slope of the tangent line to the curve at P.

Slope $= m = \tan \alpha = \dfrac{dy}{dx} = f'(x).$

Slope at $x = x_1$ is $m_1 = f'(x_1).$

Equation of *tangent line* to curve at $P_1(x_1, y_1)$ is
$$y - y_1 = m_1(x - x_1).$$

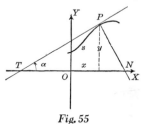

Fig. 55

Equation of *normal line* to curve at $P_1(x_1, y_1)$ is
$$y - y_1 = -\frac{1}{m_1}(x - x_1).$$

Angle (θ) *of intersection of two curves* whose slopes are m_1 and m_2 at the common point is given by
$$\tan \theta = \frac{m_2 - m_1}{1 + m_1 m_2}.$$

110. Differential. If $y = f(x)$, Δx is an increment of x, and $f'(x)$ is the derivative of $f(x)$ with respect to x, then the differential of x equals the increment of x, or $dx = \Delta x$; and the differential of y, dy, is the product of $f'(x)$ and the increment of x;

$$dy = f'(x)dx = \frac{df(x)}{dx}dx = \frac{dy}{dx}dx, \text{ and } f'(x) = \frac{dy}{dx}.$$

If $x = f(t)$, $y = \phi(t)$, then $dx = f'(t)\, dt$ and $dy = \phi'(t)\, dt$.

Every derivative formula has a corresponding differential formula. For example, from Table of §108,

$$d(\sin u) = \cos u \cdot du; \qquad d(u \cdot v) = u\, dv + v\, du.$$

111. Maximum and Minimum Values of a Function. A *maximum (minimum)* value of a function $f(x)$ in the interval (a, b) is a value of the function which is greater (less) than the values of the function in the immediate vicinity.

The values of x which give a maximum or minimum value to $y = f(x)$ are found by solving the equations $f'(x) = 0$ or ∞. If a be a root of $f'(x) = 0$ and if $f''(a) < 0$, $f(a)$ is a maximum; if $f''(a) > 0$, $f(a)$ is a minimum. If $f''(a) = 0$, $f'''(a) \neq 0$, $f(a)$ is neither a maximum or a minimum, but if $f''(a) = f'''(a) = 0$, $f(a)$ is maximum or minimum according as $f^{IV}(a) \lessgtr 0$.

In general, if the first derivative which does not vanish for $x = a$ is of an odd order, $f(a)$ is neither a maximum or a minimum; but if it is of an even order, the $2n$th, say, then $f(a)$ is a maximum or minimum according as $f^{(2n)}(a) \lessgtr 0$.

To find the largest or smallest values of a function in an interval (a, b), find $f(a)$, $f(b)$ and compare with the maximum and minimum values as found in the interval.

112. Points of Inflection of a Curve. The curve is said to have a *point of inflection* at $x = a$ if $f''(a) = 0$ and $f''(x) < 0$ on one side of $x = a$ and $f''(x) > 0$ on the other side of $x = a$. Wherever $f''(x) < 0$, the curve is *concave downward*, and wherever $f''(x) > 0$, the curve is *concave upward*.

113. Derivative of Arc Length. Radius of Curvature (See §75, §107, §126). Let s be the length of arc measured along the curve $y = f(x)$, [or in polar coördinates $r = \phi(\theta)$], from some fixed point to any point $P(x, y)$, and α be the angle of inclination of the tangent line at P with OX. Then

$$\frac{dx}{ds} = \cos \alpha = \frac{1}{\sqrt{1 + \left(\frac{dy}{dx}\right)^2}}, \quad \frac{dy}{ds} = \sin \alpha = \frac{1}{\sqrt{1 + \left(\frac{dx}{dy}\right)^2}},$$

$$ds = \sqrt{dx^2 + dy^2} = \sqrt{1 + \left(\frac{dy}{dx}\right)^2} \cdot dx = \sqrt{1 + \left(\frac{dx}{dy}\right)^2} \cdot dy.$$

$$ds = \sqrt{dr^2 + r^2 d\theta^2} = \sqrt{r^2 + \left(\frac{dr}{d\theta}\right)^2} \cdot d\theta = \sqrt{1 + r^2 \left(\frac{d\theta}{dr}\right)^2} \cdot dr.$$

If $x = r \cos \theta$, $y = r \sin \theta$,

$$dx = \cos \theta \cdot dr - r \sin \theta \cdot d\theta, \quad dy = \sin \theta \cdot dr + r \cos \theta \cdot d\theta.$$

The *radius* of *curvature* R at any point $P(x, y)$ of the curve $y = f(x)$ is

$$r = \frac{ds}{d\alpha} = \frac{\left[1 + \left(\frac{dy}{dx}\right)^2\right]^{\frac{3}{2}}}{\left(\frac{d^2y}{dx^2}\right)}, \quad = \frac{\{1 + [f'(x)]^2\}^{\frac{3}{2}}}{f''(x)},$$

$$R = \frac{\left[r^2 + \left(\frac{dr}{d\theta}\right)^2\right]^{\frac{3}{2}}}{r^2 + 2\left(\frac{dr}{d\theta}\right)^2 - r \frac{d^2r}{d\theta^2}}.$$

The *curvature* (K) at (x, y) is $\quad K = \frac{1}{R}.$

The *center* of *curvature* corresponding to the point (x, y) on $y = f(x)$ is (h, k), where

$$h = x_1 - \frac{f'(x_1) \{1 + [f'(x_1)]^2\}}{f''(x_1)},$$

$$k = y_1 + \frac{1 + [f'(x_1)]^2}{f''(x_1)}.$$

114.   Theorem of the Mean.   Rolle's Theorem. If $y = f(x)$ and its derivative $f'(x)$ be continuous on the interval (a, b), there exists a value of x somewhere between a and b such that

$$f(b) = f(a) + (b - a) f'(x_1), \quad a < x_1 < b.$$

Rolle's Theorem is a special case of the Theorem of the Mean with $f(a) = f(b) = 0$; i. e., there exists at least one value of x between a and b for which $f'(x_1) = 0$.

115.   Evaluation of Indeterminate Forms. If $f(x)$ and $F(x)$ be two continuous functions of x having continuous derivatives, $f'(x)$ and $F'(x)$, then:

(**a**)   If $\lim\limits_{x \to a} f(x) = 0$ and $\lim\limits_{x \to a} F(x) = 0$, and $\lim\limits_{x \to a} F'(x) \neq 0$,

[or if $\lim\limits_{x \to a} f(x) = \lim\limits_{x \to a} F(x) = \infty$], then

$$\lim_{x \to a} \frac{f(x)}{F(x)} = \lim_{x \to a} \frac{f'(x)}{F'(x)}.$$

(**b**)   If $\lim\limits_{x \to a} f(x) = 0$ and $\lim\limits_{x \to a} F(x) = \infty$, [i.e. $F(x)$ becomes infinite as x approaches a as a limit], then $\lim\limits_{x \to a} [f(x) \cdot F(x)]$ may often be determined by writing

$$f(x) \cdot F(x) = \frac{f(x)}{1/F(x)},$$

thus expressing the functions in the form of (**a**).

(**c**)   If $\lim\limits_{x \to a} f(x) = \infty$ and $\lim\limits_{x \to a} F(x) = \infty$, then $\lim\limits_{x \to a} [f(x) - F(x)]$ may often be determined by writing

$$f(x) - F(x) = \frac{1/F(x) - 1/f(x)}{1/[f(x) \cdot F(x)]},$$

and using (**a**).

(**d**)   The $\lim\limits_{x \to a} \left[f(x)^{F(x)} \right]$ may frequently be evaluated upon writing

$$f(x)^{F(x)} = e^{F(x) \cdot \log_e f(x)}.$$

When one factor of the last exponent approaches zero and the other becomes infinite, the exponent is of the type considered in (**b**).

Thus we are led to the indeterminate forms which are symbolized by

$$0/0, \quad \infty/\infty, \quad 0^0, \quad 1^\infty, \quad \infty^0.$$

116. Taylor's and Maclaurin's Theorem. Any function (continuous and having derivatives) may, in general, be expanded into a *Taylor's Series*,

$$f(x) = f(a) + f'(a) \cdot \frac{(x-a)}{1!} + f''(a) \cdot \frac{(x-a)^2}{2!}$$

$$+ f'''(a) \cdot \frac{(x-a)^3}{3!} + \cdots + f^{(n-1)}(a) \cdot \frac{(x-a)^{n-1}}{(n-1)!} + R_n,$$

where a is any quantity for which $f(a), f'(a), f''(a), \cdots$ are finite.

If the series is to be used for approximating $f(x)$ for some value of x, then a should be picked so that the difference $(x-a)$ is numerically very small, and thus only a few terms of the series need be used. The remainder, after n terms, is $R_n = f^{(n)}(x_1) \cdot (x-a)^n/n!$, where x_1 lies between a and x. R_n gives the limits of error in using n terms of the series for the approximation of the function.

$$[n! = n = 1 \cdot 2 \cdot 3 \cdot 4 \cdots n .]$$

If $a = 0$, the above series is called *Maclaurin's Series*.

$$f(x) = f(0) + f'(0) \frac{x}{1!} + f''(0) \frac{x^2}{2!} + f'''(0) \frac{x^3}{3!} + \cdots$$

$$+ f^{(n-1)}(0) \frac{x^{n-1}}{(n-1)!} + R_n.$$

117. Series. The following series may be obtained through the expansion of the functions by Taylor's or Maclaurin's Theorems. The expressions following a series indicate the region of convergence of the series, that is, the values of x for which R_n approaches zero as n becomes infinite, so that an approximation of the function may be obtained by using a number of terms of the series. If the region of convergence is not indicated, the series converges for all finite values of x. $(n! = 1 \cdot 2 \cdot 3 \cdots n)$. $\text{Log}_e u \equiv \text{Log } u$.

(a) *Binominal Series.*

$$(a + x)^n = a^n + na^{n-1}x + \frac{n(n-1)}{2!} a^{n-2}x^2$$
$$+ \frac{n(n-1)(n-2)}{3!} a^{n-3}x^3 + \cdots, \quad x^2 < a^2.$$

If n is a positive integer, the series consists of $(n+1)$ terms; otherwise, the number of terms is infinite.

$$(a - bx)^{-1} = \frac{1}{a}\left(1 + \frac{bx}{a} + \frac{b^2x^2}{a^2} + \frac{b^3x^3}{a^3} \cdots\right), \quad b^2x^2 < a^2.$$

(b) *Exponential, Logarithmic, and Trigonometric Series.*[*]

$$e = 1 + \frac{1}{1!} + \frac{1}{2!} + \frac{1}{3!} + \frac{1}{4!} + \cdots.$$

$$e^x = 1 + x + \frac{x^2}{2!} + \frac{x^3}{3!} + \frac{x^4}{4!} + \cdots.$$

$$a^x = 1 + x \log a + \frac{(x \log a)^2}{2!} + \frac{(x \log a)^3}{3!} + \cdots.$$

$$e^{-x^2} = 1 - x^2 + \frac{x^4}{2!} - \frac{x^6}{3!} + \frac{x^8}{4!} - \cdots.$$

$$\log x = (x - 1) - \tfrac{1}{2}(x - 1)^2 + \tfrac{1}{3}(x - 1)^3 - \cdots, \qquad 0 < x \leqq 2.$$

$$\log x = \frac{x-1}{x} + \frac{1}{2}\left(\frac{x-1}{x}\right)^2 + \frac{1}{3}\left(\frac{x-1}{x}\right)^3 + \cdots, \qquad x > \frac{1}{2}.$$

$$\log x = 2\left[\frac{x-1}{x+1} + \frac{1}{3}\left(\frac{x-1}{x+1}\right)^3 + \frac{1}{5}\left(\frac{x-1}{x+1}\right)^5 + \cdots\right], \qquad x > 0.$$

$$\log (1 + x) = x - \frac{x^2}{2} + \frac{x^3}{3} - \frac{x^4}{4} + \cdots.$$

$$\log (a + x) = \log a + 2\left[\frac{x}{2a+x} + \frac{1}{3}\left(\frac{x}{2a+x}\right)^3 + \frac{1}{5}\left(\frac{x}{2a+x}\right)^5 + \cdots\right], \quad a > 0, -a < x < +\infty.$$

$$\log\left(\frac{1+x}{1-x}\right) = 2\left(x + \frac{x^3}{3} + \frac{x^5}{5} + \frac{x^7}{7} + \cdots\right), \qquad x^2 < 1.$$

$$\log\left(\frac{x+1}{x-1}\right) = 2\left[\frac{1}{x} + \frac{1}{3}\left(\frac{1}{x}\right)^3 + \frac{1}{5}\left(\frac{1}{x}\right)^5 + \frac{1}{7}\left(\frac{1}{x}\right)^7 + \cdots\right], \quad x^2 > 1.$$

$$\log\left(\frac{x+1}{x}\right) = 2\left[\frac{1}{2x+1} + \frac{1}{3(2x+1)^3} + \frac{1}{5(2x+1)^5} + \cdots\right], x > 0.$$

[*] $\log u \equiv \log_e u.$

$$\log (x + \sqrt{1+x^2}) = x - \frac{1}{2}\frac{x^3}{3} + \frac{1 \cdot 3}{2 \cdot 4}\frac{x^5}{5} - \frac{1 \cdot 3 \cdot 5}{2 \cdot 4 \cdot 6}\frac{x^7}{7} + \cdots, \qquad x^2 < 1.$$

$$\sin x = x - \frac{x^3}{3!} + \frac{x^5}{5!} - \frac{x^7}{7!} + \cdots.$$

$$\cos x = 1 - \frac{x^2}{2!} + \frac{x^4}{4!} - \frac{x^6}{6!} + \cdots.$$

$$\tan x = x + \frac{x^3}{3} + \frac{2x^5}{15} + \frac{17x^7}{315} + \frac{62x^9}{2835} + \cdots, \qquad x^2 < \frac{\pi^2}{4}.$$

$$\sin^{-1} x = x + \frac{x^3}{6} + \frac{1}{2} \cdot \frac{3}{4} \cdot \frac{x^5}{5} + \frac{1}{2} \cdot \frac{3}{4} \cdot \frac{5}{6} \cdot \frac{x^7}{7} + \cdots, \qquad x^2 < 1.$$

$$\tan^{-1} x = x - \frac{1}{3}x^3 + \frac{1}{5}x^5 - \frac{1}{7}x^7 + \cdots, \qquad x^2 < 1.$$

$$= \frac{\pi}{2} - \frac{1}{x} + \frac{1}{3x^3} - \frac{1}{5x^5} + \cdots, \qquad x^2 > 1.$$

$$\log \sin x = \log x - \frac{x^2}{6} - \frac{x^4}{180} - \frac{x^6}{2835} - \cdots, \qquad x^2 < \pi^2.$$

$$\log \cos x = -\frac{x^2}{2} - \frac{x^4}{12} - \frac{x^6}{45} - \frac{17x^8}{2520} - \cdots, \qquad x^2 < \frac{\pi^2}{4}.$$

$$\log \tan x = \log x + \frac{x^2}{3} + \frac{7x^4}{90} + \frac{62x^6}{2835} + \cdots, \qquad x^2 < \frac{\pi^2}{4}.$$

$$e^{\sin x} = 1 + x + \frac{x^2}{2!} - \frac{3x^4}{4!} - \frac{8x^5}{5!} - \frac{3x^6}{6!} + \cdots.$$

$$e^{\cos x} = e\left(1 - \frac{x^2}{2!} + \frac{4x^4}{4!} - \frac{31x^6}{6!} + \cdots\right).$$

$$e^{\tan x} = 1 + x + \frac{x^2}{2!} + \frac{3x^3}{3!} + \frac{9x^4}{4!} + \frac{37x^5}{5!} + \cdots, \qquad x^2 < \frac{\pi^2}{4}.$$

$$\sinh x = x + \frac{x^3}{3!} + \frac{x^5}{5!} + \frac{x^7}{7!} + \cdots.$$

$$\cosh x = 1 + \frac{x^2}{2!} + \frac{x^4}{4!} + \frac{x^6}{6!} + \cdots.$$

$$\tanh x = x - \frac{x^3}{3} + \frac{2x^5}{15} + \frac{17x^7}{315} + \cdots.$$

$$\sinh^{-1} x = x - \frac{1}{2}\frac{x^3}{3} + \frac{1 \cdot 3}{2 \cdot 4}\frac{x^5}{5} - \frac{1 \cdot 3 \cdot 5}{2 \cdot 4 \cdot 6}\frac{x^7}{7} + \cdots, \qquad x^2 < 1.$$

$$\sinh^{-1} x = \log 2x + \frac{1}{2}\frac{1}{2x^2} - \frac{1 \cdot 3}{2 \cdot 4}\frac{1}{4x^4} + \frac{1 \cdot 3 \cdot 5}{2 \cdot 4 \cdot 6}\frac{1}{6x^6} \cdots, \qquad x > 1.$$

$$\cosh^{-1} x = \log 2 x - \frac{1}{2} \frac{1}{2x^2} - \frac{1 \cdot 3}{2 \cdot 4} \frac{1}{4x^4} - \frac{1 \cdot 3 \cdot 5}{2 \cdot 4 \cdot 6} \frac{1}{6x^6} - \cdots.$$

$$\tanh^{-1} x = x + \frac{x^3}{3} + \frac{x^5}{5} + \frac{x^7}{7} + \cdots, \quad x^2 < 1.$$

118. Partial Derivatives. Differentials. If $z = f(x, y)$, is a function of two variables, then the derivative of z with respect to x, as x varies while y remains constant, is called the *first partial derivative of z with respect to x* and is denoted by $\frac{\partial z}{\partial x}$. Similarly, the derivative of z with respect to y, as y varies while x remains constant, is called the *first partial derivative of z with respect to y* and is denoted by $\frac{\partial z}{\partial y}$.

Similarly, if $z = f(x, y, u, \cdots)$, then the first derivative of z with respect to x, as x varies while y, u, $\cdots$ remain constant, is called the first partial of z with respect to x and is denoted by $\frac{\partial z}{\partial x}$. Likewise, the second partial derivatives are defined as indicated below:

$$\frac{\partial^2 z}{\partial x^2} = \frac{\partial}{\partial x}\left(\frac{\partial z}{\partial x}\right); \; \frac{\partial^2 z}{\partial y^2} = \frac{\partial}{\partial y}\left(\frac{\partial z}{\partial y}\right); \; \frac{\partial^2 z}{\partial x \, \partial y} = \frac{\partial}{\partial x}\left(\frac{\partial z}{\partial y}\right) = \frac{\partial}{\partial y}\left(\frac{\partial z}{\partial x}\right) = \frac{\partial^2 z}{\partial y \, \partial x}.$$

If $z = f(x, y, \cdots, u)$, and $x, y, \cdots, u$ are functions of a single variable t, then

$$\frac{dz}{dt} = \frac{\partial z}{\partial x} \frac{dx}{dt} + \frac{\partial z}{\partial y} \frac{dy}{dt} + \cdots + \frac{\partial z}{\partial u} \frac{du}{dt},$$

$$dz = \frac{\partial z}{\partial x} dx + \frac{\partial z}{\partial y} dy + \cdots + \frac{\partial z}{\partial u} du,$$

If $F(x, y, z, \cdots, u) = 0$, then $\quad \frac{\partial F}{\partial x} dx + \frac{\partial F}{\partial y} dy + \cdots + \frac{\partial F}{\partial u} du = 0$.

119. Surfaces. Space Curves (See Analytic Geometry §97-8.) The *tangent plane* to the surface $F(x, y, z) = 0$ at the point (x_1, y_1, z_1) is

$$(x - x_1) \left(\frac{\partial F}{\partial x}\right)_1 + (y - y_1) \left(\frac{\partial F}{\partial y}\right)_1 + (z - z_1) \left(\frac{\partial F}{\partial z}\right)_1 = 0,$$

where $\left(\frac{\partial F}{\partial x}\right)_1$ is the value of $\frac{\partial F}{\partial x}$ at (x_1, y_1, z_1), etc.

The equations of the *normal* to the surface at (x_1, y_1, z_1) are

$$\frac{x - x_1}{\left(\dfrac{\partial F}{\partial x}\right)_1} = \frac{y - y_1}{\left(\dfrac{\partial F}{\partial y}\right)_1} = \frac{z - z_1}{\left(\dfrac{\partial F}{\partial z}\right)_1}.$$

The *direction cosines* of the normal to the surface are proportional to

$$\frac{\partial F}{\partial x}, \quad \frac{\partial F}{\partial y}, \quad \frac{\partial F}{\partial z}.$$

Given the *space* curve $x = x(t)$, $y = y(t)$, $z = z(t)$. The direction cosines of the tangent line to the curve at any point are proportional to

$$\frac{dx}{dt}, \quad \frac{dy}{dt}, \quad \frac{dz}{dt}, \quad \text{or to} \quad dx, \quad dy, \quad dz.$$

The equations of the *tangent line* to the curve at (x_1, y_1, z_1) are

$$\frac{x - x_1}{\left(\dfrac{dx}{dt}\right)_1} = \frac{y - y_1}{\left(\dfrac{dy}{dt}\right)_1} = \frac{z - z}{\left(\dfrac{dz}{dt}\right)_1}.$$

where $\left(\dfrac{dx}{dt}\right)_1$ is the value of $\dfrac{dx}{dt}$ at (x_1, y_1, z_1).

VI.   INTEGRAL CALCULUS

120.   Definition of Indefinite Integral. $F(x)$ is said to be an *indefinite integral* of $f(x)$, if the derivative of $F(x)$ is $f(x)$, or the differential of $F(x)$ is $f(x)dx$; symbolically:

$$F(x) = \int f(x)dx \quad \text{if} \quad \frac{dF(x)}{dx} = f(x), \quad \text{or} \quad dF(x) = f(x)dx.$$

In general: $\int f(x)dx = F(x) + C$, where C is an arbitrary constant.

121. Fundamental Theorems on Integrals. Short Table of Integrals.* (*u* and *v* denote functions of *x*; *a, b* and *C* denote constants).

1. $\int df(x) = f(x) + C.$

2. $d \int f(x)dx = f(x)dx.$

3. $\int 0 \cdot dx = C.$

4. $\int a\, f(x)\, dx = a \int f(x)\, dx.$

5. $\int (u \pm v)dx = \int u\,dx \pm \int v\,dx.$

6. $\int u\, dv = uv - \int v\, du.$

7. $\int \frac{u\, dv}{dx}\, dx = uv - \int v\, \frac{du}{dx}\, dx.$

8. $\int f(y)dx = \int \frac{f(y)dy}{\frac{dy}{dx}}.$

9. $\int u^n\, du = \frac{u^{n+1}}{n+1} + C,\ n \neq -1.$

10. $\int \frac{du}{u} = \log_e u + C.$

11. $\int e^u\, du = e^u + C.$

12. $\int b^u\, du = \frac{b^u}{\log_e b} + C.$

13. $\int \sin u\, du = -\cos u + C.$

14. $\int \cos u\, du = \sin u + C.$

*See §148.

15. $\displaystyle\int \tan u \, du \;=\; \log_e \sec u + C = -\log_e \cos u + C.$

16. $\displaystyle\int \text{ctn } u \, du \;=\; \log_e \sin u + C = -\log_e \csc u + C.$

17. $\displaystyle\int \sec u \, du \;=\; \log_e(\sec u + \tan u) + C = \log_e \tan\left(\frac{u}{2} + \frac{\pi}{4}\right) + C.$

18. $\displaystyle\int \csc u \, du \;=\; \log_e(\csc u - \text{ctn } u) + C = \log_e \tan\frac{u}{2} + C.$

19. $\displaystyle\int \sin^2 u \, du \;=\; \frac{1}{2} u - \frac{1}{2} \sin u \cos u + C.$

20. $\displaystyle\int \cos^2 u \, du \;=\; \frac{1}{2} u + \frac{1}{2} \sin u \cos u + C.$

21. $\displaystyle\int \sec^2 u \, du \;=\; \tan u + C.$

22. $\displaystyle\int \csc^2 u \, du \;=\; -\text{ctn } u + C.$

23. $\displaystyle\int \tan^2 u \, du \;=\; \tan u - u + C.$

24. $\displaystyle\int \cot^2 u \, du \;=\; -\text{ctn } u - u + C.$

25. $\displaystyle\int \frac{du}{u^2 + a^2} \;=\; \frac{1}{a} \tan^{-1} \frac{u}{a} + C.$

26. $\displaystyle\int \frac{du}{u^2 - a^2} = \frac{1}{2a} \log_e\left(\frac{u-a}{u+a}\right) + C = -\frac{1}{a} \text{ctnh}^{-1}\left(\frac{u}{a}\right) + C, \text{ if } u^2 > a^2,$

$\displaystyle\qquad\qquad = \frac{1}{2a} \log_e\left(\frac{a-u}{a+u}\right) + C = -\frac{1}{a} \tanh^{-1}\left(\frac{u}{a}\right) + C, \text{ if } u^2 < a^2.$

27. $\displaystyle\int \frac{du}{\sqrt{a^2 - u^2}} = \sin^{-1}\left(\frac{u}{a}\right) + C.$

28. $\displaystyle\int \frac{du}{\sqrt{u^2 \pm a^2}} = \log_e\left(u + \sqrt{u^2 \pm a^2}\right)^* + C.$

*See footnote on page 50.

29. $\displaystyle\int \frac{du}{\sqrt{2\,au - u^2}} = \cos^{-1}\left(\frac{a - u}{a}\right) + C.$

30. $\displaystyle\int \frac{du}{u\sqrt{u^2 - a^2}} = \frac{1}{a}\,\sec^{-1}\left(\frac{u}{a}\right) + C = \frac{1}{a}\,\cos^{-1}\frac{a}{u} + C.$

31. $\displaystyle\int \frac{du}{u\sqrt{a^2 \pm u^2}} = -\frac{1}{a}\,\log_e\left(\frac{a + \sqrt{a^2 \pm u^2}}{u}\right)^* + C.$

32. $\displaystyle\int \sqrt{a^2 - u^2}\cdot du = \frac{1}{2}\left(u\sqrt{a^2 - u^2} + a^2\sin^{-1}\frac{u}{a}\right) + C.$

33. $\displaystyle\int \sqrt{u^2 \pm a^2}\,du = \frac{1}{2}\left[u\sqrt{u^2 \pm a^2} \pm a^2\log_e\left(u + \sqrt{u^2 \pm a^2}\right)\right]^* + C.$

34. $\displaystyle\int \sinh u\,du = \cosh u + C.$

35. $\displaystyle\int \cosh u\,du = \sinh u + C.$

36. $\displaystyle\int \tanh u\,du = \log_e(\cosh u) + C.$

37. $\displaystyle\int \operatorname{ctnh} u\,du = \log_e(\sinh u) + C.$

38. $\displaystyle\int \operatorname{sech} u\,du = \sin^{-1}(\tanh u) + C.$

39. $\displaystyle\int \operatorname{csch} u\,du = \log_e\left(\tanh\frac{u}{2}\right) + C.$

40. $\displaystyle\int \operatorname{sech} u \cdot \tanh u \cdot du = -\operatorname{sech} u + C.$

41. $\displaystyle\int \operatorname{csch} u \cdot \operatorname{ctnh} u \cdot du = -\operatorname{csch} u + C.$

$* \log_e\left(\dfrac{u + \sqrt{u^2 + a^2}}{a}\right) = \sinh^{-1}\left(\dfrac{u}{a}\right);\ \log_e\left(\dfrac{a + \sqrt{a^2 - u^2}}{u}\right) = \operatorname{sech}^{-1}\left(\dfrac{u}{a}\right);$

$\log_e\left(\dfrac{u + \sqrt{u^2 - a^2}}{a}\right) = \cosh^{-1}\left(\dfrac{u}{a}\right);\ \log_e\left(\dfrac{a + \sqrt{a^2 + u^2}}{u}\right) = \operatorname{csch}^{-1}\left(\dfrac{u}{a}\right).$

Definite Integrals

122. Definition of Definite Integral. Let $f(x)$ be continuous for the interval from $x = a$ to $x = b$ inclusive. Divide this interval into n equal parts by the points a, x_1, x_2, $\cdots$, x_{n-1}, b such that $\Delta x = (b - a)/n$. The definite integral of $f(x)$ with respect to x between the limits $x = a$ to $x = b$ is

$$\int_a^b f(x)\, dx = \lim_{n \to \infty} [f(a)\Delta x + f(x_1)\Delta x + f(x_2)\Delta x + \cdots + f(x_{n-1})\Delta x],$$

$$= \left[\int f(x)\, dx \right]_a^b = \Big[F(x) \Big]_a^b = F(b) - F(a),$$

where $F(x)$ is a function whose derivative with respect to x is $f(x)$.

123. Approximate Values of Definite Integral. Approximate values of the above definite integral are given by the rules of §41, where y_0, y_1, y_2, $\cdots$, y_{n-1}, y_n are the values of $f(x)$ for $x = a$, x_1, x_2, $\cdots$, x_{n-1}, b, respectively, and $h = (b - a)/n$.

124. Some Fundamental Theorems.

$$\int_a^b [f_1(x) + f_2(x) + \cdots + f_n(x)]\, dx = \int_a^b f_1(x)\, dx$$
$$+ \int_a^b f_2(x)\, dx + \cdots + \int_a^b f_n(x)\, dx.$$

$$\int_a^b k f(x)\, dx = k \int_a^b f(x)\, dx, \quad \text{if } k \text{ is a constant.}$$

$$\int_a^b f(x)\, dx = - \int_b^a f(x)\, dx.$$

$$\int_a^b f(x)\, dx = \int_a^c f(x)\, dx + \int_c^b f(x)\, dx.$$

$$\int_a^b f(x)\, dx = (b - a) f(x_1), \quad \text{where } x_1 \text{ lies between } a \text{ and } b.$$

$$\int_a^\infty f(x)\, dx = \lim_{t \to \infty} \int_a^t f(x)\, dx.$$

$$\int_{-\infty}^b f(x)\, dx = \lim_{t \to \infty} \int_{-t}^b f(x)\, dx.$$

$$\int_{-\infty}^{+\infty} f(x)\, dx = \int_{-\infty}^{c} f(x)dx + \int_{c}^{\infty} f(x)dx.$$

If $f(x)$ has a singular point* at $x = b$, $b \neq a$,

$$\int_{a}^{b} f(x)dx = \lim_{e \to 0} \int_{a}^{b-e} f(x)dx.$$

The mean value of the function $f(x)$ on the interval (a, b) is

$$\frac{1}{b-a} \int_{a}^{b} f(x)dx.$$

Some Applications of the Definite Integral

125. Plane Area. The area bounded by $y = f(x)$, $y = 0$, $x = a$, $x = b$, where y has the same sign for all values of x between a and b, is

$$A = \int_{a}^{b} f(x)\, dx, \quad dA = f(x)\, dx.$$

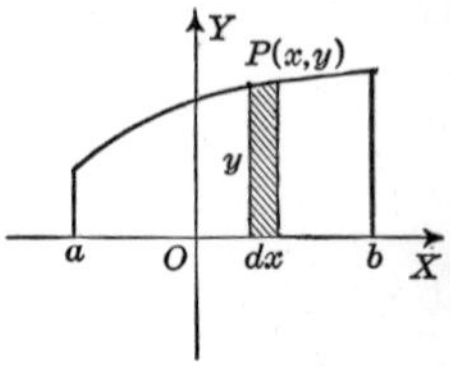

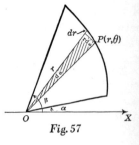

Fig. 56

The area bounded by the curve $r = f(\theta)$ and the two radii $\theta = \alpha$, $\theta = \beta$, is

$$A = \frac{1}{2} \int_{\alpha}^{\beta} [f(\theta)]^2\, d\theta, \quad dA = \frac{1}{2} r^2 \cdot d\theta.$$

126. Length of Arc (See §113). The length (s) of arc of a plane curve $f(x, y) = 0$ from the point (a, c) to the point (b, d) is

Fig. 57

$$s = \int_{a}^{b} \sqrt{1 + \left(\frac{dy}{dx}\right)^2} \cdot dx = \int_{c}^{d} \sqrt{1 + \left(\frac{dx}{dy}\right)^2} \cdot dy.$$

If the equation of the curve is $x = f(t)$, $y = f(t)$, the length of arc from $t = a$ to $t = b$ is

$$s = \int_{a}^{b} \sqrt{\left(\frac{dx}{dt}\right)^2 + \left(\frac{dy}{dt}\right)^2} \cdot dt.$$

*For example, when $\lim\limits_{x \to b} f(x) = \infty$.

If the equation of the curve is $r = f(\theta)$, then

$$s = \int_{\theta_1}^{\theta_2} \sqrt{r^2 + \left(\frac{dr}{d\theta}\right)^2} \cdot d\theta = \int_{r_1}^{r_2} \sqrt{r^2 \left(\frac{d\theta}{dr}\right)^2 + 1} \cdot dr.$$

127. Volume by Parallel Sections. If the plane perpendicular to the x-axis at $(x, 0, 0)$ cuts from a given solid a section whose area is $A(x)$, then the volume of that part of the solid between $x = a$ and $x = b$ is

$$\int_a^b A(x)\,dx.$$

128. Volume of Revolution. The volume of a solid of revolution generated by revolving that portion of the curve $y = f(x)$ between $x = a$ and $x = b$

(**a**) about the x-axis is $\pi \displaystyle\int_a^b y^2\,dx$;

(**b**) about the y-axis is $\pi \displaystyle\int_c^d x^2\,dy$, where c and d are the values of y corresponding to the values a and b of x.

129. Area of Surface of Revolution. The area of the surface of a solid of revolution generated by revolving the curve $y = f(x)$ between $x = a$ and $x = b$

(**a**) about the x-axis is $2\pi \displaystyle\int_a^b y\sqrt{1 + \left(\frac{dy}{dx}\right)^2} \cdot dx,$

(**b**) about the y-axis is $2\pi \displaystyle\int_a^b x\sqrt{1 + \left(\frac{dx}{dy}\right)^2} \cdot dy.$

130. Plane Areas by Double Integration.

(**a**) Rectangular coördinates,

$$A = \int_a^b \int_{\varphi(x)}^{f(x)} dy\,dx \quad \text{or} \quad \int_c^d \int_{\xi(y)}^{\Psi(y)} dx\,dy;$$

(**b**) Polar coördinates,

$$A = \int_{\theta_1}^{\theta_2} \int_{f_1(\theta)}^{f_2(\theta)} r\,dr\,d\theta \quad \text{or} \quad \int_{r_1}^{r_2} \int_{\phi_1(r)}^{\phi_2(r)} r\,d\theta\,dr.$$

131. Volumes by Double Integration. *If $Z = f(x,y)$,*

$$V = \int_a^b \int_{\phi(x)}^{\Psi(x)} f(x,y)\, dy\, dx \quad \text{or} \quad \int_c^d \int_{\alpha(y)}^{\beta(y)} f(x, y)\, dx\, dy.$$

132. Volumes by Triple Integration (see §102).

(*a*) Rectangular coördinates,

$$V = \int \int \int dx\, dy\, dz;$$

(*b*) Cylindrical coördinates,

$$V = \int \int \int r\, dr\, d\theta\, dz;$$

(*c*) Spherical coördinates,

$$V = \int \int \int \rho^2 \sin \phi\, d\theta\, d\phi\, d\rho.$$

where the limits of integration must be supplied. Other formulas may be obtained by changing the order of integration.

Area of Surface $z = f(x, y)$

$$A = \int \int \sqrt{\left(\frac{\partial z}{\partial x}\right)^2 + \left(\frac{\partial z}{\partial y}\right)^2 + 1} \cdot dy\, dx,$$

where the limits of integration must be supplied.

133. Mass.* The mass of a body of density δ is

$$m = \int dm, \quad dm = \delta \cdot dA, \quad \text{or} \quad \delta \cdot ds, \quad \text{or} \quad \delta \cdot dV, \quad \text{or} \quad \delta \cdot dS,$$

where dA, ds, dV, dS are, respectively, the elements of area, length, volume, surface of §125 to §132.

134. Density.* If δ is a variable (or constant) density (mass per unit of element), and $\bar{\delta}$ is the mean density of a solid of volume V, then

$$\bar{\delta} = \frac{\int \delta\, dV}{\int dV}$$

---

*The limits of integration are to be supplied.

135. Moment.* The moments M_{yz}, M_{xz}, M_{xy}, of a mass m with respect to the coordinate planes (as indicated by the subscripts) are

$$M_{yz} = \int x \, dm, \quad M_{xz} = \int y \, dm, \quad M_{xy} = \int z \, dm.$$

136. Centroid of Mass or Center of Gravity.* The coordinates $(\bar{x}, \bar{y}, \bar{z})$ of the centroid of a mass m are

$$\bar{x} = \frac{\displaystyle\int x \, dm}{\displaystyle\int dm}, \quad \bar{y} = \frac{\displaystyle\int y \, dm}{\displaystyle\int dm}, \quad \bar{z} = \frac{\displaystyle\int z \, dm}{\displaystyle\int dm}.$$

(Note: In the above equations x, y, z are the coordinates of the center of gravity of the element dm.)

137. Centroid of Several Masses. The x-coordinate $(\bar{x})$ of the centroid of several masses m_1, m_2, $\cdots$, m_n, having $\bar{x}_1$, $\bar{x}_2$, $\cdots$, $\bar{x}_n$, respectively as the x-coordinates of their centroids, is

$$\bar{x} = \frac{m_1\bar{x}_1 + m_2\bar{x}_2 + \cdots + m_n\bar{x}_n}{m_1 + m_2 + \cdots + m_n},$$

Similar formulas hold for the other coordinates $\bar{y}$, $\bar{z}$.

138. Moment of Inertia (Second Moment).* The moments of inertia (I):

(**a**) for a plane curve about the x-axis, y-axis, and origin, respectively, are:

$$I_x = \int y^2 \, ds, \quad \int I_y = \int x^2 \, ds, \quad I_0 = \int (x^2 + y^2) \, ds;$$

(**b**) for a plane area about the x-axis, y-axis, and origin, respectively, are:

$$I_x = \int y^2 \, dA, \quad I_y = \int x^2 \, dA, \quad I_0 = \int (x^2 + y^2) \, dA;$$

(**c**) for a solid of mass m about the yz, xz, xy-planes, x-axis, etc., respectively, are:

$$I_{yz} = \int x^2 \, dm, \quad I_{xz} = \int y^2 \, dm, \quad I_{xy} = \int z^2 \, dm, \quad I_x = I_{xz} + I_{xy}, \quad \text{etc.}$$

---

*The limits of integration are to be supplied.

139. Radius of Gyration. If I is the moment of inertia of a mass m, and K is the radius of gyration, $I = mK^2$. Similarly for areas, lengths, volumes, etc.

If masses (or areas, etc.) m_1, m_2, $\cdots$, m_n, have respectively the radii of gyration k_1, k_2, $\cdots$, k_n, with respect to a line or plane, then with respect to this line or plane, the several masses taken together have the radius of gyration K, where

$$K^2 = \frac{m_1 k^2_1 + m_2 k^2_2 + \cdots + m_n k^2_n}{m_1 + m_2 + \cdots + m_n}.$$

140. Work. The work W done in moving a particle from $s = a$ to $s = b$ against a force whose component expressed as function of s in the direction of motion is F_s, is

$$W = \int_{s=a}^{s=b} F_s \, ds, \quad dW = F_s \, ds.$$

141. Pressure. The pressure (p) against an area vertical to the surface of a liquid and between the depths a and b is

$$P = \int_{y=a}^{y=b} wly \, dy, \quad dp = wly \, dy,$$

where w is the weight of liquid per unit volume, y is the depth beneath surface of liquid of a horizontal element of area, and l is the length of the horizontal element of area expressed in terms of y.

142. Center of Pressure. The depth $\bar{y}$ of the center of pressure against an area vertical to the surface of the liquid and between the depths a and b is

$$\bar{y} = \frac{\displaystyle\int_{y=a}^{y=b} y \, dp}{\displaystyle\int_{y=a}^{y=b} dp} \cdot \quad \text{(for } dp \text{ see §141).}$$

VII. TABLE OF INTEGRALS

Certain Elementary Processes

143.   To integrate $\int R(x) \cdot dx$, **where** $R(x)$ **is rational function of** x.

Write $R(x)$ in the form of a fraction whose terms are polynomials. If the fraction is improper, (i.e., the degree of the denominator is less than or equal to the degree of the numerator), divide the numerator by the denominator and thus write $R(x)$ as the sum of a quotient $Q(x)$ and a proper fraction $P(x)$. (In a proper fraction the degree of the numerator is less than the degree of the denominator.) The polynomial $Q(x)$ is readily integrated. To integrate $P(x)$ separate it into a sum of partial fractions (as indicated below), and integrate each term of the sum separately.

To separate the proper fraction $P(x)$ into partial fractions, write $P(x) = f(x)/\psi(x)$, where $f(x)$ and $\psi(x)$ are polynomials,

$$\psi(x) = (x - a)^p (x - b)^q (x - c)^r \cdots ,$$

and the constants a, b, c, are all different. By algebra, there exist constants A_1, A_2, $\cdots$, B_1, B_2, $\cdots$, such that

$$\frac{f(x)}{\psi(x)} = \frac{A_1}{(x-a)} + \frac{A_2}{(x-a)^2} + \cdots + \frac{A_p}{(x-a)^p}$$

$$+ \frac{B_1}{(x-b)} + \frac{B_2}{(x-b)^2} + \cdots + \frac{B_q}{(x-b)^q} + \cdots .$$

The separate terms of this sum may be integrated by the formulas

$$\int \frac{dx}{(x-\alpha)^t} = \frac{-1}{(t-1)(x-\alpha)^{t-1}}, \ t > 1, \ \int \frac{dx}{(x-\alpha)} = \log (x-\alpha).$$

If $f(x)$ and $\psi(x)$ have real coefficients and $\psi(x) = 0$ has imaginary roots the above method leads to imaginary quantities. To avoid this, separate $P(x)$ in a different way. As before, corresponding to each p-fold real root a of $\psi(x)$, use the sum

$$\frac{A_1}{(x-a)} + \frac{A_2}{(x-a)^2} + \cdots + \frac{A_p}{(x-a)^p}.$$

To each λ-fold real quadratic factor $x^2 + \alpha x + \beta$ of $\psi(x)$ which does not factor into real linear factors, use, instead of the two sets of terms occurring in the first expansion of $R(x)$ and dependent on the conjugate complex roots of $x^2 + \alpha x + \beta = 0$, sums of the form

$$\frac{D_1 x + E_1}{(x^2 + \alpha x + \beta)} + \frac{D_2 x + E_2}{(x^2 + \alpha x + \beta)^2} + \cdots + \frac{D_\lambda x + E_\lambda}{(x^2 + \alpha x + \beta)^\lambda},$$

where the quantities $D_1, D_2, \cdots, E_1, E_2, \cdots,$ are real constants.

These new sums may be separately integrated by means of Integral formulas 128 to 134, etc.

144. To Integrate an Irrational Algebraic Function. If no convenient method of integration is apparent the integration may frequently be performed by means of a change of variable. For example, if R is a rational function of two arguments and n is an integer, then to integrate

(a) $\displaystyle\int R\left[x, (ax + b)^{\frac{1}{n}}\right] dx,$ let $(ax + b) = y^n$, whence the integral reduces to $\displaystyle\int P(y)\, dy$, where $P(y)$ is a rational function of y and may be integrated as in §143;

(b) $\displaystyle\int R\left[x, (x^2 + bx + c)^{\frac{1}{2}}\right] dx,$ let $(x^2 + bx + c)^{\frac{1}{2}} = z - x$, reduce R to a rational function of z, and proceed as in §143;

(c) $\displaystyle\int R(\sin x, \cos x)\, dx,$ let $\tan \dfrac{x}{2} = t$, whence

$$\sin x = \frac{2t}{1 + t^2}, \quad \cos x = \frac{1 - t^2}{1 + t^2}, \quad dx = \frac{2\, dt}{1 + t^2},$$

reduce R to a rational function of t and proceed as in §143.

145. To Integrate Expressions Containing $\sqrt{a^2 - x^2}$, $\sqrt{x^2 \pm a^2}$. Expressions containing these radicals can frequently be integrated after making the following transformations:

(a) if $\sqrt{a^2 - x^2}$ occurs, let $x = a \sin t$;

(b) if $\sqrt{x^2 - a^2}$ occurs, let $x = a \sec t$;

(c) if $\sqrt{x^2 + a^2}$ occurs, let $x = a \tan t$.

146. To Integrate Expressions Containing Trigonometric Functions. The integration of such functions may frequently be facilitated by the use of the identities of §58.

147. Integration by Parts. The relation

$$\int u \, dv = u \, v - \int v \, du.$$

is often effective in reducing a given integral to one or more simpler integrals.

Table of Integrals*

148. In the following table, the constant of integration, C, is omitted but should be added to the result of every integration. The letter x represents any variable; u represents any function of x; the remaining letters represent arbitrary constants, unless otherwise indicated; all angles are in radians. **Unless otherwise mentioned $\log_e u \equiv \log u$.**

Expressions Containing $(ax + b)$.

42. $\displaystyle\int (ax+b)^n dx = \frac{1}{a\,(n+1)}\,(ax+b)^{n+1},\ \ n \neq -1.$

43. $\displaystyle\int \frac{dx}{ax+b} = \frac{1}{a}\log_e (ax+b).$

44. $\displaystyle\int x(ax+b)^n\, dx = \frac{1}{a^2(n+2)}\,(ax+b)^{n+2}$
$$- \frac{b}{a^2(n+1)}\,(ax+b)^{n+1},\ n \neq -1,\ -2.$$

45. $\displaystyle\int \frac{x\,dx}{ax+b} = \frac{x}{a} - \frac{b}{a^2}\log (ax+b).$

46. $\displaystyle\int \frac{x\,dx}{(ax+b)^2} = \frac{b}{a^2(ax+b)} + \frac{1}{a^2}\log (ax+b).$

47. $\displaystyle\int x^2(ax+b)^n dx = \frac{1}{a^3}\left[\frac{(ax+b)^{n+3}}{n+3}\right.$
$$\left. - 2b\,\frac{(ax+b)^{n+2}}{n+2} + b^2\frac{(ax+b)^{n+1}}{n+1}\right],\ n \neq -1,\ -2,\ -3.$$

*See §121.

48. $\displaystyle\int \frac{x^2 dx}{ax + b} = \frac{1}{a^3}\left[\frac{1}{2}(ax + b)^2 - 2b(ax + b) + b^2\log(ax + b)\right].$

49. $\displaystyle\int \frac{x^2 dx}{(ax + b)^2} = \frac{1}{a^3}\left[(ax + b) - 2b\log(ax + b) - \frac{b^2}{ax + b}\right].$

50. $\displaystyle\int \frac{x^2\,dx}{(ax + b)^3} = \frac{1}{a^3}\left[\log(ax + b) + \frac{2b}{ax + b} - \frac{b^2}{2(ax + b)^2}\right].$

51. $\displaystyle\int x^m(ax + b)^n\,dx$
$$= \frac{1}{a(m + n + 1)}\left[x^m(ax+b)^{n+1} - mb\int x^{m-1}(ax+b)^n dx\right],$$
$$= \frac{1}{m + n + 1}\left[x^{m+1}(ax+b)^n + nb\int x^m(ax+b)^{n-1}dx\right],$$
$$m > 0,\ m + n + 1 \neq 0.$$

52. $\displaystyle\int \frac{dx}{x(ax + b)} = \frac{1}{b}\log\frac{x}{ax + b}.$

53. $\displaystyle\int \frac{dx}{x^2(ax + b)} = -\frac{1}{bx} + \frac{a}{b^2}\log\frac{ax + b}{x}.$

54. $\displaystyle\int \frac{dx}{x(ax + b)^2} = \frac{1}{b(ax + b)} - \frac{1}{b^2}\log\frac{ax + b}{x}.$

55. $\displaystyle\int \frac{dx}{x^2(ax + b)^2} = -\frac{b + 2ax}{b^2x(ax + b)} + \frac{2a}{b^3}\log\frac{ax + b}{x}.$

56. $\displaystyle\int \sqrt{ax + b}\,dx = \frac{2}{3a}\sqrt{(ax + b)^3}.$

57. $\displaystyle\int x\sqrt{ax + b}\,dx = \frac{2(3ax - 2b)}{15a^2}\sqrt{(ax + b)^3}.$

58. $\displaystyle\int x^2\sqrt{ax + b}\,dx = \frac{2(15a^2x^2 - 12abx + 8b^2)\sqrt{(ax + b)^3}}{105a^3}$

59. $\displaystyle\int \frac{\sqrt{ax + b}}{x}\,dx = 2\sqrt{ax + b} + b\int \frac{dx}{x\sqrt{ax + b}}.$

60. $\displaystyle\int \frac{dx}{\sqrt{ax + b}} = \frac{2\sqrt{ax + b}}{a}.$

61. $\displaystyle \int \frac{xdx}{\sqrt{ax+b}} = \frac{2(ax-2b)}{3a^2}\sqrt{ax+b}.$

62. $\displaystyle \int \frac{x^2dx}{\sqrt{ax+b}} = \frac{2(3a^2x^2-4abx+8b^2)}{15a^3}\sqrt{ax+b}.$

63. $\displaystyle \int \frac{dx}{x\sqrt{ax+b}} = \frac{1}{\sqrt{b}}\log\frac{\sqrt{ax+b}-\sqrt{b}}{\sqrt{ax+b}+\sqrt{b}},$ for $b>0$.

64. $\displaystyle \int \frac{dx}{x\sqrt{ax+b}} = \frac{2}{\sqrt{-b}}\tan^{-1}\sqrt{\frac{ax+b}{-b}},$ or $\frac{-2}{\sqrt{b}}\tanh^{-1}\sqrt{\frac{ax+b}{b}}, b<0.$

65. $\displaystyle \int \frac{dx}{x^2\sqrt{ax+b}} = -\frac{\sqrt{ax+b}}{bx} - \frac{a}{2b}\int\frac{dx}{x\sqrt{ax+b}}.$

66. $\displaystyle \int (ax+b)^{\pm\frac{n}{2}}dx = \frac{2(ax+b)^{\frac{2\pm n}{2}}}{a(2\pm n)}.$

67. $\displaystyle \int x(ax+b)^{\pm\frac{n}{2}}dx = \frac{2}{a^2}\left[\frac{(ax+b)^{\frac{4\pm n}{2}}}{4\pm n} - \frac{b(ax+b)^{\frac{2\pm n}{2}}}{2\pm n}\right].$

68. $\displaystyle \int \frac{dx}{x(ax+b)^{\frac{n}{2}}} = \frac{1}{b}\int\frac{dx}{x(ax+b)^{\frac{n-2}{2}}} - \frac{a}{b}\int\frac{dx}{(ax+b)^{\frac{n}{2}}}.$

69. $\displaystyle \int \frac{x^m dx}{\sqrt{ax+b}} = \frac{2x^m\sqrt{ax+b}}{(2m+1)a} - \frac{2mb}{(2m+1)a}\int\frac{x^{m-1}dx}{\sqrt{ax+b}}.$

70. $\displaystyle \int \frac{dx}{x^n\sqrt{ax+b}} = \frac{-\sqrt{ax+b}}{(n-1)bx^{n-1}} - \frac{(2n-3)a}{(2n-2)b}\int\frac{dx}{x^{n-1}\sqrt{ax+b}}.$

71. $\displaystyle \int \frac{(ax+b)^{\frac{n}{2}}}{x}dx = a\int(ax+b)^{\frac{n-2}{2}}dx + b\int\frac{(ax+b)^{\frac{n-2}{2}}}{x}dx.$

72. $\displaystyle \int \frac{dx}{(ax+b)(cx+d)} = \frac{1}{bc-ad}\log\frac{cx+d}{ax+b}, bc-ad\neq 0.$

73. $\displaystyle \int \frac{dx}{(ax+b)^2(cx+d)}$

$\displaystyle = \frac{1}{bc-ad}\left[\frac{1}{ax+b} + \frac{c}{bc-ad}\log\left(\frac{cx+d}{ax+b}\right)\right], bc-ad\neq 0.$

74. $\int (ax+b)^n (cx+d)^m \, dx = \dfrac{1}{(m+n+1)a} \Big[(ax+b)^{n+1} (cx+d)^m$

$$- m(bc-ad) \int (ax+b)^n (cx+d)^{m-1} \, dx \Big]$$

75. $\int \dfrac{dx}{(ax+b)^n (cx+d)^m} = \dfrac{1}{(m-1)(bc-ad)} \Big[\dfrac{1}{(ax+b)^{n-1}(cx+d)^{m-1}}$

$$- a(m+n-2) \int \dfrac{dx}{(ax+b)^n (cx+d)^{m-1}} \Big], \quad m>1, \, n>0, \, bc-ad \neq 0.$$

76. $\int \dfrac{(ax+b)^n}{(cx+d)^m} \, dx$

$$= - \dfrac{1}{(m-1)(bc-ad)} \Big[\dfrac{(ax+b)^{n+1}}{(cx+d)^{m-1}} + (m-n-2)a \int \dfrac{(ax+b)^n dx}{(cx+d)^{m-1}} \Big],$$

$$= \dfrac{-1}{(m-n-1)c} \Big[\dfrac{(ax+b)^n}{(cx+d)^{m-1}} + n(bc-ad) \int \dfrac{(ax+b)^{n-1}}{(cx+d)^m} \, dx \Big].$$

77. $\int \dfrac{x \, dx}{(ax+b)(cx+d)} = \dfrac{1}{bc-ad} \Big[\dfrac{b}{a} \log(ax+b)$

$$- \dfrac{d}{c} \log(cx+d) \Big], \quad bc-ad \neq 0.$$

78. $\int \dfrac{x \, dx}{(ax+b)^2(cx+d)} = \dfrac{1}{bc-ad} \Big[- \dfrac{b}{a(ax+b)}$

$$- \dfrac{d}{bc-ad} \log \dfrac{cx+d}{ax+b} \Big], \quad bc-ad \neq 0.$$

79. $\int \dfrac{cx+d}{\sqrt{ax+b}} \, dx = \dfrac{2}{3a^2} (3ad - 2bc + acx) \sqrt{ax+b}.$

80. $\int \dfrac{\sqrt{ax+b}}{cx+d} \, dx = \dfrac{2\sqrt{ax+b}}{c}$

$$- \dfrac{2}{c} \sqrt{\dfrac{ad-bc}{c}} \, \tan^{-1} \sqrt{\dfrac{c(ax+b)}{ad-bc}}, \quad c>0, \, ad>bc.$$

81. $\int \dfrac{\sqrt{ax+b}}{cx+d} \, dx = \dfrac{2\sqrt{ax+b}}{c}$

$$+ \dfrac{1}{c} \sqrt{\dfrac{bc-ad}{c}} \, \log \dfrac{\sqrt{c(ax+b)} - \sqrt{bc-ad}}{\sqrt{c(ax+b)} + \sqrt{bc-ad}}, \quad c>0, \, bc>ad.$$

82. $\displaystyle\int \frac{dx}{(cx + d)\sqrt{ax + b}} = \frac{2}{\sqrt{c}\sqrt{ad - bc}} \tan^{-1}\sqrt{\frac{c(ax + b)}{ad - bc}},$
$$c > 0 , ad > bc.$$

83. $\displaystyle\int \frac{dx}{(cx + d)\sqrt{ax + b}}$

$$= \frac{1}{\sqrt{c}\sqrt{bc - ad}}\log \frac{\sqrt{c(ax + b)} - \sqrt{bc - ad}}{\sqrt{c(ax + b)} + \sqrt{bc - ad}} \quad c > 0, bc > ad.$$

Expressions Containing $ax^2 + c$, $ax^n + c$, $x^2 \pm p^2$, and $p^2 - x^2$.

84. $\displaystyle\int \frac{dx}{p^2 + x^2} = \frac{1}{p} \tan^{-1}\frac{x}{p}.$

85. $\displaystyle\int \frac{dx}{p^2 - x^2} = \frac{1}{2p} \log \frac{p + x}{p - x}.$

86. $\displaystyle\int \frac{dx}{ax^2 + c} = \frac{1}{\sqrt{ac}} \tan^{-1}\left(x\sqrt{\frac{a}{c}}\right),$ a and $c > 0$.

87. $\displaystyle\int \frac{dx}{ax^2 + c} = \frac{1}{2\sqrt{-ac}} \log \frac{x\sqrt{a} - \sqrt{-c}}{x\sqrt{a} + \sqrt{-c}},$ $a > 0, c < 0$.

$$= \frac{1}{2\sqrt{-ac}} \log \frac{\sqrt{c} + x\sqrt{-a}}{\sqrt{c} - x\sqrt{-a}},$$ $a < 0, c > 0$.

88. $\displaystyle\int \frac{dx}{(ax^2 + c)^n} = \frac{1}{2(n - 1)c} \cdot \frac{x}{(ax^2 + c)^{n-1}}$

$$+ \frac{2n - 3}{2(n-1)c} \int \frac{dx}{(ax^2 + c)^{n-1}},$$ n a positive integer.

89. $\displaystyle\int x(ax^2 + c)^n \, dx = \frac{1}{2a} \frac{(ax^2 + c)^{n+1}}{n + 1},$ $n \neq -1$.

90. $\displaystyle\int \frac{x}{ax^2 + c} \, dx = \frac{1}{2a} \log (ax^2 + c).$

91. $\displaystyle\int \frac{dx}{x(ax^2 + c)} = \frac{1}{2c} \log \frac{ax^2}{ax^2 + c}.$

92. $\displaystyle\int \frac{x^2 \, dx}{ax^2 + c} = \frac{x}{a} - \frac{c}{a} \int \frac{dx}{ax^2 + c}.$

93. $$\int \frac{x^2 dx}{(ax^2 + c)^n} = - \frac{1}{2(n-1)a} \cdot \frac{x}{(ax^2 + c)^{n-1}}$$
$$+ \frac{1}{2(n-1)a} \int \frac{dx}{(ax^2 + c)^{n-1}}.$$

94. $$\int \frac{dx}{x^2(ax^2 + c)^n} = \frac{1}{c} \int \frac{dx}{x^2(ax^2 + c)^{n-1}} - \frac{a}{c} \int \frac{dx}{(ax^2 + c)^n}.$$

95. $$\int \sqrt{x^2 \pm p^2}\, dx = \frac{1}{2}\left[x\sqrt{x^2 \pm p^2} \pm p^2 \log(x + \sqrt{x^2 \pm p^2}) \right].$$

96. $$\int \sqrt{p^2 - x^2}\, dx = \frac{1}{2}\left[x\sqrt{p^2 - x^2} + p^2 \sin^{-1}\left(\frac{x}{p}\right) \right].$$

97. $$\int \frac{dx}{\sqrt{x^2 \pm p^2}} = \log(x + \sqrt{x^2 \pm p^2}).$$

98. $$\int \frac{dx}{\sqrt{p^2 - x^2}} = \sin^{-1}\left(\frac{x}{p}\right) \text{ or } - \cos^{-1}\left(\frac{x}{p}\right).$$

99. $$\int \sqrt{ax^2 + c}\, dx = \frac{x}{2}\sqrt{ax^2 + c}$$
$$+ \frac{c}{2\sqrt{a}} \log\left(x\sqrt{a} + \sqrt{ax^2 + c}\right), a > 0.$$

100. $$\int \sqrt{ax^2 + c}\, dx = \frac{x}{2}\sqrt{ax^2 + c} + \frac{c}{2\sqrt{-a}} \sin^{-1}\left(x\sqrt{\frac{-a}{c}}\right), a < 0.$$

101. $$\int \frac{dx}{\sqrt{ax^2 + c}} = \frac{1}{\sqrt{a}} \log(x\sqrt{a} + \sqrt{ax^2 + c}), a > 0.$$

102. $$\int \frac{dx}{\sqrt{ax^2 + c}} = \frac{1}{\sqrt{-a}} \sin^{-1}\left(x\sqrt{\frac{-a}{c}}\right), a < 0.$$

103. $$\int x\sqrt{ax^2 + c} \cdot dx = \frac{1}{3a}(ax^2 + c)^{\frac{3}{2}}.$$

104. $$\int \frac{x\,dx}{\sqrt{ax^2 + c}} = \frac{1}{a}\sqrt{ax^2 + c}.$$

105. $$\int \frac{\sqrt{ax^2 + c}}{x}\, dx = \sqrt{ax^2 + c} + \sqrt{c} \log \frac{\sqrt{ax^2 + c} - \sqrt{c}}{x}, c > 0.$$

106. $\int \dfrac{\sqrt{ax^2 + c}}{x}\, dx = \sqrt{ax^2 + c} - \sqrt{-c}\, \tan^{-1} \dfrac{\sqrt{ax^2 + c}}{\sqrt{-c}}, c < 0.$

107. $\int \dfrac{dx}{x\sqrt{ax^2 + c}} = \dfrac{1}{\sqrt{c}}\log \dfrac{\sqrt{ax^2 + c} - \sqrt{c}}{x},\quad c > 0.$

108. $\int \dfrac{dx}{x\sqrt{ax^2 + c}} = \dfrac{1}{\sqrt{-c}}\sec^{-1}\left(x\sqrt{-\dfrac{a}{c}}\right),\quad c < 0.$

109. $\int \dfrac{dx}{x^2\sqrt{ax^2 + c}} = -\dfrac{\sqrt{ax^2 + c}}{cx}.$

110. $\int \dfrac{x^n dx}{\sqrt{ax^2 + c}} = \dfrac{x^{n-1}\sqrt{ax^2 + c}}{na} - \dfrac{(n-1)c}{na}\int \dfrac{x^{n-2}dx}{\sqrt{ax^2 + c}}, n > 0.$

111. $\int x^n\sqrt{ax^2 + c}\, dx = \dfrac{x^{n-1}(ax^2 + c)^{\frac{3}{2}}}{(n+2)a}$
$$- \dfrac{(n-1)c}{(n+2)a}\int x^{n-2}\sqrt{ax^2 + c}\cdot dx, n > 0.$$

112. $\int \dfrac{\sqrt{ax^2 + c}}{x^n}\, dx = -\dfrac{(ax^2 + c)^{\frac{3}{2}}}{c(n-1)x^{n-1}}$
$$- \dfrac{(n-4)a}{(n-1)c}\int \dfrac{\sqrt{ax^2 + c}}{x^{n-2}}\, dx, n > 1.$$

113. $\int \dfrac{dx}{x^n\sqrt{ax^2 + c}} = -\dfrac{\sqrt{ax^2 + c}}{c(n-1)x^{n-1}}$
$$- \dfrac{(n-2)}{(n-1)}\dfrac{a}{c}\int \dfrac{dx}{x^{n-2}\sqrt{ax^2 + c}}, n > 1.$$

114. $\int (ax^2 + c)^{\frac{3}{2}}\, dx = \dfrac{x}{8}(2ax^2 + 5c)\sqrt{ax^2 + c}$
$$+ \dfrac{3c^2}{8\sqrt{a}}\log(x\sqrt{a} + \sqrt{ax^2 + c}), a > 0.$$

115. $\int (ax^2 + c)^{\frac{3}{2}}\, dx = \dfrac{x}{8}(2ax^2 + 5c)\sqrt{ax^2 + c}$
$$+ \dfrac{3c^2}{8\sqrt{-a}}\sin^{-1}\left(x\sqrt{\dfrac{-a}{c}}\right), a < 0.$$

116. $\int \dfrac{dx}{(ax^2 + c)^{\frac{3}{2}}} = \dfrac{x}{c\sqrt{ax^2 + c}}$

117. $\displaystyle\int x(ax^2 + c)^{\frac{3}{2}}\ dx = \frac{1}{5a}(ax^2 + c)^{\frac{5}{2}}.$

118. $\displaystyle\int \frac{xdx}{(ax^2 + c)^{\frac{3}{2}}} = -\frac{1}{a\sqrt{ax^2 + c}},$

119. $\displaystyle\int \frac{x^2dx}{(ax^2 + c)^{\frac{3}{2}}} = -\frac{x}{a\sqrt{ax^2 + c}}$
$$+ \frac{1}{a\sqrt{a}}\log\ (x\sqrt{a} + \sqrt{ax^2 + c}), \quad a > 0.$$

120. $\displaystyle\int \frac{x^2dx}{(ax^2 + c)^{\frac{3}{2}}} = -\frac{x}{a\sqrt{ax^2 + c}}$
$$+ \frac{1}{a\sqrt{-a}}\sin^{-1}\left(x\sqrt{\frac{-a}{c}}\right), \quad a < 0.$$

121. $\displaystyle\int \frac{dx}{x(ax^n + c)} = \frac{1}{cn}\log\frac{x^n}{ax^n + c}.$

122. $\displaystyle\int \frac{dx}{(ax^n + c)^m} = \frac{1}{c}\int \frac{dx}{(ax^n + c)^{m-1}} - \frac{a}{c}\int \frac{x^ndx}{(ax^n + c)^m}.$

123. $\displaystyle\int \frac{dx}{x\sqrt{ax^n + c}} = \frac{1}{n\sqrt{c}}\log\frac{\sqrt{ax^n + c} - \sqrt{c}}{\sqrt{ax^n + c} + \sqrt{c}}, \quad c > 0.$

124. $\displaystyle\int \frac{dx}{x\sqrt{ax^n + c}} = \frac{2}{n\sqrt{-c}}\sec^{-1}\sqrt{\frac{-ax^n}{c}}, \quad c < 0.$

125. $\displaystyle\int x^{m-1}(ax^n + c)^p dx$

$$= \frac{1}{m + np}\left[x^m(ax^n + c)^p + npc\int x^{m-1}(ax^n + c)^{p-1}dx\right].$$
$$= \frac{1}{cn(p+1)}\left[-x^m(ax^n+c)^{p+1} + (m+np+n)\int x^{m-1}(ax^n+c)^{p+1}dx\right].$$
$$= \frac{1}{a(m+np)}\left[x^{m-n}(ax^n + c)^{p+1} - (m-n)c\int x^{m-n-1}(ax^n + c)^p dx\right].$$
$$= \frac{1}{mc}\left[x^m(ax^n + c)^{p+1} - (m + np + n)\int x^{m+n-1}(ax^n + c)^p dx\right].$$

126. $\displaystyle\int \frac{x^m dx}{(ax^n + c)^p} = \frac{1}{a}\int \frac{x^{m-n}dx}{(ax^n + c)^{p-1}} - \frac{c}{a}\int \frac{x^{m-n}dx}{(ax^n + c)^p}.$

127. $\displaystyle\int \frac{dx}{x^m(ax^n + c)^p} = \frac{1}{c}\int \frac{dx}{x^m(ax^n + c)^{p-1}} - \frac{a}{c}\int \frac{dx}{x^{m-n}(ax^n + c)^p}.$

Expressions Containing $(ax^2 + bx + c)$.

128. $\displaystyle\int \frac{dx}{ax^2 + bx + c} = \frac{1}{\sqrt{b^2 - 4ac}}\log\frac{2ax + b - \sqrt{b^2 - 4ac}}{2ax + b + \sqrt{b^2 - 4ac}}, b^2 > 4ac.$

129. $\displaystyle\int \frac{dx}{ax^2 + bx + c} = \frac{2}{\sqrt{4ac - b^2}}\tan^{-1}\frac{2ax + b}{\sqrt{4ac - b^2}}, \qquad b^2 < 4ac.$

130. $\displaystyle\int \frac{dx}{ax^2 + bx + c} = -\frac{2}{2ax + b}, \quad b^2 = 4ac.$

131. $\displaystyle\int \frac{dx}{(ax^2 + bx + c)^{n+1}} = \frac{2ax + b}{n(4ac - b^2)(ax^2 + bx + c)^n}$
$$+ \frac{2(2n - 1)a}{n(4ac - b^2)}\int \frac{dx}{(ax^2 + bx + c)^n}.$$

132. $\displaystyle\int \frac{xdx}{ax^2 + bx + c} = \frac{1}{2a}\log(ax^2 + bx + c) - \frac{b}{2a}\int \frac{dx}{ax^2 + bx + c}.$

133. $\displaystyle\int \frac{x^2 dx}{ax^2 + bx + c} = \frac{x}{a} - \frac{b}{2a^2}\log(ax^2 + bx + c)$
$$+ \frac{b^2 - 2ac}{2a^2}\int \frac{dx}{ax^2 + bx + c}.$$

134. $\displaystyle\int \frac{xdx}{(ax^2 + bx + c)^{n+1}} = \frac{-(2c + bx)}{n(4ac - b^2)(ax^2 + bx + c)^n}$
$$- \frac{b(2n - 1)}{n(4ac - b^2)}\int \frac{dx}{(ax^2 + bx + c)^n}.$$

135. $\displaystyle\int \frac{x^m dx}{(ax^2 + bx + c)^{n+1}} = -\frac{x^{m-1}}{a(2n - m + 1)(ax^2 + bx + c)^n}$
$$- \frac{n - m + 1}{2n - m + 1}\cdot\frac{b}{a}\int \frac{x^{m-1}dx}{(ax^2 + bx + c)^{n+1}}$$
$$+ \frac{m - 1}{2n - m + 1}\cdot\frac{c}{a}\int \frac{x^{m-2}dx}{(ax^2 + bx + c)^{n+1}}.$$

136. $\int \dfrac{dx}{x(ax^2+bx+c)} = \dfrac{1}{2c} \log \dfrac{x^2}{ax^2+bx+c} - \dfrac{b}{2c} \int \dfrac{dx}{(ax^2+bx+c)}$.

137. $\int \dfrac{dx}{x^2(ax^2+bx+c)} = \dfrac{b}{2c^2} \log \left(\dfrac{ax^2+bx+c}{x^2} \right) - \dfrac{1}{cx}$

$$+ \left(\dfrac{b^2}{2c^2} - \dfrac{a}{c} \right) \int \dfrac{dx}{(ax^2+bx+c)}.$$

138. $\int \dfrac{dx}{x^m(ax^2+bx+c)^{n+1}} = -\dfrac{1}{(m-1)cx^{m-1}(ax^2+bx+c)^n}$

$$- \dfrac{(n+m-1)}{m-1} \cdot \dfrac{b}{c} \int \dfrac{dx}{x^{m-1}(ax^2+bx+c)^{n+1}}$$

$$- \dfrac{(2n+m-1)}{m-1} \cdot \dfrac{a}{c} \int \dfrac{dx}{x^{m-2}(ax^2+bx+c)^{n+1}}.$$

139. $\int \dfrac{dx}{x(ax^2+bx+c)^n} = \dfrac{1}{2c(n-1)(ax^2+bx+c)^{n-1}}$

$$- \dfrac{b}{2c} \int \dfrac{dx}{(ax^2+bx+c)^n} + \dfrac{1}{c} \int \dfrac{dx}{x(ax^2+bx+c)^{n-1}}.$$

140. $\int \dfrac{dx}{\sqrt{ax^2+bx+c}} = \dfrac{1}{\sqrt{a}} \log(2ax+b+2\sqrt{a}\sqrt{ax^2+bx+c}),\ a>0.$

141. $\int \dfrac{dx}{\sqrt{ax^2+bx+c}} = \dfrac{1}{\sqrt{-a}} \sin^{-1} \dfrac{-2ax-b}{\sqrt{b^2-4ac}},\ a<0.$

142. $\int \dfrac{xdx}{\sqrt{ax^2+bx+c}} = \dfrac{\sqrt{ax^2+bx+c}}{a} - \dfrac{b}{2a} \int \dfrac{dx}{\sqrt{ax^2+bx+c}}$.

143. $\int \sqrt{ax^2+bx+c}\, dx = \dfrac{2ax+b}{4a} \sqrt{ax^2+bx+c}$

$$+ \dfrac{4ac-b^2}{8a} \int \dfrac{dx}{\sqrt{ax^2+bx+c}}.$$

144. $\int x\sqrt{ax^2+bx+c}\, dx = \dfrac{(ax^2+bx+c)^{\frac{3}{2}}}{3a} - \dfrac{b}{2a} \int \sqrt{ax^2+bx+c}\, dx.$

145. $\int \dfrac{dx}{x\sqrt{ax^2+bx+c}} = -\dfrac{1}{\sqrt{c}} \log \left(\dfrac{\sqrt{ax^2+bx+c}+\sqrt{c}}{x} + \dfrac{b}{2\sqrt{c}} \right),\ c>0.$

146. $\displaystyle\int \frac{dx}{x\sqrt{ax^2 + bx + c}} = \frac{1}{\sqrt{-c}} \sin^{-1} \frac{bx + 2c}{x\sqrt{b^2 - 4ac}}, \; c < 0.$

147. $\displaystyle\int \frac{dx}{x\sqrt{ax^2 + bx}} = -\frac{2}{bx} \sqrt{ax^2 + bx}, \; c = 0.$

148. $\displaystyle\int \frac{dx}{(ax^2 + bx + c)^{\frac{3}{2}}} = -\frac{2(2ax + b)}{(b^2 - 4ac)\sqrt{ax^2 + bx + c}}.$

Miscellaneous Algebraic Expressions.

149. $\displaystyle\int \sqrt{2px - x^2}\, dx = \frac{1}{2}\left[\, (x - p)\sqrt{2px - x^2} + p^2 \sin^{-1}[(x - p)/p]\,\right].$

150. $\displaystyle\int \frac{dx}{\sqrt{2px - x^2}} = \cos^{-1}\left(\frac{p - x}{p}\right).$

151. $\displaystyle\int \frac{dx}{\sqrt{ax + b} \cdot \sqrt{cx + d}} = \frac{2}{\sqrt{-ac}} \tan^{-1}\sqrt{\frac{-c(ax + b)}{a(cx + d)}}$

$$\text{or } \frac{2}{\sqrt{ac}} \tanh^{-1}\sqrt{\frac{c(ax + b)}{a(cx + d)}}.$$

152. $\displaystyle\int \sqrt{ax + b} \cdot \sqrt{cx + d}\, dx =$

$$\frac{(2acx + bc + ad)\sqrt{ax + b} \cdot \sqrt{cx + d}}{4ac}$$

$$+ \frac{(ad - bc)^2}{8ac}\int \frac{dx}{\sqrt{ax + b} \cdot \sqrt{cx + d}}.$$

153. $\displaystyle\int \sqrt{\frac{cx + d}{ax + b}}\, dx = \frac{\sqrt{ax + b} \cdot \sqrt{cx + d}}{a}$

$$\mp \frac{(ad - bc)}{2a}\int \frac{dx}{\sqrt{ax + b} \cdot \sqrt{cx + d}}.$$

154. $\displaystyle\int \sqrt{\frac{x + b}{x + d}}\, dx = \sqrt{x + d} \cdot \sqrt{x + b}$

$$+ (b - d) \log[\sqrt{x + d} + \sqrt{x + b}].$$

155. $\displaystyle\int \sqrt{\frac{1 + x}{1 - x}}\, dx = \sin^{-1} x - \sqrt{1 - x^2}.$

156. $\int \sqrt{\dfrac{p-x}{q+x}}\,dx = \sqrt{p-x}\cdot\sqrt{q+x} + (p+q)\sin^{-1}\sqrt{\dfrac{x+q}{p+q}}.$

157. $\int \sqrt{\dfrac{p+x}{q-x}}\,dx = -\sqrt{p+x}\cdot\sqrt{q-x} + (p+q)\sin^{-1}\sqrt{\dfrac{q-x}{p+q}}.$

158. $\int \dfrac{dx}{\sqrt{x-p}\cdot\sqrt{q-x}} = 2\sin^{-1}\sqrt{\dfrac{x-p}{q-p}}.$

Expressions Containing sin ax.

159. $\int \sin u\,du = -\cos u,$ where u is any funtion of x.

160. $\int \sin ax\,dx = -\dfrac{1}{a}\cos ax.$

161. $\int \sin^2 ax\,dx = \dfrac{x}{2} - \dfrac{\sin 2ax}{4a}.$

162. $\int \sin^3 ax\,dx = -\dfrac{1}{a}\cos ax + \dfrac{1}{3a}\cos^3 ax.$

163. $\int \sin^n ax\,dx = -\dfrac{\sin^{n-1} ax\cos ax}{na} + \dfrac{n-1}{n}\int \sin^{n-2} ax\,dx,$
$\qquad\qquad\qquad\qquad\qquad\qquad (n \text{ pos. integer}).$

164. $\int \dfrac{dx}{\sin ax} = \dfrac{1}{a}\log\tan\dfrac{ax}{2} = \dfrac{1}{a}\log\,(\csc ax - \operatorname{ctn} ax).$

165. $\int \dfrac{dx}{\sin^2 ax} = \int \csc^2 ax\,dx = -\dfrac{1}{a}\operatorname{ctn} ax.$

166. $\int \dfrac{dx}{\sin^n ax} = -\dfrac{1}{a(n-1)}\dfrac{\cos ax}{\sin^{n-1} ax} + \dfrac{n-2}{n-1}\int \dfrac{dx}{\sin^{n-2} ax},$
$\qquad\qquad\qquad\qquad\qquad\qquad n \text{ integer} > 1.$

167. $\int \dfrac{dx}{1 \pm \sin ax} = \mp\dfrac{1}{a}\tan\left(\dfrac{\pi}{4} \mp \dfrac{ax}{2}\right).$

168. $\int \dfrac{dx}{b + c\sin ax} = \dfrac{-2}{a\sqrt{b^2-c^2}}\tan^{-1}\left[\sqrt{\dfrac{b-c}{b+c}}\tan\left(\dfrac{\pi}{4}-\dfrac{ax}{2}\right)\right], b^2 > c^2.$

169. $\int \dfrac{dx}{b + c\sin ax} = \dfrac{-1}{a\sqrt{c^2-b^2}}\log\dfrac{c + b\sin ax + \sqrt{c^2-b^2}\cdot\cos ax}{b + c\sin ax}, c^2 > b^2.$

170. $\int \sin ax\sin bx\,dx = \dfrac{\sin (a-b)x}{2(a-b)} - \dfrac{\sin (a+b)x}{2(a+b)}, a^2 \neq b^2.$

Expressions Involving cos *ax*.

171. $\int \cos u \, du = \sin u$, where u is any function of x.

172. $\int \cos ax \, dx = \dfrac{1}{a} \sin ax.$

173. $\int \cos^2 ax \, dx = \dfrac{x}{2} + \dfrac{\sin 2 \, ax}{4a}.$

174. $\int \cos^3 ax \, dx = \dfrac{1}{a} \sin ax - \dfrac{1}{3a} \sin^3 ax.$

175. $\int \cos^n ax \, dx = \dfrac{\cos^{n-1} ax \sin ax}{na} + \dfrac{n-1}{n} \int \cos^{n-2} ax \, dx,$
$$(n \text{ pos. integer}).$$

176. $\int \dfrac{dx}{\cos ax} = \dfrac{1}{a} \log \tan \left(\dfrac{ax}{2} + \dfrac{\pi}{4} \right) = \dfrac{1}{a} \log (\tan ax + \sec ax).$

177. $\int \dfrac{dx}{\cos^2 ax} = \dfrac{1}{a} \tan ax.$

178. $\int \dfrac{dx}{\cos^n ax} = \dfrac{1}{a(n-1)} \dfrac{\sin ax}{\cos^{n-1} ax} + \dfrac{n-2}{n-1} \int \dfrac{dx}{\cos^{n-2} ax},$
$$n \text{ integer} > 1.$$

179. $\int \dfrac{dx}{1 + \cos ax} = \dfrac{1}{a} \tan \dfrac{ax}{2}.$

180. $\int \dfrac{dx}{1 - \cos ax} = -\dfrac{1}{a} \operatorname{ctn} \dfrac{ax}{2}.$

131. $\int \sqrt{1 + \cos x} \cdot dx = \sqrt{2} \int \cos \dfrac{x}{2} \, dx = 2\sqrt{2} \sin \dfrac{x}{2}.$

182. $\int \sqrt{1 - \cos x} \cdot dx = \sqrt{2} \int \sin \dfrac{x}{2} \, dx = -2\sqrt{2} \cos \dfrac{x}{2}.$

183. $\int \dfrac{dx}{b + c \cos ax} = \dfrac{1}{a\sqrt{b^2 - c^2}} \cdot \tan^{-1} \left(\dfrac{\sqrt{b^2 - c^2} \cdot \sin ax}{c + b \cos ax} \right), b^2 > c^2.$

184. $\int \dfrac{dx}{b + c \cos ax} = \dfrac{1}{a\sqrt{c^2 - b^2}} \tanh^{-1} \left[\dfrac{\sqrt{c^2 - b^2} \cdot \sin ax}{c + b \cos ax} \right], c^2 > b^2.$

185. $\int \cos ax \cdot \cos bx \, dx = \dfrac{\sin (a - b)x}{2(a - b)} + \dfrac{\sin (a + b)x}{2(a + b)}, a^2 \neq b^2.$

Expressions Containing sin ax and cos ax.

186. $\int \sin ax \cos bx \, dx = -\frac{1}{2} \left[\frac{\cos(a-b)x}{a-b} + \frac{\cos(a+b)x}{a+b} \right], \ a^2 \neq b^2.$

187. $\int \sin^n ax \cos ax \, dx = \frac{1}{a(n+1)} \sin^{n+1} ax, \ n \neq -1.$

188. $\int \cos^n ax \sin ax \, dx = -\frac{1}{a(n+1)} \cos^{n+1} ax, \ n \neq -1.$

189. $\int \frac{\sin ax}{\cos ax} \, dx = -\frac{1}{a} \log \cos ax.$

190. $\int \frac{\cos ax}{\sin ax} \, dx = \frac{1}{a} \log \sin ax.$

191. $\int (b+c \sin ax)^n \cos ax \, dx = \frac{1}{ac(n+1)} (b+c \sin ax)^{n+1}, n \neq -1.$

192. $\int (b+c \cos ax)^n \sin ax \, dx = -\frac{1}{ac(n+1)} (b+c \cos ax)^{n+1}, n \neq -1.$

193. $\int \frac{\cos ax \, dx}{b+c \sin ax} = \frac{1}{ac} \log(b+c \sin ax).$

194. $\int \frac{\sin ax}{b+c \cos ax} \, dx = -\frac{1}{ac} \log(b+c \cos ax).$

195. $\int \frac{dx}{b \sin ax + c \cos ax} = \frac{1}{a\sqrt{b^2+c^2}} \left[\log \tan \frac{1}{2} \left(ax + \tan^{-1} \frac{c}{b} \right) \right]$

196. $\int \frac{dx}{b + c \cos ax + d \sin ax}$

$= \frac{-1}{a\sqrt{b^2-c^2-d^2}} \sin^{-1} \left[\frac{c^2+d^2+b(c \cos ax + a \sin ax)}{\sqrt{c^2+d^2} \cdot (b+c \cos ax + d \sin ax)} \right], \text{or}$

$= \frac{1}{a\sqrt{c^2+d^2-b^2}} \log \left[\frac{c^2+d^2+b(c \cos ax + d \sin ax) + \sqrt{c^2+d^2-b^2}(c \sin ax - d \cos ax)}{\sqrt{c^2+d^2} \cdot (b+c \cos ax + d \sin ax),} \right],$

$$-\pi < +ax < \pi$$

197. $\displaystyle\int \frac{dx}{b^2 \cos^2 ax + c^2 \sin^2 ax} = \frac{1}{abc} \tan^{-1}\left(\frac{c \tan ax}{b}\right).$

198. $\displaystyle\int \sin^2 ax \cos^2 ax \, dx = \frac{x}{8} - \frac{\sin 4 ax}{32 a}.$

199. $\displaystyle\int \frac{dx}{\sin ax \cos ax} = \frac{1}{a} \log \tan ax.$

200. $\displaystyle\int \frac{dx}{\sin^2 ax \cos^2 ax} = \frac{1}{a}\left(\tan ax - \text{ctn } ax\right).$

201. $\displaystyle\int \frac{\sin^2 ax}{\cos ax} dx = \frac{1}{a}\left[-\sin ax + \log \tan\left(\frac{ax}{2} + \frac{\pi}{4}\right)\right].$

202. $\displaystyle\int \frac{\cos^2 ax}{\sin ax} dx = \frac{1}{a}\left[\cos ax + \log \tan \frac{ax}{2}\right].$

203. $\displaystyle\int \sin^m ax \cos^n ax \, dx = -\frac{\sin^{m-1} ax \cos^{n+1} ax}{a(m+n)}$
$$+ \frac{m-1}{m+n} \int \sin^{m-2} ax \cos^n ax \, dx, \quad m, n > 0.$$

204. $\displaystyle\int \sin^m ax \cos^n ax \, dx = \frac{\sin^{m+1} ax \cos^{n-1} ax}{a(m+n)}$
$$+ \frac{n-1}{m+n} \int \sin^m ax \cos^{n-2} ax \, dx, \quad m, n > 0.$$

205. $\displaystyle\int \frac{\sin^m ax}{\cos^n ax} dx = \frac{\sin^{m+1} ax}{a(n-1)\cos^{n-1} ax}$
$$- \frac{m-n+2}{n-1} \int \frac{\sin^m ax}{\cos^{n-2} ax} dx, \quad m, n > 0, n \neq 1.$$

206. $\displaystyle\int \frac{\cos^n ax}{\sin^m ax} dx = \frac{-\cos^{n+1} ax}{a(m-1)\sin^{m-1} ax}$
$$+ \frac{m-n-2}{(m-1)} \int \frac{\cos^n ax}{\sin^{m-2} ax} dx, \quad m, n, > 0, m \neq 1.$$

207. $\displaystyle\int \frac{dx}{\sin^m ax \cos^n ax} = \frac{1}{a(n-1)} \frac{1}{\sin^{m-1} ax \cos^{n-1} ax}$
$$+ \frac{m+n-2}{(n-1)} \int \frac{dx}{\sin^m ax \cos^{n-2} ax}.$$

208. $\displaystyle\int \frac{dx}{\sin^m ax \cos^n ax} = -\frac{1}{a(m-1)}\ \frac{1}{\sin^{m-1} ax \cos^{n-1} ax}$

$$+ \frac{m+n-2}{(m-1)}\int \frac{dx}{\sin^{m-2} ax \cos^n ax}.$$

209. $\displaystyle\int \frac{\sin^{2n} ax}{\cos ax}\, dx = \int \frac{(1-\cos^2 ax)^n}{\cos ax}\, dx.$ (Expand, divide, and use 175).

210. $\displaystyle\int \frac{\cos^{2n} ax}{\sin ax}\, dx = \int \frac{(1-\sin^2 ax)^n}{\sin ax}\, dx.$ (Expand, divide, and use 163).

211. $\displaystyle\int \frac{\sin^{2n+1} ax}{\cos ax}\, dx = \int \frac{(1-\cos^2 ax)^n}{\cos ax}\sin ax\, dx.$ (Expand, divide, and use 188).

212. $\displaystyle\int \frac{\cos^{2n+1} ax}{\sin ax}\, dx = \int \frac{(1-\sin^2 ax)^n}{\sin ax}\cos ax\, dx.$ (Expand, divide, and use 187).

Expressions Containing **tan** *ax or* **ctn** *ax* ($\tan ax = 1/\operatorname{ctn} ax$).

213. $\displaystyle\int \tan u\, du = -\log \cos u,$ or $\log \sec u$, where u is any function of x.

214. $\displaystyle\int \tan ax\, dx = -\frac{1}{a}\log \cos ax.$

215. $\displaystyle\int \tan^2 ax\, dx = \frac{1}{a}\tan ax - x.$

216. $\displaystyle\int \tan^n ax\, dx = \frac{1}{a(n-1)}\tan^{n-1} ax - \int \tan^{n-2} ax\, dx,$
n integer >1.

217. $\displaystyle\int \operatorname{ctn} u\, du = \log \sin u,$ or $-\log \csc u$, where u is any function of x.

218. $\displaystyle\int \operatorname{ctn}^2 ax\, dx = \int \frac{dx}{\tan^2 ax} = -\frac{1}{a}\operatorname{ctn} ax - x.$

219. $\displaystyle\int \operatorname{ctn}^n ax\, dx = \int \frac{dx}{\tan^n ax} = -\frac{1}{a(n-1)}\operatorname{ctn}^{n-1} ax$

$$-\int \operatorname{ctn}^{n-2} ax\, dx, \ n \text{ integer} >1.$$

220. $\displaystyle\int \frac{dx}{b + c \tan ax} = \int \frac{\operatorname{ctn} ax \, dx}{b \operatorname{ctn} ax + c}$

$$= \frac{1}{b^2 + c^2}\left[bx + \frac{c}{a}\log\left(b \cos ax + c \sin ax\right)\right].$$

221. $\displaystyle\int \frac{dx}{b + c \operatorname{ctn} ax} = \int \frac{\tan ax \, dx}{b \tan ax + c}$

$$= \frac{1}{b^2 + c^2}\left[bx - \frac{c}{a}\log\left(c \cos ax + b \sin ax\right)\right].$$

222. $\displaystyle\int \frac{dx}{\sqrt{b+c \tan^2 ax}} = \frac{1}{a\sqrt{b-c}}\sin^{-1}\!\left(\sqrt{\frac{b-c}{b}}\,\sin ax\right)$, b pos., $b^2 > c^2$.

Expressions Containing $\sec ax = 1/\cos ax$ *or* $\csc ax = 1/\sin ax$.

223. $\displaystyle\int \sec u \, du = \log\left(\sec u + \tan u\right) = \log \tan\left(\frac{u}{2} + \frac{\pi}{4}\right),$
where u is any function of x.

224. $\displaystyle\int \sec ax \, dx = \frac{1}{a}\log \tan\left(\frac{ax}{2} + \frac{\pi}{4}\right).$

225. $\displaystyle\int \sec^2 ax \, dx = \frac{1}{a}\tan ax.$

226. $\displaystyle\int \sec^n ax \, dx = \frac{1}{a(n-1)}\frac{\sin ax}{\cos^{n-1}ax}$
$$+ \frac{n-2}{n-1}\int \sec^{n-2} ax \, dx, \; n \text{ integer} > 1.$$

227. $\displaystyle\int \csc u \, du = \log\left(\csc u - \operatorname{ctn} u\right) = \log \tan \frac{u}{2},$
where u is any function of x.

228. $\displaystyle\int \csc ax \, dx = \frac{1}{a}\log \tan \frac{ax}{2}.$

229. $\displaystyle\int \csc^2 ax \, dx = -\frac{1}{a}\operatorname{ctn} ax.$

230. $\displaystyle\int \csc^n ax \, dx = -\frac{1}{a(n-1)}\frac{\cos ax}{\sin^{n-1}ax}$
$$+ \frac{n-2}{n-1}\int \csc^{n-2} ax \, dx, \; n \text{ integer} > 1.$$

Expressions Containing tan ax and sec ax or ctn ax and csc ax.

231. $\displaystyle\int \tan u \sec u \; du = \sec u$, where u is any function of x.

232. $\displaystyle\int \tan ax \sec ax \; dx = \frac{1}{a} \sec ax$.

233. $\displaystyle\int \tan^n ax \sec^2 ax \; dx = \frac{1}{a(n+1)} \tan^{n+1} ax$, $n \neq -1$.

234. $\displaystyle\int \operatorname{ctn} u \csc u \; du = -\csc u$, where u is any function of x.

235. $\displaystyle\int \operatorname{ctn} ax \csc ax \; dx = -\frac{1}{a} \csc ax$.

236. $\displaystyle\int \operatorname{ctn}^n ax \csc^2 ax \; dx = -\frac{1}{a(n+1)} \operatorname{ctn}^{n+1} ax$, $n \neq -1$.

237. $\displaystyle\int \frac{\csc^2 ax \; dx}{\operatorname{ctn} ax} = -\frac{1}{a} \log \operatorname{ctn} ax$.

Expressions Containing Algebraic and Trigonometric Functions.

238. $\displaystyle\int x \sin ax \; dx = \frac{1}{a^2} \sin ax - \frac{1}{a} x \cos ax$.

239. $\displaystyle\int x^n \sin ax \; dx = -\frac{1}{a} x^n \cos ax + \frac{n}{a} \int x^{n-1} \cos ax \; dx$, $n > 0$.

240. $\displaystyle\int \frac{\sin ax \; dx}{x} = ax - \frac{(ax)^3}{3 \cdot 3!} + \frac{(ax)^5}{5 \cdot 5!} - \cdots$.

241. $\displaystyle\int \frac{\sin ax \; dx}{x^m} = \frac{-1}{(m-1)} \frac{\sin ax}{x^{m-1}} + \frac{a}{(m-1)} \int \frac{\cos ax \; dx}{x^{m-1}}$.

242. $\displaystyle\int x \cos ax \; dx = \frac{1}{a^2} \cos ax + \frac{1}{a} x \sin ax$.

243. $\displaystyle\int x^n \cos ax \; dx = \frac{1}{a} x^n \sin ax - \frac{n}{a} \int x^{n-1} \sin ax \; dx$, n pos.

244. $\displaystyle\int \frac{\cos ax \; dx}{x} = \log ax - \frac{(ax)^2}{2 \cdot 2!} + \frac{(ax)^4}{4 \cdot 4!} - \cdots$.

245. $\int \frac{\cos ax}{x^m} dx = - \frac{1}{(m-1)} \cdot \frac{\cos ax}{x^{m-1}} - \frac{a}{(m-1)} \int \frac{\sin ax \, dx}{x^{m-1}}.$

Expressions Containing Exponential and Logarithmic Functions.

246. $\int e^u \, du = e^u$, where u is any function of x.

247. $\int b^u \, du = \frac{b^u}{\log b}$, where u is any function of x.

248. $\int e^{ax} \, dx = \frac{1}{a} e^{ax}, \quad \int b^{ax} \, dx = \frac{b^{ax}}{a \log b}.$

249. $\int xe^{ax} \, dx = \frac{e^{ax}}{a^2} (ax - 1), \int xb^{ax} \, dx = \frac{xb^{ax}}{a \log b} - \frac{b^{ax}}{a^2 (\log b)^2}.$

250. $\int x^n e^{ax} \, dx = \frac{1}{a} x^n e^{ax} - \frac{n}{a} \int x^{n-1} e^{ax} \, dx, \quad n \text{ pos.}$

251. $\int x^n b^{ax} \, dx = \frac{x^n b^{ax}}{a \log b} - \frac{n}{a \log b} \int x^{n-1} b^{ax} \, dx, \quad n \text{ pos.}$

252. $\int \frac{e^{ax}}{x} \, dx = \log x + ax + \frac{(ax)^2}{2 \cdot 2!} + \frac{(ax)^2}{3 \cdot 3!} + \cdots.$

253. $\int \frac{e^{ax}}{x^n} \, dx = \frac{1}{n-1} \left[- \frac{e^{ax}}{x^{n-1}} + a \int \frac{e^{ax}}{x^{n-1}} \, dx \right], \, n \text{ integ.} > 1.$

254. $\int \frac{dx}{b + ce^{ax}} = \frac{1}{ab} [ax - \log (b + ce^{ax})].$

255. $\int \frac{e^{ax} \, dx}{b + ce^{ax}} = \frac{1}{ac} \log (b + ce^{ax}).$

256. $\int \frac{dx}{be^{ax} + ce^{-ax}} = \frac{1}{a\sqrt{bc}} \tan^{-1} \left(e^{ax} \sqrt{\frac{b}{c}} \right), b \text{ and } c \text{ pos.}$

257. $\int e^{ax} \sin bx \, dx = \frac{e^{ax}}{a^2 + b^2} \quad (a \sin bx - b \cos bx).$

258. $\displaystyle\int e^{ax} \cos bx \, dx = \frac{e^{ax}}{a^2 + b^2} \, (a \cos bx + b \sin bx).$

259. $\displaystyle\int xe^{ax} \sin bx \, dx = \frac{xe^{ax}}{a^2 + b^2} \, (a \sin bx - b \cos bx)$
$$- \frac{e^{ax}}{(a^2 + b^2)^2} \, [(a^2 - b^2) \sin bx - 2 \, ab \cos bx].$$

260. $\displaystyle\int xe^{ax} \cos bx \, dx = \frac{xe^{ax}}{a^2 + b^2} \, (a \cos bx + b \sin bx)$
$$- \frac{e^{ax}}{(a^2 + b^2)^2} [(a^2 - b^2) \cos bx + 2 \, ab \sin bx].$$

261. $\displaystyle\int e^{ax} \cos^n bx \, dx = \frac{e^{ax} \cos^{n-1} bx \, (a \cos bx + nb \sin bx)}{a^2 + n^2 b^2}$
$$+ \frac{n(n-1)b^2}{a^2 + n^2 b^2} \int e^{ax} \cos^{n-2} bx \, dx.$$

262. $\displaystyle\int e^{ax} \sin^n bx \, dx = \frac{e^{ax} \sin^{n-1} bx \, (a \sin bx - nb \cos bx)}{a^2 + n^2 b^2}$
$$+ \frac{n(n-1)b^2}{a^2 + n^2 \, b^2} \int e^{ax} \sin^{n-2} bx \, dx.$$

263. $\displaystyle\int \log ax \, dx = x \log ax - x.$

264. $\displaystyle\int (\log ax)^n \, dx = x \, (\log ax)^n - n \int (\log ax)^{n-1} \, dx, \quad n \text{ pos.}$

265. $\displaystyle\int x^n \log ax \, dx = x^{n+1} \left[\frac{\log ax}{n+1} - \frac{1}{(n+1)^2} \right], \quad n \neq -1.$

266. $\displaystyle\int x^n \, (\log ax)^m \, dx = \frac{x^{n+1}}{n+1} \, (\log ax)^m - \frac{m}{n+1} \int x^n \, (\log ax)^{m-1} dx.$

267. $\displaystyle\int \frac{(\log ax)^n}{x} \, dx = \frac{(\log ax)^{n+1}}{n+1}, \quad n \neq -1.$

268. $\displaystyle\int \frac{dx}{x \log ax} = \log \, (\log ax).$

269. $\displaystyle\int \frac{dx}{x\,(\log ax)^n} = -\frac{1}{(n-1)\,(\log ax)^{n-1}}.$

270. $\displaystyle\int \frac{x^n dx}{(\log ax)^m} = \frac{-x^{n+1}}{(m-1)\,(\log ax)^{m-1}} + \frac{n+1}{m-1}\int \frac{x^n\,dx}{(\log ax)^{m-1}}.$

271. $\displaystyle\int \frac{dx}{\log ax} = \frac{1}{a}\left[\log\,(\log ax) + \log ax + \frac{(\log ax)^2}{2\cdot 2!} \right.$
$$\left. + \frac{(\log ax)^3}{3\cdot 3!} + \cdots \right].$$

272. $\displaystyle\int \sin\,(\log ax)\,dx = \frac{x}{2}\,[\sin\,(\log ax) - \cos\,(\log ax)\,].$

273. $\displaystyle\int \cos\,(\log ax)\,dx = \frac{x}{2}\,[\sin\,(\log ax) + \cos\,(\log ax)\,].$

Expressions Containing Inverse Trigonometric Functions

274. $\displaystyle\int e^{ax} \log x\,dx = \frac{1}{a}\,e^{ax} \log x - \frac{1}{a}\int \frac{e^{ax}}{x}\,dx.$

275. $\displaystyle\int \sin^{-1} ax\,dx = x \sin^{-1} ax + \frac{1}{a}\sqrt{1-a^2x^2}.$

276. $\displaystyle\int \cos^{-1} ax\,dx = x \cos^{-1} ax - \frac{1}{a}\sqrt{1-a^2x^2}.$

277. $\displaystyle\int \tan^{-1} ax\,dx = x \tan^{-1} ax - \frac{1}{2a} \log\,(1+a^2x^2).$

278. $\displaystyle\int \text{ctn}^{-1} ax\,dx = x \, \text{ctn}^{-1} ax + \frac{1}{2a} \log\,(1+a^2x^2).$

279. $\displaystyle\int \sec^{-1} ax\,dx = x \sec^{-1} ax - \frac{1}{a} \log\,(ax + \sqrt{a^2x^2-1}).$

280. $\displaystyle\int \csc^{-1} ax\,dx = x \csc^{-1} ax + \frac{1}{a} \log\,(ax + \sqrt{a^2x^2-1}).$

Definite Integrals

281. $\int_0^\infty \dfrac{a\,dx}{a^2 + x^2} = \dfrac{\pi}{2}$, if $a > 0$; $\quad 0$, if $a = 0$; $\quad \dfrac{-\pi}{2}$, if $a < 0$.

282. $\int_0^\infty x^{n-1}e^{-x}dx = \int_0^1 \left[\log_e\dfrac{1}{x}\right]^{n-1}dx = \Gamma(n)$.

$\Gamma(n+1) = n\cdot\Gamma(n)$, if $n > 0$. $\qquad \Gamma(2) = \Gamma(1) = 1$.

$\Gamma(n+1) = n!$, if n is an integer. $\qquad \Gamma(\tfrac{1}{2}) = \sqrt{\pi}$.

$\Gamma(n) = \Pi(n-1)$. $\qquad Z(y) = D_y[\log_e\Gamma(y)]$.

$Z(1) = -0.577216$.

283. $\int_0^\infty e^{-zx} \cdot z^n \cdot x^{n-1}dx = \Gamma(n)$, $z > 0$.

284. $\int_0^1 x^{m-1}(1-x)^{n-1}dx = \int_0^\infty \dfrac{x^{m-1}dx}{(1+x)^{m+n}} = \dfrac{\Gamma(m)\Gamma(n)}{\Gamma(m+n)}$.

285. $\int_0^\infty \dfrac{x^{n-1}}{1+x}dx = \dfrac{\pi}{\sin n\pi}$, $0 < n < 1$.

286. $\int_0^{\frac{\pi}{2}} \sin^n x\,dx = \int_0^{\frac{\pi}{2}} \cos^n x\,dx$

$\qquad = \dfrac{1}{2}\sqrt{\pi} \cdot \dfrac{\Gamma\left(\dfrac{n}{2}+\dfrac{1}{2}\right)}{\Gamma\left(\dfrac{n}{2}+1\right)}$, if $n > -1$;

$\qquad = \dfrac{1 \cdot 3 \cdot 5 \cdots (n-1)}{2 \cdot 4 \cdot 6 \cdots (n)} \cdot \dfrac{\pi}{2}$, if n is an even integer;

$\qquad = \dfrac{2 \cdot 4 \cdot 6 \cdots (n-1)}{1 \cdot 3 \cdot 5 \cdot 7 \cdots n}$, if n is an odd integer.

287. $\int_0^\infty \dfrac{\sin^2 x}{x^2}dx = \dfrac{\pi}{2}$.

288. $\int_0^\infty \dfrac{\sin ax}{x}\, dx = \dfrac{\pi}{2}$, if $a > 0$.

289. $\int_0^\infty \dfrac{\sin x \cos ax}{x}\, dx = 0$, if $a < -1$, or $a > 1$;

$\qquad\qquad\qquad\qquad = \dfrac{\pi}{4}$, if $a = -1$, or $a = 1$;

$\qquad\qquad\qquad\qquad = \dfrac{\pi}{2}$, if $-1 < a < 1$.

290. $\int_0^\pi \sin^2 ax\, dx = \int_0^\pi \cos^2 ax\, dx = \dfrac{\pi}{2}$.

291. $\int_0^{\pi/a} \sin ax \cdot \cos ax\, dx = \int_0^\pi \sin ax \cdot \cos ax\, dx = 0$.

292. $\int_0^\pi \sin ax \sin bx\, dx = \int_0^\pi \cos ax \cos bx\, dx = 0, \quad a \neq b$.

293. $\int_0^\pi \sin ax \cos bx\, dx = \dfrac{2a}{a^2 - b^2}$, if $a - b$ is odd;

$\qquad\qquad\qquad\qquad = 0$, if $a - b$ is even.

294. $\int_0^\infty \dfrac{\sin ax \sin bx}{x^2}\, dx = \dfrac{1}{2}\pi a$, if $a < b$.

295. $\int_0^\infty \cos(x^2)\, dx = \int_0^\infty \sin(x^2)\, dx = \dfrac{1}{2}\sqrt{\dfrac{\pi}{2}}$.

296. $\int_0^\infty e^{-a^2 x^2}\, dx = \dfrac{\sqrt{\pi}}{2a} = \dfrac{1}{2a}\,\Gamma\!\left(\dfrac{1}{2}\right)$, if $a > 0$.

297. $\int_0^\infty x^n \cdot e^{-ax}\, dx = \dfrac{\Gamma(n+1)}{a^{n+1}}$,

$\qquad\qquad\qquad = \dfrac{n!}{a^{n+1}}$, if n is a positive integer, $a > 0$.

298. $\int_0^\infty x^{2n} e^{-ax^2}\, dx = \dfrac{1 \cdot 3 \cdot 5 \cdots (2n-1)}{2^{n+1} a^n}\sqrt{\dfrac{\pi}{a}}$.

299. $\int_0^\infty e^{-x^2 - a^2/x^2}\, dx = \dfrac{1}{2}\, e^{-2a}\sqrt{\pi}$, if $a > 0$.

300. $\displaystyle\int_0^\infty e^{-ax} \cos bx \, dx = \frac{a}{a^2 + b^2}$, if $a > 0$.

301. $\displaystyle\int_0^\infty e^{-ax} \sin bx \, dx = \frac{b}{a^2 + b^2}$, if $a > 0$.

302. $\displaystyle\int_0^\infty e^{-a^2x^2} \cos bx \, dx = \frac{\sqrt{\pi} \cdot e^{-\frac{b^2}{4a^2}}}{2a}$, if $a > 0$.

303. $\displaystyle\int_0^1 \frac{\log x}{1-x} \, dx = -\frac{\pi^2}{6}$.

304. $\displaystyle\int_0^1 \frac{\log x}{1+x} \, dx = -\frac{\pi^2}{12}$.

305. $\displaystyle\int_0^1 \frac{\log x}{1-x^2} \, dx = -\frac{\pi^2}{8}$.

306. $\displaystyle\int_0^1 \log\left(\frac{1+x}{1-x}\right) \cdot \frac{dx}{x} = \frac{\pi^2}{4}$.

307. $\displaystyle\int_0^\infty \log\left(\frac{e^x+1}{e^x-1}\right) dx = \frac{\pi^2}{4}$.

308. $\displaystyle\int_0^1 \frac{dx}{\sqrt{\log(1/x)}} = \sqrt{\pi}$.

309. $\displaystyle\int_0^{\frac{\pi}{2}} \log \sin x \, dx = \int_0^{\frac{\pi}{2}} \log \cos x \, dx = -\frac{\pi}{2} \cdot \log_e 2$.

310. $\displaystyle\int_0^\pi x \log \sin x \, dx = -\frac{\pi^2}{2} \cdot \log_e 2$.

311. $\displaystyle\int_0^1 x^m \log\left(\frac{1}{x}\right)^n dx = \frac{\Gamma(n+1)}{(m+1)^{n+1}}$, if $m+1 > 0$, $n+1 > 0$.

312. $\displaystyle\int_0^\pi \frac{\log(1+\sin a \cos x)}{\cos x} \, dx = \pi a$.

313. $\int_0^1 \dfrac{x^b - x^a}{\log x}\, dx = \log \dfrac{1+b}{1+a}.$

314. $\int_0^\pi \dfrac{dx}{a+b\cos x} = \dfrac{\pi}{\sqrt{a^2 - b^2}},$ if $a > b > 0.$

315. $\int_0^\infty \dfrac{\cos ax\, dx}{1+x^2} = \dfrac{\pi}{2}\cdot e^{-|a|},$ if $a > 0.$

316. $\int_0^\infty \dfrac{\cos x\, dx}{\sqrt{x}} = \int_0^\infty \dfrac{\sin x\, dx}{\sqrt{x}} = \sqrt{\dfrac{\pi}{2}}.$

317. $\int_0^\infty \dfrac{e^{-ax} - e^{-bx}}{x}\, dx = \log \dfrac{b}{a}.$

318. $\int_0^\infty \dfrac{\tan^{-1} ax - \tan^{-1} bx}{x}\, dx = \dfrac{\pi}{2}\log \dfrac{a}{b}.$

319. $\int_0^\infty \dfrac{\cos ax - \cos bx}{x}\, dx = \log \dfrac{b}{a}.$

320. $\int_0^{\frac{\pi}{2}} \dfrac{dx}{a^2\cos^2 x + b^2\sin^2 x} = \dfrac{\pi}{2ab}.$

321. $\int_0^{\frac{\pi}{2}} \dfrac{dx}{(a^2\cos^2 x + b^2\sin^2 x)^2} = \dfrac{\pi(a^2 + b^2)}{4a^3 b^3}.$

322. $\int_0^\pi \dfrac{(a - b\cos x)\,dx}{a^2 - 2ab\cos x + b^2} = 0,$ if $a^2 < b^2;$

$$= \dfrac{\pi}{a}, \quad \text{if } a^2 > b^2;$$

$$= \dfrac{\pi}{2a}, \quad \text{if } a = b.$$

323. $\int_0^1 \dfrac{1+x^2}{1+x^4}\, dx = \dfrac{\pi}{4}\sqrt{2}.$

324. $\int_0^1 \dfrac{\log(1+x)}{x}\, dx = \dfrac{1}{1^2} - \dfrac{1}{2^2} + \dfrac{1}{3^2} - \dfrac{1}{4^2} + \cdots = \dfrac{\pi^2}{12}.$

325. $\int_{\infty}^{1} \frac{e^{-xu}}{u} \, du = \gamma + \log x - x + \frac{x^2}{2 \cdot 2!} - \frac{x^3}{3 \cdot 3!} + \frac{x^4}{4 \cdot 4!} - \cdots,$

where $\gamma = \lim_{t \to \infty} (1 + \frac{1}{2} + \frac{1}{3} + \cdots + \frac{1}{t} - \log t) = 0.5772157 \cdots.$

326. $\int_{\infty}^{1} \frac{\cos xu}{u} \, du = \gamma + \log x - \frac{x^2}{2 \cdot 2!} + \frac{x^4}{4 \cdot 4!} - \frac{x^6}{6 \cdot 6!} + \cdots,$

where $\gamma = 0.5772157 \cdots.$

327. $\int_{0}^{1} \frac{e^{xu} - e^{-xu}}{u} \, du = 2 \left(x + \frac{x^3}{3 \cdot 3!} + \frac{x^5}{5 \cdot 5!} + \cdots \right).$

328. $\int_{0}^{1} \frac{1 - e^{-xu}}{u} \, du = x - \frac{x^2}{2 \cdot 2!} + \frac{x^3}{3 \cdot 3!} - \frac{x^4}{4 \cdot 4!} + \cdots.$

329. $\int_{0}^{\frac{\pi}{2}} \frac{dx}{\sqrt{1 - K^2 \sin^2 x}} = \frac{\pi}{2} \left[1 + \left(\frac{1}{2}\right)^2 K^2 + \left(\frac{1 \cdot 3}{2 \cdot 4}\right)^2 K^4 + \left(\frac{1 \cdot 3 \cdot 5}{2 \cdot 4 \cdot 6}\right)^2 K^6 + \cdots \right],$

$$\text{if } K^2 < 1.$$

330. $\int_{0}^{\frac{\pi}{2}} \sqrt{1 - K^2 \sin^2 x} \, dx = \frac{\pi}{2} \left[1 - \left(\frac{1}{2}\right)^2 K^2 \right.$

$$\left. - \left(\frac{1 \cdot 3}{2 \cdot 4}\right)^2 \frac{K^4}{3} - \left(\frac{1 \cdot 3 \cdot 5}{2 \cdot 4 \cdot 6}\right)^2 \frac{K^6}{5} - \cdots \right], \text{if } K^2 < 1.$$

331. $f(x) = \frac{1}{2} a_0 + a_1 \cos \frac{\pi x}{c} + a_2 \cos \frac{2\pi x}{c} + \cdots$

$$+ b_1 \sin \frac{\pi x}{c} + b_2 \sin \frac{2\pi x}{c} + \cdots, \quad -c < x < + c,$$

where $a_m = \frac{1}{c} \int_{-c}^{+c} f(x) \cdot \cos \frac{m\pi x}{c} \cdot dx,$

$$b_m = \frac{1}{c} \int_{-c}^{+c} f(x) \cdot \sin \frac{m\pi x}{c} \, dx.$$

VII. Vector Analysis

149. Definitions. Analytic Representation. A *vector V* is a quantity which is completely specified by a magnitude and a direction. A vector may be represented geometrically by a directed line segment $V = \overrightarrow{OA}$. A *scalar S* is a quantity which is completely specified by a magnitude.

Let i, j, k represent three vectors of unit magnitude along the three mutually perpendicular lines OX, OY, OZ, respectively. Let V be a vector in space, and a, b, c the magnitudes of the projections of V along the three lines OX, OY, OZ, respectively. Then V may be represented by $V = a\,i + b\,j + c\,k$. The magnitude of V is $|v| = + \sqrt{a^2 + b^2 + c^2}$, and the direction cosines of V are such that $\cos \alpha : \cos \beta : \cos \gamma = a : b : c$.

150. Vector Sum V of n vectors. Let V_1, V_2, $\cdots$, V_n be n vectors given by $V_1 = a_1\,i + b_1\,j + c_1\,k$, etc. Then the *sum* is
$$V = V_1 + V_2 + \cdots + V_n = (a_1 + a_2 + \cdots + a_n)\,i$$
$$+ (b_1 + b_2 + \cdots + b_n)\,j + (c_1 + c_2 + \cdots + c_n)\,k.$$

151. Product of a Scalar S and a Vector V.
$$SV = (Sa)i + (Sb)\,j + (Sc)k.$$
$$(S_1 + S_2)\,V = S_1\,V + S_2\,V. \quad (V_1 + V_2)\,S = V_1\,S + V_2\,S.$$

152. Scalar Product of Two Vectors: $V_1 \cdot V_2$.
$$V_1 \cdot V_2 = |V_1||V_2| \cos \phi, \text{ where } \phi \text{ is the angle from } V_1 \text{ to } V_2.$$
$$V_1 \cdot V_2 = a_1 a_2 + b_1 b_2 + c_1 c_2 = V_2 \cdot V_1. \quad V_1 \cdot V_1 = |V_1|^2.$$
$$(V_1 + V_2) \cdot V_3 = V_1 \cdot V_3 + V_2 \cdot V_3.$$
$$V_1 \cdot (V_2 + V_3) = V_1 \cdot V_2 + V_1 \cdot V_3.$$
$$i \cdot i = j \cdot j = k \cdot k = 1. \quad i \cdot j = j \cdot k = k \cdot i = 0.$$

153. Vector Product of Two Vectors: $V_1 \times V_2$.

$V_1 \times V_2 = |V_1||V_2| \sin \phi \, 1$, where ϕ is the angle from V_1 to V_2 and 1 is a unit vector perpendicular to the plane of V_1 and V_2 and so directed that a right-handed screw driven in the direction of 1 would carry V_1 into V_2.
$$V_1 \times V_2 = - V_2 \times V_1 =$$
$$(b_1 c_2 - b_2 c_1)\,i + (c_1 a_2 - c_2 a_1)\,j + (a_1 b_2 - a_2 b_1)\,k.$$
$$(V_1 + V_2) \times V_3 = V_1 \times V_3 + V_2 \times V_3.$$
$$V_1 \times (V_2 + V_3) = V_1 \times V_2 + V_1 \times V_3.$$
$$V_1 \times (V_2 \times V_3) = V_2\,(V_1 \cdot V_3) - V_3\,(V_1 \cdot V_2).$$
$$i \times i = j \times j = k \times k = 0, \ i \times j = k, \ j \times k = i, \ k \times i = j.$$
$$V_1 \cdot (V_2 \times V_3) = (V_1 \times V_2) \cdot V_3 = V_2 \cdot (V_3 \times V_1) = [V_1 V_2 V_3] = \begin{vmatrix} a_1 & a_2 & a_3 \\ b_1 & b_2 & b_3 \\ c_1 & c_2 & c_3 \end{vmatrix}.$$

154. Differentiation of Vectors. $V = a\,\boldsymbol{i} + b\,\boldsymbol{j} + c\,\boldsymbol{k}$. If V_1, V_2, $\cdots$ are functions of a scalar variable t, then

$$\frac{d}{dt}\,(V_1 + V_2 + \cdots) = \frac{dV_1}{dt} + \frac{dV_2}{dt} + \cdots, \text{ where}$$

$$\frac{dV_1}{dt} = \frac{da_1}{dt}\,\boldsymbol{i} + \frac{db_1}{dt}\,\boldsymbol{j} + \frac{dc_1}{dt}\,\boldsymbol{k}, \text{ etc.}$$

$$\frac{d}{dt}\,(V_1 \cdot V_2) = \frac{dV_1}{dt} \cdot V_2 + V_1 \cdot \frac{dV_2}{dt}.$$

$$\frac{d}{dt}\,(V_1 \times V_2) = \frac{dV_1}{dt} \times V_2 + V_1 \times \frac{dV_2}{dt}.$$

$$V \cdot \frac{dV}{dt} = |V|\,\frac{d\,|V|}{dt}. \quad \text{If } |V| \text{ is constant,} \quad V \cdot \frac{dV}{dt} = 0.$$

$$\operatorname{grad} S \equiv \nabla S \equiv \frac{\partial S}{\partial x}\,\boldsymbol{i} + \frac{\partial S}{\partial y}\,\boldsymbol{j} + \frac{\partial S}{\partial z}\,\boldsymbol{k}, \text{ where } S \text{ is a scalar.}$$

$$\operatorname{div} V \equiv \nabla \cdot V \equiv \frac{\partial a}{\partial x} + \frac{\partial b}{\partial y} + \frac{\partial c}{\partial z} \quad (\text{divergence of } S).$$

$$\operatorname{curl} V \equiv \operatorname{rot} V \equiv \begin{vmatrix} \boldsymbol{i} & \boldsymbol{j} & \boldsymbol{k} \\ \dfrac{\partial}{\partial x} & \dfrac{\partial}{\partial y} & \dfrac{\partial}{\partial z} \\ a & b & c \end{vmatrix} \equiv \nabla \times V.$$

$$\operatorname{div} \operatorname{grad} S \equiv \nabla^2 S \equiv \frac{\partial^2 S}{\partial x^2} + \frac{\partial^2 S}{\partial y^2} + \frac{\partial^2 S}{\partial z^2}.$$

$$\nabla^2 V \equiv \boldsymbol{i}\,\nabla^2 a + \boldsymbol{j}\,\nabla^2 b + \boldsymbol{k}\,\nabla^2 c.$$

$$\operatorname{curl} \operatorname{grad} S = 0. \quad \operatorname{div} \operatorname{curl} = 0.$$

$$\operatorname{curl} \operatorname{curl} V = \operatorname{grad} \operatorname{div} V - \nabla^2 V.$$

155. Green's Theorem. Let F be a vector and V be a volume bounded by a surface S. Then

$$\iiint_{(V)} \operatorname{div} F\,dV = \iiint_{(V)} \nabla \cdot F\,dV = \iint_{(S)} F \cdot dS,$$

where the integrations are to be carried out over the volume V and the surface S.

156. Stoke's Theorem. Let F be a vector and $dr = dx\,\boldsymbol{i} + dy\,\boldsymbol{j} + dz\,\boldsymbol{k}$, and S be a surface bounded by a simple closed curve C. Then

$$\int_{(C)} F \cdot dr = \iint_{(S)} \operatorname{curl} F \cdot dS = \iint_{(S)} \nabla \times F \cdot dS.$$

PART TWO—TABLES

Explanation of Tables

Table I. Five-Place Common Logarithms of Numbers from 1 to 10,000.

Definition of Logarithm. The *logarithm* x of the number N to the base b is the exponent of the power to which b must be raised to give N. That is,

$$\log_{b} N = x \quad \text{or} \quad b^{x} = N.$$

The number N is positive and b may be any positive number except 1.

Properties of Logarithms.

(*a.*) *The logarithm of a product is equal to the sum of the logarithms of the factors; thus,*

$$\log_{b} M \cdot N = \log_{b} M + \log_{b} N.$$

(*b.*) *The logarithm of a quotient is equal to the logarithm of the numerator minus the logarithm of the denominator; thus,*

$$\log_{b} \frac{M}{N} = \log_{b} M - \log_{b} N.$$

(*c.*) *The logarithm of a power of a number is equal to the logarithm of the base multiplied by the exponent of the power; thus,*

$$\log_{b} M^{p} = p \cdot \log_{b} M.$$

(*d.*) *The logarithm of a root of a number is equal to the logarithm of the number divided by the index of the root; thus,*

$$\log_{b} \sqrt[q]{M} = \frac{1}{q} \log_{b} M.$$

Other properties of logarithms:

$$\log_{b} b = 1 \qquad \qquad \log_{b} \sqrt[q]{M^{p}} = \frac{p}{q} \cdot \log_{b} M.$$

$$\log_{b} 1 = 0 \qquad \qquad \log_{b} N = \log_{a} N \cdot \log_{b} a = \frac{\log_{a} N}{\log_{a} b}.$$

$$\log_{b} (b^{N}) = N \qquad \qquad b^{\,\log_{b} N} = N.$$

Systems of Logarithms. There are two common systems of logarithms in use: (1) the *natural* (Napierian or hyperbolic) system which uses the base $e = 2.71828\cdots$; (2) the *common* (Briggsian) system which uses the base 10.

We shall use the abbreviation* log $N \equiv \log_{10} N$ in this section.

Unless otherwise stated, tables of logarithms are always tables of common logarithms.

Characteristic of a Common Logarithm of a Number. Every real positive number has a real common logarithm such that if $a < b$, log $a <$ log b. Neither zero nor any negative number has a real logarithm.

A common logarithm, in general, consists of an integer, which is called the *characteristic*, and a decimal (usually endless) which is called the *mantissa*. The characteristic of any number may be determined from the following rules.

Rule I. The characteristic of any number greater than 1 is one less than the number of digits before the decimal point.

Rule II.† *The characteristic of a number less than 1 is found by subtracting from 9 the number of ciphers between the decimal point and the first significant digit, and writing –10 after the result.*

Thus the characteristic of log 936 is 2; the characteristic of 9.36 is 0; of log 0.936 is 9 –10; of log 0.00936 is 7 –10.

Mantissa of a Common Logarithm of a Number. An important consequence of the use of base 10 is that the mantissa of a number is independent of the position of the decimal point. Thus 93,600, 93.600, 0.000936, all have the same mantissa. Hence in Tables of Common Logarithms only mantissas are given. This is done in Table I. A five place table gives the values of the mantissa correct to five places of decimals.

To Find the Logarithm of a Given Number N. By means of Rules I and II determine the characteristic. Then use Table I to find mantissa.

To find mantissa when the given number (neglecting decimal point) consists of four, or less, digits (exclusive of ciphers at the beginning or end), look in the column marked N for the first three significant digits and pick the column headed by the fourth digit— the mantissa is the number appearing at the intersection of this row and column. Thus to find the logarithm of 64030, first note (by

---

* Note, however, that log $N \equiv \log_e N$ is used in the Table of Integrals.

† Some writers use a dash over the characteristic to indicate a negative value: for example.
$$\log .004657 = 7.66811{-}10 = \bar{3}.66811.$$

Rule I) that the characteristic is 4. Next in Table I, find 640 in column marked N and opposite it in column 5 is the desired mantissa, .80638. Hence log 64030 = 4.80638. Likewise, log 0.0064030 = 7.80638 − 10; log 0.64030 = 9.80638 −10.

Interpolation. The mantissa of a number of more than four significant figures can be found approximately by assuming that the mantissa varies directly as the number in the small interval not tabulated. Thus if N has five digits (significant), and f is the fifth digit of N, the mantissa of N is

$$m = m_1 + \frac{f}{10}\left(m_2 - m_1\right),$$

where m_1 is the mantissa corresponding to the first four digits of N, m_2 is the next larger mantissa in the table. $(m_2 - m_1)$ is called a *tabular difference*. The proportional part of the difference $m_2 - m_1$ is called the *correction*. These proportional parts are printed without zeros at the right-hand side of each page as an aid to mental multiplications.

For example, find log 64034. Here $f = 4$. From the table we see $m_1 = .80638$, $m_2 = .80645$, whence $m = .80638 + (4/10)\,(.00007)$, log 64034 = 4 + m = 4.80641.

To Find the Number N when its Logarithm is Known. (The number N whose logarithm is k is called the *anti logarithm* of k.)

Case 1. If the mantissa m is found exactly in the Table I, join the figure at the top of the column containing m to the right of the figures in the column marked N and in the same row as m, and place the decimal point according to the characteristic of the logarithm.

Case 2. If the mantissa m is not found exactly in the table, interpolate as follows: find the next smaller mantissa m_1 to m; the first four significant digits of N correspond to the mantissa m_1, and the fifth digit f equals the nearest whole number to

$$f = 10\left(\frac{m - m_1}{m_2 - m_1}\right),$$

where m_2 is the next larger mantissa to m appearing in table. Then locate the decimal point according to the characteristic.

The decimal point may be located by means of the following rules:

Rule III. *If the characteristic of the logarithm is positive (then the mantissa is not followed by −10), begin at the left, count digits one more than the characteristic, and place the decimal point to the right of the last digit counted.*

Rule IV. *If the characteristic is negative (then the mantissa will be preceded by an integer n and followed by –10), prefix (9–n) ciphers, and place the decimal point to the left of these ciphers.*

Illustrations of the Use of Logarithms.

Example 1. Given log x = 2.91089, find x. The mantissa 91089 appears in the table. Join the figure 5 which appears at the top of the column to the right of the number 814 in the column N, giving the number 8145. By Rule III, the decimal point is placed to the right of 4, thus giving x = 814.5.

Example 2. Given log x = 2.34917, find x. The mantissa m = .34917 does not appear in the table. The next smaller and next larger mantissas are m_1 and m_2,

$$m_1 = .34908, \quad m = .34917, \quad m_2 = .34928.$$

The first four digits of N, corresponding to m_1, are 2234 and the fifth digit is the nearest whole number (5) to

$$10 \left(\frac{m - m_1}{m_2 - m_1} \right) = 10 \left(\frac{.00009}{.00020} \right) = 4.5$$

By Rule III, we locate decimal point, thus giving x = 223.45.

Example 3. Find x = (396.21) (.004657) (21.21).

$$\log 396.21 = 2.59792$$
$$\log .004657 = 7.66811 -10$$
$$\log 21.210 = 1.32654 \qquad \text{(add)}$$
$$\log x \qquad = 11.59257 -10, \quad x = 39.135.$$

Example 4. Find $x = \dfrac{396.21^*}{24.3}$.

$$\log 396.21 = 2.59792$$
$$\log 24.3 \quad = 1.38561 \text{ (subtract)}$$
$$\log x \qquad = 1.21231, \quad x = 16.305.$$

Example 5. Find x = (3.5273)⁴.

$$\log 3.5273 = 0.54745$$
$$\underline{\qquad\qquad 4} \text{ (multiply)}$$
$$\log x \quad = 2.18980, \quad x = 154.81.$$

---

* Some writers use *cologarithms*. The cologarithm of a number N is the negative of the logarithm of N; i. e., colog N = 10.00000 — log N — 10. Adding the cologarithm is equivalent to subtracting the logarithm. Thus in our example, colog 24.3 = (10.00000—1.38561) — 10 = 8.61439–10, log 396.21 — log 24.3 = log 396.21 + colog 24.3 = 2.59792 + 8.61439–10 = 11.21231–10 = anti log 16.305.

Example 6.   Given log x = –2.23653, to find x.   To convert this logarithm to one with a positive mantissa, add algebraically –2.23653 to 10.00000–10.   Thus

$$10.00000-10$$
$$-2.23653$$
$$\log x = \overline{7.76347-10}, \quad \text{whence } x = 0.0058006.$$

Example 7.   Find $x = \sqrt[3]{.04657}$.

$$\log x = \tfrac{1}{3} \log (.04657),$$
$$= \tfrac{1}{3}(8.66811-10) = \tfrac{1}{3}(-1.33189),$$
$$\log x = -0.44396 = 9.55604-10, \quad x = 0.35978.$$

or

$$\log x = \tfrac{1}{3}(8.66811-10) = \tfrac{1}{3}(28.66811-30)$$
$$\log x = 9.55604-10, \quad x = 0.35978.$$

Example 8.   Find $x = \dfrac{1}{21.210}$.

$$\log x = \log 1 - \log 21.210$$
$$\log 1 \quad = 10.00000-10$$
$$\log 21.210 = 1.32654 \qquad \text{(subtract)}$$
$$\log x \qquad = \overline{8.67346-10}, \quad x = 0.047148.$$

Table II.   Seven-place Common Logarithms of Numbers. This table gives seven-place logarithms for numbers of five significant figures from 10000 to 12000.

Table III.   Important Constants. This table gives the values and logarithms of a number of important constants.

Table IV.   Common Logarithms of Trigonometric Functions. In this table, the logarithmic values of the sine, cosine, tangent, and cotangent of angles at intervals of one minute from 0° to 90° are given.   Since log sec A = – log cos A and log csc A = – log sin A, log sec A and log csc A are omitted.   For angles between 0° and 45°, the number of the degrees and the name of the trigonometric function are read at the top of the page and the number of minutes in the left-hand column.   The corresponding information for angles between 45° and 90° is found at the bottom of the page and in the right-hand column.

The arrangement and the principles of interpolation are similar to those given in the explanation for Table I.   The –10 portion of the characteristic is not printed in the table but must be written down whenever such a logarithm is used.

While the logarithmic values of the trigonometric functions may be interpolated to the nearest second, interpolation for the logarithms of the sine and tangent of small angles from 0° to 3° and for the logarithms of the cosine and cotangent of angles from 87° to 90° is not accurate. Table IVa should be used in these cases.

Table IVa gives

$$S = \log \sin A - \log A' \text{ and } T = \log \tan A - \log A',$$

where A is the given angle and A' is the number of minutes in A, for values of A from 0° to 3°. Then

$$\log \sin A = \log A' + S \text{ and } \log \tan A = \log A' + T.$$

Likewise,

$$\log \cos A = \log (90° - A)' + S \text{ and } \log \text{ctn } A = \log (90° - A)' + T.$$

for values of A from 87° to 90°, the S and T corresponding to $(90° - A)'$.

For the functions of angles greater than 90°, use the relations given in §57.

Tables of proportional parts are provided in Tables IV which may be used in the interpolation of logarithmic values of the functions between 4° and 86°.

Example 1. Find log sin 21°13′26″.

Turn to the page having 21° at the top. In the row having 13 on the left, find in the column marked "L Sin" at the top log sin 21°13′ = 9.55858 −10. (The −10 portion of the characteristic is omitted in the table.) The tabular difference is 33 and is given in the column marked "*d*". In the table of proportional parts for 33, the correction for 20″ is 11.0 and for 6″ is 3.3. These two corrections must be added to the value of log sin 21°13′. Hence log sin 21°13′26″ = 9.55872 −10.

Example 2. Find log ctn 56°23′37″.

On the page having 56° at the bottom, and in the row having 23 on the right, find in the column marked "L Ctn" at the bottom, log cot 56° 23′ = 9.82270 −10. The tabular difference is 27 and is given in the column marked "*c.d.*" In the table of proportional parts for 27, we obtain 17 as the correction for 37″. Since the logarithmic value of the cotangent decreases as the angle increases from 0° to 90°, this correction for 37″ must be subtracted from log ctn 56°23′. Hence log ctn 56°23′37″ = 9.82253 −10.

Example 3. Find the acute angle A, if log tan A = 9.67341−10. The tabulated value of the logarithm of the tangent just smaller than $9.67341-10$ is $9.67327-10$. This corresponds to $25°14'$. The difference between $9.67341-10$ and $9.67327-10$ is 14 and the tabular difference to be used is 33. In the proportional parts table for 33, we find the largest value less than 14 is 11.0, which corresponds to $20''$. The difference $14 - 11.0 = 3.0$, which corresponds to $5''$. Hence, $25''$ is the approximate correction and $A = 25°14'25''$.

Example 4. Find the acute angle A, if log cos $A = 9.89317 - 10$.

The value of the logarithm of the cosine decreases as the angle increases from $0°$ to $90°$. Hence we must find in the column marked "L Cos" a value just larger than $9.89317-10$. This value is $9.89324 -10$ and corresponds to $38°33'$. The difference between $9.89324 -10$ and $9.89317-10$ is 7, and the tabular difference is 10. From the table of proportional parts we see that the largest value just smaller than 7 is 6.7, which corresponds to $40''$. The difference $7 - 6.7 = 0.3$, which corresponds to $2''$. Hence the correction is $42''$, approximately. Therefore $A = 38°33'42''$.

Example 5.   Find log sin $0°35'30''$.

Convert $35'30''$ to minutes. In table IVa, column A, we find for 35.5 minutes, $S = 6.46372-10$. By Table I, log $35.5 = 1.55023$. Hence, log sin $0°35'30'' = $ log $35.5 + S$
$$= 1.55023 + 6.46372 - 10 = 8.01395 - 10.$$

Table V. Natural Trigonometric Functions. This table gives the values of the sine, cosine, tangent, and cotangent at intervals of one minute from $0°$ to $90°$. The method of interpolation is similar to that given in the explanation of Table IV.

The following tables are self-explanatory: Table VI. Decimal Equivalents of Common Fractions.—Table VII. Minutes and Seconds to Decimal Parts of a Degree.—Table VIII. Natural Trigonometric Functions for Decimal Fractions to a Degree.—Table IX. Common Logarithms of Functions in Radian Measure.—Table X. Degrees, Minutes, and Seconds to Radians.—Table XI. Natural Trigonometric Functions in Radian Measure.—Table XII. Radians to Degrees, Minutes and Seconds.

Table XIII. Table of Powers, Roots, Reciprocals, Circumferences, and Areas of Circles. The square, cube, square root, cube root, and 1000 times the reciprocal of n are given for each integer n from 1 to 999. In the last two columns are given the circumference and area of a circle of diameter n, from $n = 1$ to 999.

Table XIV. Natural Logarithms. This table gives the logarithms of N to the Naperian base e $(= 2.71828\ldots)$ for equidistant values of N from 0.00 to 10.09 and from 10 to 1109. For values of N greater than 1109, use the formula $\log_e 10\,N$ $= \log_e N + \log_e 10 = \log_e N + 2.30258509$, or the formula $\log_e N = (\log_e 10)(\log_{10} N) = 2.30258509\ (\log_{10} N)$.

Table XV. Values and Logarithms of Exponential and Hyperbolic Functions. This table gives the values of e^x, e^{-x}, sinh x, cosh x, tanh x, and the common logarithms of e^x, sinh x, and cosh x for values of x equally spaced from 0.00 to 3.00 and for certain values of x from 3.00 to 10.00. The common logarithm of e^{-x} may be found by the relation $\log_{10} e^{-x} = -\log_{10} e^x = $ colog x. To find $\log_{10}$ tanh x, use $\log_{10}$ tanh $x = \log_{10}$ sinh $x -\log_{10}$ cosh x. This table may be extended indefinitely by means of Table XVI, since $\log_{10} e^x = M{\cdot}x$.

Table XVI. Multiples of M and 1/M. The purpose of this table is to facilitate the multiplication of a number N by M and $1/M$. This occurs whenever it is desired to change from common logarithms to natural logarithms, and conversely. Thus
$$\log_{10} x = (\log_e x)(\log_{10} e) = M \cdot \log_e x;\ \log_e x = \log_{10} x/M.$$
These multiples are also required in
$$\log_{10} e^x = Mx,\ \log_e (10^n \cdot x) = \log_e x + n(1/M),$$
and in the approximate formulae
$$\log_{10} (1 \pm x) = \pm x{\cdot}M \text{ and } 10^{\pm x} = 1 \pm (1/M)x.$$

The following tables are self-explanatory: Table XVII. Logarithms of Primes.—Table XVIII. Common Logarithms of Gamma Functions.—Table XIX. Compound Interest (See §19). —Table XX. Compound Discount (See §20).—Table XXI. Amount of an Annuity (See §23).—Table XXII. Present Value of an Annuity (See §24).—Table XXIII. Logarithms for Interest Computations.—Table XXIV. American Experience Mortality Table.—Table XXV. Probability Functions.—Table XXVb. Factors for Computing Probable Errors.—Table XXVI. Complete Elliptic Integral.—Table XXVII. Four-place Common Logarithms of Trigonometric Functions.—Table XXVIII. Four-place Natural Trigonometric Functions.—Table XXIX. Four-place Common Logarithms of Numbers.—Table XXX. Four-place Common Anti-logarithms of Numbers.

Table I

Page 95

Table I

LOGARITHMS OF NUMBERS

100 — 150

N.	L.	0	1	2	3	4	5	6	7	8	9
100	00	000	043	087	130	173	217	260	303	346	389
101		432	475	518	561	604	647	689	732	775	817
102		860	903	945	988	*030	*072	*115	*157	*199	*242
103	01	284	326	368	410	452	494	536	578	620	662
104		703	745	787	828	870	912	953	995	*036	*078
105	02	119	160	202	243	284	325	366	407	449	490
106		531	572	612	653	694	735	776	816	857	898
107		938	979	*019	*060	*100	*141	*181	*222	*262	*302
108	03	342	383	423	463	503	543	583	623	663	703
109		743	782	822	862	902	941	981	*021	*060	*100
110	04	139	179	218	258	297	336	376	415	454	493
111		532	571	610	650	689	727	766	805	844	883
112		922	961	999	*038	*077	*115	*154	*192	*231	*269
113	05	308	346	385	423	461	500	538	576	614	652
114		690	729	767	805	843	881	918	956	994	*032
115	06	070	108	145	183	221	258	296	333	371	408
116		446	483	521	558	595	633	670	707	744	781
117		819	856	893	930	967	*004	*041	*078	*115	*151
118	07	188	225	262	298	335	372	408	445	482	518
119		555	591	628	664	700	737	773	809	846	882
120		918	954	990	*027	*063	*099	*135	*171	*207	*243
121	08	279	314	350	386	422	458	493	529	565	600
122		636	672	707	743	778	814	849	884	920	955
123		991	*026	*061	*096	*132	*167	*202	*237	*272	*307
124	09	342	377	412	447	482	517	552	587	621	656
125		691	726	760	795	830	864	899	934	968	*003
126	10	037	072	106	140	175	209	243	278	312	346
127		380	415	449	483	517	551	585	619	653	687
128		721	755	789	823	857	890	924	958	992	*025
129	11	059	093	126	160	193	227	261	294	327	361
130		394	428	461	494	528	561	594	628	661	694
131		727	760	793	826	860	893	926	959	992	*024
132	12	057	090	123	156	189	222	254	287	320	352
133		385	418	450	483	516	548	581	613	646	678
134		710	743	775	808	840	872	905	937	969	*001
135	13	033	066	098	130	162	194	226	258	290	322
136		354	386	418	450	481	513	545	577	609	640
137		672	704	735	767	799	830	862	893	925	956
138		988	*019	*051	*082	*114	*145	*176	*208	*239	*270
139	14	301	333	364	395	426	457	489	520	551	582
140		613	644	675	706	737	768	799	829	860	891
141		922	953	983	*014	*045	*076	*106	*137	*168	*198
142	15	229	259	290	320	351	381	412	442	473	503
143		534	564	594	625	655	685	715	746	776	806
144		836	866	897	927	957	987	*017	*047	*077	*107
145	16	137	167	197	227	256	286	316	346	376	406
146		435	465	495	524	554	584	613	643	673	702
147		732	761	791	820	850	879	909	938	967	997
148	17	026	056	085	114	143	173	202	231	260	289
149		319	348	377	406	435	464	493	522	551	580
150		609	638	667	696	725	754	782	811	840	869
N.	L.	0	1	2	3	4	5	6	7	8	9

Proportional parts

	44	43	42
1	4.4	4.3	4.2
2	8.8	8.6	8.4
3	13.2	12.9	12.6
4	17.6	17.2	16.8
5	22.0	21.5	21.0
6	26.4	25.8	25.2
7	30.8	30.1	29.4
8	35.2	34.4	33.6
9	39.6	38.7	37.8

	41	40	39
1	4.1	4.0	3.9
2	8.2	8.0	7.8
3	12.3	12.0	11.7
4	16.4	16.0	15.6
5	20.5	20.0	19.5
6	24.6	24.0	23.4
7	28.7	28.0	27.3
8	32.8	32.0	31.2
9	36.9	36.0	35.1

	38	37	36
1	3.8	3.7	3.6
2	7.6	7.4	7.2
3	11.4	11.1	10.8
4	15.2	14.8	14.4
5	19.0	18.5	18.0
6	22.8	22.2	21.6
7	26.6	25.9	25.2
8	30.4	29.6	28.8
9	34.2	33.3	32.4

	35	34	33
1	3.5	3.4	3.3
2	7.0	6.8	6.6
3	10.5	10.2	9.9
4	14.0	13.6	13.2
5	17.5	17.0	16.5
6	21.0	20.4	19.8
7	24.5	23.8	23.1
8	28.0	27.2	26.4
9	31.5	30.6	29.7

	32	31	30
1	3.2	3.1	3.0
2	6.4	6.2	6.0
3	9.6	9.3	9.0
4	12.8	12.4	12.0
5	16.0	15.5	15.0
6	19.2	18.6	18.0
7	22.4	21.7	21.0
8	25.6	24.8	24.0
9	28.8	27.9	27.0

.00000 — .17869

LOGARITHMS OF NUMBERS

150 — 200

N.	L.	0	1	2	3	4	5	6	7	8	9	Proportional parts
150	17	609	638	667	696	725	754	782	811	840	869	
151		898	926	955	984	*013	*041	*070	*099	*127	*156	
152	18	184	213	241	270	298	327	355	384	412	441	
153		469	498	526	554	583	611	639	667	696	724	
154		752	780	808	837	865	893	921	949	977	*005	
155	19	033	061	089	117	145	173	201	229	257	285	
156		312	340	368	396	424	451	479	507	535	562	
157		590	618	645	673	700	728	756	783	811	838	
158		866	893	921	948	976	*003	*030	*058	*085	*112	
159	20	140	167	194	222	249	276	303	330	358	385	
160		412	439	466	493	520	548	575	602	629	656	
161		683	710	737	763	790	817	844	871	898	925	
162		952	978	*005	*032	*059	*085	*112	*139	*165	*192	
163	21	219	245	272	299	325	352	378	405	431	458	
164		484	511	537	564	590	617	643	669	696	722	
165		748	775	801	827	854	880	906	932	958	985	
166	22	011	037	063	089	115	141	167	194	220	246	
167		272	298	324	350	376	401	427	453	479	505	
168		531	557	583	608	634	660	686	712	737	763	
169		789	814	840	866	891	917	943	968	994	*019	
170	23	045	070	096	121	147	172	198	223	249	274	
171		300	325	350	376	401	426	452	477	502	528	
172		553	578	603	629	654	679	704	729	754	779	
173		805	830	855	880	905	930	955	980	*005	*030	
174	24	055	080	105	130	155	180	204	229	254	279	
175		304	329	353	378	403	428	452	477	502	527	
176		551	576	601	625	650	674	699	724	748	773	
177		797	822	846	871	895	920	944	969	993	*018	
178	25	042	066	091	115	139	164	188	212	237	261	
179		285	310	334	358	382	406	431	455	479	503	
180		527	551	575	600	624	648	672	696	720	744	
181		768	792	816	840	864	888	912	935	959	983	
182	26	007	031	055	079	102	126	150	174	198	221	
183		245	269	293	316	340	364	387	411	435	458	
184		482	505	529	553	576	600	623	647	670	694	
185		717	741	764	788	811	834	858	881	905	928	
186		951	975	998	*021	*045	*068	*091	*114	*138	*161	
187	27	184	207	231	254	277	300	323	346	370	393	
188		416	439	462	485	508	531	554	577	600	623	
189		646	669	692	715	738	761	784	807	830	852	
190		875	898	921	944	967	989	*012	*035	*058	*081	
191	28	103	126	149	171	194	217	240	262	285	307	
192		330	353	375	398	421	443	466	488	511	533	
193		556	578	601	623	646	668	691	713	735	758	
194		780	803	825	847	870	892	914	937	959	981	
195	29	003	026	048	070	092	115	137	159	181	203	
196		226	248	270	292	314	336	358	380	403	425	
197		447	469	491	513	535	557	579	601	623	645	
198		667	688	710	732	754	776	798	820	842	863	
199		885	907	929	951	973	994	*016	*038	*060	*081	
200	30	103	125	146	168	190	211	233	255	276	298	
N.	L.	0	1	2	3	4	5	6	7	8	9	Proportional parts

Proportional parts:

	29	28
1	2.9	2.8
2	5.8	5.6
3	8.7	8.4
4	11.6	11.2
5	14.5	14.0
6	17.4	16.8
7	20.3	19.6
8	23.2	22.4
9	26.1	25.2

	27	26
1	2.7	2.6
2	5.4	5.2
3	8.1	7.8
4	10.8	10.4
5	13.5	13.0
6	16.2	15.6
7	18.9	18.2
8	21.6	20.8
9	24.3	23.4

	25
1	2.5
2	5.0
3	7.5
4	10.0
5	12.5
6	15.0
7	17.5
8	20.0
9	22.5

	24	23
1	2.4	2.3
2	4.8	4.6
3	7.2	6.9
4	9.6	9.2
5	12.0	11.5
6	14.4	13.8
7	16.8	16.1
8	19.2	18.4
9	21.6	20.7

	22	21
1	2.2	2.1
2	4.4	4.2
3	6.6	6.3
4	8.8	8.4
5	11.0	10.5
6	13.2	12.6
7	15.4	14.7
8	17.6	16.8
9	19.8	18.9

Table I   *Page 97*

LOGARITHMS OF NUMBERS

200 — 250

N.	L.	0	1	2	3	4	5	6	7	8	9
200	30	103	125	146	168	190	211	233	255	276	298
201		320	341	363	384	406	428	449	471	492	514
202		535	557	578	600	621	643	664	685	707	728
203		750	771	792	814	835	856	878	899	920	942
204		963	984	*006	*027	*048	*069	*091	*112	*133	*154
205	31	175	197	218	239	260	281	302	323	345	366
206		387	408	429	450	471	492	513	534	555	576
207		597	618	639	660	681	702	723	744	765	785
208		806	827	848	869	890	911	931	952	973	994
209	32	015	035	056	077	098	118	139	160	181	201
210		222	243	263	284	305	325	346	366	387	408
211		428	449	469	490	510	531	552	572	593	613
212		634	654	675	695	715	736	756	777	797	818
213		838	858	879	899	919	940	960	980	*001	*021
214	33	041	062	082	102	122	143	163	183	203	224
215		244	264	284	304	325	345	365	385	405	425
216		445	465	486	506	526	546	566	586	606	626
217		646	666	686	706	726	746	766	786	806	826
218		846	866	885	905	925	945	965	985	*005	*025
219	34	044	064	084	104	124	143	163	183	203	223
220		242	262	282	301	321	341	361	380	400	420
221		439	459	479	498	518	537	557	577	596	616
222		635	655	674	694	713	733	753	772	792	811
223		830	850	869	889	908	928	947	967	986	*005
224	35	025	044	064	083	102	122	141	160	180	199
225		218	238	257	276	295	315	334	353	372	392
226		411	430	449	468	488	507	526	545	564	583
227		603	622	641	660	679	698	717	736	755	774
228		793	813	832	851	870	889	908	927	946	965
229		984	*003	*021	*040	*059	*078	*097	*116	*135	*154
230	36	173	192	211	229	248	267	286	305	324	342
231		361	380	399	418	436	455	474	493	511	530
232		549	568	586	605	624	642	661	680	698	717
233		736	754	773	791	810	829	847	866	884	903
234		922	940	959	977	996	*014	*033	*051	*070	*088
235	37	107	125	144	162	181	199	218	236	254	273
236		291	310	328	346	365	383	401	420	438	457
237		475	493	511	530	548	566	585	603	621	639
238		658	676	694	712	731	749	767	785	803	822
239		840	858	876	894	912	931	949	967	985	*003
240	38	021	039	057	075	093	112	130	148	166	184
241		202	220	238	256	274	292	310	328	346	364
242		382	399	417	435	453	471	489	507	525	543
243		561	578	596	614	632	650	668	686	703	721
244		739	757	775	792	810	828	846	863	881	899
245		917	934	952	970	987	*005	*023	*041	*058	*076
246	39	094	111	129	146	164	182	199	217	235	252
247		270	287	305	322	340	358	375	393	410	428
248		445	463	480	498	515	533	550	568	585	602
249		620	637	655	672	690	707	724	742	759	777
250		794	811	829	846	863	881	898	915	933	950
N.	L.	0	1	2	3	4	5	6	7	8	9

Proportional parts

	22	21
1	2.2	2.1
2	4.4	4.2
3	6.6	6.3
4	8.8	8.4
5	11.0	10.5
6	13.2	12.6
7	15.4	14.7
8	17.6	16.8
9	19.8	18.9

	20
1	2.0
2	4.0
3	6.0
4	8.0
5	10.0
6	12.0
7	14.0
8	16.0
9	18.0

	19
1	1.9
2	3.8
3	5.7
4	7.6
5	9.5
6	11.4
7	13.3
8	15.2
9	17.1

	18
1	1.8
2	3.6
3	5.4
4	7.2
5	9.0
6	10.8
7	12.6
8	14.4
9	16.2

	17
1	1.7
2	3.4
3	5.1
4	6.8
5	8.5
6	10.2
7	11.9
8	13.6
9	15.3

Proportional parts

.30 103 — .39 950

LOGARITHMS OF NUMBERS

250 — 300

N.	L.	0	1	2	3	4	5	6	7	8	9	Proportional parts
250	39	794	811	829	846	863	881	898	915	933	950	**18**
251		967	985	*002	*019	*037	*054	*071	*088	*106	*123	
252	40	140	157	175	192	209	226	243	261	278	295	1 1.8
253		312	329	346	364	381	398	415	432	449	466	2 3.6
254		483	500	518	535	552	569	586	603	620	637	3 5.4
												4 7.2
255		654	671	688	705	722	739	756	773	790	807	5 9.0
256		824	841	858	875	892	909	926	943	960	976	6 10.8
257		993	*010	*027	*044	*061	*078	*095	*111	*128	*145	7 12.6
258	41	162	179	196	212	229	246	263	280	296	313	8 14.4
259		330	347	363	380	397	414	430	447	464	481	9 16.2
260		497	514	531	547	564	581	597	614	631	647	**17**
261		664	681	697	714	731	747	764	780	797	814	
262		830	847	863	880	896	913	929	946	963	979	1 1.7
263		996	*012	*029	*045	*062	*078	*095	*111	*127	*144	2 3.4
264	42	160	177	193	210	226	243	259	275	292	308	3 5.1
												4 6.8
265		325	341	357	374	390	406	423	439	455	472	5 8.5
266		488	504	521	537	553	570	586	602	619	635	6 10.2
267		651	667	684	700	716	732	749	765	781	797	7 11.9
268		813	830	846	862	878	894	911	927	943	959	8 13.6
269		975	991	*008	*024	*040	*056	*072	*088	*104	*120	9 15.3
270	43	136	152	169	185	201	217	233	249	265	281	**16**
271		297	313	329	345	361	377	393	409	425	441	
272		457	473	489	505	521	537	553	569	584	600	1 1.6
273		616	632	648	664	680	696	712	727	743	759	2 3.2
274		775	791	807	823	838	854	870	886	902	917	3 4.8
												4 6.4
275		933	949	965	981	996	*012	*028	*044	*059	*075	5 8.0
276	44	091	107	122	138	154	170	185	201	217	232	6 9.6
277		248	264	279	295	311	326	342	358	373	389	7 11.2
278		404	420	436	451	467	483	498	514	529	545	8 12.8
279		560	576	592	607	623	638	654	669	685	700	9 14.4
280		716	731	747	762	778	793	809	824	840	855	**15**
281		871	886	902	917	932	948	963	979	994	*010	
282	45	025	040	056	071	086	102	117	133	148	163	1 1.5
283		179	194	209	225	240	255	271	286	301	317	2 3.0
284		332	347	362	378	393	408	423	439	454	469	3 4.5
												4 6.0
285		484	500	515	530	545	561	576	591	606	621	5 7.5
286		637	652	667	682	697	712	728	743	758	773	6 9.0
287		788	803	818	834	849	864	879	894	909	924	7 10.5
288		939	954	969	984	*000	*015	*030	*045	*060	*075	8 12.0
289	46	090	105	120	135	150	165	180	195	210	225	9 13.5
290		240	255	270	285	300	315	330	345	359	374	**14**
291		389	404	419	434	449	464	479	494	509	523	
292		538	553	568	583	598	613	627	642	657	672	1 1.4
293		687	702	716	731	746	761	776	790	805	820	2 2.8
294		835	850	864	879	894	909	923	938	953	967	3 4.2
												4 5.6
295		982	997	*012	*026	*041	*056	*070	*085	*100	*114	5 7.0
296	47	129	144	159	173	188	202	217	232	246	261	6 8.4
297		276	290	305	319	334	349	363	378	392	407	7 9.8
298		422	436	451	465	480	494	509	524	538	553	8 11.2
299		567	582	596	611	625	640	654	669	683	698	9 12.6
300		712	727	741	756	770	784	799	813	828	842	log e = 0.43429
N.	L.	0	1	2	3	4	5	6	7	8	9	Proportional parts

.39 794 — .47 842

Table I   *Page 99*

LOGARITHMS OF NUMBERS

300 — 350

N.	L.	0	1	2	3	4	5	6	7	8	9	Proportional parts
300	47	712	727	741	756	770	784	799	813	828	842	
301		857	871	885	900	914	929	943	958	972	986	
302	48	001	015	029	044	058	073	087	101	116	130	
303		144	159	173	187	202	216	230	244	259	273	**15**
304		287	302	316	330	344	359	373	387	401	416	

												Proportional parts 15
305		430	444	458	473	487	501	515	530	544	558	1 1.5
306		572	586	601	615	629	643	657	671	686	700	2 3.0
307		714	728	742	756	770	785	799	813	827	841	3 4.5
308		855	869	883	897	911	926	940	954	968	982	4 6.0
309		996	*010	*024	*038	*052	*066	*080	*094	*108	*122	5 7.5
												6 9.0
310	49	136	150	164	178	192	206	220	234	248	262	7 10.5
311		276	290	304	318	332	346	360	374	338	402	8 12.0
312		415	429	443	457	471	485	499	513	527	541	9 13.5
313		554	568	582	596	610	624	638	651	665	679	
314		693	707	721	734	748	762	776	790	803	817	

												14
315		831	845	859	872	886	900	914	927	941	955	
316		969	982	996	*010	*024	*037	*051	*065	*079	*092	1 1.4
317	50	106	120	133	147	161	174	188	202	215	229	2 2.8
318		243	256	270	284	297	311	325	338	352	365	3 4.2
319		379	393	406	420	433	447	461	474	488	501	4 5.6
												5 7.0
320		515	529	542	556	569	583	596	610	623	637	6 8.4
321		651	664	678	691	705	718	732	745	759	772	7 9.8
322		786	799	813	826	840	853	866	880	893	907	8 11.2
323		920	934	947	961	974	987	*001	*014	*028	*041	9 12.6
324	51	055	068	081	095	108	121	135	148	162	175	

												13
325		188	202	215	228	242	255	268	282	295	308	
326		322	335	348	362	375	388	402	415	428	441	
327		455	468	481	495	508	521	534	548	561	574	
328		587	601	614	627	640	654	667	630	693	706	1 1.3
329		720	733	746	759	772	786	799	812	825	838	2 2.6
												3 3.9
330		851	865	878	891	904	917	930	943	957	970	4 5.2
331		983	996	*009	*022	*035	*048	*061	*075	*088	*101	5 6.5
332	52	114	127	140	153	166	179	192	205	218	231	6 7.8
333		244	257	270	284	297	310	323	336	349	362	7 9.1
334		375	388	401	414	427	440	453	466	479	492	8 10.4
												9 11.7
335		504	517	530	543	556	569	582	595	608	621	
336		634	647	660	673	686	699	711	724	737	750	
337		763	776	789	802	815	827	840	853	866	879	
338		892	905	917	930	943	956	969	982	994	*007	12
339	53	020	033	046	058	071	084	097	110	122	135	

												12
340		148	161	173	186	199	212	224	237	250	263	1 1.2
341		275	288	301	314	326	339	352	364	377	390	2 2.4
342		403	415	428	441	453	466	479	491	504	517	3 3.6
343		529	542	555	567	580	593	605	618	631	643	4 4.8
344		656	668	681	694	706	719	732	744	757	769	5 6.0
												6 7.2
345		782	794	807	820	832	845	857	870	882	895	7 8.4
346		908	920	933	945	958	970	983	995	*008	*020	8 9.6
347	54	033	045	058	070	083	095	108	120	133	145	9 10.8
348		158	170	183	195	208	220	233	245	258	270	
349		283	295	307	320	332	345	357	370	382	394	
350		407	419	432	444	456	469	481	494	506	518	$\log \pi = 0.49715$
N.	L.	0	1	2	3	4	5	6	7	8	9	Proportional parts

.47 712 — .54 518

LOGARITHMS OF NUMBERS

350 — 400

N.	L.	0	1	2	3	4	5	6	7	8	9
350	54	407	419	432	444	456	469	481	494	506	518
351		531	543	555	568	580	593	605	617	630	642
352		654	667	679	691	704	716	728	741	753	765
353		777	790	802	814	827	839	851	864	876	888
354		900	913	925	937	949	962	974	986	998	*011
355	55	023	035	047	060	072	084	096	108	121	133
356		145	157	169	182	194	206	218	230	242	255
357		267	279	291	303	315	328	340	352	364	376
358		388	400	413	425	437	449	461	473	485	497
359		509	522	534	546	558	570	582	594	606	618
360		630	642	654	666	678	691	703	715	727	739
361		751	763	775	787	799	811	823	835	847	859
362		871	883	895	907	919	931	943	955	967	979
363		991	*003	*015	*027	*038	*050	*062	*074	*086	*098
364	56	110	122	134	146	158	170	182	194	205	217
365		229	241	253	265	277	289	301	312	324	336
366		348	360	372	384	396	407	419	431	443	455
367		467	478	490	502	514	526	538	549	561	573
368		585	597	608	620	632	644	656	667	679	691
369		703	714	726	738	750	761	773	785	797	808
370		820	832	844	855	867	879	891	902	914	926
371		937	949	961	972	984	996	*008	*019	*031	*043
372	57	054	066	078	089	101	113	124	136	148	159
373		171	183	194	206	217	229	241	252	264	276
374		287	299	310	322	334	345	357	368	380	392
375		403	415	426	438	449	461	473	484	496	507
376		519	530	542	553	565	576	588	600	611	623
377		634	646	657	669	680	692	703	715	726	738
378		749	761	772	784	795	807	818	830	841	852
379		864	875	887	898	910	921	933	944	955	967
380		978	990	*001	*013	*024	*035	*047	*058	*070	*081
381	58	092	104	115	127	138	149	161	172	184	195
382		206	218	229	240	252	263	274	286	297	309
383		320	331	343	354	365	377	388	399	410	422
384		433	444	456	467	478	490	501	512	524	535
385		546	557	569	580	591	602	614	625	636	647
386		659	670	681	692	704	715	726	737	749	760
387		771	782	794	805	816	827	838	850	861	872
388		883	894	906	917	928	939	950	961	973	984
389		995	*006	*017	*028	*040	*051	*062	*073	*084	*095
390	59	106	118	129	140	151	162	173	184	195	207
391		218	229	240	251	262	273	284	295	306	318
392		329	340	351	362	373	384	395	406	417	428
393		439	450	461	472	483	494	506	517	528	539
394		550	561	572	583	594	605	616	627	638	649
395		660	671	682	693	704	715	726	737	748	759
396		770	780	791	802	813	824	835	846	857	868
397		879	890	901	912	923	934	945	956	966	977
398		988	999	*010	*021	*032	*043	*054	*065	*076	*086
399	60	097	108	119	130	141	152	163	173	184	195
400		206	217	228	239	249	260	271	282	293	304
N.	L.	0	1	2	3	4	5	6	7	8	9

Proportional parts

	13		12		11		10
1	1.3	1	1.2	1	1.1	1	1.0
2	2.6	2	2.4	2	2.2	2	2.0
3	3.9	3	3.6	3	3.3	3	3.0
4	5.2	4	4.8	4	4.4	4	4.0
5	6.5	5	6.0	5	5.5	5	5.0
6	7.8	6	7.2	6	6.6	6	6.0
7	9.1	7	8.4	7	7.7	7	7.0
8	10.4	8	9.6	8	8.8	8	8.0
9	11.7	9	10.8	9	9.9	9	9.0

.54 407 — .60 304

Table I   *Page 101*

LOGARITHMS OF NUMBERS

400 — 450

N.	L.	0	1	2	3	4	5	6	7	8	9	Proportional parts
400	60	206	217	228	239	249	260	271	282	293	304	
401		314	325	336	347	358	369	379	390	401	412	
402		423	433	444	455	466	477	487	498	509	520	
403		531	541	552	563	574	584	595	606	617	627	
404		638	649	660	670	681	692	703	713	724	735	
405		746	756	767	778	788	799	810	821	831	842	
406		853	863	874	885	895	906	917	927	938	949	**11**
407		959	970	981	991	*002	*013	*023	*034	*045	*055	
408	61	066	077	087	098	109	119	130	140	151	162	1 | 1.1
409		172	183	194	204	215	225	236	247	257	268	2 | 2.2 3 | 3.3
410		278	289	300	310	321	331	342	352	363	374	4 | 4.4
411		384	395	405	416	426	437	448	458	469	479	5 | 5.5
412		490	500	511	521	532	542	553	563	574	584	6 | 6.6
413		595	606	616	627	637	648	658	669	679	690	7 | 7.7
414		700	711	721	731	742	752	763	773	784	794	8 | 8.8 9 | 9.9
415		805	815	826	836	847	857	868	878	888	899	
416		909	920	930	941	951	962	972	982	993	*003	
417	62	014	024	034	045	055	066	076	086	097	107	
418		118	128	138	149	159	170	180	190	201	211	
419		221	232	242	252	263	273	284	294	304	315	
420		325	335	346	356	366	377	387	397	408	418	**10**
421		428	439	449	459	469	480	490	500	511	521	
422		531	542	552	562	572	583	593	603	613	624	1 | 1.0
423		634	644	655	665	675	685	696	706	716	726	2 | 2.0
424		737	747	757	767	778	788	798	808	818	829	3 | 3.0 4 | 4.0
425		839	849	859	870	880	890	900	910	921	931	5 | 5.0
426		941	951	961	972	982	992	*002	*012	*022	*033	6 | 6.0
427	63	043	053	063	073	083	094	104	114	124	134	7 | 7.0
428		144	155	165	175	185	195	205	215	225	236	8 | 8.0
429		246	256	266	276	286	296	306	317	327	337	9 | 9.0
430		347	357	367	377	387	397	407	417	428	438	
431		448	458	468	478	488	498	508	518	528	538	
432		548	558	568	579	589	599	609	619	629	639	
433		649	659	669	679	689	699	709	719	729	739	
434		749	759	769	779	789	799	809	819	829	839	
435		849	859	869	879	889	899	909	919	929	939	**9**
436		949	959	969	979	988	998	*008	*018	*028	*038	1 | 0.9
437	64	048	058	068	078	088	098	108	118	128	137	2 | 1.8
438		147	157	167	177	187	197	207	217	227	237	3 | 2.7
439		246	256	266	276	286	296	306	316	326	335	4 | 3.6 5 | 4.5
440		345	355	365	375	385	395	404	414	424	434	6 | 5.4
441		444	454	464	473	483	493	503	513	523	532	7 | 6.3
442		542	552	562	572	582	591	601	611	621	631	8 | 7.2
443		640	650	660	670	680	689	699	709	719	729	9 | 8.1
444		738	748	758	768	777	787	797	807	816	826	
445		836	846	856	865	875	885	895	904	914	924	
446		933	943	953	963	972	982	992	*002	*011	*021	
447	65	031	040	050	060	070	079	089	099	108	118	
448		128	137	147	157	167	176	186	196	205	215	
449		225	234	244	254	263	273	283	292	302	312	
450		321	331	341	350	360	369	379	389	398	408	
N.	L.	0	1	2	3	4	5	6	7	8	9	Proportional parts

.60 206 — .65 408

LOGARITHMS OF NUMBERS

450 — 500

N.	L.	0	1	2	3	4	5	6	7	8	9	Proportional parts
450	65	321	331	341	350	360	369	379	389	398	408	
451		418	427	437	447	456	466	475	485	495	504	
452		514	523	533	543	552	562	571	581	591	600	
453		610	619	629	639	648	658	667	677	686	696	
454		706	715	725	734	744	753	763	772	782	792	
455		801	811	820	830	839	849	858	868	877	887	
456		896	906	916	925	935	944	954	963	973	982	10
457		992	*001	*011	*020	*030	*039	*049	*058	*068	*077	
458	66	087	096	106	115	124	134	143	153	162	172	1 | 1.0
459		181	191	200	210	219	229	238	247	257	266	2 | 2.0
												3 | 3.0
460		276	285	295	304	314	323	332	342	351	361	4 | 4.0
461		370	380	389	398	408	417	427	436	445	455	5 | 5.0
462		464	474	483	492	502	511	521	530	539	549	6 | 6.0
463		558	567	577	586	536	605	614	624	633	642	7 | 7.0
464		652	661	671	680	689	699	708	717	727	736	8 | 8.0
												9 | 9.0
465		745	755	764	773	783	792	801	811	820	829	
466		839	848	857	867	876	885	894	904	913	922	
467		932	941	950	960	969	978	987	997	*006	*015	
468	67	025	034	043	052	062	071	080	089	099	108	
469		117	127	136	145	154	164	173	182	191	201	
470		210	219	228	237	247	256	265	274	284	293	9
471		302	311	321	330	339	348	357	367	376	385	
472		394	403	413	422	431	440	449	459	468	477	1 | 0.9
473		486	495	504	514	523	532	541	550	560	569	2 | 1.8
474		578	587	596	605	614	624	633	642	651	660	3 | 2.7
												4 | 3.6
475		669	679	688	697	706	715	724	733	742	752	5 | 4.5
476		761	770	779	788	797	806	815	825	834	843	6 | 5.4
477		852	861	870	879	888	897	906	916	925	934	7 | 6.3
478		943	952	961	970	979	988	997	*006	*015	*024	8 | 7.2
479	68	034	043	052	061	070	079	088	097	106	115	9 | 8.1
480		124	133	142	151	160	169	178	187	196	205	
481		215	224	233	242	251	260	269	278	287	296	
482		305	314	323	332	341	350	359	368	377	386	
483		395	404	413	422	431	440	449	458	467	476	
484		485	494	502	511	520	529	538	547	556	565	
485		574	583	592	601	610	619	628	637	646	655	8
486		664	673	681	690	699	708	717	726	735	744	
487		753	762	771	780	789	797	806	815	824	833	1 | 0.8
488		842	851	860	869	878	836	895	904	913	922	2 | 1.6
489		931	940	949	958	966	975	984	993	*002	*011	3 | 2.4
												4 | 3.2
490	69	020	028	037	046	055	064	073	032	090	099	5 | 4.0
491		108	117	126	135	144	152	161	170	179	188	6 | 4.8
492		197	205	214	223	232	241	249	258	267	276	7 | 5.6
493		285	294	302	311	320	329	338	346	355	364	8 | 6.4
494		373	381	390	399	408	417	425	434	443	452	9 | 7.2
495		461	469	478	487	496	504	513	522	531	539	
496		548	557	566	574	583	592	601	609	618	627	
497		636	644	653	662	671	679	688	697	705	714	
498		723	732	740	749	758	767	775	784	793	801	
499		810	819	827	836	845	854	862	871	880	888	
500		897	906	914	923	932	940	949	958	966	975	
N.	L.	0	1	2	3	4	5	6	7	8	9	Proportional parts

.65 321 — .69 975

Table I   *Page 103*

LOGARITHMS OF NUMBERS

500 — 550

N.	L. 0	1	2	3	4	5	6	7	8	9
500	69 897	906	914	923	932	940	949	958	966	975
501	984	992	*001	*010	*018	*027	*036	*044	*053	*062
502	70 070	079	088	096	105	114	122	131	140	148
503	157	165	174	183	191	200	209	217	226	234
504	243	252	260	269	278	286	295	303	312	321
505	329	338	346	355	364	372	381	389	398	406
506	415	424	432	441	449	458	467	475	484	492
507	501	509	518	526	535	544	552	561	569	578
508	586	595	603	612	621	629	638	646	655	663
509	672	680	689	697	706	714	723	731	740	749
510	757	766	774	783	791	800	808	817	825	834
511	842	851	859	868	876	885	893	902	910	919
512	927	935	944	952	961	969	978	986	995	*003
513	71 012	020	029	037	046	054	063	071	079	088
514	096	105	113	122	130	139	147	155	164	172
515	181	189	198	206	214	223	231	240	248	257
516	265	273	282	290	299	307	315	324	332	341
517	349	357	366	374	383	391	399	408	416	425
518	433	441	450	458	466	475	483	492	500	508
519	517	525	533	542	550	559	567	575	584	592
520	600	609	617	625	634	642	650	659	667	675
521	684	692	700	709	717	725	734	742	750	759
522	767	775	784	792	800	809	817	825	834	842
523	850	858	867	875	883	892	900	908	917	925
524	933	941	950	958	966	975	983	991	999	*008
525	72 016	024	032	041	049	057	066	074	082	090
526	099	107	115	123	132	140	148	156	165	173
527	181	189	198	206	214	222	230	239	247	255
528	263	272	280	288	296	304	313	321	329	337
529	346	354	362	370	378	387	395	403	411	419
530	428	436	444	452	460	469	477	485	493	501
531	509	518	526	534	542	550	558	567	575	583
532	591	599	607	616	624	632	640	648	656	665
533	673	681	689	697	705	713	722	730	738	746
534	754	762	770	779	787	795	803	811	819	827
535	835	843	852	860	868	876	884	892	900	908
536	916	925	933	941	949	957	965	973	981	989
537	997	*006	*014	*022	*030	*038	*046	*054	*062	*070
538	73 078	086	094	102	111	119	127	135	143	151
539	159	167	175	183	191	199	207	215	223	231
540	239	247	255	263	272	280	288	296	304	312
541	320	328	336	344	352	360	368	376	384	392
542	400	408	416	424	432	440	448	456	464	472
543	480	488	496	504	512	520	528	536	544	552
544	560	568	576	584	592	600	608	616	624	632
545	640	648	656	664	672	679	687	695	703	711
546	719	727	735	743	751	759	767	775	783	791
547	799	807	815	823	830	838	846	854	862	870
548	878	886	894	902	910	918	926	933	941	949
549	957	965	973	981	989	997	*005	*013	*020	*028
550	74 036	044	052	060	068	076	084	092	099	107
N.	L. 0	1	2	3	4	5	6	7	8	9

Proportional parts

	9
1	0.9
2	1.8
3	2.7
4	3.6
5	4.5
6	5.4
7	6.3
8	7.2
9	8.1

	8
1	0.8
2	1.6
3	2.4
4	3.2
5	4.0
6	4.8
7	5.6
8	6.4
9	7.2

	7
1	0.7
2	1.4
3	2.1
4	2.8
5	3.5
6	4.2
7	4.9
8	5.6
9	6.3

LOGARITHMS OF NUMBERS

550 — 600

N.	L.	0	1	2	3	4	5	6	7	8	9	Proportional parts
550	74	036	044	052	060	068	076	084	092	099	107	
551		115	123	131	139	147	155	162	170	178	186	
552		194	202	210	218	225	233	241	249	257	265	
553		273	280	288	296	304	312	320	327	335	343	
554		351	359	367	374	382	390	398	406	414	421	
555		429	437	445	453	461	468	476	484	492	500	
556		507	515	523	531	539	547	554	562	570	578	
557		586	593	601	609	617	624	632	640	648	656	
558		663	671	679	687	695	702	710	718	726	733	
559		741	749	757	764	772	780	788	796	803	811	
560		819	827	834	842	850	858	865	873	881	889	
561		896	904	912	920	927	935	943	950	958	966	
562		974	981	989	997	*005	*012	*020	*028	*035	*043	
563	75	051	059	066	074	082	089	097	105	113	120	
564		128	136	143	151	159	166	174	182	189	197	
565		205	213	220	228	236	243	251	259	266	274	
566		282	289	297	305	312	320	328	335	343	351	
567		358	366	374	381	389	397	404	412	420	427	
568		435	442	450	458	465	473	481	488	496	504	
569		511	519	526	534	542	549	557	565	572	580	
570		587	595	603	610	618	626	633	641	648	656	
571		664	671	679	686	694	702	709	717	724	732	
572		740	747	755	762	770	778	785	793	800	808	
573		815	823	831	838	846	853	861	868	876	884	
574		891	899	906	914	921	929	937	944	952	959	
575		967	974	982	989	997	*005	*012	*020	*027	*035	
576	76	042	050	057	065	072	080	087	095	103	110	
577		118	125	133	140	148	155	163	170	178	185	
578		193	200	208	215	223	230	238	245	253	260	
579		268	275	283	290	298	305	313	320	328	335	
580		343	350	358	365	373	380	388	395	403	410	
581		418	425	433	440	448	455	462	470	477	485	
582		492	500	507	515	522	530	537	545	552	559	
583		567	574	582	589	597	604	612	619	626	634	
584		641	649	656	664	671	678	686	693	701	708	
585		716	723	730	738	745	753	760	768	775	782	
586		790	797	805	812	819	827	834	842	849	856	
587		864	871	879	886	893	901	908	916	923	930	
588		938	945	953	960	967	975	982	989	997	*004	
589	77	012	019	026	034	041	048	056	063	070	078	
590		085	093	100	107	115	122	129	137	144	151	
591		159	166	173	181	188	195	203	210	217	225	
592		232	240	247	254	262	269	276	283	291	298	
593		305	313	320	327	335	342	349	357	364	371	
594		379	386	393	401	408	415	422	430	437	444	
595		452	459	466	474	481	488	495	503	510	517	
596		525	532	539	546	554	561	568	576	583	590	
597		597	605	612	619	627	634	641	648	656	663	
598		670	677	685	692	699	706	714	721	728	735	
599		743	750	757	764	772	779	786	793	801	808	
600		815	822	830	837	844	851	859	866	873	880	
N.	L.	0	1	2	3	4	5	6	7	8	9	Proportional parts

8

1	0.8
2	1.6
3	2.4
4	3.2
5	4.0
6	4.8
7	5.6
8	6.4
9	7.2

7

1	0.7
2	1.4
3	2.1
4	2.8
5	3.5
6	4.2
7	4.9
8	5.6
9	6.3

.74 036 — .77 880

Table I   *Page 105*

LOGARITHMS OF NUMBERS

600 — 650

N.	L.	0	1	2	3	4	5	6	7	8	9
600	77	815	822	830	837	844	851	859	866	873	880
601		887	895	902	909	916	924	931	938	945	952
602		960	967	974	981	988	996	*003	*010	*017	*025
603	78	032	039	046	053	061	068	075	082	089	097
604		104	111	118	125	132	140	147	154	161	168
605		176	183	190	197	204	211	219	226	233	240
606		247	254	262	269	276	283	290	297	305	312
607		319	326	333	340	347	355	362	369	376	383
608		390	398	405	412	419	426	433	440	447	455
609		462	469	476	483	490	497	504	512	519	526
610		533	540	547	554	561	569	576	583	590	597
611		604	611	618	625	633	640	647	654	661	668
612		675	682	689	696	704	711	718	725	732	739
613		746	753	760	767	774	781	789	796	803	810
614		817	824	831	838	845	852	859	866	873	880
615		888	895	902	909	916	923	930	937	944	951
616		958	965	972	979	986	993	*000	*007	*014	*021
617	79	029	036	043	050	057	064	071	078	085	092
618		099	106	113	120	127	134	141	148	155	162
619		169	176	183	190	197	204	211	218	225	232
620		239	246	253	260	267	274	281	288	295	302
621		309	316	323	330	337	344	351	358	365	372
622		379	386	393	400	407	414	421	428	435	442
623		449	456	463	470	477	484	491	498	505	511
624		518	525	532	539	546	553	560	567	574	581
625		588	595	602	609	616	623	630	637	644	650
626		657	664	671	678	685	692	699	706	713	720
627		727	734	741	748	754	761	768	775	782	789
628		796	803	810	817	824	831	837	844	851	858
629		865	872	879	886	893	900	906	913	920	927
630		934	941	948	955	962	969	975	982	989	996
631	80	003	010	017	024	030	037	044	051	058	065
632		072	079	085	092	099	106	113	120	127	134
633		140	147	154	161	168	175	182	188	195	202
634		209	216	223	229	236	243	250	257	264	271
635		277	284	291	298	305	312	318	325	332	339
636		346	353	359	366	373	380	387	393	400	407
637		414	421	428	434	441	448	455	462	468	475
638		482	489	496	502	509	516	523	530	536	543
639		550	557	564	570	577	584	591	598	604	611
640		618	625	632	638	645	652	659	665	672	679
641		686	693	699	706	713	720	726	733	740	747
642		754	760	767	774	781	787	794	801	808	814
643		821	828	835	841	848	855	862	868	875	882
644		889	895	902	909	916	922	929	936	943	949
645		956	963	969	976	983	990	996	*003	*010	*017
646	81	023	030	037	043	050	057	064	070	077	084
647		090	097	104	111	117	124	131	137	144	151
648		158	164	171	178	184	191	198	204	211	218
649		224	231	238	245	251	258	265	271	278	285
650		291	298	305	311	318	325	331	338	345	351
N.	L.	0	1	2	3	4	5	6	7	8	9

Proportional parts

	8		7		6
1	0.8	1	0.7	1	0.6
2	1.6	2	1.4	2	1.2
3	2.4	3	2.1	3	1.8
4	3.2	4	2.8	4	2.4
5	4.0	5	3.5	5	3.0
6	4.8	6	4.2	6	3.6
7	5.6	7	4.9	7	4.2
8	6.4	8	5.6	8	4.8
9	7.2	9	6.3	9	5.4

LOGARITHMS OF NUMBERS

650 — 700

N.	L.	0	1	2	3	4	5	6	7	8	9	Proportional parts
650	81	291	298	305	311	318	325	331	338	345	351	
651		358	365	371	378	385	391	398	405	411	418	
652		425	431	438	445	451	458	465	471	478	485	
653		491	498	505	511	518	525	531	538	544	551	
654		558	564	571	578	584	591	598	604	611	617	
655		624	631	637	644	651	657	664	671	677	684	
656		690	697	704	710	717	723	730	737	743	750	
657		757	763	770	776	783	790	796	803	809	816	
658		823	829	836	842	849	856	862	869	875	882	
659		889	895	902	908	915	921	928	935	941	948	
660		954	961	968	974	981	987	994	*000	*007	*014	
661	82	020	027	033	040	046	053	060	066	073	079	
662		086	092	099	105	112	119	125	132	138	145	
663		151	158	164	171	178	184	191	197	204	210	
664		217	223	230	236	243	249	256	263	269	276	
665		282	289	295	302	308	'315	321	328	334	341	
666		347	354	360	367	373	380	387	393	400	406	
667		413	419	426	432	439	445	452	458	465	471	
668		478	484	491	497	504	510	517	523	530	536	
669		543	549	556	562	569	575	582	588	595	601	
670		607	614	620	627	633	640	646	653	659	666	
671		672	679	685	692	698	705	711	718	724	730	
672		737	743	750	756	763	769	776	782	789	795	
673		802	808	814	821	827	834	840	847	853	860	
674		866	872	879	885	892	898	905	911	918	924	
675		930	937	943	950	956	963	969	975	982	988	
676		995	*001	*008	*014	*020	*027	*033	*040	*046	*052	
677	83	059	065	072	078	085	091	097	104	110	117	
678		123	129	136	142	149	155	161	168	174	181	
679		187	193	200	206	213	219	225	232	238	245	
680		251	257	264	270	276	283	289	296	302	308	
681		315	321	327	334	340	347	353	359	366	372	
682		378	385	391	398	404	410	417	423	429	436	
683		442	448	455	461	467	474	480	487	493	499	
684		506	512	518	525	531	537	544	550	556	563	
685		569	575	582	588	594	601	607	613	620	626	
686		632	639	645	651	658	664	670	677	683	689	
687		696	702	708	715	721	727	734	740	746	753	
688		759	765	771	778	784	790	797	803	809	816	
689		822	828	835	841	847	853	860	866	872	879	
690		885	891	897	904	910	916	923	929	935	942	
691		948	954	960	967	973	979	985	992	998	*004	
692	84	011	017	023	029	036	042	048	055	061	067	
693		073	080	086	092	098	105	111	117	123	130	
694		136	142	148	155	161	167	173	180	186	192	
695		198	205	211	217	223	230	236	242	248	255	
696		261	267	273	280	286	292	298	305	311	317	
697		323	330	336	342	348	354	361	367	373	379	
698		386	392	398	404	410	417	423	429	435	442	
699		448	454	460	466	473	479	485	491	497	504	
700		510	516	522	528	535	541	547	553	559	566	
N.	L.	0	1	2	3	4	5	6	7	8	9	Proportional parts

Proportional parts:

	7
1	0.7
2	1.4
3	2.1
4	2.8
5	3.5
6	4.2
7	4.9
8	5.6
9	6.3

	6
1	0.6
2	1.2
3	1.8
4	2.4
5	3.0
6	3.6
7	4.2
8	4.8
9	5.4

Table I   **Page 107**

LOGARITHMS OF NUMBERS

700 — 750

N.	L.	0	1	2	3	4	5	6	7	8	9
700	84	510	516	522	528	535	541	547	553	559	566
701		572	578	584	590	597	603	609	615	621	628
702		634	640	646	652	658	665	671	677	683	689
703		696	702	708	714	720	726	733	739	745	751
704		757	763	770	776	782	788	794	800	807	813
705		819	825	831	837	844	850	856	862	868	874
706		880	887	893	899	905	911	917	924	930	936
707		942	948	954	960	967	973	979	985	991	997
708	85	003	009	016	022	028	034	040	046	052	058
709		065	071	077	083	089	095	101	107	114	120
710		126	132	138	144	150	156	163	169	175	181
711		187	193	199	205	211	217	224	230	236	242
712		248	254	260	266	272	278	285	291	297	303
713		309	315	321	327	333	339	345	352	358	364
714		370	376	382	388	394	400	406	412	418	425
715		431	437	443	449	455	461	467	473	479	485
716		491	497	503	509	516	522	528	534	540	546
717		552	558	564	570	576	582	588	594	600	606
718		612	618	625	631	637	643	649	655	661	667
719		673	679	685	691	697	703	709	715	721	727
720		733	739	745	751	757	763	769	775	781	788
721		794	800	806	812	818	824	830	836	842	848
722		854	860	866	872	878	884	890	896	902	908
723		914	920	926	932	938	944	950	956	962	968
724		974	980	986	992	998	*004	*010	*016	*022	*028
725	86	034	040	046	052	058	064	070	076	082	088
726		094	100	106	112	118	124	130	136	141	147
727		153	159	165	171	177	183	189	195	201	207
728		213	219	225	231	237	243	249	255	261	267
729		273	279	285	291	297	303	308	314	320	326
730		332	338	344	350	356	362	368	374	380	386
731		392	398	404	410	415	421	427	433	439	445
732		451	457	463	469	475	481	487	493	499	504
733		510	516	522	528	534	540	546	552	558	564
734		570	576	581	587	593	599	605	611	617	623
735		629	635	641	646	652	658	664	670	676	682
736		688	694	700	705	711	717	723	729	735	741
737		747	753	759	764	770	776	782	788	794	800
738		806	812	817	823	829	835	841	847	853	859
739		864	870	876	882	888	894	900	906	911	917
740		923	929	935	941	947	953	958	964	970	976
741		982	988	994	999	*005	*011	*017	*023	*029	*035
742	87	040	046	052	058	064	070	075	081	037	093
743		099	105	111	116	122	128	134	140	146	151
744		157	163	169	175	181	186	192	198	204	210
745		216	221	227	233	239	245	251	256	262	268
746		274	280	286	291	297	303	309	315	320	326
747		332	338	344	349	355	361	367	373	379	384
748		390	396	402	408	413	419	425	431	437	442
749		448	454	460	466	471	477	483	489	495	500
750		506	512	518	523	529	535	541	547	552	558
N.	L.	0	1	2	3	4	5	6	7	8	9

Proportional parts

	7
1	0.7
2	1.4
3	2.1
4	2.8
5	3.5
6	4.2
7	4.9
8	5.6
9	6.3

	6
1	0.6
2	1.2
3	1.8
4	2.4
5	3.0
6	3.6
7	4.2
8	4.8
9	5.4

	5
1	0.5
2	1.0
3	1.5
4	2.0
5	2.5
6	3.0
7	3.5
8	4.0
9	4.5

LOGARITHMS OF NUMBERS

750 — 800

N.	L.	0	1	2	3	4	5	6	7	8	9	Proportional parts
750	87	506	512	518	523	529	535	541	547	552	558	
751		564	570	576	581	587	593	599	604	610	616	
752		622	628	633	639	645	651	656	662	668	674	
753		679	685	691	697	703	708	714	720	726	731	
754		737	743	749	754	760	766	772	777	783	789	
755		795	800	806	812	818	823	829	835	841	846	
756		852	858	864	869	875	881	887	892	898	904	
757		910	915	921	927	933	938	944	950	955	961	
758		967	973	978	984	990	996	*001	*007	*013	*018	
759	88	024	030	036	041	047	053	058	064	070	076	
760		081	087	093	098	104	110	116	121	127	133	
761		138	144	150	156	161	167	173	178	184	190	
762		195	201	207	213	218	224	230	235	241	247	
763		252	258	264	270	275	281	287	292	298	304	
764		309	315	321	326	332	338	343	349	355	360	
765		366	372	377	383	389	395	400	406	412	417	
766		423	429	434	440	446	451	457	463	468	474	
767		480	485	491	497	502	508	513	519	525	530	
768		536	542	547	553	559	564	570	576	581	587	
769		593	598	604	610	615	621	627	632	638	643	
770		649	655	660	666	672	677	683	689	694	700	
771		705	711	717	722	728	734	739	745	750	756	
772		762	767	773	779	784	790	795	801	807	812	
773		818	824	829	835	840	846	852	857	863	868	
774		874	880	885	891	897	902	908	913	919	925	
775		930	936	941	947	953	958	964	969	975	981	
776		986	992	997	*003	*009	*014	*020	*025	*031	*037	
777	89	042	048	053	059	064	070	076	081	087	092	
778		098	104	109	115	120	126	131	137	143	148	
779		154	159	165	170	176	182	187	193	198	204	
780		209	215	221	226	232	237	243	248	254	260	
781		265	271	276	282	287	293	298	304	310	315	
782		321	326	332	337	343	348	354	360	365	371	
783		376	382	387	393	398	404	409	415	421	426	
784		432	437	443	448	454	459	465	470	476	481	
785		487	492	498	504	509	515	520	526	531	537	
786		542	548	553	559	564	570	575	581	586	592	
787		597	603	609	614	620	625	631	636	642	647	
788		653	658	664	669	675	680	686	691	697	702	
789		708	713	719	724	730	735	741	746	752	757	
790		763	768	774	779	785	790	796	801	807	812	
791		818	823	829	834	840	845	851	856	862	867	
792		873	878	883	889	894	900	905	911	916	922	
793		927	933	938	944	949	955	960	966	971	977	
794		982	988	993	998	*004	*009	*015	*020	*026	*031	
795	90	037	042	048	053	059	064	069	075	080	086	
796		091	097	102	108	113	119	124	129	135	140	
797		146	151	157	162	168	173	179	184	189	195	
798		200	206	211	217	222	227	233	238	244	249	
799		255	260	266	271	276	282	287	293	298	304	
800		309	314	320	325	331	336	342	347	352	358	
N.	L.	0	1	2	3	4	5	6	7	8	9	Proportional parts

Proportional parts:

6	
1	0.6
2	1.2
3	1.8
4	2.4
5	3.0
6	3.6
7	4.2
8	4.8
9	5.4

5	
1	0.5
2	1.0
3	1.5
4	2.0
5	2.5
6	3.0
7	3.5
8	4.0
9	4.5

Table 1   *Page 109*

LOGARITHMS OF NUMBERS

800 — 850

N.	L.	0	1	2	3	4	5	6	7	8	9	Proportional parts
800	90	309	314	320	325	331	336	342	347	352	358	
801		363	369	374	380	385	390	396	401	407	412	
802		417	423	428	434	439	445	450	455	461	466	
803		472	477	482	488	493	499	504	509	515	520	
804		526	531	536	542	547	553	558	563	569	574	
805		580	585	590	596	601	607	612	617	623	628	
806		634	639	644	650	655	660	666	671	677	682	
807		687	693	698	703	709	714	720	725	730	736	
808		741	747	752	757	763	768	773	779	784	789	
809		795	800	806	811	816	822	827	832	838	843	
810		849	854	859	865	870	875	881	886	891	897	
811		902	907	913	918	924	929	934	940	945	950	
812		956	961	966	972	977	982	988	993	998	*004	
813	91	009	014	020	025	030	036	041	046	052	057	
814		062	068	073	078	084	089	094	100	105	110	
815		116	121	126	132	137	142	148	153	158	164	
816		169	174	180	185	190	196	201	206	212	217	
817		222	228	233	238	243	249	254	259	265	270	
818		275	281	286	291	297	302	307	312	318	323	
819		328	334	339	344	350	355	360	365	371	376	
820		381	387	392	397	403	408	413	418	424	429	
821		434	440	445	450	455	461	466	471	477	482	
822		487	492	498	503	508	514	519	524	529	535	
823		540	545	551	556	561	566	572	577	582	587	
824		593	598	603	609	614	619	624	630	635	640	
825		645	651	656	661	666	672	677	682	687	693	
826		698	703	709	714	719	724	730	735	740	745	
827		751	756	761	766	772	777	782	787	793	798	
828		803	808	814	819	824	829	834	840	845	850	
829		855	861	866	871	876	882	887	892	897	903	
830		908	913	918	924	929	934	939	944	950	955	
831		960	965	971	976	981	986	991	997	*002	*007	
832	92	012	018	023	028	033	038	044	049	054	059	
833		065	070	075	080	085	091	096	101	106	111	
834		117	122	127	132	137	143	148	153	158	163	
835		169	174	179	184	189	195	200	205	210	215	
836		221	226	231	236	241	247	252	257	262	267	
837		273	278	283	288	293	298	304	309	314	319	
838		324	330	335	340	345	350	355	361	366	371	
839		376	381	387	392	397	402	407	412	418	423	
840		428	433	438	443	449	454	459	464	469	474	
841		480	485	490	495	500	505	511	516	521	526	
842		531	536	542	547	552	557	562	567	572	578	
843		583	588	593	598	603	609	614	619	624	629	
844		634	639	645	650	655	660	665	670	675	681	
845		686	691	696	701	706	711	716	722	727	732	
846		737	742	747	752	758	763	768	773	778	783	
847		788	793	799	804	809	814	819	824	829	834	
848		840	845	850	855	860	865	870	875	881	886	
849		891	896	901	906	911	916	921	927	932	937	
850		942	947	952	957	962	967	973	978	983	988	
N.	L.	0	1	2	3	4	5	6	7	8	9	Proportional parts

Proportional parts

	6
1	0.6
2	1.2
3	1.8
4	2.4
5	3.0
6	3.6
7	4.2
8	4.8
9	5.4

	5
1	0.5
2	1.0
3	1.5
4	2.0
5	2.5
6	3.0
7	3.5
8	4.0
9	4.5

LOGARITHMS OF NUMBERS

850 — 900

N.	L.	0	1	2	3	4	5	6	7	8	9	Proportional parts
850	92	942	947	952	957	962	967	973	978	983	988	
851		993	998	*003	*008	*013	*018	*024	*029	*034	*039	
852	93	044	049	054	059	064	069	075	080	085	090	
853		095	100	105	110	115	120	125	131	136	141	
854		146	151	156	161	166	171	176	181	186	192	
855		197	202	207	212	217	222	227	232	237	242	6
856		247	252	258	263	268	273	278	283	288	293	
857		298	303	308	313	318	323	328	334	339	344	1 0.6
858		349	354	359	364	369	374	379	384	389	394	2 1.2
859		399	404	409	414	420	425	430	435	440	445	3 1.8
												4 2.4
860		450	455	460	465	470	475	480	485	490	495	5 3.0
861		500	505	510	515	520	526	531	536	541	546	6 3.6
862		551	556	561	566	571	576	581	586	591	596	7 4.2
863		601	606	611	616	621	626	631	636	641	646	8 4.8
864		651	656	661	666	671	676	682	687	692	697	9 5.4
865		702	707	712	717	722	727	732	737	742	747	
866		752	757	762	767	772	777	782	787	792	797	
867		802	807	812	817	822	827	832	837	842	847	
868		852	857	862	867	872	877	882	887	892	897	
869		902	907	912	917	922	927	932	937	942	947	
												5
870		952	957	962	967	972	977	982	987	992	997	
871	94	002	007	012	017	022	027	032	037	042	047	1 0.5
872		052	057	062	067	072	077	082	086	091	096	2 1.0
873		101	106	111	116	121	126	131	136	141	146	3 1.5
874		151	156	161	166	171	176	181	186	191	196	4 2.0
												5 2.5
875		201	206	211	216	221	226	231	236	240	245	6 3.0
876		250	255	260	265	270	275	280	285	290	295	7 3.5
877		300	305	310	315	320	325	330	335	340	345	8 4.0
878		349	354	359	364	369	374	379	384	389	394	9 4.5
879		399	404	409	414	419	424	429	433	438	443	
880		448	453	458	463	468	473	478	483	488	493	
881		498	503	507	512	517	522	527	532	537	542	
882		547	552	557	562	567	571	576	581	586	591	
883		596	601	606	611	616	621	626	630	635	640	
884		645	650	655	660	665	670	675	680	685	689	
												4
885		694	699	704	709	714	719	724	729	734	738	
886		743	748	753	758	763	768	773	778	783	787	1 0.4
887		792	797	802	807	812	817	822	827	832	836	2 0.8
888		841	846	851	856	861	866	871	876	880	885	3 1.2
889		890	895	900	905	910	915	919	924	929	934	4 1.6
												5 2.0
890		939	944	949	954	959	963	968	973	978	983	6 2.4
891		988	993	998	*002	*007	*012	*017	*022	*027	*032	7 2.8
892	95	036	041	046	051	056	061	066	071	075	080	8 3.2
893		085	090	095	100	105	109	114	119	124	129	9 3.6
894		134	139	143	148	153	158	163	168	173	177	
895		182	187	192	197	202	207	211	216	221	226	
896		231	236	240	245	250	255	260	265	270	274	
897		279	284	289	294	299	303	308	313	318	323	
898		328	332	337	342	347	352	357	361	366	371	
899		376	381	386	390	395	400	405	410	415	419	
900		424	429	434	439	444	448	453	458	463	468	
N.	L.	0	1	2	3	4	5	6	7	8	9	Proportional parts

.92 942 — .95 468

Table I   *Page 111*

LOGARITHMS OF NUMBERS

900 — 950

N.	L.	0	1	2	3	4	5	6	7	8	9	Proportional parts
900	95	424	429	434	439	444	448	453	458	463	468	
901		472	477	482	487	492	497	501	506	511	516	
902		521	525	530	535	540	545	550	554	559	564	
903		569	574	578	583	588	593	598	602	607	612	
904		617	622	626	631	636	641	646	650	655	660	
905		665	670	674	679	684	689	694	698	703	708	
906		713	718	722	727	732	737	742	746	751	756	
907		761	766	770	775	780	785	789	794	799	804	
908		809	813	818	823	828	832	837	842	847	852	
909		856	861	866	871	875	880	885	890	895	899	
910		904	909	914	918	923	928	933	938	942	947	
911		952	957	961	966	971	976	980	985	990	995	**5**
912		999	*004	*009	*014	*019	*023	*028	*033	*038	*042	1 0.5
913	96	047	052	057	061	066	071	076	030	085	090	2 1.0
914		095	099	104	109	114	118	123	128	133	137	3 1.5
915		142	147	152	156	161	166	171	175	180	185	4 2.0
916		190	194	199	204	209	213	218	223	227	232	5 2.5
917		237	242	246	251	256	261	265	270	275	280	6 3.0
918		284	289	294	298	303	308	313	317	322	327	7 3.5
919		332	336	341	346	350	355	360	365	369	374	8 4.0
920		379	384	388	393	398	402	407	412	417	421	9 4.5
921		426	431	435	440	445	450	454	459	464	468	
922		473	478	483	487	492	497	501	506	511	515	
923		520	525	530	534	539	544	548	553	558	562	
924		567	572	577	581	586	591	595	600	605	609	
925		614	619	624	628	633	638	642	647	652	656	
926		661	666	670	675	680	685	639	694	699	703	
927		708	713	717	722	727	731	736	741	745	750	
928		755	759	764	769	774	778	783	788	792	797	
929		802	806	811	816	820	825	830	834	839	844	
930		848	853	858	862	867	872	876	881	836	890	
931		895	900	904	909	914	918	923	928	932	937	**4**
932		942	946	951	956	960	965	970	974	979	984	1 0.4
933		988	993	997	*002	*007	*011	*016	*021	*025	*030	2 0.8
934	97	035	039	044	049	053	058	063	067	072	077	3 1.2
935		081	086	090	095	100	104	109	114	118	123	4 1.6
936		128	132	137	142	146	151	155	160	165	169	5 2.0
937		174	179	183	188	192	197	202	206	211	216	6 2.4
938		220	225	230	234	239	243	248	253	257	262	7 2.8
939		267	271	276	280	285	290	294	299	304	308	8 3.2
940		313	317	322	327	331	336	340	345	350	354	9 3.6
941		359	364	368	373	377	332	387	391	396	400	
942		405	410	414	419	424	428	433	437	442	447	
943		451	456	460	465	470	474	479	483	488	493	
944		497	502	506	511	516	520	525	529	534	539	
945		543	548	552	557	562	566	571	575	580	585	
946		589	594	598	603	607	612	617	621	626	630	
947		635	640	644	649	653	658	663	667	672	676	
948		681	685	690	695	699	704	708	713	717	722	
949		727	731	736	740	745	749	754	759	763	768	
950		772	777	782	786	791	795	800	804	809	813	
N.	L.	0	1	2	3	4	5	6	7	8	9	Proportional parts

.95 424 — .97 813

LOGARITHMS OF NUMBERS

950 — 1000

N.	L.	0	1	2	3	4	5	6	7	8	9	Proportional parts
950	97	772	777	782	786	791	795	800	804	809	813	
951		818	823	827	832	836	841	845	850	855	859	
952		864	868	873	877	882	886	891	896	900	905	
953		909	914	918	923	928	932	937	941	946	950	
954		955	959	964	968	973	978	982	987	991	996	
955	98	000	005	009	014	019	023	028	032	037	041	
956		046	050	055	059	064	068	073	078	082	087	
957		091	096	100	105	109	114	118	123	127	132	
958		137	141	146	150	155	159	164	168	173	177	
959		182	186	191	195	200	204	209	214	218	223	
960		227	232	236	241	245	250	254	259	263	268	
961		272	277	281	286	290	295	299	304	308	313	
962		318	322	327	331	336	340	345	349	354	358	
963		363	367	372	376	381	385	390	394	399	403	
964		408	412	417	421	426	430	435	439	444	448	
965		453	457	462	466	471	475	480	484	489	493	
966		498	502	507	511	516	520	525	529	534	538	
967		543	547	552	556	561	565	570	574	579	583	
968		588	592	597	601	605	610	614	619	623	628	
969		632	637	641	646	650	655	659	664	668	673	
970		677	682	686	691	695	700	704	709	713	717	
971		722	726	731	735	740	744	749	753	758	762	
972		767	771	776	780	784	789	793	798	802	807	
973		811	816	820	825	829	834	838	843	847	851	
974		856	860	865	869	874	878	883	887	892	896	
975		900	905	909	914	918	923	927	932	936	941	
976		945	949	954	958	963	967	972	976	981	985	
977		989	994	998	*003	*007	*012	*016	*021	*025	*029	
978	99	034	038	043	047	052	056	061	065	069	074	
979		078	083	087	092	096	100	105	109	114	118	
980		123	127	131	136	140	145	149	154	158	162	
981		167	171	176	180	185	189	193	198	202	207	
982		211	216	220	224	229	233	238	242	247	251	
983		255	260	264	269	273	277	282	286	291	295	
984		300	304	308	313	317	322	326	330	335	339	
985		344	348	352	357	361	366	370	374	379	383	
986		388	392	396	401	405	410	414	419	423	427	
987		432	436	441	445	449	454	458	463	467	471	
988		476	480	484	489	493	498	502	506	511	515	
989		520	524	528	533	537	542	546	550	555	559	
990		564	568	572	577	581	585	590	594	599	603	
991		607	612	616	621	625	629	634	638	642	647	
992		651	656	660	664	669	673	677	682	686	691	
993		695	699	704	708	712	717	721	726	730	734	
994		739	743	747	752	756	760	765	769	774	778	
995		782	787	791	795	800	804	808	813	817	822	
996		826	830	835	839	843	848	852	856	861	865	
997		870	874	878	883	887	891	896	900	904	909	
998		913	917	922	926	930	935	939	944	948	952	
999		957	961	965	970	974	978	983	987	991	996	
1000	00	000	004	009	013	017	022	026	030	035	039	
N.	L.	0	1	2	3	4	5	6	7	8	9	Proportional parts

Proportional parts:

	5
1	0.5
2	1.0
3	1.5
4	2.0
5	2.5
6	3.0
7	3.5
8	4.0
9	4.5

	4
1	0.4
2	0.8
3	1.2
4	1.6
5	2.0
6	2.4
7	2.8
8	3.2
9	3.6

Table II

LOGARITHMS OF NUMBERS

1000 — 1050

N.	L.	0	1	2	3	4	5	6	7	8	9	d.
1000	000	0000	0434	0869	1303	1737	2171	2605	3039	3473	3907	434
1001		4341	4775	5208	5642	6076	6510	6943	7377	7810	8244	434
1002		8677	9111	9544	9977	*0411	*0844	*1277	*1710	*2143	*2576	433
1003	001	3009	3442	3875	4308	4741	5174	5607	6039	6472	6905	433
1004		7337	7770	8202	8635	9067	9499	9932	*0364	*0796	*1228	432
1005	002	1661	2093	2525	2957	3389	3821	4253	4685	5116	5548	432
1006		5980	6411	6843	7275	7706	8138	8569	9001	9432	9863	431
1007	003	0295	0726	1157	1588	2019	2451	2882	3313	3744	4174	431
1008		4605	5036	5467	5898	6328	6759	7190	7620	8051	8481	431
1009		8912	9342	9772	*0203	*0633	*1063	*1493	*1924	*2354	*2784	430
1010	004	3214	3644	4074	4504	4933	5363	5793	6223	6652	7082	430
1011		7512	7941	8371	8800	9229	9659	*0088	*0517	*0947	*1376	429
1012	005	1805	2234	2663	3092	3521	3950	4379	4808	5237	5666	429
1013		6094	6523	6952	7380	7809	8238	8666	9094	9523	9951	429
1014	006	0380	0808	1236	1664	2092	2521	2949	3377	3805	4233	428
1015		4660	5088	5516	5944	6372	6799	7227	7655	8082	8510	428
1016		8937	9365	9792	*0219	*0647	*1074	*1501	*1928	*2355	*2782	427
1017	007	3210	3637	4064	4490	4917	5344	5771	6198	6624	7051	427
1018		7478	7904	8331	8757	9184	9610	*0037	*0463	*0889	*1316	426
1019	008	1742	2168	2594	3020	3446	3872	4298	4724	5150	5576	426
1020		6002	6427	6853	7279	7704	8130	8556	8981	9407	9832	426
1021	009	0257	0683	1108	1533	1959	2384	2809	3234	3659	4084	425
1022		4509	4934	5359	5784	6208	6633	7058	7483	7907	8332	425
1023		8756	9181	9605	*0030	*0454	*0878	*1303	*1727	*2151	*2575	424
1024	010	3000	3424	3848	4272	4696	5120	5544	5967	6391	6815	424
1025		7239	7662	8086	8510	8933	9357	9780	*0204	*0627	*1050	424
1026	011	1474	1897	2320	2743	3166	3590	4013	4436	4859	5282	423
1027		5704	6127	6550	6973	7396	7818	8241	8664	9086	9509	423
1028		9931	*0354	*0776	*1198	*1621	*2043	*2465	*2887	*3310	*3732	422
1029	012	4154	4576	4998	5420	5842	6264	6685	7107	7529	7951	422
1030		8372	8794	9215	9637	*0059	*0480	*0901	*1323	*1744	*2165	422
1031	013	2587	3008	3429	3850	4271	4692	5113	5534	5955	6376	421
1032		6797	7218	7639	8059	8480	8901	9321	9742	*0162	*0583	421
1033	014	1003	1424	1844	2264	2685	3105	3525	3945	4365	4785	420
1034		5205	5625	6045	6465	6885	7305	7725	8144	8564	8984	420
1035		9403	9823	*0243	*0662	*1082	*1501	*1920	*2340	*2759	*3178	420
1036	015	3598	4017	4436	4855	5274	5693	6112	6531	6950	7369	419
1037		7788	8206	8625	9044	9462	9881	*0300	*0718	*1137	*1555	419
1038	016	1974	2392	2810	3229	3647	4065	4483	4901	5319	5737	418
1039		6155	6573	6991	7409	7827	8245	8663	9080	9498	9916	418
1040	017	0333	0751	1168	1586	2003	2421	2838	3256	3673	4090	417
1041		4507	4924	5342	5759	6176	6593	7010	7427	7844	8260	417
1042		8677	9094	9511	9927	*0344	*0761	*1177	*1594	*2010	*2427	417
1043	018	2843	3259	3676	4092	4508	4925	5341	5757	6173	6589	416
1044		7005	7421	7837	8253	8669	9084	9500	9916	*0332	*0747	416
1045	019	1163	1578	1994	2410	2825	3240	3656	4071	4486	4902	415
1046		5317	5732	6147	6562	6977	7392	7807	8222	8637	9052	415
1047		9467	9882	*0296	*0711	*1126	*1540	*1955	*2369	*2784	*3198	415
1048	020	3613	4027	4442	4856	5270	5684	6099	6513	6927	7341	414
1049		7755	8169	8583	8997	9411	9824	*0238	*0652	*1066	*1479	414
1050	021	1893	2307	2720	3134	3547	3961	4374	4787	5201	5614	413
N.	L.	0	1	2	3	4	5	6	7	8	9	d.

LOGARITHMS OF NUMBERS

1050 — 1100

N.	L.	0	1	2	3	4	5	6	7	8	9	d.
1050	021	1893	2307	2720	3134	3547	3961	4374	4787	5201	5614	413
1051		6027	6440	6854	7267	7680	8093	8506	8919	9332	9745	413
1052	022	0157	0570	0983	1396	1808	2221	2634	3046	3459	3871	413
1053		4284	4696	5109	5521	5933	6345	6758	7170	7582	7994	412
1054		8406	8818	9230	9642	*0054	*0466	*0878	*1289	*1701	*2113	412
1055	023	2525	2936	3348	3759	4171	4582	4994	5405	5817	6228	411
1056		6639	7050	7462	7873	8284	8695	9106	9517	9928	*0339	411
1057	024	0750	1161	1572	1982	2393	2804	3214	3625	4036	4446	411
1058		4857	5267	5678	6088	6498	6909	7319	7729	8139	8549	410
1059		8960	9370	9780	*0190	*0600	*1010	*1419	*1829	*2239	*2649	410
1060	025	3059	3468	3878	4288	4697	5107	5516	5926	6335	6744	410
1061		7154	7563	7972	8382	8791	9200	9609	*0018	*0427	*0836	409
1062	026	1245	1654	2063	2472	2881	3289	3698	4107	4515	4924	409
1063		5333	5741	6150	6558	6967	7375	7783	8192	8600	9008	408
1064		9416	9824	*0233	*0641	*1049	*1457	*1865	*2273	*2680	*3088	408
1065	027	3496	3904	4312	4719	5127	5535	5942	6350	6757	7165	408
1066		7572	7979	8387	8794	9201	9609	*0016	*0423	*0830	*1237	407
1067	028	1644	2051	2458	2865	3272	3679	4086	4492	4899	5306	407
1068		5713	6119	6526	6932	7339	7745	8152	8558	8964	9371	406
1069		9777	*0183	*0590	*0996	*1402	*1808	*2214	*2620	*3026	*3432	406
1070	029	3838	4244	4649	5055	5461	5867	6272	6678	7084	7489	406
1071		7895	8300	8706	9111	9516	9922	*0327	*0732	*1138	*1543	405
1072	030	1948	2353	2758	3163	3568	3973	4378	4783	5188	5592	405
1073		5997	6402	6807	7211	7616	8020	8425	8830	9234	9638	405
1074	031	0043	0447	0851	1256	1660	2064	2468	2872	3277	3681	404
1075		4085	4489	4893	5296	5700	6104	6508	6912	7315	7719	404
1076		8123	8526	8930	9333	9737	*0140	*0544	*0947	*1350	*1754	403
1077	032	2157	2560	2963	3367	3770	4173	4576	4979	5382	5785	403
1078		6188	6590	6993	7396	7799	8201	8604	9007	9409	9812	403
1079	033	0214	0617	1019	1422	1824	2226	2629	3031	3433	3835	402
1080		4238	4640	5042	5444	5846	6248	6650	7052	7453	7855	402
1081		8257	8659	9060	9462	9864	*0265	*0667	*1068	*1470	*1871	402
1082	034	2273	2674	3075	3477	3878	4279	4680	5081	5482	5884	401
1083		6285	6686	7087	7487	7888	8289	8690	9091	9491	9892	401
1084	035	0293	0693	1094	1495	1895	2296	2696	3096	3497	3897	400
1085		4297	4698	5098	5498	5898	6298	6698	7098	7498	7898	400
1086		8298	8698	9098	9498	9898	*0297	*0697	*1097	*1496	*1896	400
1087	036	2295	2695	3094	3494	3893	4293	4692	5091	5491	5890	399
1088		6289	6688	7087	7486	7885	8284	8683	9082	9481	9880	399
1089	037	0279	0678	1076	1475	1874	2272	2671	3070	3468	3867	399
1090		4265	4663	5062	5460	5858	6257	6655	7053	7451	7849	398
1091		8248	8646	9044	9442	9839	*0237	*0635	*1033	*1431	*1829	398
1092	038	2226	2624	3022	3419	3817	4214	4612	5009	5407	5804	398
1093		6202	6599	6996	7393	7791	8188	8585	8982	9379	9776	397
1094	039	0173	0570	0967	1364	1761	2158	2554	2951	3348	3745	397
1095		4141	4538	4934	5331	5727	6124	6520	6917	7313	7709	397
1096		8106	8502	8898	9294	9690	*0086	*0482	*0878	*1274	*1670	396
1097	040	2066	2462	2858	3254	3650	4045	4441	4837	5232	5628	396
1098		6023	6419	6814	7210	7605	8001	8396	8791	9187	9582	395
1099		9977	*0372	*0767	*1162	*1557	*1952	*2347	*2742	*3137	*3532	395
1100	041	3927	4322	4716	5111	5506	5900	6295	6690	7084	7479	395
N.	L.	0	1	2	3	4	5	6	7	8	9	d.

.021 1893 — .041 7479

Table II   *Page 115*

LOGARITHMS OF NUMBERS

1100 — 1150

N.	L.	0	1	2	3	4	5	6	7	8	9	d.
1100	041 3927	4322	4716	5111	5506	5900	6295	6690	7084	7479		395
1101	7873	8268	8662	9056	9451	9845	*0239	*0633	*1028	*1422		394
1102	042 1816	2210	2604	2998	3392	3786	4180	4574	4968	5361		394
1103	5755	6149	6543	6936	7330	7723	8117	8510	8904	9297		394
1104	9691	*0084	*0477	*0871	*1264	*1657	*2050	*2444	*2837	*3230		393
1105	043 3623	4016	4409	4802	5195	5587	5980	6373	6766	7159		393
1106	7551	7944	8337	8729	9122	9514	9907	*0299	*0692	*1084		393
1107	044 1476	1869	2261	2653	3045	3437	3829	4222	4614	5006		392
1108	5398	5790	6181	6573	6965	7357	7749	8140	8532	8924		392
1109	9315	9707	*0099	*0490	*0882	*1273	*1664	*2056	*2447	*2839		392
1110	045 3230	3621	4012	4403	4795	5186	5577	5968	6359	6750		391
1111	7141	7531	7922	8313	8704	9095	9485	9876	*0267	*0657		391
1112	046 1048	1438	1829	2219	2610	3000	3391	3781	4171	4561		390
1113	4952	5342	5732	6122	6512	6902	7292	7682	8072	8462		390
1114	8852	9242	9632	*0021	*0411	*0801	*1190	*1580	*1970	*2359		390
1115	047 2749	3138	3528	3917	4306	4696	5085	5474	5864	6253		389
1116	6642	7031	7420	7809	8198	8587	8976	9365	9754	*0143		389
1117	048 0532	0921	1309	1698	2087	2475	2864	3253	3641	4030		389
1118	4418	4806	5195	5583	5972	6360	6748	7136	7525	7913		388
1119	8301	8689	9077	9465	9853	*0241	*0629	*1017	*1405	*1792		388
1120	049 2180	2568	2956	3343	3731	4119	4506	4894	5281	5669		388
1121	6056	6444	6831	7218	7606	7993	8380	8767	9154	9541		387
1122	9929	*0316	*0703	*1090	*1477	*1863	*2250	*2637	*3024	*3411		387
1123	050 3798	4184	4571	4958	5344	5731	6117	6504	6890	7277		387
1124	7663	8049	8436	8822	9208	9595	9981	*0367	*0753	*1139		386
1125	051 1525	1911	2297	2683	3069	3455	3841	4227	4612	4998		386
1126	5384	5770	6155	6541	6926	7312	7697	8083	8468	8854		386
1127	9239	9624	*0010	*0395	*0780	*1166	*1551	*1936	*2321	*2706		385
1128	052 3091	3476	3861	4246	4631	5016	5400	5785	6170	6555		385
1129	6939	7324	7709	8093	8478	8862	9247	9631	*0016	*0400		385
1130	053 0734	1169	1553	1937	2321	2706	3090	3474	3858	4242		384
1131	4626	5010	5394	5778	6162	6546	6929	7313	7697	8081		384
1132	8434	8848	9232	9615	9999	*0382	*0766	*1149	*1532	*1916		384
1133	054 2299	2682	3066	3449	3832	4215	4598	4981	5365	5748		383
1134	6131	6514	6896	7279	7662	8045	8428	8811	9193	9576		383
1135	9959	*0341	*0724	*1106	*1489	*1871	*2254	*2636	*3019	*3401		382
1136	055 3783	4166	4548	4930	5312	5694	6077	6459	6841	7223		382
1137	7605	7987	8369	8750	9132	9514	9896	*0278	*0659	*1041		382
1138	056 1423	1804	2186	2567	2949	3330	3712	4093	4475	4856		381
1139	5237	5619	6000	6381	6762	7143	7524	7905	8287	8668		381
1140	9049	9429	9810	*0191	*0572	*0953	*1334	*1714	*2095	*2476		381
1141	057 2856	3237	3618	3998	4379	4759	5140	5520	5900	6281		381
1142	6661	7041	7422	7802	8182	8562	8942	9322	9702	*0082		380
1143	058 0462	0842	1222	1602	1982	2362	2741	3121	3501	3881		380
1144	4260	4640	5019	5399	5778	6158	6537	6917	7296	7676		380
1145	8055	8434	8813	9193	9572	9951	*0330	*0709	*1088	*1467		379
1146	059 1846	2225	2604	2983	3362	3741	4119	4498	4877	5256		379
1147	5634	6013	6391	6770	7148	7527	7905	8284	8662	9041		379
1148	9419	9797	*0175	*0554	*0932	*1310	*1688	*2066	*2444	*2822		378
1149	060 3200	3578	3956	4334	4712	5090	5468	5845	6223	6601		378
1150	6978	7356	7734	8111	8489	8866	9244	9621	9999	*0376		378
N.	L.	0	1	2	3	4	5	6	7	8	9	d.

LOGARITHMS OF NUMBERS

1150 — 1200

N.	L.	0	1	2	3	4	5	6	7	8	9	d.
1150	060	6978	7356	7734	8111	8489	8866	9244	9621	9999	*0376	378
1151	061	0753	1131	1508	1885	2262	2639	3017	3394	3771	4148	377
1152		4525	4902	5279	5656	6032	6409	6786	7163	7540	7916	377
1153		8293	8670	9046	9423	9799	*0176	*0552	*0929	*1305	*1682	377
1154	062	2058	2434	2811	3187	3563	3939	4316	4692	5068	5444	376
1155		5820	6196	6572	6948	7324	7699	8075	8451	8827	9203	376
1156		9578	9954	*0330	*0705	*1081	*1456	*1832	*2207	*2583	*2958	376
1157	063	3334	3709	4084	4460	4835	5210	5585	5960	6335	6711	375
1158		7086	7461	7836	8211	8585	8960	9335	9710	*0085	*0460	375
1159	064	0834	1209	1584	1958	2333	2708	3082	3457	3831	4205	375
1160		4580	4954	5329	5703	6077	6451	6826	7200	7574	7948	374
1161		8322	8696	9070	9444	9818	*0192	*0566	*0940	*1314	*1688	374
1162	065	2061	2435	2809	3182	3556	3930	4303	4677	5050	5424	374
1163		5797	6171	6544	6917	7291	7664	8037	8410	8784	9157	373
1164		9530	9903	*0276	*0649	*1022	*1395	*1768	*2141	*2514	*2886	373
1165	066	3259	3632	4005	4377	4750	5123	5495	5868	6241	6613	373
1166		6986	7358	7730	8103	8475	8847	9220	9592	9964	*0336	372
1167	067	0709	1081	1453	1825	2197	2569	2941	3313	3685	4057	372
1168		4428	4800	5172	5544	5915	6287	6659	7030	7402	7774	372
1169		8145	8517	8888	9259	9631	*0002	*0374	*0745	*1116	*1487	371
1170	068	1859	2230	2601	2972	3343	3714	4085	4456	4827	5198	371
1171		5569	5940	6311	6681	7052	7423	7794	8164	8535	8906	371
1172		9276	9647	*0017	*0388	*0758	*1129	*1499	*1869	*2240	*2610	370
1173	069	2980	3350	3721	4091	4461	4831	5201	5571	5941	6311	370
1174		6681	7051	7421	7791	8160	8530	8900	9270	9639	*0009	370
1175	070	0379	0748	1118	1487	1857	2226	2596	2965	3335	3704	369
1176		4073	4442	4812	5181	5550	5919	6288	6658	7027	7396	369
1177		7765	8134	8503	8871	9240	9609	9978	*0347	*0715	*1084	369
1178	071	1453	1822	2190	2559	2927	3296	3664	4033	4401	4770	369
1179		5138	5506	5875	6243	6611	6979	7348	7716	8084	8452	368
1180		8820	9188	9556	9924	*0292	*0660	*1028	*1396	*1763	*2131	368
1181	072	2499	2867	3234	3602	3970	4337	4705	5072	5440	5807	368
1182		6175	6542	6910	7277	7644	8011	8379	8746	9113	9480	367
1183		9847	*0215	*0582	*0949	*1316	*1683	*2050	*2416	*2783	*3150	367
1184	073	3517	3884	4251	4617	4984	5351	5717	6084	6450	6817	367
1185		7184	7550	7916	8283	8649	9016	9382	9748	*0114	*0481	366
1186	074	0847	1213	1579	1945	2311	2677	3043	3409	3775	4141	366
1187		4507	4873	5239	5605	5970	6336	6702	7068	7433	7799	366
1188		8164	8530	8895	9261	9626	9992	*0357	*0723	*1088	*1453	365
1189	075	1819	2184	2549	2914	3279	3644	4010	4375	4740	5105	365
1190		5470	5835	6199	6564	6929	7294	7659	8024	8388	8753	365
1191		9118	9482	9847	*0211	*0576	*0940	*1305	*1669	*2034	*2398	364
1192	076	2763	3127	3491	3855	4220	4584	4948	5312	5676	6040	364
1193		6404	6768	7132	7496	7860	8224	8588	8952	9316	9680	364
1194	077	0043	0407	0771	1134	1498	1862	2225	2589	2952	3316	364
1195		3679	4042	4406	4769	5133	5496	5859	6222	6585	6949	363
1196		7312	7675	8038	8401	8764	9127	9490	9853	*0216	*0579	363
1197	078	0942	1304	1667	2030	2393	2755	3118	3480	3843	4206	363
1198		4568	4931	5293	5656	6018	6380	6743	7105	7467	7830	362
1199		8192	8554	8916	9278	9640	*0003	*0365	*0727	*1089	*1451	362
1200	079	1812	2174	2536	2898	3260	3622	3983	4345	4707	5068	362
N.	L.	0	1	2	3	4	5	6	7	8	9	d.

Table III

IMPORTANT CONSTANTS

N	Log N	N	Log N
$\pi = 3.14159265$	0.4971499	$\pi^2 = 9.86960440$	0.9942997
$2\pi = 6.28318531$	0.7981799	$\dfrac{1}{\pi^2} = 0.10132118$	9.0057003–10
$4\pi = 12.56637061$	1.0992099	$\sqrt{\pi} = 1.77245385$	0.2485749
$\dfrac{\pi}{2} = 1.57079633$	0.1961199	$\dfrac{1}{\sqrt{\pi}} = 0.56418958$	9.7514251–10
$\dfrac{\pi}{3} = 1.04719755$	0.0200286	$\sqrt{\dfrac{3}{\pi}} = 0.97720502$	9.9899857–10
$\dfrac{4\pi}{3} = 4.18879020$	0.6220886	$\sqrt{\dfrac{4}{\pi}} = 1.12837917$	0.0524551
$\dfrac{\pi}{4} = 0.78539816$	9.8950899–10	$\sqrt[3]{\pi} = 1.46459189$	0.1657166
$\dfrac{\pi}{6} = 0.52359878$	9.7189986–10	$\dfrac{1}{\sqrt[3]{\pi}} = 0.68278406$	9.8342834–10
$\dfrac{1}{\pi} = 0.31830989$	9.5028501–10	$\sqrt[3]{\pi^2} = 2.14502940$	0.3314332
$\dfrac{1}{2\pi} = 0.15915494$	9.2018201–10	$\sqrt[3]{\dfrac{3}{4\pi}} = 0.62035049$	9.7926371–10
$\dfrac{3}{\pi} = 0.95492966$	9.9799714–10	$\sqrt[3]{\dfrac{\pi}{6}} = 0.80599598$	9.9063329–10
$\dfrac{4}{\pi} = 1.27323954$	0.1049101		

$e =$ Naperian Base	$= 2.71828183$	0.43429448
$M = \log_{10} e$	$= 0.43429448$	9.63778431—10
$1 \div M = \log_e 10$	$= 2.30258509$	0.36221569
$180 \div \pi =$ degrees in 1 radian	$= 57.2957795$	1.75812263
$\pi \div 180 =$ radians in 1°	$= 0.01745329$	8.24187737—10
$\pi \div 10800 =$ radians in 1'	$= 0.0002908882$	6.46372612—10
$\pi \div 648000 =$ radians in 1''	$= 0.00000484813 6811095$	4.68557487—10
sin 1''	$= 0.00000484813 6811076$	4.68557487—10
tan 1''	$= 0.00000484813 6811152$	4.68557487—10
centimeters in 1 ft. (U.S.)	$= 30.48006096$ (legal)	1.4840158
feet in 1 cm.	$= 0.03280833$	8.5159842—10
inches in 1 m.	$= 39.37$ (exact legal value)	1.5951654
pounds in 1 kg.	$= 2.204622341$	0.3433342
kilograms in 1 lb.	$= 0.4535924277$	9.6566660—10
cu. in. in 1 (U.S.) gallon	$= 231$ (exact legal value)	2.3636120
g (average value)	$= 32.16$ ft./sec./sec.	1.5073
g (legal)	$= 980.665$ cm./sec.^{2}	2.9915207
weight of 1 cu. ft. of water	$= 62.425$ lb. (max. density)	1.7953586
weight of 1 cu. ft. of air	$= 0.0807$ lb. (at 32° F.)	8.907 —10
ft. lb. per sec. in 1 H. P.	$= 550$ (exact legal value)	2.7403627
kg. m. per sec. in 1 H. P.	$= 76.0404$	1.8810445
watts in 1 H. P. (legal)	$= 745.70$	2.8725649

$\pi =$	3.14159	26535	89793	23846
$e =$	2.71828	18284	59045	23536
$M =$	0.43429	44819	03251	82765
$1 \div M =$	2.30258	50929	94045	68402
$\log_{10} \pi =$	0.49714	98726	94133	85435
$\log_{10} M =$	9.63778	43113	00536	78912

Table IV

COMMON LOGARITHMS
OF THE TRIGONOMETRIC FUNCTIONS
FROM 0° TO 90°

At Intervals Of One Minute
To Five Decimal Places

Table IVa

AUXILIARY TABLE OF S AND T FOR A IN MINUTES

$$S = \log \sin A - \log A' \quad \text{and} \quad T = \log \tan A - \log A'$$

$A' =$ number of minutes in A, and $(90° - A)' =$ number of minutes in $90° - A$.

A'	S	A'	T	A'	T
0 to 13	6.46373 — 10	0 to 26	6.46373 — 10	131 to 133	6.46394 — 10
14 to 42	72 — 10	27 to 39	74 — 10	134 to 136	95 — 10
43 to 58	71 — 10	40 to 48	75 — 10	137 to 139	96 — 10
59 to 71	6.46370 — 10	49 to 56	6.46376 — 10	140 to 142	6.46397 — 10
72 to 81	69 — 10	57 to 63	77 — 10	143 to 145	98 — 10
82 to 91	68 — 10	64 to 69	78 — 10	146 to 148	99 — 10
92 to 99	6.46367 — 10	70 to 74	6.46379 — 10	149 to 150	6.46400 — 10
100 to 107	66 — 10	75 to 80	80 — 10	151 to 153	01 — 10
108 to 115	65 — 10	81 to 85	81 — 10	154 to 156	02 — 10
116 to 121	6.46364 — 10	86 to 89	6.46382 — 10	157 to 158	6.46403 — 10
122 to 128	63 — 10	90 to 94	83 — 10	159 to 161	04 — 10
129 to 134	62 — 10	95 to 98	84 — 10	162 to 163	05 — 10
135 to 140	6.46361 — 10	99 to 102	6.46385 — 10	164 to 165	6.46406 — 10
141 to 146	60 — 10	103 to 106	86 — 10	167 to 168	07 — 10
147 to 151	59 — 10	107 to 110	87 — 10	169 to 171	08 — 10
152 to 157	6.46358 — 10	111 to 113	6.46388 — 10	172 to 173	6.46409 — 10
158 to 162	57 — 10	114 to 117	89 — 10	174 to 175	10 — 10
163 to 167	56 — 10	118 to 120	90 — 10	176 to 178	11 — 10
168 to 171	6.46355 — 10	121 to 124	6.46391 — 10	179 to 180	6.46412 — 10
172 to 176	54 — 10	125 to 127	92 — 10	181 to 182	13 — 10
177 to 181	53 — 10	128 to 130	93 — 10	183 to 184	14 — 10

For small angles, log sin A = log A' + S and log tan A = log A' + T; for angles near 90°, log cos A = log $(90° - A)'$ + S and log ctn A = log $(90° - A)'$ + T.

Table IV   *Page 119*

0°—LOGARITHMS OF TRIGONOMETRIC FUNCTIONS

′	L Sin	d	L Tan	c d	L Ctn	L Cos	
0					3.53 627	0.00 000	60
1	6.46 373		6.46 373		3.23 524	0.00 000	59
2	6.76 476	30103	6.76 476	30103	3.05 915	0.00 000	58
3	6.94 085	17609	6.94 085	17609	2.93 421	0.00 000	57
4	7.06 579	12494	7.06 579	12494		0.00 000	56
		9691		9691			
5	7.16 270		7.16 270		2.83 730	0.00 000	55
6	7.24 188	7918	7.24 188	7918	2.75 812	0.00 000	54
7	7.30 882	6694	7.30 882	6694	2.69 118	0.00 000	53
8	7.36 682	5800	7.36 682	5800	2.63 318	0.00 000	52
9	7.41 797	5115	7.41 797	5115	2.58 203	0.00 000	51
		4576		4576			
10	7.46 373		7.46 373		2.53 627	0.00 000	50
11	7.50 512	4139	7.50 512	4139	2.49 488	0.00 000	49
12	7.54 291	3779	7.54 291	3779	2.45 709	0.00 000	48
13	7.57 767	3476	7.57 767	3476	2.42 233	0.00 000	47
14	7.60 985	3218	7.60 986	3219	2.39 014	0.00 000	46
		2997		2996			
15	7.63 982		7.63 982		2.36 018	0.00 000	45
16	7.66 784	2802	7.66 785	2803	2.33 215	0.00 000	44
17	7.69 417	2633	7.69 418	2633	2.30 582	9.99 999	43
18	7.71 900	2483	7.71 900	2482	2.28 100	9.99 999	42
19	7.74 248	2348	7.74 248	2348	2.25 752	9.99 999	41
		2227		2228			
20	7.76 475		7.76 476		2.23 524	9.99 999	40
21	7.78 594	2119	7.78 595	2119	2.21 405	9.99 999	39
22	7.80 615	2021	7.80 615	2020	2.19 385	9.99 999	38
23	7.82 545	1930	7.82 546	1931	2.17 454	9.99 999	37
24	7.84 393	1848	7.84 394	1848	2.15 606	9.99 999	36
		1773		1773			
25	7.86 166		7.86 167		2.13 833	9.99 999	35
26	7.87 870	1704	7.87 871	1704	2.12 129	9.99 999	34
27	7.89 509	1639	7.89 510	1639	2.10 490	9.99 999	33
28	7.91 088	1579	7.91 009	1579	2.08 911	9.99 999	32
29	7.92 612	1524	7.92 613	1524	2.07 387	9.99 998	31
		1472		1473			
30	7.94 084		7.94 006		2.05 914	9.99 998	30
31	7.95 503	1424	7.95 510	1424	2.04 490	9.99 998	29
32	7.96 887	1379	7.96 889	1379	2.03 111	9.99 998	28
33	7.98 223	1336	7.98 225	1336	2.01 775	9.99 998	27
34	7.99 520	1297	7.99 522	1297	2.00 478	9.99 998	26
		1259		1259			
35	8.00 779		8.00 781		1.99 219	9.99 998	25
36	8.02 002	1223	8.02 004	1223	1.97 996	9.99 998	24
37	8.03 192	1190	8.03 194	1190	1.96 806	9.99 997	23
38	8.04 350	1158	8.04 353	1159	1.95 647	9.99 997	22
39	8.05 478	1128	8.05 481	1128	1.94 519	9.99 997	21
		1100		1100			
40	8.06 578		8.06 581		1.93 419	9.99 997	20
41	8.07 650	1072	8.07 653	1072	1.92 347	9.99 997	19
42	8.08 696	1046	8.08 700	1047	1.91 300	9.99 997	18
43	8.09 718	1022	8.09 722	1022	1.90 278	9.99 997	17
44	8.10 717	999	8.10 720	998	1.89 280	9.99 996	16
		976		976			
45	8.11 693		8.11 696		1.88 304	9.99 996	15
46	8.12 647	954	8.12 651	955	1.87 349	9.99 996	14
47	8.13 581	934	8.13 585	934	1.86 415	9.99 996	13
48	8.14 495	914	8.14 500	915	1.85 500	9.99 996	12
49	8.15 391	896	8.15 395	895	1.84 605	9.99 996	11
		877		878			
50	8.16 268		8.16 273		1.83 727	9.99 995	10
51	8.17 128	860	8.17 133	860	1.82 867	9.99 995	9
52	8.17 971	843	8.17 976	843	1.82 024	9.99 995	8
53	8.18 798	827	8.18 804	828	1.81 196	9.99 995	7
54	8.19 610	812	8.19 616	812	1.80 384	9.99 995	6
		797		797			
55	8.20 407		8.20 413		1.79 587	9.99 994	5
56	8.21 189	782	8.21 195	782	1.78 805	9.99 994	4
57	8.21 958	769	8.21 964	769	1.78 036	9.99 994	3
58	8.22 713	755	8.22 720	756	1.77 280	9.99 994	2
59	8.23 456	743	8.23 462	742	1.76 538	9.99 994	1
		730		730			
60	8.24 186		8.24 192		1.75 808	9.99 993	0
—	L Cos	d	L Ctn	c d	L Tan	L Sin	′

For more accurate values of L sin and L tan for interpolated values of angles less than 3° (or L cos or L ctn of angles greater than 87°) use Table IVa, Page 118.

1°—LOGARITHMS OF TRIGONOMETRIC FUNCTIONS

′	L Sin	d	L Tan	c d	L Ctn	L Cos	
0	8.24 186	717	8.24 192	718	1.75 808	9.99 993	60
1	8.24 903	706	8.24 910	706	1.75 090	9.99 993	59
2	8.25 609	695	8.25 616	696	1.74 384	9.99 993	58
3	8.26 304	684	8.26 312	684	1.73 688	9.99 993	57
4	8.26 988	673	8.26 996	673	1.73 004	9.99 992	56
5	8.27 661	663	8.27 669	663	1.72 331	9.99 992	55
6	8.28 324	653	8.28 332	654	1.71 668	9.99 992	54
7	8.28 977	644	8.28 986	643	1.71 014	9.99 992	53
8	8.29 621	634	8.29 629	634	1.70 371	9.99 992	52
9	8.30 255	624	8.30 263	625	1.69 737	9.99 991	51
10	8.30 879	616	8.30 888	617	1.69 112	9.99 991	50
11	8.31 495	608	8.31 505	607	1.68 495	9.99 991	49
12	8.32 103	599	8.32 112	599	1.67 888	9.99 990	48
13	8.32 702	590	8.32 711	591	1.67 289	9.99 990	47
14	8.33 292	583	8.33 302	584	1.66 698	9.99 990	46
15	8.33 875	575	8.33 886	575	1.66 114	9.99 990	45
16	8.34 450	568	8.34 461	568	1.65 539	9.99 989	44
17	8.35 018	560	8.35 029	561	1.64 971	9.99 989	43
18	8.35 578	553	8.35 590	553	1.64 410	9.99 989	42
19	8.36 131	547	8.36 143	546	1.63 857	9.99 989	41
20	8.36 678	539	8.36 689	540	1.63 311	9.99 988	40
21	8.37 217	533	8.37 229	533	1.62 771	9.99 988	39
22	8.37 750	526	8.37 762	527	1.62 238	9.99 988	38
23	8.38 276	520	8.38 289	520	1.61 711	9.99 987	37
24	8.38 796	514	8.38 809	514	1.61 191	9.99 987	36
25	8.39 310	508	8.39 323	509	1.60 677	9.99 987	35
26	8.39 818	502	8.39 832	502	1.60 168	9.99 986	34
27	8.40 320	496	8.40 334	496	1.59 666	9.99 986	33
28	8.40 816	491	8.40 830	491	1.59 170	9.99 986	32
29	8.41 307	485	8.41 321	486	1.58 679	9.99 985	31
30	8.41 792	480	8.41 807	480	1.58 193	9 99 985	30
31	8.42 272	474	8.42 287	475	1.57 713	9.99 985	29
32	8.42 746	470	8.42 762	470	1.57 238	9.99 984	28
33	8.43 216	464	8.43 232	464	1.56 768	9.99 984	27
34	8.43 680	459	8.43 696	460	1.56 304	9.99 984	26
35	8.44 139	455	8.44 156	455	1.55 844	9.99 983	25
36	8.44 594	450	8.44 611	450	1.55 389	9.99 983	24
37	8.45 044	445	8.45 061	446	1.54 939	9.99 983	23
38	8.45 489	441	8.45 507	441	1.54 493	9.99 982	22
39	8.45 930	436	8.45 948	437	1.54 052	9.99 982	21
40	8.46 366	433	8.46 385	432	1.53 615	9.99 982	20
41	8.46 799	427	8.46 817	428	1.53 183	9.99 981	19
42	8.47 226	424	8.47 245	424	1.52 755	9.99 981	18
43	8.47 650	419	8.47 669	420	1.52 331	9.99 981	17
44	8.48 069	416	8.48 089	416	1.51 911	9.99 980	16
45	8.48 485	411	8.48 505	412	1.51 495	9.99 980	15
46	8.48 896	408	8.48 917	408	1.51 083	9.99 979	14
47	8.49 304	404	8.49 325	404	1.50 675	9.99 979	13
48	8.49 703	400	8.49 729	401	1.50 271	9.99 979	12
49	8.50 108	396	8.50 130	397	1.49 870	9.99 978	11
50	8.50 504	393	8.50 527	393	1.49 473	9.99 978	10
51	8.50 897	390	8.50 920	390	1.49 080	9.99 977	9
52	8.51 287	386	8.51 310	386	1.48 690	9.99 977	8
53	8.51 673	382	8.51 696	383	1.48 304	9.99 977	7
54	8.52 055	379	8.52 079	380	1.47 921	9.99 976	6
55	8.52 434	376	8.52 459	376	1.47 541	9.99 976	5
56	8.52 810	373	8.52 835	373	1.47 165	9.99 975	4
57	8.53 183	369	8.53 208	370	1.46 792	9.99 975	3
58	8.53 552	367	8.53 578	367	1.46 422	9.99 974	2
59	8.53 919	363	8.53 945	363	1.46 055	9.99 974	1
60	8.54 282		8.54 308		1.45 692	9.99 974	0
	L Cos	d	L Ctn	c d	L Tan	L Sin	′

For more accurate values of L sin and L tan for interpolated values of angles less than 3° (or L cos or L ctn of angles greater than 87°) use Table IVa, Page 118.

88°

Table IV　　　　　　　　　　　　　　　　　　　　　*Page 121*

2°—LOGARITHMS OF TRIGONOMETRIC FUNCTIONS

′	L Sin	d	L Tan	c d	L Ctn	L Cos	
0	8.54 282		8.54 308		1.45 692	9.99 974	60
1	8.54 642	360	8.54 669	361	1.45 331	9.99 973	59
2	8.54 999	357	8.55 027	358	1.44 973	9.99 973	58
3	8.55 354	355	8.55 382	355	1.44 618	9.99 972	57
4	8.55 705	351	8.55 734	352	1.44 266	9.99 972	56
		349		349			
5	8.56 054		8.56 083		1.43 917	9.99 971	55
6	8.56 400	346	8.56 429	346	1.43 571	9.99 971	54
7	8.56 743	343	8.56 773	344	1.43 227	9.99 970	53
8	8.57 084	341	8.57 114	341	1.42 886	9.99 970	52
9	8.57 421	337	8.57 452	338	1.42 548	9.99 969	51
		336		336			
10	8.57 757		8.57 788		1.42 212	9.99 969	50
11	8.58 089	332	8.58 121	333	1.41 879	9.99 968	49
12	8.58 419	330	8.58 451	330	1.41 549	9.99 968	48
13	8.58 747	328	8.58 779	328	1.41 221	9.99 967	47
14	8.59 072	325	8.59 105	326	1.40 895	9.99 967	46
		323		323			
15	8.59 395		8.59 428		1.40 572	9.99 967	45
16	8.59 715	320	8.59 749	321	1.40 251	9.99 966	44
17	8.60 033	318	8.60 068	319	1.39 932	9.99 966	43
18	8.60 349	316	8.60 384	316	1.39 616	9.99 965	42
19	8.60 662	313	8.60 698	314	1.39 302	9.99 964	41
		311		311			
20	8.60 973		8.61 009		1.38 991	9.99 964	40
21	8.61 282	309	8.61 319	310	1.38 681	9.99 963	39
22	8.61 589	307	8.61 626	307	1.38 374	9.99 963	38
23	8.61 894	305	8.61 931	305	1.38 069	9.99 962	37
24	8.62 196	302	8.62 234	303	1.37 766	9.99 962	36
		301		301			
25	8.62 497		8.62 535		1.37 465	9.99 961	35
26	8.62 795	298	8.62 834	299	1.37 166	9.99 961	34
27	8.63 091	296	8.63 131	297	1.36 869	9.99 960	33
28	8.63 385	294	8.63 426	295	1.36 574	9.99 960	32
29	8.63 678	293	8.63 718	292	1.36 282	9.99 959	31
		290		291			
30	8.63 968		8.64 009		1.35 991	9.99 959	30
31	8.64 256	288	8.64 298	289	1.35 702	9.99 958	29
32	8.64 543	287	8.64 585	287	1.35 415	9.99 958	28
33	8.64 827	284	8.64 870	285	1.35 130	9.99 957	27
34	8.65 110	283	8.65 154	284	1.34 846	9.99 956	26
		281		281			
35	8.65 391		8.65 435		1.34 565	9.99 956	25
36	8.65 670	279	8.65 715	280	1.34 285	9.99 955	24
37	8.65 947	277	8.65 993	278	1.34 007	9.99 955	23
38	8.66 223	276	8.66 269	276	1.33 731	9.99 954	22
39	8.66 497	274	8.66 543	274	1.33 457	9.99 954	21
		272		273			
40	8.66 769		8.66 816		1.33 184	9.99 953	20
41	8.67 039	270	8.67 087	271	1.32 913	9.99 952	19
42	8.67 308	269	8.67 356	269	1.32 644	9.99 952	18
43	8.67 575	267	8.67 624	268	1.32 376	9.99 951	17
44	8.67 841	266	8.67 890	266	1.32 110	9.99 951	16
		263		264			
45	8.68 104		8.68 154		1.31 846	9.99 950	15
46	8.68 367	263	8.68 417	263	1.31 583	9.99 949	14
47	8.68 627	260	8.68 678	261	1.31 322	9.99 949	13
48	8.68 886	259	8.68 938	260	1.31 062	9.99 948	12
49	8.69 144	258	8.69 196	258	1.30 804	9.99 948	11
		256		257			
50	8.69 400		8.69 453		1.30 547	9.99 947	10
51	8.69 654	254	8.69 708	255	1.30 292	9.99 946	9
52	8.69 907	253	8.69 962	254	1.30 038	9.99 946	8
53	8.70 159	252	8.70 214	252	1.29 786	9.99 945	7
54	8.70 409	250	8.70 465	251	1.29 535	9.99 944	6
		249		249			
55	8.70 658		8.70 714		1.29 286	9.99 944	5
56	8.70 905	247	8.70 962	248	1.29 038	9.99 943	4
57	8.71 151	246	8.71 208	246	1.28 792	9.99 942	3
58	8.71 395	244	8.71 453	245	1.28 547	9.99 942	2
59	8.71 638	243	8.71 697	244	1.28 303	9.99 941	1
		242		243			
60	8.71 880		8.71 940		1.28 060	9.99 940	0
	L Cos	d	L Ctn	c d	L Tan	L Sin	′

For more accurate values of L sin and L tan for interpolated values of angles less than 3° (or L cos or L ctn of angles greater than 87°) use Table IVa, Page 118.

3°—LOGARITHMS OF TRIGONOMETRIC FUNCTIONS

'	L Sin	d	L Tan	c d	L Ctn	L Cos		Proportional parts				
0	8.71 880	240	8.71 940	241	1.28 060	9.99 940	60	''	241	239	237	235	234
1	8.72 120	239	8.72 181	239	1.27 819	9.99 940	59	1	4.0	4.0	4.0	3.9	3.9
2	8.72 359	238	8.72 420	239	1.27 580	9.99 939	58	2	8.0	8.0	7.9	7.8	7.8
3	8.72 597	237	8.72 659	237	1.27 341	9.99 938	57	3	12.0	12.0	11.8	11.8	11.7
4	8.72 834	235	8.72 896	236	1.27 104	9.99 938	56	4	16.1	15.9	15.8	15.7	15.6
5	8.73 069	234	8.73 132	234	1.26 868	9.99 937	55	5	20.1	19.9	19.8	19.6	19.5
6	8.73 303	232	8.73 366	234	1.26 634	9.99 936	54	6	24.1	23.9	23.7	23.5	23.4
7	8.73 535	232	8.73 600	232	1.26 400	9.99 936	53	7	28.1	27.9	27.6	27.4	27.3
8	8.73 767	230	8.73 832	231	1.26 168	9.99 935	52	8	32.1	31.9	31.6	31.3	31.2
9	8.73 997	229	8.74 063	229	1.25 937	9.99 934	51	9	36.2	35.8	35.6	35.2	35.1
10	8.74 226	228	8.74 292	229	1.25 703	9.99 934	50	''	232	229	227	225	223
11	8.74 454	226	8.74 521	227	1.25 479	9.99 933	49	1	3.9	3.8	3.8	3.8	3.7
12	8.74 680	226	8.74 748	226	1.25 252	9.99 932	48	2	7.7	7.6	7.6	7.5	7.4
13	8.74 906	224	8.74 974	225	1.25 026	9.99 932	47	3	11.6	11.4	11.4	11.2	11.2
14	8.75 130	223	8.75 199	224	1.24 801	9.99 931	46	4	15.5	15.3	15.1	15.0	14.9
15	8.75 353	222	8.75 423	222	1.24 577	9.99 930	45	5	19.3	19.1	18.9	18.8	18.6
16	8.75 575	220	8.75 645	222	1.24 355	9.99 929	44	6	23.2	22.9	22.7	22.5	22.3
17	8.75 795	220	8.75 867	220	1.24 133	9.99 929	43	7	27.1	26.7	26.5	26.2	26.0
18	8.76 015	219	8.76 087	219	1.23 913	9.99 928	42	8	30.9	30.5	30.3	30.0	29.7
19	8.76 234	217	8.76 306	219	1.23 694	9.99 927	41	9	34.8	34.4	34.0	33.8	33.4
20	8.76 451	216	8.76 525	217	1.23 475	9.99 926	40	''	222	220	217	215	213
21	8.76 667	216	8.76 742	216	1.23 258	9.99 926	39	1	3.7	3.7	3.6	3.6	3.6
22	8.76 883	214	8.76 958	215	1.23 042	9.99 925	38	2	7.4	7.3	7.2	7.2	7.1
23	8.77 097	213	8.77 173	214	1.22 827	9.99 924	37	3	11.1	11.0	10.8	10.8	10.6
24	8.77 310	212	8.77 387	213	1.22 613	9.99 923	36	4	14.8	14.7	14.5	14.3	14.2
25	8.77 522	211	8.77 600	211	1.22 400	9.99 923	35	5	18.5	18.3	18.1	17.9	17.8
26	8.77 733	210	8.77 811	211	1.22 189	9.99 922	34	6	22.2	22.0	21.7	21.5	21.3
27	8.77 943	209	8.78 022	210	1.21 978	9.99 921	33	7	25.9	25.7	25.3	25.1	24.8
28	8.78 152	208	8.78 232	209	1.21 768	9.99 920	32	8	29.6	29.3	28.9	28.7	28.4
29	8.78 360	208	8.78 441	208	1.21 559	9.99 920	31	9	33.3	33.0	32.6	32.2	32.0
30	8.78 568	206	8.78 649	206	1.21 351	9.99 919	30						
31	8.78 774	205	8.78 855	206	1.21 145	9.99 918	29	''	211	208	206	203	201
32	8.78 979	204	8.79 061	205	1.20 939	9.99 917	28	1	3.5	3.5	3.4	3.4	3.4
33	8.79 183	203	8.79 266	204	1.20 734	9.99 917	27	2	7.0	6.9	6.9	6.8	6.7
34	8.79 386	202	8.79 470	203	1.20 530	9.99 916	26	3	10.6	10.4	10.3	10.2	10.0
35	8.79 588	201	8.79 673	202	1.20 327	9.99 915	25	4	14.1	13.9	13.7	13.5	13.4
36	8.79 789	201	8.79 875	201	1.20 125	9.99 914	24	5	17.6	17.3	17.2	16.9	16.8
37	8.79 990	199	8.80 076	201	1.19 924	9.99 913	23	6	21.1	20.8	20.6	20.3	20.1
38	8.80 189	199	8.80 277	199	1.19 723	9.99 913	22	7	24.6	24.3	24.0	23.7	23.4
39	8.80 388	197	8.80 476	198	1.19 524	9.99 912	21	8	28.1	27.7	27.5	27.1	26.8
40	8.80 585	197	8.80 674	198	1.19 326	9.99 911	20	9	31.6	31.2	30.9	30.4	30.2
41	8.80 782	196	8.80 872	196	1.19 128	9.99 910	19	''	199	197	195	193	192
42	8.80 978	195	8.81 068	196	1.18 932	9.99 909	18	1	3.3	3.3	3.2	3.2	3.2
43	8.81 173	194	8.81 264	195	1.18 736	9.99 909	17	2	6.6	6.6	6.5	6.4	6.4
44	8.81 367	193	8.81 459	194	1.18 541	9.99 908	16	3	10.0	9.8	9.8	9.6	9.6
45	8.81 560	192	8.81 653	193	1.18 347	9.99 907	15	4	13.3	13.1	13.0	12.9	12.8
46	8.81 752	192	8.81 846	192	1.18 154	9.99 906	14	5	16.6	16.4	16.2	16.1	16.0
47	8.81 944	190	8.82 038	192	1.17 962	9.99 905	13	6	19.9	19.7	19.5	19.3	19.2
48	8.82 134	190	8.82 230	190	1.17 770	9.99 904	12	7	23.2	23.0	22.8	22.5	22.4
49	8.82 324	189	8.82 420	190	1.17 580	9.99 904	11	8	26.5	26.3	26.0	25.7	25.6
50	8.82 513	188	8.82 610	189	1.17 390	9.99 903	10	9	29.8	29.6	29.2	29.0	28.8
51	8.82 701	187	8.82 799	188	1.17 201	9.99 902	9	''	189	187	185	183	181
52	8.82 888	187	8.82 987	188	1.17 013	9.99 901	8	1	3.2	3.1	3.1	3.0	3.0
53	8.83 075	186	8.83 175	186	1.16 825	9.99 900	7	2	6.3	6.2	6.2	6.1	6.0
54	8.83 261	185	8.83 361	186	1.16 639	9.99 899	6	3	9.4	9.4	9.2	9.2	9.0
55	8.83 446	184	8.83 547	185	1.16 453	9.99 898	5	4	12.6	12.5	12.3	12.2	12.1
56	8.83 630	183	8.83 732	184	1.16 268	9.99 898	4						
57	8.83 813	183	8.83 916	184	1.16 084	9.99 897	3	5	15.8	15.6	15.4	15.2	15.1
58	8.83 996	181	8.84 100	182	1.15 900	9.99 896	2	6	18.9	18.7	18.5	18.3	18.1
59	8.84 177	181	8.84 282	182	1.15 718	9.99 895	1	7	22.0	21.8	21.6	21.4	21.1
								8	25.2	24.9	24.7	24.4	24.1
60	8.84 358		8.84 464		1.15 536	9.99 894	0	9	28.4	28.0	27.8	27.4	27.2
	L Cos	d	L Ctn	c d	L Tan	L Sin	'		Proportional parts				

86°

Table IV   **Page 123**

4°—LOGARITHMS OF TRIGONOMETRIC FUNCTIONS

′	L Sin	d	L Tan	c d	L Ctn	L Cos	
0	8.84 358	181	8.84 464	182	1.15 536	9.99 894	60
1	8.84 539	179	8.84 646	180	1.15 354	9.99 893	59
2	8.84 718	179	8.84 826	180	1.15 174	9.99 892	58
3	8.84 897	178	8.85 006	179	1.14 994	9.99 891	57
4	8.85 075	177	8.85 185	178	1.14 815	9.99 891	56
5	8.85 252	177	8.85 363	177	1.14 637	9.99 890	55
6	8.85 429	176	8.85 540	177	1.14 460	9.99 889	54
7	8.85 605	175	8.85 717	176	1.14 283	9.99 888	53
8	8.85 780	175	8.85 893	176	1.14 107	9.99 887	52
9	8.85 955	173	8.86 069	174	1.13 931	9.99 886	51
10	8.86 128	173	8.86 243	174	1.13 757	9.99 885	50
11	8.86 301	173	8.86 417	174	1.13 583	9.99 884	49
12	8.86 474	171	8.86 591	172	1.13 409	9.99 883	48
13	8.86 645	171	8.86 763	172	1.13 237	9.99 882	47
14	8.86 816	171	8.86 935	171	1.13 065	9.99 881	46
15	8.86 987	169	8.87 106	171	1.12 894	9.99 880	45
16	8.87 156	169	8.87 277	170	1.12 723	9.99 879	44
17	8.87 325	169	8.87 447	169	1.12 553	9.99 879	43
18	8.87 494	167	8.87 616	169	1.12 384	9.99 878	42
19	8.87 661	168	8.87 785	168	1.12 215	9.99 877	41
20	8.87 829	166	8.87 953	167	1.12 047	9.99 876	40
21	8.87 995	166	8.88 120	167	1.11 880	9.99 875	39
22	8.88 161	165	8.88 287	166	1.11 713	9.99 874	38
23	8.88 326	164	8.88 453	165	1.11 547	9.99 873	37
24	8.88 490	164	8.88 618	165	1.11 382	9.99 872	36
25	8.88 654	163	8.88 783	165	1.11 217	9.99 871	35
26	8.88 817	163	8.88 948	163	1.11 052	9.99 870	34
27	8.88 980	162	8.89 111	163	1.10 889	9.99 869	33
28	8.89 142	162	8.89 274	163	1.10 726	9.99 868	32
29	8.89 304	160	8.89 437	161	1.10 563	9.99 867	31
30	8.89 464	161	8.89 598	162	1.10 402	9.99 866	30
31	8.89 625	159	8.89 760	160	1.10 240	9.99 865	29
32	8.89 784	159	8.89 920	160	1.10 030	9.99 864	28
33	8.89 943	159	8.90 030	160	1.09 920	9.99 863	27
34	8.90 102		8.90 240	159	1.09 760	9.99 862	26
35	8.90 260	157	8.90 399	158	1.09 601	9.99 861	25
36	8.90 417	157	8.90 557	158	1.09 443	9.99 860	24
37	8.90 574	156	8.90 715	157	1.09 285	9.99 859	23
38	8.90 730	155	8.90 872	157	1.09 128	9.99 858	22
39	8.90 885	155	8.91 029	156	1.08 971	9.99 857	21
40	8.91 040	155	8.91 185	155	1.08 815	9.99 856	20
41	8.91 195	154	8.91 340	155	1.08 660	9.99 855	19
42	8.91 349	153	8.91 495	155	1.08 505	9.99 854	18
43	8.91 502	153	8.91 650	153	1.08 350	9.99 853	17
44	8.91 655	152	8.91 803	154	1.08 197	9.99 852	16
45	8.91 807	152	8.91 957	153	1.08 043	9.99 851	15
46	8.91 959	151	8.92 110	152	1.07 890	9.99 850	14
47	8.92 110	151	8.92 262	152	1.07 738	9.99 848	13
48	8.92 261	150	8.92 414	151	1.07 586	9.99 847	12
49	8.92 411	150	8.92 565	151	1.07 435	9.99 846	11
50	8.92 561	149	8.92 716	150	1.07 284	9.99 845	10
51	8.92 710	149	8.92 866	150	1.07 134	9.99 844	9
52	8.92 859	148	8.93 016	150	1.06 984	9.99 843	8
53	8.93 007	147	8.93 165	148	1.06 835	9.99 842	7
54	8.93 154	147	8.93 313	149	1.06 687	9.99 841	6
55	8.93 301	147	8.93 462	147	1.06 538	9.99 840	5
56	8.93 448	146	8.93 609	147	1.06 391	9.99 839	4
57	8.93 594	146	8.93 756	147	1.06 244	9.99 838	3
58	8.93 740	145	8.93 903	146	1.06 097	9.99 837	2
59	8.93 885	145	8.94 049	146	1.05 951	9.99 836	1
60	8.94 030		8.94 195		1.05 805	9.99 834	0

| | L Cos | d | L Ctn | c d | L Tan | L Sin | ′ |

Proportional parts

″	182	181	179	178	177
1	3.0	3.0	3.0	3.0	3.0
2	6.1	6.0	6.0	5.9	5.9
3	9.1	9.0	9.0	8.9	8.8
4	12.1	12.1	11.9	11.9	11.8
5	15.2	15.1	14.9	14.8	14.8
6	18.2	18.1	17.9	17.8	17.7
7	21.2	21.1	20.9	20.8	20.6
8	24.3	24.1	23.9	23.7	23.6
9	27.3	27.2	26.8	26.7	26.6

″	176	175	174	173	172
1	2.9	2.9	2.9	2.9	2.9
2	5.9	5.8	5.8	5.8	5.7
3	8.8	8.8	8.7	8.6	8.6
4	11.7	11.7	11.6	11.5	11.5
5	14.7	14.6	14.5	14.4	14.3
6	17.6	17.5	17.4	17.3	17.2
7	20.5	20.4	20.3	20.2	20.1
8	23.5	23.3	23.2	23.1	22.9
9	26.4	26.2	26.1	26.0	25.8

″	171	170	169	168	167
1	2.8	2.8	2.8	2.8	2.8
2	5.7	5.7	5.6	5.6	5.6
3	8.6	8.5	8.4	8.4	8.4
4	11.4	11.3	11.3	11.2	11.1
5	14.2	14.2	14.1	14.0	13.9
6	17.1	17.0	16.9	16.8	16.7
7	20.0	19.8	19.7	19.6	19.5
8	22.8	22.7	22.5	22.4	22.3
9	25.6	25.5	25.4	25.2	25.0

″	166	165	164	163	162
1	2.8	2.8	2.7	2.7	2.7
2	5.5	5.5	5.5	5.4	5.4
3	8.3	8.2	8.2	8.2	8.1
4	11.1	11.0	10.9	10.9	10.8
5	13.8	13.8	13.7	13.6	13.5
6	16.6	16.5	16.4	16.3	16.2
7	19.4	19.2	19.1	19.0	18.9
8	22.1	22.0	21.9	21.7	21.6
9	24.9	24.8	24.6	24.4	24.3

″	161	160	159	158	157
1	2.7	2.7	2.6	2.6	2.6
2	5.4	5.3	5.3	5.3	5.2
3	8.0	8.0	8.0	7.9	7.8
4	10.7	10.7	10.6	10.5	10.5
5	13.4	13.3	13.2	13.2	13.1
6	16.1	16.0	15.9	15.8	15.7
7	18.8	18.7	18.6	18.4	18.3
8	21.5	21.3	21.2	21.1	20.9
9	24.2	24.0	23.8	23.7	23.6

″	156	155	154	153	152
1	2.6	2.6	2.6	2.6	2.5
2	5.2	5.2	5.1	5.1	5.1
3	7.8	7.8	7.7	7.6	7.6
4	10.4	10.3	10.3	10.2	10.1
5	13.0	12.9	12.8	12.8	12.7
6	15.6	15.5	15.4	15.3	15.2
7	18.2	18.1	18.0	17.8	17.7
8	20.8	20.7	20.5	20.4	20.3
9	23.4	23.2	23.1	23.0	22.8

5°—LOGARITHMS OF TRIGONOMETRIC FUNCTIONS

'	L Sin	d	L Tan	c d	L Ctn	L Cos	
0	8.94 030	144	8.94 195	145	1.05 805	9.99 834	60
1	8.94 174	143	8.94 340	145	1.05 660	9.99 833	59
2	8.94 317	144	8.94 485	145	1.05 515	9.99 832	58
3	8.94 461	142	8.94 630	143	1.05 370	9.99 831	57
4	8.94 603	143	8.94 773	144	1.05 227	9.99 830	56
5	8.94 746	141	8.94 917	143	1.05 083	9.99 829	55
6	8.94 887	142	8.95 060	142	1.04 940	9.99 828	54
7	8.95 029	141	8.95 202	142	1.04 798	9.99 827	53
8	8.95 170	140	8.95 344	142	1.04 656	9.99 825	52
9	8.95 310	140	8.95 486	141	1.04 514	9.99 824	51
10	8.95 450	139	8.95 627	140	1.04 373	9.99 823	50
11	8.95 589	139	8.95 767	141	1.04 233	9.99 822	49
12	8.95 728	139	8.95 908	139	1.04 092	9.99 821	48
13	8.95 867	138	8.96 047	140	1.03 953	9.99 820	47
14	8.96 005	138	8.96 187	138	1.03 813	9.99 819	46
15	8.96 143	137	8.96 325	139	1.03 675	9.99 817	45
16	8.96 280	137	8.96 464	138	1.03 536	9.99 816	44
17	8.96 417	136	8.96 602	137	1.03 398	9.99 815	43
18	8.96 553	136	8.96 739	138	1.03 261	9.99 814	42
19	8.96 689	136	8.96 877	136	1.03 123	9.99 813	41
20	8.96 825	135	8.97 013	137	1.02 987	9.99 812	40
21	8.96 960	135	8.97 150	135	1.02 850	9.99 810	39
22	8.97 095	134	8.97 285	136	1.02 715	9.99 809	38
23	8.97 229	134	8.97 421	135	1.02 579	9.99 808	37
24	8.97 363	133	8.97 556	135	1.02 444	9.99 807	36
25	8.97 496	133	8.97 691	134	1.02 309	9.99 806	35
26	8.97 629	133	8.97 825	134	1.02 175	9.99 804	34
27	8.97 762	132	8.97 959	133	1.02 041	9.99 803	33
28	8.97 894	132	8.98 092	133	1.01 908	9.99 802	32
29	8.98 026	131	8.98 225	133	1.01 775	9.99 801	31
30	8.98 157	131	8.98 358	132	1.01 642	9.99 800	30
31	8.98 288	131	8.98 490	132	1.01 510	9.99 798	29
32	8.98 419	130	8.98 622	131	1.01 378	9.99 797	28
33	8.98 549	130	8.98 753	131	1.01 247	9.99 796	27
34	8.98 679	129	8.98 884	131	1.01 116	9.99 795	26
35	8.98 808	129	8.99 015	130	1.00 985	9.99 793	25
36	8.98 937	129	8.99 145	130	1.00 855	9.99 792	24
37	8.99 066	128	8.99 275	130	1.00 725	9.99 791	23
38	8.99 194	128	8.99 405	129	1.00 595	9.99 790	22
39	8.99 322	128	8.99 534	128	1.00 466	9.99 788	21
40	8.99 450	127	8.99 662	129	1.00 338	9.99 787	20
41	8.99 577	127	8.99 791	128	1.00 209	9.99 786	19
42	8.99 704	126	8.99 919	127	1.00 081	9.99 785	18
43	8.99 830	126	9.00 046	128	0.99 954	9.99 783	17
44	8.99 956	126	9.00 174	127	0.99 826	9.99 782	16
45	9.00 082	125	9.00 301	126	0.99 699	9.99 781	15
46	9.00 207	125	9.00 427	126	0.99 573	9.99 780	14
47	9.00 332	124	9.00 553	126	0.99 447	9.99 778	13
48	9.00 456	125	9.00 679	126	0.99 321	9.99 777	12
49	9.00 581	123	9.00 805	125	0.99 195	9.99 776	11
50	9.00 704	124	9.00 930	125	0.99 070	9.99 775	10
51	9.00 828	123	9.01 055	124	0.98 945	9.99 773	9
52	9.00 951	123	9.01 179	124	0.98 821	9.99 772	8
53	9.01 074	122	9.01 303	124	0.98 697	9.99 771	7
54	9.01 196	122	9.01 427	123	0.98 573	9.99 769	6
55	9.01 318	122	9.01 550	123	0.98 450	9.99 768	5
56	9.01 440	121	9.01 673	123	0.98 327	9.99 767	4
57	9.01 561	121	9.01 796	122	0.98 204	9.99 765	3
58	9.01 682	121	9.01 918	122	0.98 082	9.99 764	2
59	9.01 803	120	9.02 040	122	0.97 960	9.99 763	1
60	9.01 923		9.02 162		0.97 838	9.99 761	0
	L Cos	d	L Ctn	c d	L Tan	L Sin	'

Proportional parts

''	151	149	148	147	146
1	2.5	2.5	2.5	2.4	2.4
2	5.0	5.0	4.9	4.9	4.9
3	7.6	7.4	7.4	7.4	7.3
4	10.1	9.9	9.9	9.8	9.7
5	12.6	12.4	12.3	12.2	12.2
6	15.1	14.9	14.8	14.7	14.6
7	17.6	17.4	17.3	17.2	17.0
8	20.1	19.9	19.7	19.6	19.5
9	22.6	22.4	22.2	22.0	21.9

''	145	144	143	142	141
1	2.4	2.4	2.4	2.4	2.4
2	4.8	4.8	4.8	4.7	4.7
3	7.2	7.2	7.2	7.1	7.0
4	9.7	9.6	9.5	9.5	9.4
5	12.1	12.0	11.9	11.8	11.8
6	14.5	14.4	14.3	14.2	14.1
7	16.9	16.8	16.7	16.6	16.4
8	19.3	19.2	19.1	18.9	18.8
9	21.8	21.6	21.4	21.3	21.2

''	140	139	138	137	136
1	2.3	2.3	2.3	2.3	2.3
2	4.7	4.6	4.6	4.6	4.5
3	7.0	7.0	6.9	6.8	6.8
4	9.3	9.3	9.2	9.1	9.1
5	11.7	11.6	11.5	11.4	11.3
6	14.0	13.9	13.8	13.7	13.6
7	16.3	16.2	16.1	16.0	15.9
8	18.7	18.5	18.4	18.3	18.1
9	21.0	20.8	20.7	20.6	20.4

''	135	134	133	132	131
1	2.2	2.2	2.2	2.2	2.2
2	4.5	4.5	4.4	4.4	4.4
3	6.8	6.7	6.6	6.6	6.6
4	9.0	8.9	8.9	8.8	8.7
5	11.2	11.2	11.1	11.0	10.9
6	13.5	13.4	13.3	13.2	13.1
7	15.8	15.6	15.5	15.4	15.3
8	18.0	17.9	17.7	17.6	17.5
9	20.2	20.1	20.0	19.8	19.6

''	130	129	128	127	126
1	2.2	2.2	2.1	2.1	2.1
2	4.3	4.3	4.3	4.2	4.2
3	6.5	6.4	6.4	6.4	6.3
4	8.7	8.6	8.5	8.5	8.4
5	10.8	10.8	10.7	10.6	10.5
6	13.0	12.9	12.8	12.7	12.6
7	15.2	15.0	14.9	14.8	14.7
8	17.3	17.2	17.1	16.9	16.8
9	19.5	19.4	19.2	19.0	18.9

''	125	124	123	122	121
1	2.1	2.1	2.0	2.0	2.0
2	4.2	4.1	4.1	4.1	4.0
3	6.2	6.2	6.2	6.1	6.0
4	8.3	8.3	8.2	8.1	8.1
5	10.4	10.3	10.2	10.2	10.1
6	12.5	12.4	12.3	12.2	12.1
7	14.6	14.5	14.4	14.2	14.1
8	16.7	16.5	16.4	16.3	16.1
9	18.8	18.6	18.4	18.3	18.2

Proportional parts

6°—LOGARITHMS OF TRIGONOMETRIC FUNCTIONS

′	L Sin	d	L Tan	c d	L Ctn	L Cos		Proportional parts			
0	9.01 923	120	9.02 162	121	0.97 838	9.99 761	60	″	121	120	119	118
1	9.02 043	120	9.02 283	121	0.97 717	9.99 760	59	1	2.0	2.0	2.0	2.0
2	9.02 163	120	9.02 404	121	0.97 596	9.99 759	58	2	4.0	4.0	4.0	3.9
3	9.02 283	119	9.02 525	120	0.97 475	9.99 757	57	3	6.0	6.0	6.0	5.9
4	9.02 402	118	9.02 645	121	0.97 355	9.99 756	56	4	8.1	8.0	7.9	7.9
5	9.02 520	119	9.02 766	119	0.97 234	9.99 755	55	5	10.1	10.0	9.9	9.8
6	9.02 639	118	9.02 885	120	0.97 115	9.99 753	54	6	12.1	12.0	11.9	11.8
7	9.02 757	117	9.03 005	119	0.96 995	9.99 752	53	7	14.1	14.0	13.9	13.8
8	9.02 874	118	9.03 124	118	0.96 876	9.99 751	52	8	16.1	16.0	15.9	15.7
9	9.02 992	117	9.03 242	119	0.96 758	9.99 749	51	9	18.2	18.0	17.8	17.7
10	9.03 109	117	9.03 361	118	0.96 639	9.99 748	50	10	20.2	20.0	19.8	19.7
11	9.03 226	116	9.03 479	118	0.96 521	9.99 747	49	20	40.3	40.0	39.7	39.3
12	9.03 342	116	9.03 597	117	0.96 403	9.99 745	48	30	60.5	60.0	59.5	59.0
13	9.03 458	116	9.03 714	118	0.96 286	9.99 744	47	40	80.7	80.0	79.3	78.7
14	9.03 574	116	9.03 832	116	0.96 168	9.99 742	46	50	100.8	100.0	99.2	98.3
15	9.03 690	115	9.03 948	117	0.96 052	9.99 741	45	″	117	116	115	114
16	9.03 805	115	9.04 065	116	0.95 935	9.99 740	44	1	2.0	1.9	1.9	1.9
17	9.03 920	114	9.04 181	116	0.95 819	9.99 738	43	2	3.9	3.9	3.8	3.8
18	9.04 034	115	9.04 297	116	0.95 703	9.99 737	42	3	5.8	5.8	5.8	5.7
19	9.04 149	113	9.04 413	115	0.95 587	9.99 736	41	4	7.8	7.7	7.7	7.6
20	9.04 262	114	9.04 528	115	0.95 472	9.99 734	40	5	9.8	9.7	9.6	9.5
21	9.04 376	114	9.04 643	115	0.95 357	9.99 733	39	6	11.7	11.6	11.5	11.4
22	9.04 490	113	9.04 758	115	0.95 242	9.99 731	38	7	13.6	13.5	13.4	13.3
23	9.04 603	112	9.04 873	114	0.95 127	9.99 730	37	8	15.6	15.5	15.3	15.2
24	9.04 715	113	9.04 987	114	0.95 013	9.99 728	36	9	17.6	17.4	17.2	17.1
25	9.04 828	112	9.05 101	113	0.94 899	9.99 727	35	10	19.5	19.3	19.2	19.0
26	9.04 940	112	9.05 214	114	0.94 786	9.99 726	34	20	39.0	38.7	38.3	38.0
27	9.05 052	112	9.05 328	113	0.94 672	9.99 724	33	30	58.5	58.0	57.5	57.0
28	9.05 164	111	9.05 441	112	0.94 559	9.99 723	32	40	78.0	77.3	76.7	76.0
29	9.05 275	111	9.05 553	113	0.94 447	9.99 721	31	50	97.5	96.7	95.8	95.0
30	9.05 386	111	9.05 666	112	0.94 334	9.99 720	30	″	113	112	111	110
31	9.05 497	110	9.05 778	112	0.94 222	9.99 718	29	1	1.9	1.9	1.8	1.8
32	9.05 607	110	9.05 890	112	0.94 110	9.99 717	28	2	3.8	3.7	3.7	3.7
33	9.05 717	110	9.06 002	111	0.93 998	9.99 716	27	3	5.6	5.6	5.6	5.5
34	9.05 827	110	9.06 113	111	0.93 887	9.99 714	26	4	7.5	7.5	7.4	7.3
35	9.05 937	109	9.06 224	111	0.93 776	9.99 713	25	5	9.4	9.3	9.2	9.2
36	9.06 046	109	9.06 335	110	0.93 665	9.99 711	24	6	11.3	11.2	11.1	11.0
37	9.06 155	109	9.06 445	111	0.93 555	9.99 710	23	7	13.2	13.1	13.0	12.8
38	9.06 264	108	9.06 556	110	0.93 444	9.99 708	22	8	15.1	14.9	14.8	14.7
39	9.06 372	109	9.06 666	109	0.93 334	9.99 707	21	9	17.0	16.8	16.6	16.5
40	9.06 481	108	9.06 775	110	0.93 225	9.99 705	20	10	18.8	18.7	18.5	18.3
41	9.06 589	107	9.06 885	109	0.93 115	9.99 704	19	20	37.7	37.3	37.0	36.7
42	9.06 696	108	9.06 994	109	0.93 006	9.99 702	18	30	56.5	56.0	55.5	55.0
43	9.06 804	107	9.07 103	108	0.92 897	9.99 701	17	40	75.3	74.7	74.0	73.3
44	9.06 911	107	9.07 211	109	0.92 789	9.99 699	16	50	94.2	93.3	92.5	91.7
45	9.07 018	106	9.07 320	108	0.92 680	9.99 698	15	″	109	108	107	106
46	9.07 124	107	9.07 428	108	0.92 572	9.99 696	14	1	1.8	1.8	1.8	1.8
47	9.07 231	106	9.07 536	107	0.92 464	9.99 695	13	2	3.6	3.6	3.6	3.5
48	9.07 337	105	9.07 643	108	0.92 357	9.99 693	12	3	5.4	5.4	5.4	5.3
49	9.07 442	106	9.07 751	107	0.92 249	9.99 692	11	4	7.3	7.2	7.1	7.1
50	9.07 548	105	9.07 858	106	0.92 142	9.99 690	10	5	9.1	9.0	8.9	8.8
51	9.07 653	105	9.07 964	107	0.92 036	9.99 689	9	6	10.9	10.8	10.7	10.6
52	9.07 758	105	9.08 071	106	0.91 929	9.99 687	8	7	12.7	12.6	12.5	12.4
53	9.07 863	105	9.08 177	106	0.91 823	9.99 686	7	8	14.5	14.4	14.3	14.1
54	9.07 968	104	9.08 283	106	0.91 717	9.99 684	6	9	16.4	16.2	16.0	15.9
55	9.08 072	104	9.08 389	106	0.91 611	9.99 683	5	10	18.2	18.0	17.8	17.7
56	9.08 176	104	9.08 495	105	0.91 505	9.99 681	4	20	36.3	36.0	35.7	35.3
57	9.08 280	103	9.08 600	105	0.91 400	9.99 680	3	30	54.5	54.0	53.5	53.0
58	9.08 383	103	9.08 705	105	0.91 295	9.99 678	2	40	72.7	72.0	71.3	70.7
59	9.08 486	103	9.08 810	104	0.91 190	9.99 677	1	50	90.8	90.0	89.2	88.3
60	9.08 589		9.08 914		0.91 086	9.99 675	0					
′	L Cos	d	L Ctn	c d	L Tan	L Sin	′	Proportional parts			

7°—LOGARITHMS OF TRIGONOMETRIC FUNCTIONS

'	L Sin	d	L Tan	c d	L Ctn	L Cos	
0	9.08 589		9.08 914		0.91 086	9.99 675	60
1	9.08 692	103	9.09 019	105	0.90 981	9.99 674	59
2	9.08 795	103	9.09 123	104	0.90 877	9.99 672	58
3	9.08 897	102	9.09 227	104	0.90 773	9.99 670	57
4	9.08 999	102	9.09 330	103	0.90 670	9.99 669	56
5	9.09 101	102	9.09 434	104	0.90 566	9.99 667	55
6	9.09 202	101	9.09 537	103	0.90 463	9.99 666	54
7	9.09 304	102	9.09 640	103	0.90 360	9.99 664	53
8	9.09 405	101	9.09 742	102	0.90 258	9.99 663	52
9	9.09 506	101	9.09 845	103	0.90 155	9.99 661	51
10	9.09 606	100	9.09 947	102	0.90 053	9.99 659	50
11	9.09 707	101	9.10 049	102	0.89 951	9.99 658	49
12	9.09 807	100	9.10 150	101	0.89 850	9.99 656	48
13	9.09 907	100	9.10 252	102	0.89 748	9.99 655	47
14	9.10 006	99	9.10 353	101	0.89 647	9.99 653	46
15	9.10 106	100	9.10 454	101	0.89 546	9.99 651	45
16	9.10 205	99	9.10 555	101	0.89 445	9.99 650	44
17	9.10 304	99	9.10 656	100	0.89 344	9.99 648	43
18	9.10 402	98	9.10 756	100	0.89 244	9.99 647	42
19	9.10 501	99	9.10 856	100	0.89 144	9.99 645	41
20	9.10 599	98	9.10 956	100	0.89 044	9.99 643	40
21	9.10 697	98	9.11 056	99	0.88 944	9.99 642	39
22	9.10 795	98	9.11 155	99	0.88 845	9.99 640	38
23	9.10 893	97	9.11 254	99	0.88 746	9.99 638	37
24	9.10 990	97	9.11 353	99	0.88 647	9.99 637	36
25	9.11 087	97	9.11 452	99	0.88 548	9.99 635	35
26	9.11 184	97	9.11 551	98	0.88 449	9.99 633	34
27	9.11 281	96	9.11 649	98	0.88 351	9.99 632	33
28	9.11 377	97	9.11 747	98	0.88 253	9.99 630	32
29	9.11 474	96	9.11 845	98	0.88 155	9.99 629	31
30	9.11 570	96	9.11 943	97	0.88 057	9.99 627	30
31	9.11 666	95	9.12 040	98	0.87 960	9.99 625	29
32	9.11 761	96	9.12 138	97	0.87 862	9.99 624	28
33	9.11 857	95	9.12 235	97	0.87 765	9.99 622	27
34	9.11 952	95	9.12 332	96	0.87 668	9.99 620	26
35	9.12 047	95	9.12 428	97	0.87 572	9.99 618	25
36	9.12 142	94	9.12 525	96	0.87 475	9.99 617	24
37	9.12 236	95	9.12 621	96	0.87 379	9.99 615	23
38	9.12 331	94	9.12 717	96	0.87 283	9.99 613	22
39	9.12 425	94	9.12 813	96	0.87 187	9.99 612	21
40	9.12 519	93	9.12 909	95	0.87 091	9.99 610	20
41	9.12 612	94	9.13 004	95	0.86 996	9.99 608	19
42	9.12 706	93	9.13 099	95	0.86 901	9.99 607	18
43	9.12 799	93	9.13 194	95	0.86 806	9.99 605	17
44	9.12 892	93	9.13 289	95	0.86 711	9.99 603	16
45	9.12 985	93	9.13 384	94	0.86 616	9.99 601	15
46	9.13 078	93	9.13 478	95	0.86 522	9.99 600	14
47	9.13 171	92	9.13 573	94	0.86 427	9.99 598	13
48	9.13 263	92	9.13 667	94	0.86 333	9.99 596	12
49	9.13 355	92	9.13 761	93	0.86 239	9.99 595	11
50	9.13 447	92	9.13 854	94	0.86 146	9.99 593	10
51	9.13 539	91	9.13 948	93	0.86 052	9.99 591	9
52	9.13 630	92	9.14 041	93	0.85 959	9.99 589	8
53	9.13 722	91	9.14 134	93	0.85 866	9.99 588	7
54	9.13 813	91	9.14 227	93	0.85 773	9.99 586	6
55	9.13 904	90	9.14 320	92	0.85 680	9.99 584	5
56	9.13 994	91	9.14 412	92	0.85 588	9.99 582	4
57	9.14 085	90	9.14 504	93	0.85 496	9.99 581	3
58	9.14 175	91	9.14 597	91	0.85 403	9.99 579	2
59	9.14 266	90	9.14 688	92	0.85 312	9.99 577	1
60	9.14 356		9.14 780		0.85 220	9.99 575	0
	L Cos	d	L Ctn	c d	L Tan	L Sin	'

Proportional parts

''	105	104	103	102
1	1.8	1.7	1.7	1.7
2	3.5	3.5	3.4	3.4
3	5.2	5.2	5.2	5.1
4	7.0	6.9	6.9	6.8
5	8.8	8.7	8.6	8.5
6	10.5	10.4	10.3	10.2
7	12.2	12.1	12.0	11.9
8	14.0	13.9	13.7	13.6
9	15.8	15.6	15.4	15.3
10	17.5	17.3	17.2	17.0
20	35.0	34.7	34.3	34.0
30	52.5	52.0	51.5	51.0
40	70.0	69.3	68.7	68.0
50	87.5	86.7	85.8	85.0

''	101	100	99	98
1	1.7	1.7	1.6	1.6
2	3.4	3.3	3.3	3.3
3	5.0	5.0	5.0	4.9
4	6.7	6.7	6.6	6.5
5	8.4	8.3	8.2	8.2
6	10.1	10.0	9.9	9.8
7	11.8	11.7	11.6	11.4
8	13.5	13.3	13.2	13.1
9	15.2	15.0	14.8	14.7
10	16.8	16.7	16.5	16.3
20	33.7	33.3	33.0	32.7
30	50.5	50.0	49.5	49.0
40	67.3	66.7	66.0	65.3
50	84.2	83.3	82.5	81.7

''	97	96	95	94
1	1.6	1.6	1.6	1.6
2	3.2	3.2	3.2	3.1
3	4.8	4.8	4.8	4.7
4	6.5	6.4	6.3	6.3
5	8.1	8.0	7.9	7.8
6	9.7	9.6	9.5	9.4
7	11.3	11.2	11.1	11.0
8	12.9	12.8	12.7	12.5
9	14.6	14.4	14.2	14.1
10	16.2	16.0	15.8	15.7
20	32.3	32.0	31.7	31.3
30	48.5	48.0	47.5	47.0
40	64.7	64.0	63.3	62.7
50	80.8	80.0	79.2	78.3

''	93	92	91	90
1	1.6	1.5	1.5	1.5
2	3.1	3.1	3.0	3.0
3	4.6	4.6	4.6	4.5
4	6.2	6.1	6.1	6.0
5	7.8	7.7	7.6	7.5
6	9.3	9.2	9.1	9.0
7	10.8	10.7	10.6	10.5
8	12.4	12.3	12.1	12.0
9	14.0	13.8	13.6	13.5
10	15.5	15.3	15.2	15.0
20	31.0	30.7	30.3	30.0
30	46.5	46.0	45.5	45.0
40	62.0	61.3	60.7	60.0
50	77.5	76.7	75.8	75.0

Proportional parts

82°

Table IV   *Page 127*

8°—LOGARITHMS OF TRIGONOMETRIC FUNCTIONS

′	L Sin	d	L Tan	c d	L Ctn	L Cos	
0	9.14 356		9.14 780		0.85 220	9.99 575	60
1	9.14 445	89	9.14 872	92	0.85 128	9.99 574	59
2	9.14 535	90	9.14 963	91	0.85 037	9.99 572	58
3	9.14 624	89	9.15 054	91	0.84 946	9.99 570	57
4	9.14 714	90	9.15 145	91	0.84 855	9.99 568	56
		89		91			
5	9.14 803		9.15 236		0.84 764	9.99 566	55
6	9.14 891	88	9.15 327	91	0.84 673	9.99 565	54
7	9.14 980	89	9.15 417	90	0.84 583	9.99 563	53
8	9.15 069	89	9.15 508	91	0.84 492	9.99 561	52
9	9.15 157	88	9.15 598	90	0.84 402	9.99 559	51
		88		90			
10	9.15 245		9.15 688		0.84 312	9.99 557	50
11	9.15 333	88	9.15 777	89	0.84 223	9.99 556	49
12	9.15 421	88	9.15 867	90	0.84 133	9.99 554	48
13	9.15 508	87	9.15 956	89	0.84 044	9.99 552	47
14	9.15 596	88	9.16 046	90	0.83 954	9.99 550	46
		87		89			
15	9.15 683		9.16 135		0.83 865	9.99 548	45
16	9.15 770	87	9.16 224	89	0.83 776	9.99 546	44
17	9.15 857	87	9.16 312	88	0.83 688	9.99 545	43
18	9.15 944	87	9.16 401	89	0.83 599	9.99 543	42
19	9.16 030	86	9.16 489	88	0.83 511	9.99 541†	41
		86		88			
20	9.16 116		9.16 577		0.83 423	9.99 539	40
21	9.16 203	87	9.16 665	88	0.83 335	9.99 537	39
22	9.16 289	86	9.16 753	88	0.83 247	9.99 535	38
23	9.16 374	85	9.16 841	88	0.83 159	9.99 533	37
24	9.16 460	86	9.16 928	87	0.83 072	9.99 532	36
		85		88			
25	9.16 545		9.17 016		0.82 984	9.99 530	35
26	9.16 631	86	9.17 103	87	0.82 897	9.99 528	34
27	9.16 716	85	9.17 190	87	0.82 810	9.99 526	33
28	9.16 801	85	9.17 277	87	0.82 723	9.99 524	32
29	9.16 886	85	9.17 363	86	0.82 637	9.99 522	31
		84		87			
30	9.16 970		9.17 450		0.82 550	9.99 520	30
31	9.17 055	85	9.17 536	86	0.82 464	9.99 518	29
32	9.17 139	84	9.17 622	86	0.82 378	9.99 517	28
33	9.17 223	84	9.17 708	86	0.82 292	9.99 515	27
34	9.17 307	84	9.17 794	86	0.82 206	9.99 513	26
		84		86			
35	9.17 391		9.17 880		0.82 120	9.99 511	25
36	9.17 474	83	9.17 965	85	0.82 035	9.99 509	24
37	9.17 558	84	9.18 051	86	0.81 949	9.99 507	23
38	9.17 641	83	9.18 136	85	0.81 864	9.99 505	22
39	9.17 724	83	9.18 221	85	0.81 779	9.99 503	21
		83		85			
40	9.17 807		9.18 306		0.81 694	9.99 501	20
41	9.17 890	83	9.18 391	85	0.81 609	9.99 499	19
42	9.17 973	83	9.18 475	84	0.81 525	9.99 497	18
43	9.18 055	82	9.18 560	85	0.81 440	9.99 495	17
44	9.18 137	82	9.18 644	84	0.81 356	9.99 494	16
		83		84			
45	9.18 220		9.18 728		0.81 272	9.99 492	15
46	9.18 302	82	9.18 812	84	0.81 188	9.99 490	14
47	9.18 383	81	9.18 896	84	0.81 104	9.99 488	13
48	9.18 465	82	9.18 979	83	0.81 021	9.99 486	12
49	9.18 547	82	9.19 063	84	0.80 937	9.99 484	11
		81		83			
50	9.18 628		9.19 146		0.80 854	9.99 482	10
51	9.18 709	81	9.19 229	83	0.80 771	9.99 480	9
52	9.18 790	81	9.19 312	83	0.80 688	9.99 478	8
53	9.18 871	81	9.19 395	83	0.80 605	9.99 476	7
54	9.18 952	81	9.19 478	83	0.80 522	9.99 474	6
		81		83			
55	9.19 033		9.19 561		0.80 439	9.99 472	5
56	9.19 113	80	9.19 643	82	0.80 357	9.99 470	4
57	9.19 193	80	9.19 725	82	0.80 275	9.99 468	3
58	9.19 273	80	9.19 807	82	0.80 193	9.99 466	2
59	9.19 353	80	9.19 889	82	0.80 111	9.99 464	1
		80		82			
60	9.19 433		9.19 971		0.80 029	9.99 462	0
	L Cos	d	L Ctn	c d	L Tan	L Sin	′

Proportional parts

″	92	91	90
1	1.5	1.5	1.5
2	3.1	3.0	3.0
3	4.6	4.6	4.5
4	6.1	6.1	6.0
5	7.7	7.6	7.5
6	9.2	9.1	9.0
7	10.7	10.6	10.5
8	12.3	12.1	12.0
9	13.8	13.6	13.5
10	15.3	15.2	15.0
20	30.7	30.3	30.0
30	46.0	45.5	45.0
40	61.3	60.7	60.0
50	76.7	75.8	75.0

″	89	88	87
1	1.5	1.5	1.4
2	3.0	2.9	2.9
3	4.4	4.4	4.4
4	5.9	5.9	5.8
5	7.4	7.3	7.2
6	8.9	8.8	8.7
7	10.4	10.3	10.2
8	11.9	11.7	11.6
9	13.4	13.2	13.0
10	14.8	14.7	14.5
20	29.7	29.3	29.0
30	44.5	44.0	43.5
40	59.3	58.7	58.0
50	74.2	73.3	72.5

″	86	85	84
1	1.4	1.4	1.4
2	2.9	2.8	2.8
3	4.3	4.2	4.2
4	5.7	5.7	5.6
5	7.2	7.1	7.0
6	8.6	8.5	8.4
7	10.0	9.9	9.8
8	11.5	11.3	11.2
9	12.9	12.8	12.6
10	14.3	14.2	14.0
20	28.7	28.3	28.0
30	43.0	42.5	42.0
40	57.3	56.7	56.0
50	71.7	70.8	70.0

″	83	82	81
1	1.4	1.4	1.4
2	2.8	2.7	2.7
3	4.2	4.1	4.0
4	5.5	5.5	5.4
5	6.9	6.8	6.8
6	8.3	8.2	8.1
7	9.7	9.6	9.4
8	11.1	10.9	10.8
9	12.4	12.3	12.2
10	13.8	13.7	13.5
20	27.7	27.3	27.0
30	41.5	41.0	40.5
40	55.3	54.7	54.0
50	69.2	68.3	67.5

9°—LOGARITHMS OF TRIGONOMETRIC FUNCTIONS

′	L Sin	d	L Tan	c d	L Ctn	L Cos	.
0	9.19 433	80	9.19 971	82	0.80 029	9.99 462	60
1	9.19 513	79	9.20 053	81	0.79 947	9.99 460	59
2	9.19 592	80	9.20 134	82	0.79 866	9.99 458	58
3	9.19 672	79	9.20 216	81	0.79 784	9.99 456	57
4	9.19 751	79	9.20 297	81	0.79 703	9.99 454	56
5	9.19 830	79	9.20 378	81	0.79 622	9.99 452	55
6	9.19 909	79	9.20 459	81	0.79 541	9.99 450	54
7	9.19 988	79	9.20 540	81	0.79 460	9.99 448	53
8	9.20 067	78	9.20 621	80	0.79 379	9.99 446	52
9	9.20 145	78	9.20 701	81	0.79 299	9.99 444	51
10	9.20 223	79	9.20 782	80	0.79 218	9.99 442	50
11	9.20 302	78	9.20 862	80	0.79 138	9.99 440	49
12	9.20 380	78	9.20 942	80	0.79 058	9.99 438	48
13	9.20 458	77	9.21 022	80	0.78 978	9.99 436	47
14	9.20 535	78	9.21 102	80	0.78 898	9.99 434	46
15	9.20 613	78	9.21 182	79	0.78 818	9.99 432	45
16	9.20 691	77	9.21 261	80	0.78 739	9.99 429	44
17	9.20 768	77	9.21 341	79	0.78 659	9.99 427	43
18	9.20 845	77	9.21 420	79	0.78 580	9.99 425	42
19	9.20 922	77	9.21 499	79	0.78 501	9.99 423	41
20	9.20 999	77	9.21 578	79	0.78 422	9.99 421	40
21	9.21 076	77	9.21 657	79	0.78 343	9.99 419	39
22	9.21 153	76	9.21 736	78	0.78 264	9.99 417	38
23	9.21 229	77	9.21 814	79	0.78 186	9.99 415	37
24	9.21 306	76	9.21 893	78	0.78 107	9.99 413	36
25	9.21 382	76	9.21 971	78	0.78 029	9.99 411	35
26	9.21 458	76	9.22 049	78	0.77 951	9.99 409	34
27	9.21 534	76	9.22 127	78	0.77 873	9.99 407	33
28	9.21 610	75	9.22 205	78	0.77 795	9.99 404	32
29	9.21 685	76	9.22 283	78	0.77 717	9.99 402	31
30	9.21 761	75	9.22 361	77	0.77 639	9.99 400	30
31	9.21 836	76	9.22 438	78	0.77 562	9.99 398	29
32	9.21 912	75	9.22 516	77	0.77 484	9.99 396	28
33	9.21 987	75	9.22 593	77	0.77 407	9.99 394	27
34	9.22 062	75	9.22 670	77	0.77 330	9.99 392	26
35	9.22 137	74	9.22 747	77	0.77 253	9.99 390	25
36	9.22 211	75	9.22 824	77	0.77 176	9.99 388	24
37	9.22 286	75	9.22 901	76	0.77 099	9.99 385	23
38	9.22 361	74	9.22 977	77	0.77 023	9.99 383	22
39	9.22 435	74	9.23 054	76	0.76 946	9.99 381	21
40	9.22 509	74	9.23 130	76	0.76 870	9.99 379	20
41	9.22 583	74	9.23 206	77	0.76 794	9.99 377	19
42	9.22 657	74	9.23 283	76	0.76 717	9.99 375	18
43	9.22 731	74	9.23 359	76	0.76 641	9.99 372	17
44	9.22 805	73	9.23 435	75	0.76 565	9.99 370	16
45	9.22 878	74	9.23 510	76	0.76 490	9.99 368	15
46	9.22 952	73	9.23 586	75	0.76 414	9.99 366	14
47	9.23 025	73	9.23 661	76	0.76 339	9.99 364	13
48	9.23 098	73	9.23 737	75	0.76 263	9.99 362	12
49	9.23 171	73	9.23 812	75	0.76 188	9.99 359	11
50	9.23 244	73	9.23 887	75	0.76 113	9.99 357	10
51	9.23 317	73	9.23 962	75	0.76 038	9.99 355	9
52	9.23 390	72	9.24 037	75	0.75 963	9.99 353	8
53	9.23 462	73	9.24 112	74	0.75 888	9.99 351	7
54	9.23 535	72	9.24 186	75	0.75 814	9.99 348	6
55	9.23 607	72	9.24 261	74	0.75 739	9.99 346	5
56	9.23 679	73	9.24 335	75	0.75 665	9.99 344	4
57	9.23 752	71	9.24 410	74	0.75 590	9.99 342	3
58	9.23 823	72	9.24 484	74	0.75 516	9.99 340	2
59	9.23 895	72	9.24 558	74	0.75 442	9.99 337	1
60	9.23 967		9.24 632		0.75 368	9.99 335	0
	L Cos	d	L Ctn	c d	L Tan	L Sin	′

Proportional parts

″	80	79	78	77
1	1.3	1.3	1.3	1.3
2	2.7	2.6	2.6	2.6
3	4.0	4.0	3.9	3.8
4	5.3	5.3	5.2	5.1
5	6.7	6.6	6.5	6.4
6	8.0	7.9	7.8	7.7
7	9.3	9.2	9.1	9.0
8	10.7	10.5	10.4	10.3
9	12.0	11.8	11.7	11.6
10	13.3	13.2	13.0	12.8
20	26.7	26.3	26.0	25.7
30	40.0	39.5	39.0	38.5
40	53.3	52.7	52.0	51.3
50	66.7	65.8	65.0	64.2

″	76	75	74	73
1	1.3	1.2	1.2	1.2
2	2.5	2.5	2.5	2.4
3	3.8	3.8	3.7	3.6
4	5.1	5.0	4.9	4.9
5	6.3	6.2	6.2	6.1
6	7.6	7.5	7.4	7.3
7	8.9	8.8	8.6	8.5
8	10.1	10.0	9.9	9.7
9	11.4	11.2	11.1	11.0
10	12.7	12.5	12.3	12.2
20	25.3	25.0	24.7	24.3
30	38.0	37.5	37.0	36.5
40	50.7	50.0	49.3	48.7
50	63.3	62.5	61.7	60.8

″	72	71	3	2
1	1.2	1.2	0.0	0.0
2	2.4	2.4	0.1	0.1
3	3.6	3.6	0.2	0.1
4	4.8	4.7	0.2	0.1
5	6.0	5.9	0.2	0.2
6	7.2	7.1	0.3	0.2
7	8.4	8.3	0.4	0.2
8	9.6	9.5	0.4	0.3
9	10.8	10.6	0.4	0.3
10	12.0	11.8	0.5	0.3
20	24.0	23.7	1.0	0.7
30	36.0	35.5	1.5	1.0
40	48.0	47.3	2.0	1.3
50	60.0	59.2	2.5	1.7

Proportional parts

80°

Table IV   *Page 129*

10°—LOGARITHMS OF TRIGONOMETRIC FUNCTIONS

'	L Sin	d	L Tan	c d	L Ctn	L Cos	d		Proportional parts

'	L Sin	d	L Tan	c d	L Ctn	L Cos	d					
0	9.23 967	72	9.24 632	74	0.75 368	9.99 335	2	60				
1	9.24 039	71	9.24 706	73	0.75 294	9.99 333	2	59				
2	9.24 110	71	9.24 779	74	0.75 221	9.99 331	3	58				
3	9.24 181	72	9.24 853	73	0.75 147	9.99 328	2	57				
4	9.24 253	71	9.24 926	74	0.75 074	9.99 326	2	56				
5	9.24 324	71	9.25 000	73	0.75 000	9.99 324	2	55	''	74	73	72
6	9.24 395	71	9.25 073	73	0.74 927	9.99 322	3	54				
7	9.24 466	70	9.25 146	73	0.74 854	9.99 319	2	53	1	1.2	1.2	1.2
8	9.24 536	71	9.25 219	73	0.74 781	9.99 317	2	52	2	2.5	2.4	2.4
9	9.24 607	70	9.25 292	73	0.74 708	9.99 315	2	51	3	3.7	3.6	3.6
									4	4.9	4.9	4.8
10	9.24 677	71	9.25 365	72	0.74 635	9.99 313	3	50				
11	9.24 748	70	9.25 437	73	0.74 563	9.99 310	2	49	5	6.2	6.1	6.0
12	9.24 818	70	9.25 510	72	0.74 490	9.99 308	2	48	6	7.4	7.3	7.2
13	9.24 888	70	9.25 582	73	0.74 418	9.99 306	2	47	7	8.6	8.5	8.4
14	9.24 958	70	9.25 655	72	0.74 345	9.99 304	3	46	8	9.9	9.7	9.6
									9	11.1	11.0	10.8
15	9.25 028	70	9.25 727	72	0.74 273	9.99 301	2	45				
16	9.25 098	70	9.25 799	72	0.74 201	9.99 299	2	44	10	12.3	12.2	12.0
17	9.25 168	69	9.25 871	72	0.74 129	9.99 297	3	43	20	24.7	24.3	24.0
18	9.25 237	70	9.25 943	72	0.74 057	9.99 294	2	42	30	37.0	36.5	36.0
19	9.25 307	69	9.26 015	71	0.73 985	9.99 292	2	41	40	49.3	48.7	48.0
									50	61.7	60.8	60.0
20	9.25 376	69	9.26 086	72	0.73 914	9.99 290	2	40				
21	9.25 445	69	9.26 158	71	0.73 842	9.99 288	3	39				
22	9.25 514	69	9.26 229	72	0.73 771	9.99 285	2	38				
23	9.25 583	69	9.26 301	71	0.73 699	9.99 283	2	37	''	71	70	69
24	9.25 652	69	6.26 372	71	0.73 628	9.99 281	3	36				
									1	1.2	1.2	1.2
25	9.25 721	69	9.26 443	71	0.73 557	9.99 278	2	35	2	2.4	2.3	2.3
26	9.25 790	68	9.26 514	71	0.73 486	9.99 276	2	34	3	3.6	3.5	3.4
27	9.25 858	69	9.26 585	70	0.73 415	9.99 274	3	33	4	4.7	4.7	4.6
28	9.25 927	68	9.26 655	71	0.73 345	9.99 271	2	32				
29	9.25 995	68	9.26 726	71	0.73 274	9.99 269	2	31	5	5.9	5.8	5.8
									6	7.1	7.0	6.9
30	9.26 063	68	9.26 797	70	0.73 203	9.99 267	3	30	7	8.3	8.2	8.0
31	9.26 131	68	9.26 867	70	0.73 133	9.99 264	2	29	8	9.5	9.3	9.2
32	9.26 199	68	9.26 937	71	0.73 063	9.99 262	2	28	9	10.6	10.5	10.4
33	9.26 267	68	9.27 008	70	0.72 992	9.99 260	3	27				
34	9.26 335	68	9.27 078	70	0.72 922	9.99 257	2	26	10	11.8	11.7	11.5
									20	23.7	23.3	23.0
35	9.26 403	67	9.27 148	70	0.72 852	9.99 255	3	25	30	35.5	35.0	34.5
36	9.26 470	68	9.27 218	70	0.72 782	9.99 252	2	24	40	47.3	46.7	46.0
37	9.26 538	67	9.27 288	69	0.72 712	9.99 250	2	23	50	59.2	58.3	57.5
38	9.26 605	67	9.27 357	70	0.72 643	9.99 248	3	22				
39	9.26 672	67	9.27 427	69	0.72 573	9.99 245	2	21				
40	9.26 739	67	9.27 496	70	0.72 504	9.99 243	2	20	''	68	67	66
41	9.26 806	67	9.27 566	69	0.72 434	9.99 241	3	19				
42	9.26 873	67	9.27 635	69	0.72 365	9.99 238	2	18	1	1.1	1.1	1.1
43	9.26 940	67	9.27 704	69	0.72 296	9.99 236	3	17	2	2.3	2.2	2.2
44	9.27 007	66	9.27 773	69	0.72 227	9.99 233	2	16	3	3.4	3.4	3.3
									4	4.5	4.5	4.4
45	9.27 073	67	9.27 842	69	0.72 158	9.99 231	2	15				
46	9.27 140	66	9.27 911	69	0.72 089	9.99 229	3	14	5	5.7	5.6	5.5
47	9.27 206	67	9.27 980	69	0.72 020	9.99 226	2	13	6	6.8	6.7	6.6
48	9.27 273	66	9.28 049	68	0.71 951	9.99 224	3	12	7	7.9	7.8	7.7
49	9.27 339	66	9.28 117	69	0.71 883	9.99 221	2	11	8	9.1	8.9	8.8
									9	10.2	10.0	9.9
50	9.27 405	66	9.28 186	68	0.71 814	9.99 219	2	10				
51	9.27 471	66	9.28 254	69	0.71 746	9.99 217	3	9	10	11.3	11.2	11.0
52	9.27 537	65	9.28 323	68	0.71 677	9.99 214	2	8	20	22.7	22.3	22.0
53	9.27 602	66	9.28 391	68	0.71 609	9.99 212	3	7	30	34.0	33.5	33.0
54	9.27 668	66	9.28 459	68	0.71 541	9.99 209	2	6	40	45.3	44.7	44.0
									50	56.7	55.8	55.0
55	9.27 734	65	9.28 527	68	0.71 473	9.99 207	3	5				
56	9.27 799	65	9.28 595	67	0.71 405	9.99 204	2	4				
57	9.27 864	66	9.28 662	68	0.71 338	9.99 202	2	3				
58	9.27 930	65	9.28 730	68	0.71 270	9.99 200	3	2				
59	9.27 995	65	9.28 798	67	0.71 202	9.99 197	2	1				
60	9.28 060		9.28 865		0.71 135	9.99 195		0				

| | L Cos | d | L Ctn | c d | L Tan | L Sin | d | ' | | Proportional parts | |

79°

11°—LOGARITHMS OF TRIGONOMETRIC FUNCTIONS

′	L Sin	d	L Tan	c d	L Ctn	L Cos	d		Proportional parts

′	L Sin	d	L Tan	c d	L Ctn	L Cos	d	
0	9.28 060	65	9.28 865	68	0.71 135	9.99 195	3	60
1	9.28 125	65	9.28 933	67	0.71 067	9.99 192	2	59
2	9.28 190	64	9.29 000	67	0.71 000	9.99 190	3	58
3	9.28 254	65	9.29 067	67	0.70 933	9.99 187	2	57
4	9.28 319	65	9.29 134	67	0.70 866	9.99 185	3	56
5	9.28 384	64	9.29 201	67	0.70 799	9.99 182	2	55
6	9.28 448	64	9.29 268	67	0.70 732	9.99 180	3	54
7	9.28 512	65	9.29 335	67	0.70 665	9.99 177	2	53
8	9.28 577	64	9.29 402	66	0.70 598	9.99 175	3	52
9	9.28 641	64	9.29 468	67	0.70 532	9.99 172	2	51
10	9.28 705	64	9.29 535	66	0.70 465	9.99 170	3	50
11	9.28 769	64	9.29 601	67	0.70 399	9.99 167	2	49
12	9.28 833	63	9.29 668	66	0.70 332	9.99 165	3	48
13	9.28 896	64	9.29 734	66	0.70 266	9.99 162	2	47
14	9.28 960	64	9.29 800	66	0.70 200	9.99 160	3	46
15	9.29 024	63	9.29 866	66	0.70 134	9.99 157	2	45
16	9.29 087	63	9.29 932	66	0.70 068	9.99 155	3	44
17	9.29 150	64	9.29 998	66	0.70 002	9.99 152	2	43
18	9.29 214	63	9.30 064	66	0.69 936	9.99 150	3	42
19	9.29 277	63	9.30 130	65	0.69 870	9.99 147	2	41
20	9.29 340	63	9.30 195	66	0.69 805	9.99 145	3	40
21	9.29 403	63	9.30 261	65	0.69 739	9.99 142	2	39
22	9.29 466	63	9.30 326	65	0.69 674	9.99 140	3	38
23	9.29 529	62	9.30 391	66	0.69 609	9.99 137	2	37
24	9.29 591	63	9.30 457	65	0.69 543	9.99 135	3	36
25	9.29 654	62	9.30 522	65	0.69 478	9.99 132	2	35
26	9.29 716	63	9.30 587	65	0.69 413	9.99 130	3	34
27	9.29 779	62	9.30 652	65	0.69 348	9.99 127	3	33
28	9.29 841	62	9.30 717	65	0.69 283	9.99 124	2	32
29	9.29 903	63	9.30 782	64	0.69 218	9.99 122	3	31
30	9.29 966	62	9.30 846	65	0.69 154	9.99 119	2	30
31	9.30 028	62	9.30 911	64	0.69 039	9.99 117	3	29
32	9.30 090	61	9.30 975	65	0.69 025	9.99 114	2	28
33	9.30 151	62	9.31 040	64	0.68 960	9.99 112	3	27
34	9.30 213	62	9.31 104	64	0.68 896	9.99 109	3	26
35	9.30 275	61	9.31 168	65	0.68 832	9.99 106	2	25
36	9.30 336	62	9.31 233	64	0.68 767	9.99 104	3	24
37	9.30 398	61	9.31 297	64	0.68 703	9.99 101	2	23
38	9.30 459	62	9.31 361	64	0.68 639	9.99 099	3	22
39	9.30 521	61	9.31 425	64	0.68 575	9.99 096	3	21
40	9.30 582	61	9.31 489	63	0.68 511	9.99 093	2	20
41	9.30 643	61	9.31 552	64	0.68 448	9.99 091	3	19
42	9.30 704	61	9.31 616	63	0.68 384	9.99 088	2	18
43	9.30 765	61	9.31 679	64	0.68 321	9.99 086	3	17
44	9.30 826	61	9.31 743	63	0.68 257	9.99 083	3	16
45	9.30 887	60	9.31 806	64	0.68 194	9.99 080	2	15
46	9.30 947	61	9.31 870	63	0.68 130	9.99 078	3	14
47	9.31 008	60	9.31 933	63	0.68 067	9.99 075	3	13
48	9.31 068	61	9.31 996	63	0.68 004	9.99 072	2	12
49	9.31 129	60	9.32 059	63	0.67 941	9.99 070	3	11
50	9.31 189	61	9.32 122	63	0.67 878	9.99 067	3	10
51	9.31 250	60	9.32 185	63	0.67 815	9.99 064	2	9
52	9.31 310	60	9.32 248	63	0.67 752	9.99 062	3	8
53	9.31 370	60	9.32 311	62	0.67 689	9.99 059	3	7
54	9.31 430	60	9.32 373	63	0.67 627	9.99 056	2	6
55	9.31 490	59	9.32 436	62	0.67 564	9.99 054	3	5
56	9.31 549	60	9.32 498	63	0.67 502	9.99 051	3	4
57	9.31 609	60	9.32 561	62	0.67 439	9.99 048	2	3
58	9.31 669	59	9.32 623	62	0.67 377	9.99 046	3	2
59	9.31 728	60	9.32 685	62	0.67 315	9.99 043	3	1
60	9.31 788		9.32 747		0.67 253	9.99 040		0

	L Cos	d	L Ctn	c d	L Tan	L Sin	d	′

Proportional parts

″	65	64	63
1	1.1	1.1	1.0
2	2.2	2.1	2.1
3	3.2	3.2	3.2
4	4.3	4.3	4.2
5	5.4	5.3	5.2
6	6.5	6.4	6.3
7	7.6	7.5	7.4
8	8.7	8.5	8.4
9	9.8	9.6	9.4
10	10.8	10.7	10.5
20	21.7	21.3	21.0
30	32.5	32.0	31.5
40	43.3	42.7	42.0
50	54.2	53.3	52.5

″	62	61	60
1	1.0	1.0	1.0
2	2.1	2.0	2.0
3	3.1	3.0	3.0
4	4.1	4.1	4.0
5	5.2	5.1	5.0
6	6.2	6.1	6.0
7	7.2	7.1	7.0
8	8.3	8.1	8.0
9	9.3	9.2	9.0
10	10.3	10.2	10.0
20	20.7	20.3	20.0
30	31.0	30.5	30.0
40	41.3	40.7	40.0
50	51.7	50.8	50.0

″	59	3	2
1	1.0	0.0	0.0
2	2.0	0.1	0.1
3	3.0	0.2	0.1
4	3.9	0.2	0.1
5	4.9	0.2	0.2
6	5.9	0.3	0.2
7	6.9	0.4	0.2
8	7.9	0.4	0.3
9	8.8	0.4	0.3
10	9.8	0.5	0.3
20	19.7	1.0	0.7
30	29.5	1.5	1.0
40	39.3	2.0	1.3
50	49.2	2.5	1.7

Proportional parts

78°

Table IV   *Page 131*

12°—LOGARITHMS OF TRIGONOMETRIC FUNCTIONS

'	L Sin	d	L Tan	c d	L Ctn	L Cos	d	
0	9.31 788	59	9.32 747	63	0.67 253	9.99 040	2	60
1	9.31 847	60	9.32 810	62	0.67 190	9.99 038	3	59
2	9.31 907	59	9.32 872	61	0.67 128	9.99 035	3	58
3	9.31 966	59	9.32 933	62	0.67 067	9.99 032	2	57
4	9.32 025	59	9.32 995	62	0.67 005	9.99 030	3	56
5	9.32 084	59	9.33 057	62	0.66 943	9.99 027	3	55
6	9.32 143	59	9.33 119	61	0.66 881	9.99 024	2	54
7	9.32 202	59	9.33 180	62	0.66 820	9.99 022	3	53
8	9.32 261	58	9.33 242	61	0.66 758	9.99 019	3	52
9	9.32 319	59	9.33 303	62	0.66 697	9.99 016	3	51
10	9.32 378	59	9.33 365	61	0.66 635	9.99 013	2	50
11	9.32 437	58	9.33 426	61	0.66 574	9.99 011	3	49
12	9.32 495	58	9.33 487	61	0.66 513	9.99 008	3	48
13	9.32 553	59	9.33 548	61	0.66 452	9.99 005	3	47
14	9.32 612	58	9.33 609	61	0.66 391	9.99 002	2	46
15	9.32 670	58	9.33 670	61	0.66 330	9.99 000	3	45
16	9.32 728	58	9.33 731	61	0.66 269	9.98 997	3	44
17	9.32 786	58	9.33 792	61	0.66 208	9.98 994	3	43
18	9.32 844	58	9.33 853	60	0.66 147	9.98 991	2	42
19	9.32 902	58	9.33 913	61	0.66 087	9.98 989	3	41
20	9.32 960	58	9.33 974	60	0.66 026	9.98 986	3	40
21	9.33 018	57	9.34 034	61	0.65 966	9.98 983	3	39
22	9.33 075	58	9.34 095	60	0.65 905	9.98 980	2	38
23	9.33 133	57	9.34 155	60	0 65 845	9.98 978	3	37
24	9.33 190	58	9.34 215	61	0.65 785	9.98 975	3	36
25	9.33 248	57	9.34 276	60	0.65 724	9.98 972	3	35
26	9.33 305	57	9.34 336	60	0.65 664	9.98 969	2	34
27	9.33 362	58	9.34 396	60	0.65 604	9.98 967	3	33
28	9.33 420	57	9.34 456	60	0.65 544	9.98 964	3	32
29	9.33 477	57	9.34 516	60	0.65 484	9.98 961	3	31
30	9.33 534	57	9.34 576	59	0.65 424	9.98 958	3	30
31	9.33 591	56	9.34 635	60	0.65 365	9.98 955	2	29
32	9.33 647	57	9.34 695	60	0.65 305	9.98 953	3	28
33	9.33 704	57	9.34 755	59	0.65 245	9.98 950	3	27
34	9.33 761	57	9.34 814	60	0.65 186	9.98 947	3	26
35	9.33 818	56	9.34 874	59	0.65 126	9.98 944	3	25
36	9.33 874	57	9.34 933	59	0.65 067	9.98 941	3	24
37	9.33 931	56	9.34 992	59	0.65 008	9.98 938	2	23
38	9.33 987	56	9.35 051	60	0.64 949	9.98 936	3	22
39	9.34 043	57	9.35 111	59	0.64 889	9.98 933	3	21
40	9.34 100	56	9.35 170	59	0.64 830	9.98 930	3	20
41	9.34 156	56	9.35 229	59	0.64 771	9.98 927	3	19
42	9.34 212	56	9.35 288	59	0.64 712	9.98 924	3	18
43	9.34 268	56	9.35 347	58	0.64 653	9.98 921	2	17
44	9.34 324	56	9.35 405	59	0.64 595	9.98 919	3	16
45	9.34 380	56	9.35 464	59	0.64 535	9.98 916	3	15
46	9.34 436	55	9.35 523	58	0.64 477	9.98 913	3	14
47	9.34 491	56	9.35 581	59	0.64 419	9.98 910	3	13
48	9.34 547	55	9.35 640	58	0.64 360	9.98 907	3	12
49	9.34 602	56	9.35 698	59	0.64 302	9.98 904	3	11
50	9.34 658	55	9.35 757	58	0.64 243	9.98 901	3	10
51	9.34 713	56	9.35 815	58	0.64 185	9.98 898	2	9
52	9.34 769	55	9.35 873	58	0.64 127	9.98 896	3	8
53	9.34 824	55	9.35 931	58	0.64 069	9.98 893	3	7
54	9.34 879	55	9.35 989	58	0.64 011	9.98 890	3	6
55	9.34 934	55	9.36 047	58	0.63 953	9.98 887	3	5
56	9.34 989	55	9.36 105	58	0.63 895	9.98 884	3	4
57	9.35 044	55	9.36 163	58	0.63 837	9.98 881	3	3
58	9.35 099	55	9.36 221	58	0.63 779	9.98 878	3	2
59	9.35 154	55	9.36 279	57	0.63 721	9.98 875	3	1
60	9.35 209		9.36 336		0.63 664	9.98 872		0
	L Cos	d	L Ctn	c d	L Tan	L Sin	d	'

Proportional parts

''	63	62	61
1	1.0	1.0	1.0
2	2.1	2.1	2.0
3	3.2	3.1	3.0
4	4.2	4.1	4.1
5	5.2	5.2	5.1
6	6.3	6.2	6.1
7	7.4	7.2	7.1
8	8.4	8.3	8.1
9	9.4	9.3	9.2
10	10.5	10.3	10.2
20	21.0	20.7	20.3
30	31.5	31.0	30.5
40	42.0	41.3	40.7
50	52.5	51.7	50.8

''	60	59	58
1	1.0	1.0	1.0
2	2.0	2.0	1.9
3	3.0	3.0	2.9
4	4.0	3.9	3.9
5	5.0	4.9	4.8
6	6.0	5.9	5.8
7	7.0	6.9	6.8
8	8.0	7.9	7.7
9	9.0	8.8	8.7
10	10.0	9.8	9.7
20	20.0	19.7	19.3
30	30.0	29.5	29.0
40	40.0	39.3	38.7
50	50.0	49.2	48.3

''	57	56	55
1	1.0	0.9	0.9
2	1.9	1.9	1.8
3	2.8	2.8	2.8
4	3.8	3.7	3.7
5	4.8	4.7	4.6
6	5.7	5.6	5.5
7	6.6	6.5	6.4
8	7.6	7.5	7.3
9	8.6	8.4	8.2
10	9.5	9.3	9.2
20	19.0	18.7	18.3
30	28.5	28.0	27.5
40	38.0	37.3	36.7
50	47.5	46.7	45.8

Proportional parts

77°

13°—LOGARITHMS OF TRIGONOMETRIC FUNCTIONS

′	L Sin	d	L Tan	c d	L Ctn	L Cos	d		Proportional parts
0	9.35 209	54	9.36 336	58	0.63 664	9.98 872	3	60	
1	9.35 263	55	9.36 394	58	0.63 606	9.98 869	2	59	
2	9.35 318	55	9.36 452	57	0.63 548	9.98 867	3	58	
3	9.35 373	54	9.36 509	57	0.63 491	9.98 864	3	57	
4	9.35 427	54	9.36 566	58	0.63 434	9.98 861	3	56	

′	L Sin	d	L Tan	c d	L Ctn	L Cos	d				
5	9.35 481	55	9.36 624	57	0.63 376	9.98 858	3	55	″	57	56	55
6	9.35 536	54	9.36 681	57	0.63 319	9.98 855	3	54	1	1.0	0.9	0.9
7	9.35 590	54	9.36 738	57	0.63 262	9.98 852	3	53	2	1.9	1.9	1.8
8	9.35 644	54	9.36 795	57	0.63 205	9.98 849	3	52	3	2.8	2.8	2.8
9	9.35 698	54	9.36 852	57	0.63 148	9.98 846	3	51	4	3.8	3.7	3.7
10	9.35 752	54	9.36 909	57	0.63 091	9.98 843	3	50	5	4.8	4.7	4.6
11	9.35 806	54	9.36 966	57	0.63 034	9.98 840	3	49	6	5.7	5.6	5.5
12	9.35 860	54	9.37 023	57	0.62 977	9.98 837	3	48	7	6.6	6.5	6.4
13	9.35 914	54	9.37 080	57	0.62 920	9.98 834	3	47	8	7.6	7.5	7.3
14	9.35 968	54	9.37 137	56	0.62 863	9.98 831	3	46	9	8.6	8.4	8.2
15	9.36 022	53	9.37 193	57	0.62 807	9.98 828	3	45	10	9.5	9.3	9.2
16	9.36 075	54	9.37 250	56	0.62 750	9.98 825	3	44	20	19.0	18.7	18.3
17	9.36 129	53	9.37 306	57	0.62 694	9.98 822	3	43	30	28.5	28.0	27.5
18	9.36 182	54	9.37 363	56	0.62 637	9.98 819	3	42	40	38.0	37.3	36.7
19	9.36 236	53	9.37 419	57	0.62 581	9.98 816	3	41	50	47.5	46.7	45.8
20	9.36 289	53	9.37 476	56	0.62 524	9.98 813	3	40				
21	9.36 342	53	9.37 532	56	0.62 468	9.98 810	3	39				
22	9.36 395	54	9.37 588	56	0.62 412	9.98 807	3	38	″	54	53	52
23	9.36 449	53	9.37 644	56	0.62 356	9.98 804	3	37	1	0.9	0.9	0.9
24	9.36 502	53	9.37 700	56	0.62 300	9.98 801	3	36	2	1.8	1.8	1.7
25	9.36 555	53	9.37 756	56	0.62 244	9.98 798	3	35	3	2.7	2.6	2.6
26	9.36 608	52	9.37 812	56	0.62 188	9.98 795	3	34	4	3.6	3.5	3.5
27	9.36 660	53	9.37 868	56	0.62 132	9.98 792	3	33				
28	9.36 713	53	9.37 924	56	0.62 076	9.98 789	3	32	5	4.5	4.4	4.3
29	9.36 766	53	9.37 980	55	0.62 020	9.98 786	3	31	6	5.4	5.3	5.2
30	9.36 819	52	9.38 035	56	0.61 965	9.98 783	3	30	7	6.3	6.2	6.1
31	9.36 871	53	9.38 091	56	0.61 909	9.98 780	3	29	8	7.2	7.1	6.9
32	9.36 924	52	9.38 147	55	0.61 853	9.98 777	3	28	9	8.1	8.0	7.8
33	9.36 976	52	9.38 202	55	0.61 798	9.98 774	3	27	10	9.0	8.8	8.7
34	9.37 028	53	9.38 257	56	0.61 743	9.98 771	3	26	20	18.0	17.7	17.3
35	9.37 081	52	9.38 313	55	0.61 687	9.98 768	3	25	30	27.0	26.5	26.0
36	9.37 133	52	9.38 368	55	0.61 632	9.98 765	3	24	40	36.0	35.3	34.7
37	9.37 185	52	9.38 423	56	0.61 577	9.98 762	3	23	50	45.0	44.2	43.3
38	9.37 237	52	9.38 479	55	0.61 521	9.98 759	3	22				
39	9.37 289	52	9.38 534	55	0.61 466	9.98 756	3	21	″	51	4	3	2
40	9.37 341	52	9.38 589	55	0.61 411	9.98 753	3	20	1	0.8	0.1	0.0	0.0
41	9.37 393	52	9.38 644	55	0.61 356	9.98 750	4	19	2	1.7	0.1	0.1	0.1
42	9.37 445	52	9.38 699	55	0.61 301	9.98 746	3	18	3	2.6	0.2	0.2	0.1
43	9.37 497	52	9.38 754	54	0.61 246	9.98 743	3	17	4	3.4	0.3	0.2	0.1
44	9.37 549	51	9.38 808	55	0.61 192	9.98 740	3	16					
									5	4.2	0.3	0.2	0.2
45	9.37 600	52	9.38 863	55	0.61 137	9.98 737	3	15	6	5.1	0.4	0.3	0.2
46	9.37 652	51	9.38 918	55	0.61 082	9.98 734	3	14	7	6.0	0.5	0.4	0.2
47	9.37 703	52	9.38 972	55	0.61 028	9.98 731	3	13	8	6.8	0.5	0.4	0.3
48	9.37 755	51	9.39 027	55	0.60 973	9.98 728	3	12	9	7.6	0.6	0.4	0.3
49	9.37 806	52	9.39 082	54	0.60 918	9.98 725	3	11					
									10	8.5	0.7	0.5	0.3
50	9.37 858	51	9.39 136	54	0.60 864	9.98 722	3	10	20	17.0	1.3	1.0	0.7
51	9.37 909	51	9.39 190	55	0.60 810	9.98 719	4	9	30	25.5	2.0	1.5	1.0
52	9.37 960	51	9.39 245	54	0.60 755	9.98 715	3	8	40	34.0	2.7	2.0	1.3
53	9.38 011	51	9.39 299	54	0.60 701	9.98 712	3	7	50	42.5	3.3	2.5	1.7
54	9.38 062	51	9.39 353	54	0.60 647	9.98 709	3	6					
55	9.38 113	51	9.39 407	54	0.60 593	9.98 706	3	5				
56	9.38 164	51	9.39 461	54	0.60 539	9.98 703	3	4				
57	9.38 215	51	9.39 515	54	0.60 485	9.98 700	3	3				
58	9.38 266	51	9.39 569	54	0.60 431	9.98 697	3	2				
59	9.38 317	51	9.39 623	54	0.60 377	9.98 694	4	1				
60	9.38 368		9.39 677		0.60 323	9.98 690		0				

	L Cos	d	L Ctn	c d	L Tan	L Sin	d	′	Proportional parts

Table IV   Page 133

14°—LOGARITHMS OF TRIGONOMETRIC FUNCTIONS

'	L Sin	d	L Tan	c d	L Ctn	L Cos	d		Proportional parts
0	9.38 368		9.39 677		0.60 323	9.98 690	3	60	
1	9.38 418	50	9.39 731	54	0.60 269	9.98 687	3	59	
2	9.38 469	51	9.39 785	54	0.60 215	9.98 684	3	58	
3	9.38 519	50	9.39 838	53	0.60 162	9.98 681	3	57	
4	9.38 570	51	9.39 892	54	0.60 108	9.98 678	3	56	
		50		53			3		

'	L Sin	d	L Tan	c d	L Ctn	L Cos	d					
5	9.38 620	50	9.39 945	54	0.60 055	9.98 675	4	55				
6	9.38 670	51	9.39 999	53	0.60 001	9.98 671	3	54				
7	9.38 721	50	9.40 052	54	0.59 948	9.98 668	3	53	''	54	53	52
8	9.38 771	50	9.40 106	53	0.59 894	9.98 665	3	52				
9	9.38 821	50	9.40 159	53	0.59 841	9.98 662	3	51	1	0.9	0.9	0.9
									2	1.8	1.8	1.7
10	9.38 871	50	9.40 212	54	0.59 788	9.98 659	3	50	3	2.7	2.6	2.6
11	9.38 921	50	9.40 266	53	0.59 734	9.98 656	4	49	4	3.6	3.5	3.5
12	9.38 971	50	9.40 319	53	0.59 681	9.98 652	3	48				
13	9.39 021	50	9.40 372	53	0.59 628	9.98 649	3	47	5	4.5	4.4	4.3
14	9.39 071	50	9.40 425	53	0.59 575	9.98 646	3	46	6	5.4	5.3	5.2
									7	6.3	6.2	6.1
15	9.39 121	49	9.40 478	53	0.59 522	9.98 643	3	45	8	7.2	7.1	6.9
16	9.39 170	50	9.40 531	53	0.59 469	9.98 640	4	44	9	8.1	8.0	7.8
17	9.39 220	50	9.40 584	52	0.59 416	9.98 636	3	43				
18	9.39 270	49	9.40 636	53	0.59 364	9.98 633	3	42	10	9.0	8.8	8.7
19	9.39 319	50	9.40 689	53	0.59 311	9.98 630	3	41	20	18.0	17.7	17.3
									30	27.0	26.5	26.0
20	9.39 369	49	9.40 742	53	0.59 258	9.98 627	3	40	40	36.0	35.3	34.7
21	9.39 418	49	9.40 795	52	0.59 205	9.98 623	3	39	50	45.0	44.2	43.3
22	9.39 467	50	9.40 347	53	0.59 153	9.98 620	3	38				
23	9.39 517	49	9.40 900	52	0.59 100	9.98 617	3	37	''	51	50	49
24	9.39 566	49	9.40 952	53	0.59 048	9.98 614	4	36				
									1	0.8	0.8	0.8
25	9.39 615	49	9.41 005	52	0.58 995	9.98 610	3	35	2	1.7	1.7	1.6
26	9.39 664	49	9.41 057	52	0.58 943	9.98 607	3	34	3	2.6	2.5	2.4
27	9.39 713	49	9.41 109	52	0.58 891	9.98 604	3	33	4	3.4	3.3	3.3
28	9.39 762	49	9.41 161	53	0.58 839	9.98 601	4	32				
29	9.39 811	49	9.41 214	52	0.58 786	9.98 597	3	31	5	4.2	4.2	4.1
									6	5.1	5.0	4.9
30	9.39 860	49	9.41 266	52	0.58 734	9.98 594	3	30	7	6.0	5.8	5.7
31	9.39 909	49	9.41 318	52	0.58 682	9.98 591	3	29	8	6.8	6.7	6.5
32	9.39 958	48	9.41 370	52	0.58 630	9.98 588	4	23	9	7.6	7.5	7.4
33	9.40 006	49	9.41 422	52	0.58 578	9.98 584	3	27				
34	9.40 055	48	9.41 474	52	0.58 526	9.98 581	3	26	10	8.5	8.3	8.2
									20	17.0	16.7	16.3
35	9.40 103	49	9.41 526	52	0.58 474	9.98 578	4	25	30	25.5	25.0	24.5
36	9.40 152	48	9.41 578	51	0.58 422	9.98 574	3	24	40	34.0	33.3	32.7
37	9.40 200	49	9.41 629	52	0.58 371	9.98 571	3	23	50	42.5	41.7	40.8
38	9.40 249	48	9.41 681	52	0.58 319	9.98 568	3	22				
39	9.40 297	49	9.41 733	51	0.58 267	9.98 565	4	21				
									''	48	47	4	3
40	9.40 346	48	9.41 784	52	0.58 216	9.98 561	3	20				
41	9.40 394	48	9.41 836	51	0.58 164	9.98 558	3	19	1	0.8	0.8	0.1	0.0
42	9.40 442	48	9.41 887	52	0.58 113	9.98 555	4	18	2	1.6	1.6	0.1	0.1
43	9.40 490	48	9.41 939	51	0.58 061	9.98 551	3	17	3	2.4	2.4	0.2	0.2
44	9.40 538	48	9.41 990	51	0.58 010	9.98 548	3	16	4	3.2	3.1	0.3	0.2
45	9.40 586	48	9.42 041	52	0.57 959	9.98 545	4	15	5	4.0	3.9	0.3	0.2
46	9.40 634	48	9.42 093	51	0.57 907	9.98 541	3	14	6	4.8	4.7	0.4	0.3
47	9.40 682	48	9.42 144	51	0.57 856	9.98 538	3	13	7	5.6	5.5	0.5	0.4
48	9.40 730	48	9.42 195	51	0.57 805	9.98 535	4	12	8	6.4	6.3	0.5	0.4
49	9.40 778	47	9.42 246	51	0.57 754	9.98 531	3	11	9	7.2	7.0	0.6	0.4
50	9.40 825	48	9.42 297	51	0.57 703	9.98 528	3	10	10	8.0	7.8	0.7	0.5
51	9.40 873	48	9.42 348	51	0.57 652	9.98 525	4	9	20	16.0	15.7	1.3	1.0
52	9.40 921	47	9.42 399	51	0.57 601	9.98 521	3	8	30	24.0	23.5	2.0	1.5
53	9.40 968	48	9.42 450	51	0.57 550	9.98 518	3	7	40	32.0	31.3	2.7	2.0
54	9.41 016	47	9.42 501	51	0.57 499	9.98 515	4	6	50	40.0	39.2	3.3	2.5
55	9.41 063	48	9.42 552	51	0.57 448	9.98 511	3	5				
56	9.41 111	47	9.42 603	50	0.57 397	9.98 508	3	4				
57	9.41 158	47	9.42 653	51	0.57 347	9.98 505	4	3				
58	9.41 205	47	9.42 704	51	0.57 296	9.98 501	3	2				
59	9.41 252	48	9.42 755	50	0.57 245	9.98 498	4	1				
60	9.41 300		9.42 805		0.57 195	9.98 494		0				
	L Cos	d	L Ctn	c d	L Tan	L Sin	d	'	Proportional parts			

75°

15°—LOGARITHMS OF TRIGONOMETRIC FUNCTIONS

′	L Sin	d	L Tan	c d	L Ctn	L Cos	d		Proportional parts			
0	9.41 300	47	9.42 805	51	0.57 195	9.98 494	3	60				
1	9.41 347	47	9.42 856	50	0.57 144	9.98 491	3	59				
2	9.41 394	47	9.42 906	51	0.57 094	9.98 488	4	58				
3	9.41 441	47	9.42 957	50	0.57 043	9.98 484	3	57				
4	9.41 488	47	9.43 007	50	0.56 993	9.98 481	4	56				
5	9.41 535	47	9.43 057	51	0.56 943	9.98 477	3	55				
6	9.41 582	46	9.43 108	50	0.56 892	9.98 474	3	54	″	51	50	49
7	9.41 628	47	9.43 158	50	0.56 842	9.98 471	3	53				
8	9.41 675	47	9.43 208	50	0.56 792	9.98 467	3	52	1	0.8	0.8	0.8
9	9.41 722	46	9.43 258	50	0.56 742	9.96 464	4	51	2	1.7	1.7	1.6
10	9.41 768	47	9.43 308	50	0.56 692	9.98 460	3	50	3	2.6	2.5	2.4
11	9.41 815	46	9.43 358	50	0.56 642	9.98 457	4	49	4	3.4	3.3	3.3
12	9.41 861	47	9.43 408	50	0.56 592	9.98 453	3	48				
13	9.41 908	46	9.43 458	50	0.56 542	9.98 450	3	47	5	4.2	4.2	4.1
14	9.41 954	47	9.43 508	50	0.56 492	9.98 447	4	46	6	5.1	5.0	4.9
15	9.42 001	46	9.43 558	49	0.56 442	9.98 443	3	45	7	6.0	5.8	5.7
16	9.42 047	46	9.43 607	50	0.56 393	9.98 440	4	44	8	6.8	6.7	6.5
17	9.42 093	47	9.43 657	50	0.56 343	9.98 436	3	43	9	7.6	7.5	7.4
18	9.42 140	46	9.43 707	49	0.56 293	9.98 433	4	42				
19	9.42 186	46	9.43 756	50	0.56 244	9.98 429	3	41	10	8.5	8.3	8.2
20	9.42 232	46	9.43 806	49	0.56 194	9.98 426	4	40	20	17.0	16.7	16.3
21	9.42 278	46	9.43 855	50	0.56 145	9.98 422	3	39	30	25.5	25.0	24.5
22	9.42 324	46	9.43 905	49	0.56 095	9.98 419	4	38	40	34.0	33.3	32.7
23	9.42 370	46	9.43 954	50	0.56 046	9.98 415	3	37	50	42.5	41.7	40.8
24	9.42 416	45	9.44 004	49	0.55 996	9.98 412	3	36				
25	9.42 461	46	9.44 053	49	0.55 947	9.98 409	4	35	″	48	47	46
26	9.42 507	46	9.44 102	49	0.55 898	9.98 405	3	34	1	0.8	0.8	0.8
27	9.42 553	46	9.44 151	50	0.55 849	9.98 402	4	33	2	1.6	1.6	1.5
28	9.42 599	45	9.44 201	49	0.55 799	9.98 398	3	32	3	2.4	2.4	2.3
29	9.42 644	46	9.44 250	49	0.55 750	9.98 395	4	31	4	3.2	3.1	3.1
30	9.42 690	45	9.44 299	49	0.55 701	9.98 391	3	30	5	4.0	3.9	3.8
31	9.42 735	46	9.44 348	49	0.55 652	9.98 388	4	29	6	4.8	4.7	4.6
32	9.42 781	45	9.44 397	49	0.55 603	9.98 384	3	28	7	5.6	5.5	5.4
33	9.42 826	46	9.44 446	49	0.55 554	9.98 381	4	27	8	6.4	6.3	6.1
34	9.42 872	45	9.44 495	49	0.55 505	9.98 377	4	26	9	7.2	7.0	6.9
35	9.42 917	45	9.44 544	48	0.55 456	9.98 373	3	25	10	8.0	7.8	7.7
36	9.42 962	46	9.44 592	49	0.55 408	9.98 370	4	24	20	16.0	15.7	15.3
37	9.43 008	45	9.44 641	49	0.55 359	9.98 366	3	23	30	24.0	23.5	23.0
38	9.43 053	45	9.44 690	49	0.55 310	9.98 363	4	22	40	32.0	31.3	30.7
39	9.43 098	45	9.44 738	49	0.55 262	9.98 359	3	21	50	40.0	39.2	38.3
40	9.43 143	45	9.44 787	49	0.55 213	9.98 356	4	20	″	45	44	4	3
41	9.43 188	45	9.44 836	48	0.55 164	9.98 352	3	19					
42	9.43 233	45	9.44 884	49	0.55 116	9.98 349	4	18	1	0.8	0.7	0.1	0.0
43	9.43 278	45	9.44 933	48	0.55 067	9.98 345	3	17	2	1.5	1.5	0.1	0.1
44	9.43 323	44	9.44 981	48	0.55 019	9.98 342	4	16	3	2.2	2.2	0.2	0.2
45	9.43 367	45	9.45 029	49	0.54 971	9.98 338	4	15	4	3.0	2.9	0.3	0.2
46	9.43 412	45	9.45 078	48	0.54 922	9.98 334	3	14	5	3.8	3.7	0.3	0.2
47	9.43 457	45	9.45 126	48	0.54 874	9.98 331	4	13	6	4.5	4.4	0.4	0.3
48	9.43 502	44	9.45 174	48	0.54 826	9.98 327	3	12	7	5.2	5.1	0.5	0.4
49	9.43 546	45	9.45 222	49	0.54 778	9.98 324	4	11	8	6.0	5.9	0.5	0.4
50	9.43 591	44	9.45 271	48	0.54 729	9.98 320	3	10	9	6.8	6.6	0.6	0.4
51	9.43 635	45	9.45 319	48	0.54 681	9.98 317	4	9	10	7.5	7.3	0.7	0.5
52	9.43 680	44	9.45 367	48	0.54 633	9.98 313	4	8	20	15.0	14.7	1.3	1.0
53	9.43 724	45	9.45 415	48	0.54 585	9.98 309	3	7	30	22.5	22.0	2.0	1.5
54	9.43 769	44	9.45 463	48	0.54 537	9.98 306	4	6	40	30.0	29.3	2.7	2.0
55	9.43 813	44	9.45 511	48	0.54 489	9.98 302	3	5	50	37.5	36.7	3.3	2.5
56	9.43 857	44	9.45 559	47	0.54 441	9.98 299	4	4					
57	9.43 901	45	9.45 606	48	0.54 394	9.98 295	4	3					
58	9.43 946	44	9.45 654	48	0.54 346	9.98 291	3	2					
59	9.43 990	44	9.45 702	48	0.54 298	9.98 288	4	1					
60	9.44 034		9.45 750		0.54 250	9.98 284		0					
′′	L Cos	d	L Ctn	c d	L Tan	L Sin	d	′		Proportional parts		

Table IV   *Page 135*

16°—LOGARITHMS OF TRIGONOMETRIC FUNCTIONS

′	L Sin	d	L Tan	c d	L Ctn	L Cos	d	
0	9.44 034	44	9.45 750	47	0.54 250	9.98 284	3	60
1	9.44 078	44	9.45 797	48	0.54 203	9.98 281	4	59
2	9.44 122	44	9.45 845	47	0.54 155	9.98 277	4	58
3	9.44 166	44	9.45 892	48	0.54 108	9.98 273	3	57
4	9.44 210	43	9.45 940	47	0.54 060	9.98 270	4	56
5	9.44 253	44	9.45 987	48	0.54 013	9.98 266	4	55
6	9.44 297	44	9.46 035	47	0.53 965	9.98 262	3	54
7	9.44 341	44	9.46 082	48	0.53 918	9.98 259	4	53
8	9.44 385	43	9.46 130	47	0.53 870	9.98 255	4	52
9	9.44 428	44	9.46 177	47	0.53 823	9.98 251	3	51
10	9.44 472	44	9.46 224	47	0.53 776	9.98 248	4	50
11	9.44 516	43	9.46 271	48	0.53 729	9.98 244	4	49
12	9.44 559	43	9.46 319	47	0.53 681	9.98 240	3	48
13	9.44 602	44	9.46 366	47	0.53 634	9.98 237	4	47
14	9.44 646	43	9.46 413	47	0.53 587	9.98 233	4	46
15	9.44 689	44	9.46 460	47	0.53 540	9.98 229	3	45
16	9.44 733	43	9.46 507	47	0.53 493	9.98 226	4	44
17	9.44 776	43	9.46 554	47	0.53 446	9.98 222	4	43
18	9.44 819	43	9.46 601	47	0.53 399	9.98 218	3	42
19	9.44 862	43	9.46 648	46	0.53 352	9.98 215	4	41
20	9.44 905	43	9.46 694	47	0.53 306	9.98 211	4	40
21	9.44 948	44	9.46 741	47	0.53 259	9.98 207	3	39
22	9.44 992	43	9.46 788	47	0.53 212	9.98 204	4	38
23	9.45 035	42	9.46 835	46	0.53 165	9.98 200	4	37
24	9.45 077	43	9.46 881	47	0.53 119	9.98 196	4	36
25	9.45 120	43	9.46 928	47	0.53 072	9.98 192	3	35
26	9.45 163	43	9.46 975	46	0.53 025	9.98 189	4	34
27	9.45 206	43	9.47 021	47	0.52 979	9.98 185	4	33
28	9.45 249	43	9.47 068	46	0.52 932	9.98 181	4	32
29	9.45 292	42	9.47 114	46	0.52 886	9.98 177	3	31
30	9.45 334	43	9.47 160	47	0.52 840	9.98 174	4	30
31	9.45 377	42	9.47 207	46	0.52 793	9.98 170	4	29
32	9.45 419	43	9.47 253	46	0.52 747	9.98 166	4	28
33	9.45 462	42	9.47 299	47	0.52 701	9.98 162	3	27
34	9.45 504	43	9.47 346	46	0.52 654	9.98 159	4	26
35	9.45 547	42	9.47 392	46	0.52 608	9.98 155	4	25
36	9.45 589	43	9.47 438	46	0.52 562	9.98 151	4	24
37	9.45 632	42	9.47 484	46	0.52 516	9.98 147	3	23
38	9.45 674	42	9.47 530	46	0.52 470	9.98 144	4	22
39	9.45 716	42	9.47 576	46	0.52 424	9.98 140	4	21
40	9.45 758	43	9.47 622	46	0.52 378	9.98 136	4	20
41	9.45 801	42	9.47 668	46	0.52 332	9.98 132	3	19
42	9.45 843	42	9.47 714	46	0.52 286	9.98 129	4	18
43	9.45 885	42	9.47 760	46	0.52 240	9.98 125	4	17
44	9.45 927	42	9.47 806	46	0.52 194	9.98 121	4	16
45	9.45 969	42	9.47 852	45	0.52 148	9.98 117	4	15
46	9.46 011	42	9.47 897	46	0.52 103	9.98 113	3	14
47	9.46 053	42	9.47 943	46	0.52 057	9.98 110	4	13
48	9.46 095	41	9.47 989	46	0.52 011	9.98 106	4	12
49	9.46 136	42	9.48 035	45	0.51 965	9.98 102	4	11
50	9.46 178	42	9.48 080	46	0.51 920	9.98 098	4	10
51	9.46 220	42	9.48 126	45	0.51 874	9.98 094	4	9
52	9.46 262	41	9.48 171	46	0.51 829	9.98 090	3	8
53	9.46 303	42	9.48 217	45	0.51 783	9.98 087	4	7
54	9.46 345	41	9.48 262	45	0.51 738	9.98 083	4	6
55	9.46 386	42	9.48 307	46	0.51 693	9.98 079	4	5
56	9.46 428	41	9.48 353	45	0.51 647	9.98 075	4	4
57	9.46 469	42	9.48 398	45	0.51 602	9.98 071	4	3
58	9.46 511	41	9.48 443	46	0.51 557	9.98 067	4	2
59	9.46 552	42	9.48 489	45	0.51 511	9.98 063	3	1
60	9.46 594		9.48 534		0.51 466	9.98 060		0
	L Cos	d	L Ctn	c d	L Tan	L Sin	d	′

Proportional parts

′′	48	47	46
1	0.8	0.8	0.8
2	1.6	1.6	1.5
3	2.4	2.4	2.3
4	3.2	3.1	3.1
5	4.0	3.9	3.8
6	4.8	4.7	4.6
7	5.6	5.5	5.4
8	6.4	6.3	6.1
9	7.2	7.0	6.9
10	8.0	7.8	7.7
20	16.0	15.7	15.3
30	24.0	23.5	23.0
40	32.0	31.3	30.7
50	40.0	39.2	38.3

′′	45	44	43
1	0.8	0.7	0.7
2	1.5	1.5	1.4
3	2.2	2.2	2.2
4	3.0	2.9	2.9
5	3.8	3.7	3.6
6	4.5	4.4	4.3
7	5.2	5.1	5.0
8	6.0	5.9	5.7
9	6.8	6.6	6.4
10	7.5	7.3	7.2
20	15.0	14.7	14.3
30	22.5	22.0	21.5
40	30.0	29.3	28.7
50	37.5	36.7	35.8

′′	42	41	4	3
1	0.7	0.7	0.1	0.0
2	1.4	1.4	0.1	0.1
3	2.1	2.0	0.2	0.2
4	2.8	2.7	0.3	0.2
5	3.5	3.4	0.3	0.2
6	4.2	4.1	0.4	0.3
7	4.9	4.8	0.5	0.4
8	5.6	5.5	0.5	0.4
9	6.3	6.2	0.6	0.4
10	7 0	6.8	0.7	0.5
20	14.0	13.7	1.3	1.0
30	21.0	20.5	2.0	1.5
40	28.0	27.3	2.7	2.0
50	35.0	34.2	3.3	2.5

17°—LOGARITHMS OF TRIGONOMETRIC FUNCTIONS

′	L Sin	d	L Tan	c d	L Ctn	L Cos	d		Proportional parts			
0	9.46 594	41	9.48 534	45	0.51 466	9.98 060	4	60				
1	9.46 635	41	9.48 579	45	0.51 421	9.98 056	4	59				
2	9.46 676	41	9.48 624	45	0.51 376	9.98 052	4	58				
3	9.46 717	41	9.48 669	45	0.51 331	9.98 048	4	57				
4	9.46 758	42	9.48 714	45	0.51 286	9.98 044	4	56				
5	9.46 800	41	9.48 759	45	0.51 241	9.98 040	4	55	″	45	44	43
6	9.46 841	41	9.48 804	45	0.51 196	9.98 036	4	54				
7	9.46 882	41	9.48 849	45	0.51 151	9.98 032	4	53	1	0.8	0.7	0.7
8	9.46 923	41	9.48 894	45	0.51 106	9.98 029	3	52	2	1.5	1.5	1.4
9	9.46 964	41	9.48 939	45	0.51 061	9.98 025	4	51	3	2.2	2.2	2.2
									4	3.0	2.9	2.9
10	9.47 005	40	9.48 984	45	0.51 016	9.98 021	4	50				
11	9.47 045	41	9.49 029	44	0.50 971	9.98 017	4	49	5	3.8	3.7	3.6
12	9.47 086	41	9.49 073	45	0.50 927	9.98 013	4	48	6	4.5	4.4	4.3
13	9.47 127	41	9.49 118	45	0.50 882	9.98 009	4	47	7	5.2	5.1	5.0
14	9.47 168	41	9.49 163	44	0.50 837	9.98 005	4	46	8	6.0	5.9	5.7
									9	6.8	6.6	6.4
15	9.47 209	40	9.49 207	45	0.50 793	9.98 001	4	45				
16	9.47 249	41	9.49 252	44	0.50 748	9.97 997	4	44	10	7.5	7.3	7.2
17	9.47 290	40	9.49 296	45	0.50 704	9.97 993	4	43	20	15.0	14.7	14.3
18	9.47 330	41	9.49 341	44	0.50 659	9.97 989	3	42	30	22.5	22.0	21.5
19	9.47 371	40	9.49 385	45	0.50 615	9.97 986	4	41	40	30.0	29.3	28.7
									50	37.5	36.7	35.8
20	9.47 411	41	9.49 430	44	0.50 570	9.97 982	4	40				
21	9.47 452	40	9.49 474	45	0.50 526	9.97 978	4	39				
22	9.47 492	41	9.49 519	44	0.50 481	9.97 974	4	38				
23	9.47 533	40	9.49 563	44	0.50 437	9.97 970	4	37	″	42	41	40
24	9.47 573	40	9.49 607	45	0.50 393	9.97 966	4	36				
									1	0.7	0.7	0.7
25	9.47 613	41	9.49 652	44	0.50 348	9.97 962	4	35	2	1.4	1.4	1.3
26	9.47 654	40	9.49 696	44	0.50 304	9.97 958	4	34	3	2.1	2.0	2.0
27	9.47 694	40	9.49 740	44	0.50 260	9.97 954	4	33	4	2.8	2.7	2.7
28	9.47 734	40	9.49 784	44	0.50 216	9.97 950	4	32				
29	9.47 774	40	9.49 828	44	0.50 172	9.97 946	4	31	5	3.5	3.4	3.3
									6	4.2	4.1	4.0
30	9.47 814	40	9.49 872	44	0.50 128	9.97 942	4	30	7	4.9	4.8	4.7
31	9.47 854	40	9.49 916	44	0.50 084	9.97 938	4	29	8	5.6	5.5	5.3
32	9.47 894	40	9.49 960	44	0.50 040	9.97 934	4	28	9	6.3	6.2	6.0
33	9.47 934	40	9.50 004	44	0.49 996	9.97 930	4	27				
34	9.47 974	40	9.50 048	44	0.49 952	9.97 926	4	26	10	7.0	6.8	6.7
									20	14.0	13.7	13.3
35	9.48 014	40	9.50 092	44	0.49 908	9.97 922	4	25	30	21.0	20.5	20.0
36	9.48 054	40	9.50 136	44	0.49 864	9.97 918	4	24	40	28.0	27.3	26.7
37	9.48 094	39	9.50 180	43	0.49 820	9.97 914	4	23	50	35.0	34.2	33.3
38	9.48 133	40	9.50 223	44	0.49 777	9.97 910	4	22				
39	9.48 173	40	9.50 267	44	0.49 733	9.97 906	4	21				
40	9.48 213	39	9.50 311	44	0.49 689	9.97 902	4	20	″	39	5	4	3
41	9.48 252	40	9.50 355	43	0.49 645	9.97 898	4	19				
42	9.48 292	40	9.50 398	44	0.49 602	9.97 894	4	18	1	0.6	0.1	0.1	0.0
43	9.48 332	39	9.50 442	43	0.49 558	9.97 890	4	17	2	1.3	0.2	0.1	0.1
44	9.48 371	40	9.50 485	44	0.49 515	9.97 886	4	16	3	2.0	0.2	0.2	0.2
									4	2.6	0.3	0.3	0.2
45	9.48 411	39	9.50 529	43	0.49 471	9.97 882	4	15				
46	9.48 450	40	9.50 572	44	0.49 428	9.97 878	4	14	5	3.2	0.4	0.3	0.2
47	9.48 490	39	9.50 616	43	0.49 384	9.97 874	4	13	6	3.9	0.5	0.4	0.3
48	9.48 529	39	9.50 659	44	0.49 341	9.97 870	4	12	7	4.6	0.6	0.5	0.4
49	9.48 568	39	9.50 703	43	0.49 297	9.97 866	5	11	8	5.2	0.7	0.5	0.4
									9	5.8	0.8	0.6	0.4
50	9.48 607	40	9.50 746	43	0.49 254	9.97 861	4	10				
51	9.48 647	39	9.50 789	44	0.49 211	9.97 857	4	9	10	6.5	0.8	0.7	0.5
52	9.48 686	39	9.50 833	43	0.49 167	9.97 853	4	8	20	13.0	1.7	1.3	1.0
53	9.48 725	39	9.50 876	43	0.49 124	9.97 849	4	7	30	19.5	2.5	2.0	1.5
54	9.48 764	39	9.50 919	43	0.49 081	9.97 845	4	6	40	26.0	3.3	2.7	2.0
									50	32.5	4.2	3.3	2.5
55	9.48 803	39	9.50 962	43	0.49 038	9.97 841	4	5				
56	9.48 842	39	9.51 005	43	0.48 995	9.97 837	4	4				
57	9.48 881	39	9.51 048	44	0.48 952	9.97 833	4	3				
58	9.48 920	39	9.51 092	43	0.48 908	9.97 829	4	2				
59	9.48 959	39	9.51 135	43	0.48 865	9.97 825	4	1				
60	9.48 998		9.51 178		0.48 822	9.97 821		0				
	L Cos	d	L Ctn	c d	L Tan	L Sin	d	′		Proportional parts		

72°

Table IV　　　　　　　　　　　　　　　　　　　　　　*Page 137*

18°—LOGARITHMS OF TRIGONOMETRIC FUNCTIONS

′	L Sin	d	L Tan	c d	L Ctn	L Cos	d		Proportional parts			
0	9.48 998	39	9.51 178	43	0.48 822	9.97 821	4	60				
1	9.49 037	39	9.51 221	43	0.48 779	9.97 817	5	59				
2	9.49 076	39	9.51 264	42	0.48 736	9.97 812	4	58				
3	9.49 115	38	9.51 306	43	0.48 694	9.97 808	4	57				
4	9.49 153	39	9.51 349	43	0.48 651	9.97 804	4	56				
5	9.49 192	39	9.51 392	43	0.48 608	9.97 800	4	55				
6	9.49 231	38	9.51 435	43	0.48 565	9.97 796	4	54	′′	43	42	41
7	9.49 269	39	9.51 478	42	0.48 522	9.97 792	4	53				
8	9.49 308	39	9.51 520	43	0.48 480	9.97 788	4	52	1	0.7	0.7	0.7
9	9.49 347	38	9.51 563	43	0.48 437	9.97 784	5	51	2	1.4	1.4	1.4
									3	2.2	2.1	2.0
10	9.49 385	39	9.51 606	42	0.48 394	9.97 779	4	50	4	2.9	2.8	2.7
11	9.49 424	38	9.51 648	43	0.48 352	9.97 775	4	49				
12	9.49 462	38	9.51 691	43	0.48 309	9.97 771	4	48	5	3.6	3.5	3.4
13	9.49 500	39	9.51 734	42	0.48 266	9.97 767	4	47	6	4.3	4.2	4.1
14	9.49 539	38	9.51 776	43	0.48 224	9.97 763	4	46	7	5.0	4.9	4.8
									8	5.7	5.6	5.5
15	9.49 577	38	9.51 819	42	0.48 181	9.97 759	5	45	9	6.4	6.3	6.2
16	9.49 615	39	9.51 861	42	0.48 139	9.97 754	4	44				
17	9.49 654	38	9.51 903	43	0.48 097	9.97 750	4	43	10	7.2	7.0	6.8
18	9.49 692	38	9.51 946	42	0.48 054	9.97 746	4	42	20	14.3	14.0	13.7
19	9.49 730	38	9.51 988	43	0.48 012	9.97 742	4	41	30	21.5	21.0	20.5
									40	28.7	28.0	27.3
20	9.49 768	38	9.52 031	42	0.47 969	9.97 738	4	40	50	35.8	35.0	34.2
21	9.49 806	38	9.52 073	42	0.47 927	9.97 734	5	39				
22	9.49 844	38	9.52 115	42	0.47 885	9.97 729	4	38				
23	9.49 882	38	9.52 157	43	0.47 843	9.97 725	4	37	′′	39	38	37
24	9.49 920	38	9.52 200	42	0.47 800	9.97 721	4	36				
									1	0.6	0.6	0.6
25	9.49 958	38	9.52 242	42	0.47 758	9.97 717	4	35	2	1.3	1.3	1.2
26	9.49 996	38	9.52 284	42	0.47 716	9.97 713	5	34	3	2.0	1.9	1.8
27	9.50 034	38	9.52 326	42	0.47 674	9.97 708	4	33	4	2.6	2.5	2.5
28	9.50 072	38	9.52 368	42	0.47 632	9.97 704	4	32				
29	9.50 110	38	9.52 410	42	0.47 590	9.97 700	4	31	5	3.2	3.2	3.1
									6	3.9	3.8	3.7
30	9.50 148	37	9.52 452	42	0.47 548	9.97 696	5	30	7	4.6	4.4	4.3
31	9.50 185	38	9.52 494	42	0.47 506	9.97 691	4	29	8	5.2	5.1	4.9
32	9.50 223	38	9.52 536	42	0.47 464	9.97 687	4	28	9	5.8	5.7	5.6
33	9.50 261	37	9.52 578	42	0.47 422	9.97 683	4	27				
34	9.50 298	38	9.52 620	41	0.47 380	9.97 679	5	26	10	6.5	6.3	6.2
									20	13.0	12.7	12.3
35	9.50 336	38	9.52 661	42	0.47 339	9.97 674	4	25	30	19.5	19.0	18.5
36	9.50 374	37	9.52 703	42	0.47 297	9.97 670	4	24	40	26.0	25.3	24.7
37	9.50 411	38	9.52 745	42	0.47 255	9.97 666	4	23	50	32.5	31.7	30.8
38	9.50 449	37	9.52 787	42	0.47 213	9.97 662	5	22				
39	9.50 486	37	9.52 829	41	0.47 171	9.97 657	4	21				
									′′	36	5	4
40	9.50 523	38	9.52 870	42	0.47 130	9.97 653	4	20				
41	9.50 561	37	9.52 912	41	0.47 088	9.97 649	4	19	1	0.6	0.1	0.1
42	9.50 598	37	9.52 953	42	0.47 047	9.97 645	4	18	2	1.2	0.2	0.1
43	9.50 635	38	9.52 995	42	0.47 005	9.97 640	4	17	3	1.8	0.2	0.2
44	9.50 673	37	9.53 037	41	0.46 963	9.97 636	4	16	4	2.4	0.3	0.3
45	9.50 710	37	9.53 078	42	0.46 922	9.97 632	4	15	5	3.0	0.4	0.3
46	9.50 747	37	9.53 120	41	0.46 880	9.97 628	5	14	6	3.6	0.5	0.4
47	9.50 784	37	9.53 161	41	0.46 839	9.97 623	4	13	7	4.2	0.6	0.5
48	9.50 821	37	9.53 202	42	0.46 798	9.97 619	4	12	8	4.8	0.7	0.5
49	9.50 858	38	9.53 244	41	0.46 756	9.97 615	5	11	9	5.4	0.8	0.6
50	9.50 896	37	9.53 285	42	0.46 715	9.97 610	4	10	10	6.0	0.8	0.7
51	9.50 933	37	9.53 327	41	0.46 673	9.97 606	4	9	20	12.0	1.7	1.3
52	9.50 970	37	9.53 368	41	0.46 632	9.97 602	5	8	30	18.0	2.5	2.0
53	9.51 007	36	9.53 409	41	0.46 591	9.97 597	4	7	40	24.0	3.3	2.7
54	9.51 043	37	9.53 450	42	0.46 550	9.97 593	4	6	50	30.0	4.2	3.3
55	9.51 080	37	9.53 492	41	0.46 508	9.97 589	5	5				
56	9.51 117	37	9.53 533	41	0.46 467	9.97 584	4	4				
57	9.51 154	37	9.53 574	41	0.46 426	9.97 580	4	3				
58	9.51 191	36	9.53 615	41	0.46 385	9.97 576	5	2				
59	9.51 227	37	9.53 656	41	0.46 344	9.97 571	4	1				
60	9.51 264		9.53 697		0.46 303	9.97 567		0				
	L Cos	d	L Ctn	c d	L Tan	L Sin	d	′	Proportional parts			

71°

19°—LOGARITHMS OF TRIGONOMETRIC FUNCTIONS

'	L Sin	d	L Tan	c d	L Ctn	L Cos	d	
0	9.51 264	37	9.53 697	41	0.46 303	9.97 567	4	60
1	9.51 301	37	9.53 738	41	0.46 262	9.97 563	5	59
2	9.51 338	36	9.53 779	41	0.46 221	9.97 558	4	58
3	9.51 374	37	9.53 820	41	0.46 180	9.97 554	4	57
4	9.51 411	36	9.53 861	41	0.46 139	9.97 550	4	56
5	9.51 447	37	9.53 902	41	0.46 098	9.97 545	4	55
6	9.51 484	36	9.53 943	41	0.46 057	9.97 541	5	54
7	9.51 520	37	9.53 984	41	0.46 016	9.97 536	4	53
8	9.51 557	36	9.54 025	41	0.45 975	9.97 532	4	52
9	9.51 593	36	9.54 065	40	0.45 935	9.97 528	5	51
10	9.51 629	37	9.54 106	41	0.45 894	9.97 523	4	50
11	9.51 666	36	9.54 147	40	0.45 853	9.97 519	4	49
12	9.51 702	36	9.54 187	41	0.45 813	9.97 515	5	48
13	9.51 738	36	9.54 228	41	0.45 772	9.97 510	4	47
14	9.51 774	37	9.54 269	40	0.45 731	9.97 506	5	46
15	9.51 811	36	9.54 309	41	0.45 691	9.97 501	4	45
16	9.51 847	36	9.54 350	40	0.45 650	9.97 497	5	44
17	9.51 883	36	9.54 390	41	0.45 610	9.97 492	4	43
18	9.51 919	36	9.54 431	40	0.45 569	9.97 488	4	42
19	9 51 955	36	9.54 471	41	0.45 529	9.97 484	5	41
20	9.51 991	36	9.54 512	40	0.45 488	9.97 479	4	40
21	9.52 027	36	9.54 552	41	0.45 448	9.97 475	5	39
22	9.52 063	36	9.54 593	40	0.45 407	9.97 470	4	38
23	9.52 099	36	9.54 633	40	0.45 367	9.97 466	5	37
24	9.52 135	36	9.54 673	41	0.45 327	9.97 461	5	36
25	9.52 171	36	9.54 714	40	0.45 286	9.97 457	4	35
26	9.52 207	35	9.54 754	40	0.45 246	9.97 453	5	34
27	9.52 242	36	9.54 794	41	0.45 206	9.97 448	4	33
28	9.52 278	36	9.54 835	40	0.45 165	9.97 444	5	32
29	9.52 314	36	9.54 875	40	0.45 125	9.97 439	4	31
30	9.52 350	35	9.54 915	40	0.45 085	9.97 435	5	30
31	9.52 385	36	9.54 955	40	0.45 045	9.97 430	4	29
32	9.52 421	35	9.54 995	40	0.45 005	9.97 426	5	28
33	9.52 456	36	9.55 035	40	0.44 965	9.97 421	4	27
34	9.52 492	35	9.55 075	40	0.44 925	9.97 417	4	26
35	9.52 527	36	9.55 115	40	0.44 885	9.97 412	4	25
36	9.52 563	35	9.55 155	40	0.44 845	9.97 408	5	24
37	9.52 598	36	9.55 195	40	0.44 805	9.97 403	4	23
38	9.52 634	35	9.55 235	40	0.44 765	9.97 399	5	22
39	9.52 669	36	9.55 275	40	0.44 725	9.97 394	4	21
40	9.52 705	35	9.55 315	40	0.44 685	9.97 390	5	20
41	9.52 740	35	9.55 355	40	0.44 645	9.97 385	4	19
42	9.52 775	36	9.55 395	39	0.44 605	9.97 381	5	18
43	9.52 811	35	9.55 434	40	0.44 566	9.97 376	4	17
44	9.52 846	35	9.55 474	40	0.44 526	9.97 372	5	16
45	9.52 881	35	9.55 514	40	0.44 486	9.97 367	4	15
46	9.52 916	35	9.55 554	39	0.44 446	9.97 363	5	14
47	9.52 951	35	9.55 593	40	0.44 407	9.97 358	5	13
48	9.52 986	35	9.55 633	40	0.44 367	9.97 353	4	12
49	9.53 021	35	9.55 673	39	0.44 327	9.97 349	5	11
50	9.53 056	36	9.55 712	40	0.44 288	9.97 344	4	10
51	9.53 092	34	9.55 752	39	0.44 248	9.97 340	5	9
52	9.53 126	35	9.55 791	40	0.44 209	9.97 335	4	8
53	9.53 161	35	9.55 831	39	0.44 169	9.97 331	5	7
54	9.53 196	35	9.55 870	40	0.44 130	9.97 326	4	6
55	9.53 231	35	9.55 910	39	0.44 090	9.97 322	5	5
56	9.53 266	35	9.55 949	40	0.44 051	9.97 317	5	4
57	9.53 301	35	9.55 989	39	0.44 011	9.97 312	4	3
58	9.53 336	34	9.56 028	39	0.43 972	9.97 308	5	2
59	9.53 370	35	9.56 067	40	0.43 933	9.97 303	4	1
60	9.53 405		9.56 107		0.43 893	9.97 299		0
	L Cos	d	L Ctn	c d	L Tan	L Sin	d	'

Proportional parts

''	41	40	39
1	0.7	0.7	0.6
2	1.4	1.3	1.3
3	2.0	2.0	2.0
4	2.7	2.7	2.6
5	3.4	3.3	3.2
6	4.1	4.0	3.9
7	4.8	4.7	4.6
8	5.5	5.3	5.2
9	6.2	6.0	5.8
10	6.8	6.7	6.5
20	13.7	13.3	13.0
30	20.5	20.0	19.5
40	27.3	26.7	26.0
50	34.2	33.3	32.5

''	37	36	35
1	0.6	0.6	0.6
2	1.2	1.2	1.2
3	1.8	1.8	1.8
4	2.5	2.4	2.3
5	3.1	3.0	2.9
6	3.7	3.6	3.5
7	4.3	4.2	4.1
8	4.9	4.8	4.7
9	5 6	5.4	5.2
10	6..	6.0	5.8
20	12.3	12.0	11.7
30	18.5	18.0	17.5
40	24.7	24 0	23.3
50	30.8	30.0	29.2

''	34	5	4
1	0.6	0.1	0.1
2	1.1	0.2	0.1
3	1.7	0.2	0.2
4	2.3	0.3	0.3
5	2.8	0.4	0.3
6	3.4	0.5	0.4
7	4.0	0.6	0.5
8	4.5	0.7	0.5
9	5.1	0.8	0.6
10	5.7	0.8	0.7
20	11.3	1.7	1.3
30	17.0	2.5	2.0
40	22.7	3.3	2.7
50	28.3	4.2	3.3

Proportional parts

70°

Table IV   Page 139

20°—LOGARITHMS OF TRIGONOMETRIC FUNCTIONS

'	L Sin	d	L Tan	c d	L Ctn	L Cos	d	
0	9.53 405	35	9.56 107	39	0.43 893	9.97 299	5	60
1	9.53 440	35	9.56 146	39	0.43 854	9.97 294	5	59
2	9.53 475	34	9.56 185	39	0.43 815	9.97 289	4	58
3	9.53 509	35	9.56 224	40	0.43 776	9.97 285	5	57
4	9.53 544	34	9.56 264	39	0.43 736	9.97 280	4	56
5	9.53 578	35	9.56 303	39	0.43 697	9.97 276	5	55
6	9.53 613	34	9.56 342	39	0.43 658	9.97 271	5	54
7	9.53 647	35	9.56 381	39	0.43 619	9.97 266	4	53
8	9.53 682	34	9.56 420	39	0.43 580	9.97 262	5	52
9	9.53 716	35	9.56 459	39	0.43 541	9.97 257	5	51
10	9.53 751	34	9.56 498	39	0.43 502	9.97 252	4	50
11	9.53 785	34	9.56 537	39	0.43 463	9.97 248	5	49
12	9.53 819	35	9.56 576	39	0.43 424	9.97 243	5	48
13	9.53 854	34	9.56 615	39	0.43 385	9.97 238	4	47
14	9.53 888	34	9.56 654	39	0.43 346	9.97 234	5	46
15	9.53 922	35	9.56 693	39	0.43 307	9.97 229	5	45
16	9.53 957	34	9.56 732	39	0.43 268	9.97 224	4	44
17	9.53 991	34	9.56 771	39	0.43 229	9.97 220	5	43
18	9.54 025	34	9.56 810	39	0.43 190	9.97 215	5	42
19	9.54 059	34	9.56 849	38	0.43 151	9.97 210	4	41
20	9.54 093	34	9.56 887	39	0.43 113	9.97 206	5	40
21	9.54 127	34	9.56 926	39	0.43 074	9.97 201	5	39
22	9.54 161	34	9.56 965	39	0.43 035	9.97 196	4	38
23	9.54 195	34	9.57 004	38	0.42 996	9.97 192	5	37
24	9.54 229	34	9.57 042	39	0.42 958	9.97 187	5	36
25	9.54 263	34	9.57 081	39	0.42 919	9.97 182	4	35
26	9.54 297	34	9.57 120	38	0.42 880	9.97 178	5	34
27	9.54 331	34	9.57 158	39	0.42 842	9.97 173	5	33
28	9.54 365	34	9.57 197	38	0.42 803	9.97 168	5	32
29	9.54 399	34	9.57 235	39	0.42 765	9.97 163	4	31
30	9.54 433	33	9.57 274	38	0.42 726	9.97 159	5	30
31	9.54 466	34	9.57 312	39	0.42 688	9.97 154	5	29
32	9.54 500	34	9.57 351	38	0.42 649	9.97 149	4	28
33	9.54 534	33	9.57 389	39	0.42 611	9.97 145	5	27
34	9.54 567	34	9.57 428	38	0.42 572	9.97 140	5	26
35	9.54 601	34	9.57 466	38	0.42 534	9.97 135	5	25
36	9.54 635	34	9.57 504	39	0.42 496	9.97 130	4	24
37	9.54 668	33	9.57 543	38	0.42 457	9.97 126	5	23
38	9.54 702	34	9.57 581	38	0.42 419	9.97 121	5	22
39	9.54 735	34	9.57 619	39	0.42 381	9.97 116	5	21
40	9.54 769	33	9.57 658	38	0.42 342	9.97 111	4	20
41	9.54 802	34	9.57 696	38	0.42 304	9.97 107	5	19
42	9.54 836	33	9.57 734	38	0.42 266	9.97 102	5	18
43	9.54 869	34	9.57 772	38	0.42 228	9.97 097	5	17
44	9.54 903	33	9.57 810	39	0.42 190	9.97 092	5	16
45	9.54 936	33	9.57 849	38	0.42 151	9.97 087	4	15
46	9.54 969	34	9.57 887	38	0.42 113	9.97 083	5	14
47	9.55 003	33	9.57 925	38	0.42 075	9.97 078	5	13
48	9.55 036	33	9.57 963	38	0.42 037	9.97 073	5	12
49	9.55 069	33	9.58 001	38	0.41 999	9.97 068	5	11
50	9.55 102	34	9.58 039	38	0.41 961	9.97 063	4	10
51	9.55 136	33	9.58 077	38	0.41 923	9.97 059	5	9
52	9.55 169	33	9.58 115	38	0.41 885	9.97 054	5	8
53	9.55 202	33	9.58 153	38	0.41 847	9.97 049	5	7
54	9.55 235	33	9.58 191	38	0.41 809	9.97 044	5	6
55	9.55 268	33	9.58 229	38	0.41 771	9.97 039	4	5
56	9.55 301	33	9.58 267	37	0.41 733	9.97 035	5	4
57	9.55 334	33	9.58 304	38	0.41 696	9.97 030	5	3
58	9.55 367	33	9.58 342	38	0.41 658	9.97 025	5	2
59	9.55 400	33	9.58 380	38	0.41 620	9.97 020	5	1
60	9.55 433		9.58 418		0.41 582	9.97 015		0
	L Cos	d	L Ctn	c d	L Tan	L Sin	d	'

Proportional parts

''	40	39	38
1	0.7	0.6	0.6
2	1.3	1.3	1.3
3	2.0	2.0	1.9
4	2.7	2.6	2.5
5	3.3	3.2	3.2
6	4.0	3.9	3.8
7	4.7	4.6	4.4
8	5.3	5.2	5.1
9	6.0	5.8	5.7
10	6.7	6.5	6.3
20	13.3	13.0	12.7
30	20.0	19.5	19.0
40	26.7	26.0	25.3
50	33.3	32.5	31.7

''	37	35	34
1	0.6	0.6	0.6
2	1.2	1.2	1.1
3	1.8	1.8	1.7
4	2.5	2.3	2.3
5	3.1	2.9	2.8
6	3.7	3.5	3.4
7	4.3	4.1	4.0
8	4.9	4.7	4.5
9	5.6	5.2	5.1
10	6.2	5.8	5.7
20	12.3	11.7	11.3
30	18.5	17.5	17.0
40	24.7	23.3	22.7
50	30.8	29.2	28.3

''	33	5	4
1	0.6	0.1	0.1
2	1.1	0.2	0.1
3	1.6	0.2	0.2
4	2.2	0.3	0.3
5	2.8	0.4	0.3
6	3.3	0.5	0.4
7	3.8	0.6	0.5
8	4.4	0.7	0.5
9	5.0	0.8	0.6
10	5.5	0.8	0.7
20	11.0	1.7	1.3
30	16.5	2.5	2.0
40	22.0	3.3	2.7
50	27.5	4.2	3.3

Proportional parts

21°—LOGARITHMS OF TRIGONOMETRIC FUNCTIONS

′	L Sin	d	L Tan	c d	L Ctn	L Cos	d		Proportional parts		
0	9.55 433	33	9.58 418	37	0.41 582	9.97 015	5	60			
1	9.55 466	33	9.58 455	38	0.41 545	9.97 010	5	59			
2	9.55 499	33	9.58 493	38	0.41 507	9.97 005	4	58			
3	9.55 532	32	9.58 531	38	0.41 469	9.97 001	5	57			
4	9.55 564	33	9.58 569	37	0.41 431	9.96 996	5	56			
									″	38	37	36
5	9.55 597	33	9.58 606	38	0.41 394	9.96 991	5	55				
6	9.55 630	33	9.58 644	37	0.41 356	9.96 986	5	54	1	0.6	0.6	0.6
7	9.55 663	32	9.58 681	38	0.41 319	9.96 981	5	53	2	1.3	1.2	1.2
8	9.55 695	33	9.58 719	38	0.41 281	9.96 976	5	52	3	1.9	1.8	1.8
9	9.55 728	33	9.58 757	37	0.41 243	9.96 971	5	51	4	2.5	2.5	2.4
10	9.55 761	32	9.58 794	38	0.41 206	9.96 966	4	50	5	3.2	3.1	3.0
11	9.55 793	33	9.58 832	37	0.41 168	9.96 962	5	49	6	3.8	3.7	3.6
12	9.55 826	32	9.58 869	38	0.41 131	9.96 957	5	48	7	4.4	4.3	4.2
13	9.55 858	33	9.58 907	37	0.41 093	9.96 952	5	47	8	5.1	4.9	4.8
14	9.55 891	32	9.58 944	37	0.41 056	9.96 947	5	46	9	5.7	5.6	5.4
15	9.55 923	33	9.58 981	38	0.41 019	9.96 942	5	45				
16	9.55 956	32	9.59 019	37	0.40 981	9.96 937	5	44	10	6.3	6.2	6.0
17	9.55 988	33	9.59 056	38	0.40 944	9.96 932	5	43	20	12.7	12.3	12.0
18	9.56 021	32	9.59 094	37	0.40 906	9.96 927	5	42	30	19.0	18.5	18.0
19	9.56 053	32	9.59 131	37	0.40 869	9.96 922	5	41	40	25.3	24.7	24.0
									50	31.7	30.8	30.0
20	9.56 085	33	9.59 168	37	0.40 832	9.96 917	5	40				
21	9.56 118	32	9.59 205	38	0.40 795	9.96 912	5	39				
22	9.56 150	32	9.59 243	37	0.40 757	9.96 907	4	38				
23	9.56 182	33	9.59 280	37	0.40 720	9.96 903	5	37	″	33	32	31
24	9.56 215	32	9.59 317	37	0.40 683	9.96 898	5	36				
									1	0.6	0.5	0.5
25	9.56 247	32	9.59 354	37	0.40 646	9.96 893	5	35	2	1.1	1.1	1.0
26	9.56 279	32	9.59 391	38	0.40 609	9.96 888	5	34	3	1.6	1.6	1.6
27	9.56 311	32	9.59 429	37	0.40 571	9.96 883	5	33	4	2.2	2.1	2.1
28	9.56 343	32	9.59 466	37	0.40 534	9.96 878	5	32				
29	9.56 375	33	9.59 503	37	0.40 497	9.96 873	5	31	5	2.8	2.7	2.6
									6	3.3	3.2	3.1
30	9.56 408	32	9.59 540	37	0.40 460	9.96 868	5	30	7	3.8	3.7	3.6
31	9.56 440	32	9.59 577	37	0.40 423	9.96 863	5	29	8	4.4	4.3	4.1
32	9.56 472	32	9.59 614	37	0.40 386	9.96 858	5	28	9	5.0	4.8	4.6
33	9.56 504	32	9.59 651	37	0.40 349	9.96 853	5	27				
34	9.56 536	32	9.59 688	37	0.40 312	9.96 848	5	26	10	5.5	5.3	5.2
									20	11.0	10.7	10.3
35	9.56 568	31	9.59 725	37	0.40 275	9.96 843	5	25	30	16.5	16.0	15.5
36	9.56 599	32	9.59 762	37	0.40 238	9.96 838	5	24	40	22.0	21.3	20.7
37	9.56 631	32	9.59 799	36	0.40 201	9.96 833	5	23	50	27.5	26.7	25.8
38	9.56 663	32	9.59 835	37	0.40 165	9.96 828	5	22				
39	9.56 695	32	9.59 872	37	0.40 128	9.96 823	5	21				
40	9.56 727	32	9.59 909	37	0.40 091	9.96 818	5	20	″	6	5	4
41	9.56 759	31	9.59 946	37	0.40 054	9.96 813	5	19				
42	9.56 790	32	9.59 983	36	0.40 017	9.96 808	5	18	1	0.1	0.1	0.1
43	9.56 822	32	9.60 019	37	0.39 981	9.96 803	5	17	2	0.2	0.2	0.1
44	9.56 854	32	9.60 056	37	0.39 944	9.96 798	5	16	3	0.3	0.2	0.2
									4	0.4	0.3	0.3
45	9.56 886	31	9.60 093	37	0.39 907	9.96 793	5	15	5	0.5	0.4	0.3
46	9.56 917	32	9.60 130	36	0.39 870	9.96 788	5	14	6	0.6	0.5	0.4
47	9.56 949	31	9.60 166	37	0.39 834	9.96 783	5	13	7	0.7	0.6	0.5
48	9.56 980	32	9.60 203	37	0.39 797	9.96 778	6	12	8	0.8	0.7	0.5
49	9.57 012	32	9.60 240	36	0.39 760	9.96 772	5	11	9	0.9	0.8	0.6
50	9.57 044	31	9.60 276	37	0.39 724	9.96 767	5	10				
51	9.57 075	32	9.60 313	36	0.39 687	9.96 762	5	9	10	1.0	0.8	0.7
52	9.57 107	31	9.60 349	37	0.39 651	9.96 757	5	8	20	2.0	1.7	1.3
53	9.57 138	31	9.60 386	36	0.39 614	9.96 752	5	7	30	3.0	2.5	2.0
54	9.57 169	32	9.60 422	37	0.39 578	9.96 747	5	6	40	4.0	3.3	2.7
									50	5.0	4.2	3.3
55	9.57 201	31	9.60 459	36	0.39 541	9.96 742	5	5				
56	9.57 232	32	9.60 495	37	0.39 505	9.96 737	5	4				
57	9.57 264	31	9.60 532	36	0.39 468	9.96 732	5	3				
58	9.57 295	31	9.60 568	37	0.39 432	9.96 727	5	2				
59	9.57 326	32	9.60 605	36	0.39 395	9.96 722	5	1				
60	9.57 358		9.60 641		0.39 359	9.96 717		0				
	L Cos	d	L Ctn	c d	L Tan	L Sin	d	′	Proportional parts		

68°

Table IV   Page 141

22°—LOGARITHMS OF TRIGONOMETRIC FUNCTIONS

′	L Sin	d	L Tan	c d	L Ctn	L Cos	d		Proportional parts		
0	9.57 358	31	9.60 641	36	0.39 359	9.96 717	6	60			
1	9.57 389	31	9.60 677	37	0.39 323	9.96 711	5	59			
2	9.57 420	31	9.60 714	36	0.39 286	9.96 706	5	58			
3	9.57 451	31	9.60 750	36	0.39 250	9.96 701	5	57			
4	9.57 482	32	9.60 786	37	0.39 214	9.96 696	5	56			
									″	37	36	35
5	9.57 514	31	9.60 823	36	0.39 177	9.96 691	5	55				
6	9.57 545	31	9.60 859	36	0.39 141	9.96 686	5	54	1	0.6	0.6	0.6
7	9.57 576	31	9.60 895	36	0.39 105	9.96 681	5	53	2	1.2	1.2	1.2
8	9.57 607	31	9.60 931	36	0.39 069	9.96 676	6	52	3	1.8	1.8	1.8
9	9.57 638	31	9.60 967	37	0.39 033	9.96 670	5	51	4	2.5	2.4	2.3
10	9.57 669	31	9.61 004	36	0.38 996	9.96 665	5	50	5	3.1	3.0	2.9
11	9.57 700	31	9.61 040	36	0.38 960	9.96 660	5	49	6	3.7	3.6	3.5
12	9.57 731	31	9.61 076	36	0.38 924	9.96 655	5	48	7	4.3	4.2	4.1
13	9.57 762	31	9.61 112	36	0.38 888	9.96 650	5	47	8	4.9	4.8	4.7
14	9.57 793	31	9.61 148	36	0.38 852	9.96 645	5	46	9	5.6	5.4	5.2
15	9.57 824	31	9.61 184	36	0.38 816	9.96 640	6	45	10	6.2	6.0	5.8
16	9.57 855	30	9.61 220	36	0.38 780	9.96 634	5	44	20	12.3	12.0	11.7
17	9.57 885	31	9.61 256	36	0.38 744	9.96 629	5	43	30	18.5	18.0	17.5
18	9.57 916	31	9.61 292	36	0.38 708	9.96 624	5	42	40	24.7	24.0	23.3
19	9.57 947	31	9.61 328	36	0.38 672	9.96 619	5	41	50	30.8	30.0	29.2
20	9.57 978	30	9.61 364	36	0.38 636	9.96 614	6	40				
21	9.58 008	31	9.61 400	36	0.38 600	9.96 608	5	39				
22	9.58 039	31	9.61 436	36	0.38 564	9.96 603	5	38				
23	9.58 070	31	9.61 472	36	0.38 528	9.96 598	5	37	″	32	31	30
24	9.58 101	30	9.61 508	36	0.38 492	9.96 593	5	36	1	0.5	0.5	0.5
25	9.58 131	31	9.61 544	35	0.38 456	9.96 588	6	35	2	1.1	1.0	1.0
26	9.58 162	30	9.61 579	36	0.38 421	9.96 582	5	34	3	1.6	1.6	1.5
27	9.58 192	31	9.61 615	36	0.38 385	9.96 577	5	33	4	2.1	2.1	2.0
28	9.58 223	30	9.61 651	36	0.38 349	9.96 572	5	32				
29	9.58 253	31	9.61 687	35	0.38 313	9.96 567	5	31	5	2.7	2.6	2.5
									6	3.2	3.1	3.0
30	9.58 284	30	9.61 722	36	0.38 278	9.96 562	6	30	7	3.7	3.6	3.5
31	9.58 314	31	9.61 758	36	0.38 242	9.96 556	5	29	8	4.3	4.1	4.0
32	9.58 345	30	9.61 794	36	0.38 206	9.96 551	5	28	9	4.8	4.6	4.5
33	9.58 375	31	9.61 830	35	0.38 170	9.96 546	5	27				
34	9.58 406	30	9.61 865	36	0.38 135	9.96 541	6	26	10	5.3	5.2	5.0
									20	10.7	10.3	10.0
35	9.58 436	31	9.61 901	35	0.38 099	9.96 535	5	25	30	16.0	15.5	15.0
36	9.58 467	30	9.61 936	36	0.38 064	9.96 530	5	24	40	21.3	20.7	20.0
37	9.58 497	30	9.61 972	36	0.38 028	9.96 525	5	23	50	26.7	25.8	25.0
38	9.58 527	30	9.62 008	35	0.37 992	9.96 520	6	22				
39	9.58 557	31	9.62 043	36	0.37 957	9.96 514	5	21				
40	9.58 588	30	9.62 079	35	0.37 921	9.96 509	5	20	″	29	6	5
41	9.58 618	30	9.62 114	36	0.37 886	9.96 504	6	19				
42	9.58 648	30	9.62 150	35	0.37 850	9.96 498	5	18	1	0.5	0.1	0.1
43	9.58 678	31	9.62 185	36	0.37 815	9.96 493	5	17	2	1.0	0.2	0.2
44	9.58 709	30	9.62 221	35	0.37 779	9.96 488	5	16	3	1.4	0.3	0.2
									4	1.9	0.4	0.3
45	9.58 739	30	9.62 256	36	0.37 744	9.96 483	6	15				
46	9.58 769	30	9.62 292	35	0.37 708	9.96 477	5	14	5	2.4	0.5	0.4
47	9.58 799	30	9.62 327	35	0.37 673	9.96 472	5	13	6	2.9	0.6	0.5
48	9.58 829	30	9.62 362	36	0.37 638	9.96 467	6	12	7	3.4	0.7	0.6
49	9.58 859	30	9.62 398	35	0.37 602	9.96 461	5	11	8	3.9	0.8	0.7
									9	4.4	0.9	0.8
50	9.58 889	30	9.62 433	35	0.37 567	9.96 456	5	10				
51	9.58 919	30	9.62 468	36	0.37 532	9.96 451	6	9	10	4.8	1.0	0.8
52	9.58 949	30	9.62 504	35	0.37 496	9.96 445	5	8	20	9.7	2.0	1.7
53	9.58 979	30	9.62 539	35	0.37 461	9.96 440	5	7	30	14.5	3.0	2.5
54	9.59 009	30	9.62 574	35	0.37 426	9.96 435	6	6	40	19.3	4.0	3.3
									50	24.2	5.0	4.2
55	9.59 039	30	9.62 609	36	0.37 391	9.96 429	5	5				
56	9.59 069	29	9.62 645	35	0.37 355	9.96 424	5	4				
57	9.59 098	30	9.62 680	35	0.37 320	9.96 419	6	3				
58	9.59 128	30	9.62 715	35	0.37 285	9.96 413	5	2				
59	9.59 158	30	9.62 750	35	0.37 250	9.96 408	5	1				
60	9.59 188		9.62 785		0.37 215	9.96 403		0				
	L Cos	d	L Ctn	c d	L Tan	L Sin	d	′	Proportional parts		

23°—LOGARITHMS OF TRIGONOMETRIC FUNCTIONS

'	L Sin	d	L Tan	c d	L Ctn	L Cos	d	'
0	9.59 188	30	9.62 785	35	0.37 215	9.96 403	6	60
1	9.59 218	29	9.62 820	35	0.37 180	9.96 397	5	59
2	9.59 247	30	9.62 855	35	0.37 145	9.96 392	5	58
3	9.59 277	30	9.62 890	36	0.37 110	9.96 387	6	57
4	9.59 307	29	9.62 926	35	0.37 074	9.96 381	5	56
5	9.59 336	30	9.62 961	35	0.37 039	9.96 376	6	55
6	9.59 366	30	9.62 996	35	0.37 004	9.96 370	5	54
7	9.59 396	29	9.63 031	35	0.36 969	9.96 365	5	53
8	9.59 425	30	9.63 066	35	0.36 934	9.96 360	6	52
9	9.59 455	29	9.63 101	34	0.36 899	9.96 354	5	51
10	9.59 484	30	9.63 135	35	0.36 865	9.96 349	6	50
11	9.59 514	29	9.63 170	35	0.36 830	9.96 343	5	49
12	9.59 543	30	9.63 205	35	0.36 795	9.96 338	5	48
13	9.59 573	29	9.63 240	35	0.36 760	9.96 333	6	47
14	9.59 602	30	9.63 275	35	0.36 725	9.96 327	5	46
15	9.59 632	29	9.63 310	35	0.36 690	9.96 322	6	45
16	9.59 661	29	9.63 345	34	0.36 655	9.96 316	5	44
17	9.59 690	30	9.63 379	35	0.36 621	9.96 311	6	43
18	9.59 720	29	9.63 414	35	0.36 586	9.96 305	5	42
19	9.59 749	29	9.63 449	35	0.36 551	9.96 300	6	41
20	9.59 778	30	9.63 484	35	0.36 516	9.96 294	5	40
21	9.59 808	29	9.63 519	34	0.36 481	9.96 289	5	39
22	9.59 837	29	9.63 553	35	0.36 447	9.96 284	6	38
23	9.59 866	29	9.63 588	35	0.36 412	9.96 278	5	37
24	9.59 895	29	9.63 623	34	0.36 377	9.96 273	6	36
25	9.59 924	30	9.63 657	35	0.36 343	9.96 267	5	35
26	9.59 954	29	9.63 692	34	0.36 308	9.96 262	6	34
27	9.59 983	29	9.63 726	35	0.36 274	9.96 256	5	33
28	9.60 012	29	9.63 761	35	0.36 239	9.96 251	6	32
29	9.60 041	29	9.63 796	34	0.36 204	9.96 245	5	31
30	9.60 070	29	9.63 830	35	0.36 170	9.96 240	6	30
31	9.60 099	29	9.63 865	34	0.36 135	9.96 234	5	29
32	9.60 128	29	9.63 899	35	0.36 101	9.96 229	6	28
33	9.60 157	29	9.63 934	34	0.36 066	9.96 223	5	27
34	9.60 186	29	9.63 968	35	0.36 032	9.96 218	6	26
35	9.60 215	29	9.64 003	34	0.35 997	9.96 212	5	25
36	9.60 244	29	9.64 037	35	0.35 963	9.96 207	6	24
37	9.60 273	29	9.64 072	34	0.35 928	9.96 201	5	23
38	9.60 302	29	9.64 106	34	0.35 894	9.96 196	6	22
39	9.60 331	28	9.64 140	35	0.35 860	9.96 190	5	21
40	9.60 359	29	9.64 175	34	0.35 825	9.96 185	6	20
41	9.60 388	29	9.64 209	34	0.35 791	9.96 179	5	19
42	9.60 417	29	9.64 243	35	0.35 757	9.96 174	6	18
43	9.60 446	28	9.64 278	34	0.35 722	9.96 168	6	17
44	9.60 474	29	9.64 312	34	0.35 688	9.96 162	5	16
45	9.60 503	29	9.64 346	35	0.35 654	9.96 157	6	15
46	9.60 532	29	9.64 381	34	0.35 619	9.96 151	5	14
47	9.60 561	28	9.64 415	34	0.35 585	9.96 146	6	13
48	9.60 589	29	9.64 449	34	0.35 551	9.96 140	5	12
49	9.60 618	28	9.64 483	34	0.35 517	9.96 135	6	11
50	9.60 646	29	9.64 517	35	0.35 483	9.96 129	6	10
51	9.60 675	29	9.64 552	34	0.35 448	9.96 123	5	9
52	9.60 704	28	9.64 586	34	0.35 414	9.96 118	6	8
53	9.60 732	29	9.64 620	34	0.35 380	9.96 112	5	7
54	9.60 761	28	9.64 654	34	0.35 346	9.96 107	6	6
55	9.60 789	29	9.64 688	34	0.35 312	9.96 101	6	5
56	9.60 818	28	9.64 722	34	0.35 278	9.96 095	5	4
57	9.60 846	29	9.64 756	34	0.35 244	9.96 090	6	3
58	9.60 875	28	9.64 790	34	0.35 210	9.96 084	5	2
59	9.60 903	28	9.64 824	34	0.35 176	9.96 079	6	1
60	9.60 931		9.64 858		0.35 142	9.96 073		0
	L Cos	d	L Ctn	c d	L Tan	L Sin	d	'

Proportional parts

''	36	35	34
1	0.6	0.6	0.6
2	1.2	1.2	1.1
3	1.8	1.8	1.7
4	2.4	2.3	2.3
5	3.0	2.9	2.8
6	3.6	3.5	3.4
7	4.2	4.1	4.0
8	4.8	4.7	4.5
9	5.4	5.2	5.1
10	6.0	5.8	5.7
20	12.0	11.7	11.3
30	18.0	17.5	17.0
40	24.0	23.3	22.7
50	30.0	29.2	28.3

''	30	29	28
1	0.5	0.5	0.5
2	1.0	1.0	0.9
3	1.5	1.4	1.4
4	2.0	1.9	1.9
5	2.5	2.4	2.3
6	3.0	2.9	2.8
7	3.5	3.4	3.3
8	4.0	3.9	3.7
9	4.5	4.4	4.2
10	5.0	4.8	4.7
20	10.0	9.7	9.3
30	15.0	14.5	14.0
40	20.0	19.3	18.7
50	25.0	24.2	23.3

''	6	5
1	0.1	0.1
2	0.2	0.2
3	0.3	0.2
4	0.4	0.3
5	0.5	0.4
6	0.6	0.5
7	0.7	0.6
8	0.8	0.7
9	0.9	0.8
10	1.0	0.8
20	2.0	1.7
30	3.0	2.5
40	4.0	3.3
50	5.0	4.2

Proportional parts

66°

Table IV   Page 143
24°—LOGARITHMS OF TRIGONOMETRIC FUNCTIONS

'	L Sin	d	L Tan	c d	L Ctn	L Cos	d	'
0	9.60 931	29	9.64 858	34	0.35 142	9.96 073	6	60
1	9.60 960	28	9.64 892	34	0.35 108	9.96 067	6	59
2	9.60 988	28	9.64 926	34	0.35 074	9.96 062	5	58
3	9.61 016	29	9.64 960	34	0.35 040	9.96 056	6	57
4	9.61 045	28	9.64 994	34	0.35 006	9.96 050	6	56
5	9.61 073	28	9.65 028	34	0.34 972	9.96 045	5	55
6	9.61 101	28	9.65 062	34	0.34 938	9.96 039	6	54
7	9.61 129	29	9.65 096	34	0.34 904	9.96 034	5	53
8	9.61 158	28	9.65 130	34	0.34 870	9.96 028	6	52
9	9.61 186	28	9.65 164	33	0.34 836	9.96 022	5	51
10	9.61 214	28	9.65 197	34	0.34 803	9.96 017	6	50
11	9.61 242	28	9.65 231	34	0.34 769	9.96 011	6	49
12	9.61 270	28	9.65 265	34	0.34 735	9.96 005	5	48
13	9.61 298	28	9.65 299	34	0.34 701	9.96 000	6	47
14	9.61 326	28	9.65 333	33	0.34 667	9.95 994	6	46
15	9.61 354	28	9.65 366	34	0.34 634	9.95 988	6	45
16	9.61 382	29	9.65 400	34	0.34 600	9.95 982	5	44
17	9.61 411	27	9.65 434	33	0.34 566	9.95 977	6	43
18	9.61 438	28	9.65 467	34	0.34 533	9.95 971	6	42
19	9.61 466	28	9.65 501	34	0.34 499	9.95 965	5	41
20	9.61 494	28	9.65 535	33	0.34 465	9.95 960	6	40
21	9.61 522	28	9.65 568	34	0.34 432	9.95 954	6	39
22	9.61 550	28	9.65 602	34	0.34 398	9.95 948	6	38
23	9.61 578	28	9.65 636	33	0.34 364	9.95 942	5	37
24	9.61 606	28	9.65 669	34	0.34 331	9.95 937	6	36
25	9.61 634	28	9.65 703	33	0.34 297	9.95 931	6	35
26	9.61 662	27	9.65 736	34	0.34 264	9.95 925	5	34
27	9.61 689	28	9.65 770	33	0.34 230	9.95 920	6	33
28	9.61 717	28	9.65 803	34	0.34 197	9.95 914	6	32
29	9.61 745	28	9.65 837	33	0.34 163	9.95 908	6	31
30	9.61 773	27	9.65 870	34	0.34 130	9.95 902	5	30
31	9.61 800	28	9.65 904	33	0.34 096	9.95 897	6	29
32	9.61 828	28	9.65 937	34	0.34 063	9.95 891	6	28
33	9.61 856	27	9.65 971	33	0.34 029	9.95 885	6	27
34	9.61 883	28	9.66 004	34	0.33 996	9.95 879	6	26
35	9.61 911	28	9.66 038	33	0.33 962	9.95 873	5	25
36	9.61 939	27	9.66 071	33	0.33 929	9.95 868	6	24
37	9.61 966	28	9.66 104	34	0.33 896	9.95 862	6	23
38	9.61 994	27	9.66 138	33	0.33 862	9.95 856	6	22
39	9.62 021	28	9.66 171	33	0.33 829	9.95 850	6	21
40	9.62 049	27	9.66 204	34	0.33 796	9.95 844	5	20
41	9.62 076	28	9.66 238	33	0.33 762	9.95 839	6	19
42	9.62 104	27	9.66 271	33	0.33 729	9.95 833	6	18
43	9.62 131	28	9.66 304	33	0.33 696	9.95 827	6	17
44	9.62 159	27	9.66 337	34	0.33 663	9.95 821	6	16
45	9.62 186	28	9.66 371	33	0.33 629	9.95 815	5	15
46	9.62 214	27	9.66 404	33	0.33 596	9.95 810	6	14
47	9.62 241	27	9.66 437	33	0.33 563	9.95 804	6	13
48	9.62 268	28	9.66 470	33	0.33 530	9.95 798	6	12
49	9.62 296	27	9.66 503	34	0.33 497	9.95 792	6	11
50	9.62 323	27	9.66 537	33	0.33 463	9.95 786	6	10
51	9.62 350	27	9.66 570	33	0.33 430	9.95 780	5	9
52	9.62 377	28	9.66 603	33	0.33 397	9.95 775	6	8
53	9.62 405	27	9.66 636	33	0.33 364	9.95 769	6	7
54	9.62 432	27	9.66 669	33	0.33 331	9.95 763	6	6
55	9.62 459	27	9.66 702	33	0.33 298	9.95 757	6	5
56	9.62 486	27	9.66 735	33	0.33 265	9.95 751	6	4
57	9.62 513	28	9.66 768	33	0.33 232	9.95 745	6	3
58	9.62 541	27	9.66 801	33	0.33 199	9.95 739	6	2
59	9.62 568	27	9.66 834	33	0.33 166	9.95 733	5	1
60	9.62 595		9.66 867		0.33 133	9.95 728		0
	L Cos	d	L Ctn	c d	L Tan	L Sin	d	'

Proportional parts

''	34	33
1	0.6	0.6
2	1.1	1.1
3	1.7	1.6
4	2.3	2.2
5	2.8	2.8
6	3.4	3.3
7	4.0	3.8
8	4.5	4.4
9	5.1	5.0
10	5.7	5.5
20	11.3	11.0
30	17.0	16.5
40	22.7	22.0
50	28.3	27.5

''	29	28	27
1	0.5	0.5	0.4
2	1.0	0.9	0.9
3	1.4	1.4	1.4
4	1.9	1.9	1.8
5	2.4	2.3	2.2
6	2.9	2.8	2.7
7	3.4	3.3	3.2
8	3.9	3.7	3.6
9	4.4	4.2	4.0
10	4.8	4.7	4.5
20	9.7	9.3	9.0
30	14.5	14.0	13.5
40	19.3	18.7	18.0
50	24.2	23.3	22.5

''	6	5
1	0.1	0.1
2	0.2	0.2
3	0.3	0.2
4	0.4	0.3
5	0.5	0.4
6	0.6	0.5
7	0.7	0.6
8	0.8	0.7
9	0.9	0.8
10	1.0	0.8
20	2.0	1.7
30	3.0	2.5
40	4.0	3.3
50	5.0	4.2

Proportional parts

65°

25°—LOGARITHMS OF TRIGONOMETRIC FUNCTIONS

′	L Sin	d	L Tan	c d	L Ctn	L Cos	d	′	Proportional parts
0	9.62 595	27	9.66 867	33	0.33 133	9.95 728	6	60	
1	9.62 622	27	9.66 900	33	0.33 100	9.95 722	6	59	
2	9.62 649	27	9.66 933	33	0.33 067	9.95 716	6	58	
3	9.62 676	27	9.66 966	33	0.33 034	9.95 710	6	57	
4	9.62 703	27	9.66 999	33	0.33 001	9.95 704	6	56	
5	9.62 730	27	9.67 032	33	0.32 968	9.95 698	6	55	
6	9.62 757	27	9.67 065	33	0.32 935	9.95 692	6	54	
7	9.62 784	27	9.67 098	33	0.32 902	9.95 686	6	53	
8	9.62 811	27	9.67 131	32	0.32 869	9.95 680	6	52	
9	9.62 838	27	9.67 163	33	0.32 837	9.95 674	6	51	
10	9.62 865	27	9.67 196	33	0.32 804	9.95 668	5	50	
11	9.62 892	26	9.67 229	33	0.32 771	9.95 663	6	49	
12	9.62 918	27	9.67 262	33	0.32 738	9.95 657	6	48	
13	9.62 945	27	9.67 295	32	0.32 705	9.95 651	6	47	
14	9.62 972	27	9.67 327	33	0.32 673	9.95 645	6	46	
15	9.62 999	27	9.67 360	33	0.32 640	9.95 639	6	45	
16	9.63 026	26	9.67 393	33	0.32 607	9.95 633	6	44	
17	9.63 052	27	9.67 426	32	0.32 574	9.95 627	6	43	
18	9.63 079	27	9.67 458	33	0.32 542	9.95 621	6	42	
19	9.63 106	27	9.67 491	33	0.32 509	9.95 615	6	41	
20	9.63 133	26	9.67 524	32	0.32 476	9.95 609	6	40	
21	9.63 159	27	9.67 556	33	0.32 444	9.95 603	6	39	
22	9.63 186	27	9.67 589	33	0.32 411	9.95 597	6	38	
23	9.63 213	26	9.67 622	32	0.32 378	9.95 591	6	37	
24	9.63 239	27	9.67 654	33	0.32 346	9.95 585	6	36	
25	9.63 266	26	9.67 687	32	0.32 313	9.95 579	6	35	
26	9.63 292	27	9.67 719	33	0.32 281	9.95 573	6	34	
27	9.63 319	26	9.67 752	33	0.32 248	9.95 567	6	33	
28	9.63 345	27	9.67 785	32	0.32 215	9.95 561	6	32	
29	9.63 372	26	9.67 817	33	0.32 183	9.95 555	6	31	
30	9.63 398	27	9.67 850	32	0.32 150	9.95 549	6	30	
31	9.63 425	26	9.67 882	33	0.32 118	9.95 543	6	29	
32	9.63 451	27	9.67 915	32	0.32 085	9.95 537	6	28	
33	9.63 478	26	9.67 947	33	0.32 053	9.95 531	6	27	
34	9.63 504	27	9.67 980	32	0.32 020	9.95 525	6	26	
35	9.63 531	26	9.68 012	32	0.31 988	9.95 519	6	25	
36	9.63 557	26	9.68 044	33	0.31 956	9.95 513	6	24	
37	9.63 583	27	9.68 077	32	0.31 923	9.95 507	7	23	
38	9.63 610	26	9.68 109	33	0.31 891	9.95 500	6	22	
39	9.63 636	26	9.68 142	32	0.31 858	9.95 494	6	21	
40	9.63 662	27	9.68 174	32	0.31 826	9.95 488	6	20	
41	9.63 689	26	9.68 206	33	0.31 794	9.95 482	6	19	
42	9.63 715	26	9.68 239	32	0.31 761	9.95 476	6	18	
43	9.63 741	26	9.68 271	32	0.31 729	9.95 470	6	17	
44	9.63 767	27	9.68 303	33	0.31 697	9.95 464	6	16	
45	9.63 794	26	9.68 336	32	0.31 664	9.95 458	6	15	
46	9.63 820	26	9.68 368	32	0.31 632	9.95 452	6	14	
47	9.63 846	26	9.68 400	32	0.31 600	9.95 446	6	13	
48	9.63 872	26	9.68 432	33	0.31 568	9.95 440	6	12	
49	9.63 898	26	9.68 465	32	0.31 535	9.95 434	7	11	
50	9.63 924	26	9.68 497	32	0.31 503	9.95 427	6	10	
51	9.63 950	26	9.68 529	32	0.31 471	9.95 421	6	9	
52	9.63 976	26	9.68 561	32	0.31 439	9.95 415	6	8	
53	9.64 002	26	9.68 593	33	0.31 407	9.95 409	6	7	
54	9.64 028	26	9.68 626	32	0.31 374	9.95 403	6	6	
55	9.64 054	26	9.68 658	32	0.31 342	9.95 397	6	5	
56	9.64 080	26	9.68 690	32	0.31 310	9.95 391	7	4	
57	9.64 106	26	9.68 722	32	0.31 278	9.95 384	6	3	
58	9.64 132	26	9.68 754	32	0.31 246	9.95 378	6	2	
59	9.64 158	26	9.68 786	32	0.31 214	9.95 372	6	1	
60	9.64 184		9.68 818		0.31 182	9.95 366		0	
	L Cos	d	L Ctn	c d	L Tan	L Sin	d	′	Proportional parts

Proportional parts:

″	33	32
1	0.6	0.5
2	1.1	1.1
3	1.6	1.6
4	2.2	2.1
5	2.8	2.7
6	3.3	3.2
7	3.8	3.7
8	4.4	4.3
9	5.0	4.8
10	5.5	5.3
20	11.0	10.7
30	16.5	16.0
40	22.0	21.3
50	27.5	26.7

″	27	26
1	0.4	0.4
2	0.9	0.9
3	1.4	1.3
4	1.8	1.7
5	2.2	2.2
6	2.7	2.6
7	3.2	3.0
8	3.6	3.5
9	4.0	3.9
10	4.5	4.3
20	9.0	8.7
30	13.5	13.0
40	18.0	17.3
50	22.5	21.7

″	7	6	5
1	0.1	0.1	0.1
2	0.2	0.2	0.2
3	0.4	0.3	0.2
4	0.5	0.4	0.3
5	0.6	0.5	0.4
6	0.7	0.6	0.5
7	0.8	0.7	0.6
8	0.9	0.8	0.7
9	1.0	0.9	0.8
10	1.2	1.0	0.8
20	2.3	2.0	1.7
30	3.5	3.0	2.5
40	4.7	4.0	3.3
50	5.8	5.0	4.2

64°

Table IV   *Page 145*

26°—LOGARITHMS OF TRIGONOMETRIC FUNCTIONS

'	L Sin	d	L Tan	c d	L Ctn	L Cos	d	
0	9.64 184		9.68 818		0.31 182	9.95 366	6	60
1	9.64 210	26	9.68 850	32	0.31 150	9.95 360	6	59
2	9.64 236	26	9.68 882	32	0.31 118	9.95 354	6	58
3	9.64 262	26	9.68 914	32	0.31 086	9.95 348	7	57
4	9.64 288	26 25	9.68 946	32	0.31 054	9.95 341	7	56
5	9.64 313	26	9.68 978	32	0.31 022	9.95 335	6	55
6	9.64 339	26	9.69 010	32	0.30 990	9.95 329	6	54
7	9.64 365	26	9.69 042	32	0.30 958	9.95 323	6	53
8	9.64 391	26	9.69 074	32	0.30 926	9.95 317	7	52
9	9.64 417	25	9.69 106	32	0.30 894	9.95 310	6	51
10	9.64 442	26	9.69 138	32	0.30 862	9.95 304	6	50
11	9.64 468	26	9.69 170	32	0.30 830	9.95 298	6	49
12	9.64 494	25	9.69 202	32	0.30 798	9.95 292	6	48
13	9.64 519	26	9.69 234	32	0.30 766	9.95 286	7	47
14	9.64 545	26	9.69 266	32	0.30 734	9.95 279	6	46
15	9.64 571	25	9.69 298	31	0.30 702	9.95 273	6	45
16	9.64 596	26	9.69 329	32	0.30 671	9.95 267	6	44
17	9.64 622	25	9.69 361	32	0.30 639	9.95 261	7	43
18	9.64 647	25	9.69 393	32	0.30 607	9.95 254	6	42
19	9.64 673	25	9.69 425	32	0.30 575	9.95 248	6	41
20	9.64 698	26	9.69 457	31	0.30 543	9.95 242	6	40
21	9.64 724	25	9.69 488	32	0.30 512	9.95 236	7	39
22	9.64 749	26	9.69 520	32	0.30 480	9.95 229	6	38
23	9.64 775	25	9.69 552	32	0.30 448	9.95 223	6	37
24	9.64 800	26	9.69 584	31	0.30 416	9.95 217	6	36
25	9.64 826	25	9.69 615	32	0.30 385	9.95 211	7	35
26	9.64 851	26	9.69 647	32	0.30 353	9.95 204	6	34
27	9.64 877	25	9.69 679	31	0.30 321	9.95 198	6	33
28	9.64 902	25	9.69 710	32	0.30 290	9.95 192	7	32
29	9.64 927	26	9.69 742	32	0.30 258	9.95 185	6	31
30	9.64 953	25	9.69 774	31	0.30 226	9.95 179	6	30
31	9.64 978	25	9.69 805	32	0.30 195	9.95 173	6	29
32	9.65 003	26	9.69 837	31	0.30 163	9.95 167	7	28
33	9.65 029	25	9.69 868	32	0.30 132	9.95 160	6	27
34	9.65 054	25	9.69 900	32	0.30 100	9.95 154	6	26
35	9.65 079	25	9.69 932	31	0.30 068	9.95 148	7	25
36	9.65 104	26	9.69 963	32	0.30 037	9.95 141	6	24
37	9.65 130	25	9.69 995	31	0.30 005	9.95 135	6	23
38	9.65 155	25	9.70 026	32	0.29 974	9.95 129	7	22
39	9.65 180	25	9.70 058	31	0.29 942	9.95 122	6	21
40	9.65 205	25	9.70 089	32	0.29 911	9.95 116	6	20
41	9.65 230	25	9.70 121	31	0.29 879	9.95 110	7	19
42	9.65 255	26	9.70 152	32	0.29 848	9.95 103	6	18
43	9.65 281	25	9.70 184	31	0.29 816	9.95 097	7	17
44	9.65 306	25	9.70 215	32	0.29 785	9.95 090	6	16
45	9.65 331	25	9.70 247	31	0.29 753	9.95 084	6	15
46	9.65 356	25	9.70 278	31	0.29 722	9.95 078	7	14
47	9.65 381	25	9.70 309	32	0.29 691	9.95 071	6	13
48	9.65 406	25	9.70 341	31	0.29 659	9.95 065	6	12
49	9.65 431	25	9.70 372	32	0.29 628	9.95 059	7	11
50	9.65 456	25	9.70 404	31	0.29 596	9.95 052	6	10
51	9.65 481	25	9.70 435	31	0.29 565	9.95 046	7	9
52	9.65 506	25	9.70 466	32	0.29 534	9.95 039	6	8
53	9.65 531	25	9.70 498	31	0.29 502	9.95 033	6	7
54	9.65 556	24	9.70 529	31	0.29 471	9.95 027	7	6
55	9.65 580	25	9.70 560	32	0.29 440	9.95 020	6	5
56	9.65 605	25	9.70 592	31	0.29 408	9.95 014	7	4
57	9.65 630	25	9.70 623	31	0.29 377	9.95 007	6	3
58	9.65 655	25	9.70 654	31	0.29 346	9.95 001	6	2
59	9.65 680	25	9.70 685	32	0.29 315	9.94 995	7	1
60	9.65 705		9.70 717		0.29 283	9.94 988		0
	L Cos	d	L Ctn	c d	L Tan	L Sin	d	'

Proportional parts

''	32	31
1	0.5	0.5
2	1.1	1.0
3	1.6	1.6
4	2.1	2.1
5	2.7	2.6
6	3.2	3.1
7	3.7	3.6
8	4.3	4.1
9	4.8	4.6
10	5.3	5.2
20	10.7	10.3
30	16.0	15.5
40	21.3	20.7
50	26.7	25.8

''	26	25	24
1	0.4	0.4	0.4
2	0.9	0.8	0.8
3	1.3	1.2	1.2
4	1.7	1.7	1.6
5	2.2	2.1	2.0
6	2.6	2.5	2.4
7	3.0	2.9	2.8
8	3.5	3.3	3.2
9	3.9	3.8	3.6
10	4.3	4.2	4.0
20	8.7	8.3	8.0
30	13.0	12.5	12.0
40	17.3	16.7	16.0
50	21.7	20.8	20.0

''	7	6
1	0.1	0.1
2	0.2	0.2
3	0.4	0.3
4	0.5	0.4
5	0.6	0.5
6	0.7	0.6
7	0.8	0.7
8	0.9	0.8
9	1.0	0.9
10	1.2	1.0
20	2.3	2.0
30	3.5	3.0
40	4.7	4.0
50	5.8	5.0

Proportional parts

63°

27°—LOGARITHMS OF TRIGONOMETRIC FUNCTIONS

'	L Sin	d	L Tan	c d	L Ctn	L Cos	d	
0	9.65 705	24	9.70 717	31	0.29 283	9.94 988	6	60
1	9.65 729	25	9.70 748	31	0.29 252	9.94 982	7	59
2	9.65 754	25	9.70 779	31	0.29 221	9.94 975	6	58
3	9.65 779	25	9.70 810	31	0.29 190	9.94 969	7	57
4	9.65 804	24	9.70 841	32	0.29 159	9.94 962	6	56
5	9.65 828	25	9.70 873	31	0.29 127	9.94 956	7	55
6	9.65 853	25	9.70 904	31	0.29 096	9.94 949	6	54
7	9.65 878	24	9.70 935	31	0.29 065	9.94 943	7	53
8	9.65 902	25	9.70 966	31	0.29 034	9.94 936	6	52
9	9.65 927	25	9.70 997	31	0.29 003	9.94 930	7	51
10	9.65 952	24	9.71 028	31	0.28 972	9.94 923	6	50
11	9.65 976	25	9.71 059	31	0.28 941	9.94 917	6	49
12	9.66 001	24	9.71 090	31	0.28 910	9.94 911	7	48
13	9.66 025	25	9.71 121	32	0.28 879	9.94 904	6	47
14	9.66 050	25	9.71 153	31	0.28 847	9.94 898	7	46
15	9.66 075	24	9.71 184	31	0.28 816	9.94 891	6	45
16	9.66 099	25	9.71 215	31	0.28 785	9.94 885	7	44
17	9.66 124	24	9.71 246	31	0.28 754	9.94 878	7	43
18	9.66 148	25	9.71 277	31	0.28 723	9.94 871	6	42
19	9.66 173	24	9.71 308	31	0.28 692	9.94 865	7	41
20	9.66 197	24	9.71 339	31	0.28 661	9.94 858	6	40
21	9.66 221	25	9.71 370	31	0.28 630	9.94 852	7	39
22	9.66 246	24	9.71 401	30	0.28 599	9.94 845	6	38
23	9.66 270	25	9.71 431	31	0.28 569	9.94 839	7	37
24	9.66 295	24	9.71 462	31	0.28 538	9.94 832	6	36
25	9.66 319	24	9.71 493	31	0.28 507	9.94 826	7	35
26	9.66 343	25	9.71 524	31	0.28 476	9.94 819	6	34
27	9.66 368	24	9.71 555	31	0.28 445	9.94 813	7	33
28	9.66 392	24	9.71 586	31	0.28 414	9.94 806	7	32
29	9.66 416	25	9.71 617	31	0.28 383	9.94 799	6	31
30	9.66 441	24	9.71 648	31	0.28 352	9.94 793	7	30
31	9.66 465	24	9.71 679	30	0.28 321	9.94 786	6	29
32	9.66 489	24	9.71 709	31	0.28 291	9.94 780	7	28
33	9.66 513	24	9.71 740	31	0.28 260	9.94 773	6	27
34	9.66 537	25	9.71 771	31	0.28 229	9.94 767	7	26
35	9.66 562	24	9.71 802	31	0.28 198	9.94 760	7	25
36	9.66 586	24	9.71 833	30	0.28 167	9.94 753	6	24
37	9.66 610	24	9.71 863	31	0.28 137	9.94 747	7	23
38	9.66 634	24	9.71 894	31	0.28 106	9.94 740	6	22
39	9.66 658	24	9.71 925	30	0.28 075	9.94 734	7	21
40	9.66 682	24	9.71 955	31	0.28 045	9.94 727	7	20
41	9.66 706	25	9.71 986	31	0.28 014	9.94 720	6	19
42	9.66 731	24	9.72 017	31	0.27 983	9.94 714	7	18
43	9.66 755	24	9.72 048	30	0.27 952	9.94 707	7	17
44	9.66 779	24	9.72 078	31	0.27 922	9.94 700	6	16
45	9.66 803	24	9.72 109	31	0.27 891	9.94 694	7	15
46	9.66 827	24	9.72 140	30	0.27 860	9.94 687	7	14
47	9.66 851	24	9.72 170	31	0.27 830	9.94 680	6	13
48	9.66 875	24	9.72 201	30	0.27 799	9.94 674	7	12
49	9.66 899	23	9.72 231	31	0.27 769	9.94 667	7	11
50	9.66 922	24	9.72 262	31	0.27 738	9.94 660	6	10
51	9.66 946	24	9.72 293	30	0.27 707	9.94 654	7	9
52	9.66 970	24	9.72 323	31	0.27 677	9.94 647	7	8
53	9.66 994	24	9.72 354	30	0.27 646	9.94 640	6	7
54	9.67 018	24	9.72 384	31	0.27 616	9.94 634	7	6
55	9.67 042	24	9.72 415	30	0.27 585	9.94 627	7	5
56	9.67 066	24	9.72 445	31	0.27 555	9.94 620	6	4
57	9.67 090	23	9.72 476	30	0.27 524	9.94 614	7	3
58	9.67 113	24	9.72 506	31	0.27 494	9.94 607	7	2
59	9.67 137	24	9.72 537	30	0.27 463	9.94 600	7	1
60	9.67 161		9.72 567		0.27 433	9.94 593		0
	L Cos	d	L Ctn	c d	L Tan	L Sin	d	'

Proportional parts

''	32	31	30
1	0.5	0.5	0.5
2	1.1	1.0	1.0
3	1.6	1.6	1.5
4	2.1	2.1	2.0
5	2.7	2.6	2.5
6	3.2	3.1	3.0
7	3.7	3.6	3.5
8	4.3	4.1	4.0
9	4.8	4.6	4.5
10	5.3	5.2	5.0
20	10.7	10.3	10.0
30	16.0	15.5	15.0
40	21.3	20.7	20.0
50	26.7	25.8	25.0

''	25	24	23
1	0.4	0.4	0.4
2	0.8	0.8	0.8
3	1.2	1.2	1.2
4	1.7	1.6	1.5
5	2.1	2.0	1.9
6	2.5	2.4	2.3
7	2.9	2.8	2.7
8	3.3	3.2	3.1
9	3.8	3.6	3.4
10	4.2	4.0	3.8
20	8.3	8.0	7.7
30	12.5	12.0	11.5
40	16.7	16.0	15.3
50	20.8	20.0	19.2

''	7	6
1	0.1	0.1
2	0.2	0.2
3	0.4	0.3
4	0.5	0.4
5	0.6	0.5
6	0.7	0.6
7	0.8	0.7
8	0.9	0.8
9	1.0	0.9
10	1.2	1.0
20	2.3	2.0
30	3.5	3.0
40	4.7	4.0
50	5.8	5.0

Proportional parts

62°

28°—LOGARITHMS OF TRIGONOMETRIC FUNCTIONS

′	L Sin	d	L Tan	c d	L Ctn	L Cos	d		Proportional parts			
0	9.67 161		9.72 567		0.27 433	9.94 593		60				
1	9.67 185	24	9.72 598	31	0.27 402	9.94 587	6	59				
2	9.67 208	23	9.72 628	30	0.27 372	9.94 580	7	58				
3	9.67 232	24	9.72 659	31	0.27 341	9.94 573	7	57				
4	9.67 256	24	9.72 689	30	0.27 311	9.94 567	6	56				
		24		31			7		″	31	30	29
5	9.67 280		9.72 720		0.27 280	9.94 560		55				
6	9.67 303	23	9.72 750	30	0.27 250	9.94 553	7	54				
7	9.67 327	24	9.72 780	30	0.27 220	9.94 546	7	53	1	0.5	0.5	0.5
8	9.67 350	23	9.72 811	31	0.27 189	9.94 540	6	52	2	1.0	1.0	1.0
9	9.67 374	24	9.72 841	30	0.27 159	9.94 533	7	51	3	1.6	1.5	1.4
		24		31			7		4	2.1	2.0	1.9
10	9.67 398		9.72 872		0.27 128	9.94 526		50				
11	9.67 421	23	9.72 902	30	0.27 098	9.94 519	7	49	5	2.6	2.5	2.4
12	9.67 445	24	9.72 932	30	0.27 068	9.94 513	6	48	6	3.1	3.0	2.9
13	9.67 468	23	9.72 963	31	0.27 037	9.94 506	7	47	7	3.6	3.5	3.4
14	9.67 492	24	9.72 993	30	0.27 007	9.94 499	7	46	8	4.1	4.0	3.9
		23		30			7		9	4.6	4.5	4.4
15	9.67 515		9.73 023		0.26 977	9.94 492		45				
16	9.67 539	24	9.73 054	31	0.26 946	9.94 485	7	44	10	5.2	5.0	4.8
17	9.67 562	23	9.73 084	30	0.26 916	9.94 479	6	43	20	10.3	10.0	9.7
18	9.67 586	24	9.73 114	30	0.26 886	9.94 472	7	42	30	15.5	15.0	14.5
19	9.67 609	23	9.73 144	30	0.26 856	9.94 465	7	41	40	20.7	20.0	19.3
		24		31			7		50	25.8	25.0	24.2
20	9.67 633		9.73 175		0.26 825	9.94 458		40				
21	9.67 656	23	9.73 205	30	0.26 795	9.94 451	7	39				
22	9.67 680	24	9.73 235	30	0.26 765	9.94 445	6	38				
23	9.67 703	23	9.73 265	30	0.26 735	9.94 438	7	37	″	24	23	22
24	9.67 726	23	9.73 295	30	0.26 705	9.94 431	7	36				
		24		31			7		1	0.4	0.4	0.4
25	9.67 750		9.73 326		0.26 674	9.94 424		35	2	0.8	0.8	0.7
26	9.67 773	23	9.73 356	30	0.26 644	9.94 417	7	34	3	1.2	1.2	1.1
27	9.67 796	23	9.73 386	30	0.26 614	9.94 410	7	33	4	1.6	1.5	1.5
28	9.67 820	24	9.73 416	30	0.26 584	9.94 404	6	32				
29	9.67 843	23	9.73 446	30	0.26 554	9.94 397	7	31	5	2.0	1.9	1.8
		23		30			7		6	2.4	2.3	2.2
30	9.67 866		9.73 476		0.26 524	9.94 390		30	7	2.8	2.7	2.6
31	9.67 890	24	9.73 507	31	0.26 493	9.94 383	7	29	8	3.2	3.1	2.9
32	9.67 913	23	9.73 537	30	0.26 463	9.94 376	7	28	9	3.6	3.4	3.3
33	9.67 936	23	9.73 567	30	0.26 433	9.94 369	7	27				
34	9.67 959	23	9.73 597	30	0.26 403	9.94 362	7	26	10	4.0	3.8	3.7
		23		30			7		20	8.0	7.7	7.3
35	9.67 982		9.73 627		0.26 373	9.94 355		25	30	12.0	11.5	11.0
36	9.68 006	24	9.73 657	30	0.26 343	9.94 349	6	24	40	16.0	15.3	14.7
37	9.68 029	23	9.73 687	30	0.26 313	9.94 342	7	23	50	20.0	19.2	18.3
38	9.68 052	23	9.73 717	30	0.26 283	9.94 335	7	22				
39	9.68 075	23	9.73 747	30	0.26 253	9.94 328	7	21				
		23		30			7		″	7	6	
40	9.68 098		9.73 777		0.26 223	9.94 321		20				
41	9.68 121	23	9.73 807	30	0.26 193	9.94 314	7	19	1	0.1	0.1	
42	9.68 144	23	9.73 837	30	0.26 163	9.94 307	7	18	2	0.2	0.2	
43	9.68 167	23	9.73 867	30	0.26 133	9.94 300	7	17	3	0.4	0.3	
44	9.68 190	23	9.73 897	30	0.26 103	9.94 293	7	16	4	0.5	0.4	
		23		30			7					
45	9.68 213		9.73 927		0.26 073	9.94 286		15	5	0.6	0.5	
46	9.68 237	24	9.73 957	30	0.26 043	9.94 279	7	14	6	0.7	0.6	
47	9.68 260	23	9.73 987	30	0.26 013	9.94 273	6	13	7	0.8	0.7	
48	9.68 283	23	9.74 017	30	0.25 983	9.94 266	7	12	8	0.9	0.8	
49	9.68 305	22	9.74 047	30	0.25 953	9.94 259	7	11	9	1.0	0.9	
		23		30			7					
50	9.68 328		9.74 077		0.25 923	9.94 252		10	10	1.2	1.0	
51	9.68 351	23	9.74 107	30	0.25 893	9.94 245	7	9	20	2.3	2.0	
52	9.68 374	23	9.74 137	30	0.25 863	9.94 238	7	8	30	3.5	3.0	
53	9.68 397	23	9.74 166	29	0.25 834	9.94 231	7	7	40	4.7	4.0	
54	9.68 420	23	9.74 196	30	0.25 804	9.94 224	7	6	50	5.8	5.0	
		23		30			7					
55	9.68 443		9.74 226		0.25 774	9.94 217		5				
56	9.68 466	23	9.74 256	30	0.25 744	9.94 210	7	4				
57	9.68 489	23	9.74 286	30	0.25 714	9.94 203	7	3				
58	9.68 512	23	9.74 316	30	0.25 684	9.94 196	7	2				
59	9.68 534	22	9.74 345	29	0.25 655	9.94 189	7	1				
		23		30			7					
60	9.68 557		9.74 375		0.25 625	9.94 182		0				
―	L Cos	d	L Ctn	c d	L Tan	L Sin	d	′		Proportional parts		

29°—LOGARITHMS OF TRIGONOMETRIC FUNCTIONS

′	L Sin	d	L Tan	c d	L Ctn	L Cos	d	
0	9.68 557	23	9.74 375	30	0.25 625	9.94 182	7	60
1	9.68 580	23	9.74 405	30	0.25 595	9.94 175	7	59
2	9.68 603	22	9.74 435	30	0.25 565	9.94 168	7	58
3	9.68 625	23	9.74 465	29	0.25 535	9.94 161	7	57
4	9.68 648	23	9.74 494	30	0.25 506	9.94 154	7	56
5	9.68 671	23	9.74 524	30	0.25 476	9.94 147	7	55
6	9.68 694	22	9.74 554	29	0.25 446	9.94 140	7	54
7	9.68 716	23	9.74 583	30	0.25 417	9.94 133	7	53
8	9.68 739	23	9.74 613	30	0.25 387	9.94 126	7	52
9	9.68 762	22	9.74 643	30	0.25 357	9.94 119	7	51
10	9.68 784	23	9.74 673	29	0.25 327	9.94 112	7	50
11	9.68 807	22	9.74 702	30	0.25 298	9.94 105	7	49
12	9.68 829	23	9.74 732	30	0.25 268	9.94 098	8	48
13	9.68 852	23	9.74 762	29	0.25 238	9.94 090	7	47
14	9.68 875	22	9.74 791	30	0.25 209	9.94 083	7	46
15	9.68 897	23	9.74 821	30	0.25 179	9.94 076	7	45
16	9.68 920	22	9.74 851	29	0.25 149	9.94 069	7	44
17	9.68 942	23	9.74 880	30	0.25 120	9.94 062	7	43
18	9.68 965	22	9.74 910	29	0.25 090	9.94 055	7	42
19	9.68 987	23	9.74 939	30	0.25 061	9.94 048	7	41
20	9.69 010	22	9.74 969	29	0.25 031	9.94 041	7	40
21	9.69 032	23	9.74 998	30	0.25 002	9.94 034	7	39
22	9.69 055	22	9.75 028	30	0.24 972	9.94 027	7	38
23	9.69 077	23	9.75 058	29	0.24 942	9.94 020	8	37
24	9.69 100	22	9.75 087	30	0.24 913	9.94 012	7	36
25	9.69 122	22	9.75 117	29	0.24 883	9.94 005	7	35
26	9.69 144	23	9.75 146	30	0.24 854	9.93 998	7	34
27	9.69 167	22	9.75 176	29	0.24 824	9.93 991	7	33
28	9.69 189	23	9.75 205	30	0.24 795	9.93 984	7	32
29	9.69 212	22	9.75 235	30	0.24 765	9.93 977	7	31
30	9.69 234	22	9.75 264	30	0.24 736	9.93 970	7	30
31	9.69 256	23	9.75 294	29	0.24 706	9.93 963	8	29
32	9.69 279	22	9.75 323	30	0.24 677	9.93 955	7	28
33	9.69 301	22	9.75 353	29	0.24 647	9.93 948	7	27
34	9.69 323	22	9.75 382	29	0.24 618	9.93 941	7	26
35	9.69 345	23	9.75 411	30	0.24 589	9.93 934	7	25
36	9.69 368	22	9.75 441	29	0.24 559	9.93 927	7	24
37	9.69 390	22	9.75 470	30	0.24 530	9.93 920	8	23
38	9.69 412	22	9.75 500	29	0.24 500	9.93 912	7	22
39	9.69 434	22	9.75 529	29	0.24 471	9.93 905	7	21
40	9.69 456	23	9.75 558	30	0.24 442	9.93 898	7	20
41	9.69 479	22	9.75 588	29	0.24 412	9.93 891	7	19
42	9.69 501	22	9.75 617	30	0.24 383	9.93 884	8	18
43	9.69 523	22	9.75 647	29	0.24 353	9.93 876	7	17
44	9.69 545	22	9.75 676	29	0.24 324	9.93 869	7	16
45	9.69 567	22	9.75 705	30	0.24 295	9.93 862	7	15
46	9.69 589	22	9.75 735	29	0.24 265	9.93 855	8	14
47	9.69 611	22	9.75 764	29	0.24 236	9.93 847	7	13
48	9.69 633	22	9.75 793	29	0.24 207	9.93 840	7	12
49	9.69 655	22	9.75 822	30	0.24 178	9.93 833	7	11
50	9.69 677	22	9.75 852	29	0.24 148	9.93 826	7	10
51	9.69 699	22	9.75 881	29	0.24 119	9.93 819	8	9
52	9.69 721	22	9.75 910	29	0.24 090	9.93 811	7	8
53	9.69 743	22	9.75 939	30	0.24 061	9.93 804	7	7
54	9.69 765	22	9.75 969	29	0.24 031	9.93 797	8	6
55	9.69 787	22	9.75 998	29	0.24 002	9.93 789	7	5
56	9.69 809	22	9.76 027	29	0.23 973	9.93 782	7	4
57	9.69 831	22	9.76 056	30	0.23 944	9.93 775	7	3
58	9.69 853	22	9.76 086	29	0.23 914	9.93 768	8	2
59	9.69 875	22	9.76 115	29	0.23 885	9.93 760	7	1
60	9.69 897		9.76 144		0.23 856	9.93 753		0
	L Cos	d	L Ctn	c d	L Tan	L Sin	d	′

Proportional parts

″	30	29	23
1	0.5	0.5	0.4
2	1.0	1.0	0.8
3	1.5	1.4	1.2
4	2.0	1.9	1.5
5	2.5	2.4	1.9
6	3.0	2.9	2.3
7	3.5	3.4	2.7
8	4.0	3.9	3.1
9	4.5	4.4	3.4
10	5.0	4.8	3.8
20	10.0	9.7	7.7
30	15.0	14.5	11.5
40	20.0	19.3	15.3
50	25.0	24.2	19.2

″	22	8	7
1	0.4	0.1	0.1
2	0.7	0.3	0.2
3	1.1	0.4	0.4
4	1.5	0.5	0.5
5	1.8	0.7	0.6
6	2.2	0.8	0.7
7	2.6	0.9	0.8
8	2.9	1.1	0.9
9	3.3	1.2	1.0
10	3.7	1.3	1.2
20	7.3	2.7	2.3
30	11.0	4.0	3.5
40	14.7	5.3	4.7
50	18.3	6.7	5.8

Proportional parts

60°

Table IV   Page 149

30°—LOGARITHMS OF TRIGONOMETRIC FUNCTIONS

′	L Sin	d	L Tan	c d	L Ctn	L Cos	d	
0	9.69 897		9.76 144		0.23 856	9.93 753		60
1	9.69 919	22	9.76 173	29	0.23 827	9.93 746	7	59
2	9.69 941	22	9.76 202	29	0.23 798	9.93 738	8	58
3	9.69 963	22	9.76 231	29	0.23 769	9.93 731	7	57
4	9.69 984	21	9.76 261	30	0.23 739	9.93 724	7	56
		22		29			7	
5	9.70 006	22	9.76 290	29	0.23 710	9.93 717	8	55
6	9.70 028	22	9.76 319	29	0.23 681	9.93 709	7	54
7	9.70 050	22	9.76 348	29	0.23 652	9.93 702	7	53
8	9.70 072	21	9.76 377	29	0.23 623	9.93 695	8	52
9	9.70 093	22	9.76 406	29	0.23 594	9.93 687	7	51
10	9.70 115	22	9.76 435	29	0.23 565	9.93 680	7	50
11	9.70 137	22	9.76 464	29	0.23 536	9.93 673	8	49
12	9.70 159	21	9.76 493	29	0.23 507	9.93 665	7	48
13	9.70 180	22	9.76 522	29	0.23 478	9.93 658	8	47
14	9.70 202	22	9.76 551	29	0.23 449	9.93 650	7	46
15	9.70 224	21	9.76 580	29	0.23 420	9.93 643	7	45
16	9.70 245	22	9.76 609	30	0.23 391	9.93 636	8	44
17	9.70 267	21	9.76 639	29	0.23 361	9.93 628	7	43
18	9.70 288	22	9.76 668	29	0.23 332	9.93 621	7	42
19	9.70 310	22	9.76 697	28	0.23 303	9.93 614	8	41
20	9.70 332	21	9.76 725	29	0.23 275	9.93 606	7	40
21	9.70 353	22	9.76 754	29	0.23 246	9.93 599	8	39
22	9.70 375	21	9.76 783	29	0.23 217	9.93 591	7	38
23	9.70 396	22	9.76 812	29	0.23 188	9.93 584	7	37
24	9.70 418	21	9.76 841	29	0.23 159	9.93 577	8	36
25	9.70 439	22	9.76 870	29	0.23 130	9.93 569	7	35
26	9.70 461	21	9.76 899	29	0.23 101	9.93 562	8	34
27	9.70 482	22	9.76 928	29	0.23 072	9.93 554	7	33
28	9.70 504	21	9.76 957	29	0.23 043	9.93 547	8	32
29	9.70 525	22	9.76 986	29	0.23 014	9.93 539	7	31
30	9.70 547	21	9.77 015	29	0.22 985	9.93 532	7	30
31	9.70 568	22	9.77 044	29	0.22 956	9.93 525	8	29
32	9.70 590	21	9.77 073	28	0.22 927	9.93 517	7	28
33	9.70 611	22	9.77 101	29	0.22 899	9.93 510	8	27
34	9.70 633	21	9.77 130	29	0.22 870	9.93 502	7	26
35	9.70 654	21	9.77 159	29	0.22 841	9.93 495	8	25
36	9.70 675	22	9.77 188	29	0.22 812	9.93 487	7	24
37	9.70 697	21	9.77 217	29	0.22 783	9.93 480	8	23
38	9.70 718	21	9.77 246	28	0.22 754	9.93 472	7	22
39	9.70 739	22	9.77 274	29	0.22 726	9.93 465	8	21
40	9.70 761	21	9.77 303	29	0.22 697	9.93 457	7	20
41	9.70 782	21	9.77 332	29	0.22 668	9.93 450	8	19
42	9.70 803	21	9.77 361	29	0.22 639	9.93 442	7	18
43	9.70 824	22	9.77 390	28	0.22 610	9.93 435	8	17
44	9.70 846	21	9.77 418	29	0.22 582	9.93 427	7	16
45	9.70 867	21	9.77 447	29	0.22 553	9.93 420	8	15
46	9.70 888	21	9.77 476	29	0.22 524	9.93 412	7	14
47	9.70 909	22	9.77 505	28	0.22 495	9.93 405	8	13
48	9.70 931	21	9.77 533	29	0.22 467	9.93 397	7	12
49	9.70 952	21	9.77 562	29	0.22 438	9.93 390	8	11
50	9.70 973	21	9.77 591	28	0.22 409	9.93 382	7	10
51	9.70 994	21	9.77 619	29	0.22 381	9.93 375	8	9
52	9.71 015	21	9.77 648	29	0.22 352	9.93 367	7	8
53	9.71 036	22	9.77 677	29	0.22 323	9.93 360	8	7
54	9.71 058	21	9.77 706	28	0.22 294	9.93 352	8	6
55	9.71 079	21	9.77 734	29	0.22 266	9.93 344	7	5
56	9.71 100	21	9.77 763	28	0.22 237	9.93 337	8	4
57	9.71 121	21	9.77 791	29	0.22 209	9.93 329	7	3
58	9.71 142	21	9.77 820	29	0.22 180	9.93 322	8	2
59	9.71 163	21	9.77 849	28	0.22 151	9.93 314	7	1
60	9.71 184		9.77 877		0.22 123	9.93 307		0
	L Cos	d	L Ctn	c d	L Tan	L Sin	d	′

Proportional parts

″	30	29	28
1	0.5	0.5	0.5
2	1.0	1.0	0.9
3	1.5	1.4	1.4
4	2.0	1.9	1.9
5	2.5	2.4	2.3
6	3.0	2.9	2.8
7	3.5	3.4	3.3
8	4.0	3.9	3.7
9	4.5	4.4	4.2
10	5.0	4.8	4.7
20	10.0	9.7	9.3
30	15.0	14.5	14.0
40	20.0	19.3	18.7
50	25.0	24.2	23.3

″	22	21
1	0.4	0.4
2	0.7	0.7
3	1.1	1.0
4	1.5	1.4
5	1.8	1.8
6	2.2	2.1
7	2.6	2.4
8	2.9	2.8
9	3.3	3.2
10	3.7	3.5
20	7.3	7.0
30	11.0	10.5
40	14.7	14.0
50	18.3	17.5

″	8	7
1	0.1	0.1
2	0.3	0.2
3	0.4	0.4
4	0.5	0.5
5	0.7	0.6
6	0.8	0.7
7	0.9	0.8
8	1.1	0.9
9	1.2	1.0
10	1.3	1.2
20	2.7	2.3
30	4.0	3.5
40	5.3	4.7
50	6.7	5.8

31°—LOGARITHMS OF TRIGONOMETRIC FUNCTIONS

'	L Sin	d	L Tan	c d	L Ctn	L Cos	d		Proportional parts	
0	9.71 184	21	9.77 877	29	0.22 123	9.93 307	8	60		
1	9.71 205	21	9.77 906	29	0.22 094	9.93 299	8	59		
2	9.71 226	21	9.77 935	28	0.22 065	9.93 291	7	58		
3	9.71 247	21	9.77 963	29	0.22 037	9.93 284	8	57		
4	9.71 268	21	9.77 992	28	0.22 008	9.93 276	7	56		
									''	29	28
5	9.71 289	21	9.78 020	29	0.21 980	9.93 269	8	55			
6	9.71 310	21	9.78 049	28	0.21 951	9.93 261	8	54	1	0.5	0.5
7	9.71 331	21	9.78 077	29	0.21 923	9.93 253	7	53	2	1.0	0.9
8	9.71 352	21	9.78 106	29	0.21 894	9.93 246	8	52	3	1.4	1.4
9	9.71 373	20	9.78 135	28	0.21 865	9.93 238	8	51	4	1.9	1.9
10	9.71 393	21	9.78 163	29	0.21 837	9.93 230	7	50			
11	9.71 414	21	9.78 192	28	0.21 808	9.93 223	8	49	5	2.4	2.3
12	9.71 435	21	9.78 220	29	0.21 780	9.93 215	8	48	6	2.9	2.8
13	9.71 456	21	9.78 249	28	0.21 751	9.93 207	7	47	7	3.4	3.3
14	9.71 477	21	9.78 277	29	0.21 723	9.93 200	8	46	8	3.9	3.7
									9	4.4	4.2
15	9.71 498	21	9.78 306	28	0.21 694	9.93 192	8	45			
16	9.71 519	20	9.78 334	29	0.21 666	9.93 184	7	44	10	4 8	4.7
17	9.71 539	21	9.78 363	28	0.21 637	9.93 177	8	43	20	9.7	9.3
18	9.71 560	21	9.78 391	28	0.21 609	9.93 169	8	42	30	14.5	14.0
19	9.71 581	21	9.78 419	29	0.21 581	9.93 161	7	41	40	19.3	18.7
									50	24.2	23.3
20	9.71 602	20	9.78 448	28	0.21 552	9.93 154	8	40			
21	9.71 622	21	9.78 476	28	0.21 524	9.93 146	8	39			
22	9.71 643	21	9.78 505	28	0.21 495	9.93 138	7	38			
23	9.71 664	21	9.78 533	29	0.21 467	9.93 131	8	37	''	21	20
24	9.71 685	20	9.78 562	28	0.21 438	9.93 123	8	36			
									1	0.4	0.3
25	9.71 705	21	9.78 590	28	0.21 410	9.93 115	7	35	2	0.7	0.7
26	9.71 726	21	9.78 618	29	0.21 382	9.93 108	8	34	3	1.0	1.0
27	9.71 747	20	9.78 647	28	0.21 353	9.93 100	8	33	4	1.4	1.3
28	9.71 767	21	9.78 675	29	0.21 325	9.93 092	8	32			
29	9.71 788	21	9.78 704	28	0.21 296	9.93 084	7	31	5	1.8	1.7
									6	2.1	2.0
30	9.71 809	20	9.78 732	28	0.21 268	9.93 077	8	30	7	2.4	2.3
31	9.71 829	21	9.78 760	29	0.21 240	9.93 069	8	29	8	2.8	2.7
32	9.71 850	20	9.78 789	28	0.21 211	9.93 061	8	28	9	3.2	3.0
33	9.71 870	21	9.78 817	28	0.21 183	9.93 053	7	27			
34	9.71 891	20	9.78 845	29	0.21 155	9.93 046	8	26	10	3.5	3.3
									20	7.0	6.7
35	9.71 911	21	9.78 874	28	0.21 126	9.93 038	8	25	30	10.5	10.0
36	9.71 932	20	9.78 902	28	0.21 098	9.93 030	8	24	40	14.0	13.3
37	9.71 952	21	9.78 930	29	0.21 070	9.93 022	8	23	50	17.5	16.7
38	9.71 973	21	9.78 959	28	0.21 041	9.93 014	7	22			
39	9.71 994	21	9.78 987	28	0.21 013	9.93 007	8	21			
40	9.72 014	20	9.79 015	28	0.20 985	9.92 999	8	20	''	8	7
41	9.72 034	21	9.79 043	29	0.20 957	9.92 991	8	19			
42	9.72 055	20	9.79 072	28	0.20 928	9.92 983	7	18	1	0.1	0.1
43	9.72 075	21	9.79 100	28	0.20 900	9.92 976	8	17	2	0.3	0.2
44	9.72 096	20	9.79 128	28	0.20 872	9.92 968	8	16	3	0.4	0.4
									4	0.5	0.5
45	9.72 116	21	9.79 156	29	0.20 844	9.92 960	8	15			
46	9.72 137	20	9.79 185	28	0.20 815	9.92 952	8	14	5	0.7	0.6
47	9.72 157	20	9.79 213	28	0.20 787	9.92 944	8	13	6	0.8	0.7
48	9.72 177	21	9.79 241	28	0.20 759	9.92 936	7	12	7	0.9	0.8
49	9.72 198	20	9.79 269	28	0.20 731	9.92 929	8	11	8	1.1	0.9
									9	1.2	1.0
50	9.72 218	20	9.79 297	29	0.20 703	9.92 921	8	10			
51	9.72 238	21	9.79 326	28	0.20 674	9.92 913	8	9	10	1.3	1.2
52	9.72 259	20	9.79 354	28	0.20 646	9.92 905	8	8	20	2.7	2.3
53	9.72 279	20	9.79 382	28	0.20 618	9.92 897	8	7	30	4.0	3.5
54	9.72 299	21	9.79 410	28	0.20 590	9.92 889	8	6	40	5.3	4.7
									50	6.7	5.8
55	9.72 320	20	9.79 438	28	0.20 562	9.92 881	7	5			
56	9.72 340	20	9.79 466	29	0.20 534	9.92 874	8	4			
57	9.72 360	21	9.79 495	28	0.20 505	9.92 866	8	3			
58	9.72 381	20	9.79 523	28	0.20 477	9.92 858	8	2			
59	9.72 401	20	9.79 551	28	0.20 449	9.92 850	8	1			
60	9.72 421		9.79 579		0.20 421	9.92 842		0			
	L Cos	d	L Ctn	c d	L Tan	L Sin	d	'	Proportional parts		

58°

Table IV

32°—LOGARITHMS OF TRIGONOMETRIC FUNCTIONS

′	L Sin	d	L Tan	c d	L Ctn	L Cos	d	
0	9.72 421	20	9.79 579	28	0.20 421	9.92 842	8	60
1	9.72 441	20	9.79 607	28	0.20 393	9.92 834	8	59
2	9.72 461	21	9.79 635	28	0.20 365	9.92 826	8	58
3	9.72 482	20	9.79 663	28	0.20 337	9.92 818	8	57
4	9.72 502	20	9.79 691	28	0.20 309	9.92 810	7	56
5	9.72 522	20	9.79 719	28	0.20 281	9.92 803	8	55
6	9.72 542	20	9.79 747	29	0.20 253	9.92 795	8	54
7	9.72 562	20	9.79 776	28	0.20 224	9.92 787	8	53
8	9.72 582	20	9.79 804	28	0.20 196	9.92 779	8	52
9	9.72 602	20	9.79 832	28	0.20 168	9.92 771	8	51
10	9.72 622	21	9.79 860	28	0.20 140	9.92 763	8	50
11	9.72 643	20	9.79 888	28	0.20 112	9.92 755	8	49
12	9.72 663	20	9.79 916	28	0.20 084	9.92 747	8	48
13	9.72 683	20	9.79 944	28	0.20 056	9.92 739	8	47
14	9.72 703	20	9.79 972	28	0.20 028	9.92 731	8	46
15	9.72 723	20	9.80 000	28	0.20 000	9.92 723	8	45
16	9.72 743	20	9.80 028	28	0.19 972	9.92 715	8	44
17	9.72 763	20	9.80 056	28	0.19 944	9.92 707	8	43
18	9.72 783	20	9.80 084	28	0.19 916	9.92 699	8	42
19	9.72 803	20	9.80 112	28	0.19 888	9.92 691	8	41
20	9.72 823	20	9.80 140	28	0.19 860	9.92 683	8	40
21	9.72 843	20	9.80 168	27	0.19 832	9.92 675	8	39
22	9.72 863	20	9.80 195	28	0.19 805	9.92 667	8	38
23	9.72 883	19	9.80 223	28	0.19 777	9.92 659	8	37
24	9.72 902	20	9.80 251	28	0.19 749	9.92 651	8	36
25	9.72 922	20	9.80 279	28	0.19 721	9.92 643	8	35
26	9.72 942	20	9.80 307	28	0.19 693	9.92 635	8	34
27	9.72 962	20	9.80 335	28	0.19 665	9.92 627	8	33
28	9.72 982	20	9.80 363	28	0.19 637	9.92 619	8	32
29	9.73 002	20	9.80 391	28	0.19 609	9.92 611	8	31
30	9.73 022	19	9.80 419	28	0.19 581	9.92 603	8	30
31	9.73 041	20	9.80 447	27	0.19 553	9.92 595	8	29
32	9.73 061	20	9.80 474	28	0.19 526	9.92 587	8	28
33	9.73 081	20	9.80 502	28	0.19 498	9.92 579	8	27
34	9.73 101	20	9.80 530	28	0.19 470	9.92 571	8	26
35	9.73 121	19	9.80 558	28	0.19 442	9.92 563	8	25
36	9.73 140	20	9.80 586	28	0.19 414	9.92 555	9	24
37	9.73 160	20	9.80 614	28	0.19 386	9.92 546	8	23
38	9.73 180	20	9.80 642	27	0.19 358	9.92 538	8	22
39	9.73 200	19	9.80 669	28	0.19 331	9.92 530	8	21
40	9.73 219	20	9.80 697	28	0.19 303	9.92 522	8	20
41	9.73 239	20	9.80 725	28	0.19 275	9.92 514	8	19
42	9.73 259	19	9.80 753	28	0.19 247	9.92 506	8	18
43	9.73 278	20	9.80 781	27	0.19 219	9.92 498	8	17
44	9.73 298	20	9.80 808	28	0.19 192	9.92 490	8	16
45	9.73 318	19	9.80 836	28	0.19 164	9.92 482	9	15
46	9.73 337	20	9.80 864	28	0.19 136	9.92 473	8	14
47	9.73 357	20	9.80 892	27	0.19 108	9.92 465	8	13
48	9.73 377	19	9.80 919	28	0.19 081	9.92 457	8	12
49	9.73 396	20	9.80 947	28	0.19 053	9.92 449	8	11
50	9.73 416	19	9.80 975	28	0.19 025	9.92 441	8	10
51	9.73 435	20	9.81 003	27	0.18 997	9.92 433	8	9
52	9.73 455	19	9.81 030	28	0.18 970	9.92 425	9	8
53	9.73 474	20	9.81 058	28	0.18 942	9.92 416	8	7
54	9.73 494	19	9.81 086	27	0.18 914	9.92 408	8	6
55	9.73 513	20	9.81 113	28	0.18 887	9.92 400	8	5
56	9.73 533	19	9.81 141	28	0.18 859	9.92 392	8	4
57	9.73 552	20	9.81 169	27	0.18 831	9.92 384	8	3
58	9.73 572	19	9.81 196	28	0.18 804	9.92 376	9	2
59	9.73 591	20	9.81 224	28	0.18 776	9.92 367	8	1
60	9.73 611		9.81 252		0.18 748	9.92 359		0
—	L Cos	d	L Ctn	c d	L Tan	L Sin	d	′

Proportional parts

″	29	28	27
1	0.5	0.5	0.4
2	1.0	0.9	0.9
3	1.4	1.4	1.4
4	1.9	1.9	1.8
5	2.4	2.3	2.2
6	2.9	2.8	2.7
7	3.4	3.3	3.2
8	3.9	3.7	3.6
9	4.4	4.2	4.0
10	4.8	4.7	4.5
20	9.7	9.3	9.0
30	14.5	14.0	13.5
40	19.3	18.7	18.0
50	24.2	23.3	22.5

″	21	20	19
1	0.4	0.3	0.3
2	0.7	0.7	0.6
3	1.0	1.0	1.0
4	1.4	1.3	1.3
5	1.8	1.7	1.6
6	2.1	2.0	1.9
7	2.4	2.3	2.2
8	2.8	2.7	2.5
9	3.2	3.0	2.8
10	3.5	3.3	3.2
20	7.0	6.7	6.3
30	10.5	10.0	9.5
40	14.0	13.3	12.7
50	17.5	16.7	15.8

″	9	8	7
1	0.2	0.1	0.1
2	0.3	0.3	0.2
3	0.4	0.4	0.4
4	0.6	0.5	0.5
5	0.8	0.7	0.6
6	0.9	0.8	0.7
7	1.0	0.9	0.8
8	1.2	1.1	0.9
9	1.4	1.2	1.0
10	1.5	1.3	1.2
20	3.0	2.7	2.3
30	4.5	4.0	3.5
40	6.0	5.3	4.7
50	7.5	6.7	5.8

Proportional parts

57°

33°—LOGARITHMS OF TRIGONOMETRIC FUNCTIONS

′	L Sin	d	L Tan	c d	L Ctn	L Cos	d		Proportional parts
0	9.73 611	19	9.81 252	27	0.18 748	9.92 359	8	60	
1	9.73 630	20	9.81 279	28	0.18 721	9.92 351	8	59	
2	9.73 650	19	9.81 307	28	0.18 693	9.92 343	8	58	
3	9.73 669	20	9.81 335	27	0.18 665	9.92 335	9	57	
4	9.73 689	19	9.81 362	28	0.18 638	9.92 326	8	56	
5	9.73 708	19	9.81 390	28	0.18 610	9.92 318	8	55	
6	9.73 727	20	9.81 418	27	0.18 582	9.92 310	8	54	
7	9.73 747	19	9.81 445	28	0.18 555	9.92 302	9	53	″ 28 27
8	9.73 766	19	9.81 473	27	0.18 527	9.92 293	8	52	
9	9.73 785	20	9.81 500	28	0.18 500	9.92 285	8	51	1 0.5 0.4
									2 0.9 0.9
10	9.73 805	19	9.81 528	28	0.18 472	9.92 277	8	50	3 1.4 1.4
11	9.73 824	19	9.81 556	27	0.18 444	9.92 269	9	49	4 1.9 1.8
12	9.73 843	20	9.81 583	28	0.18 417	9.92 260	8	48	
13	9.73 863	19	9.81 611	27	0.18 389	9.92 252	8	47	5 2.3 2.2
14	9.73 882	19	9.81 638	28	0.18 362	9.92 244	9	46	6 2.8 2.7
									7 3.3 3.2
15	9.73 901	20	9.81 666	27	0.18 334	9.92 235	8	45	8 3.7 3.6
16	9.73 921	19	9.81 693	28	0.18 307	9.92 227	8	44	9 4.2 4.0
17	9.73 940	19	9.81 721	27	0.18 279	9.92 219	8	43	
18	9.73 959	19	9.81 748	28	0.18 252	9.92 211	9	42	10 4.7 4.5
19	9.73 978	19	9.81 776	27	0.18 224	9.92 202	8	41	20 9.3 9.0
									30 14.0 13.5
20	9.73 997	20	9.81 803	28	0.18 197	9.92 194	8	40	40 18.7 18.0
21	9.74 017	19	9.81 831	27	0.18 169	9.92 186	8	39	50 23.3 22.5
22	9.74 036	19	9.81 858	28	0.18 142	9.92 177	8	38	
23	9.74 055	19	9.81 886	27	0.18 114	9.92 169	8	37	
24	9.74 074	19	9.81 913	28	0.18 087	9.92 161	9	36	″ 20 19 18
25	9.74 093	20	9.81 941	27	0.18 059	9.92 152	8	35	1 0.3 0.3 0.3
26	9.74 113	19	9.81 968	28	0.18 032	9.92 144	8	34	2 0.7 0.6 0.6
27	9.74 132	19	9.81 996	28	0.18 004	9.92 136	9	33	3 1.0 1.0 0.9
28	9.74 151	19	9.82 023	28	0.17 977	9.92 127	8	32	4 1.3 1.3 1.2
29	9.74 170	19	9.82 051	27	0.17 949	9.92 119	8	31	
									5 1.7 1.6 1.5
30	9.74 189	19	9.82 078	28	0.17 922	9.92 111	9	30	6 2.0 1.9 1.8
31	9.74 208	19	9.82 106	27	0.17 894	9.92 102	8	29	7 2.3 2.2 2.1
32	9.74 227	19	9.82 133	28	0.17 867	9.92 094	8	28	8 2.7 2.5 2.4
33	9.74 246	19	9.82 161	27	0.17 839	9.92 086	9	27	9 3.0 2.8 2.7
34	9.74 265	19	9.82 188	27	0.17 812	9.92 077	8	26	
									10 3.3 3.2 3.0
35	9.74 284	19	9.82 215	28	0.17 785	9.92 069	9	25	20 6.7 6.3 6.0
36	9.74 303	19	9.82 243	27	0.17 757	9.92 060	8	24	30 10.0 9.5 9.0
37	9.74 322	19	9.82 270	28	0.17 730	9.92 052	8	23	40 13.3 12.7 12.0
38	9.74 341	19	9.82 298	27	0.17 702	9.92 044	9	22	50 16.7 15.8 15.0
39	9.74 360	19	9.82 325	27	0.17 675	9.92 035	8	21	
40	9.74 379	19	9.82 352	28	0.17 648	9.92 027	9	20	″ 9 8
41	9.74 398	19	9.82 380	27	0.17 620	9.92 018	8	19	
42	9.74 417	19	9.82 407	28	0.17 593	9.92 010	8	18	1 0.2 0.1
43	9.74 436	19	9.82 435	27	0.17 565	9.92 002	9	17	2 0.3 0.3
44	9.74 455	19	9.82 462	27	0.17 538	9.91 993	8	16	3 0.4 0.4
									4 0.6 0.5
45	9.74 474	19	9.82 489	28	0.17 511	9.91 985	9	15	
46	9.74 493	19	9.82 517	27	0.17 483	9.91 976	8	14	5 0.8 0.7
47	9.74 512	19	9.82 544	27	0.17 456	9.91 968	9	13	6 0.9 0.8
48	9.74 531	19	9.82 571	28	0.17 429	9.91 959	8	12	7 1.0 0.9
49	9.74 549	19	9.82 599	27	0.17 401	9.91 951	9	11	8 1.2 1.1
									9 1.4 1.2
50	9.74 568	19	9.82 626	27	0.17 374	9.91 942	8	10	
51	9.74 587	19	9.82 653	28	0.17 347	9.91 934	9	9	10 1.5 1.3
52	9.74 606	19	9.82 681	27	0.17 319	9.91 925	8	8	20 3.0 2.7
53	9.74 625	19	9.82 708	27	0.17 292	9.91 917	9	7	30 4.5 4.0
54	9.74 644	18	9.82 735	27	0.17 265	9.91 908	8	6	40 6.0 5.3
									50 7.5 6.7
55	9.74 662	19	9.82 762	28	0.17 238	9.91 900	9	5	
56	9.74 681	19	9.82 790	27	0.17 210	9.91 891	8	4	
57	9.74 700	19	9.82 817	27	0.17 183	9.91 883	9	3	
58	9.74 719	18	9.82 844	27	0.17 156	9.91 874	8	2	
59	9.74 737	19	9.82 871	28	0.17 129	9.91 866	9	1	
60	9.74 756		9.82 899		0.17 101	9.91 857		0	
	L Cos	d	L Ctn	c d	L Tan	L Sin	d	′	Proportional parts

Table IV   Page 153

34°—LOGARITHMS OF TRIGONOMETRIC FUNCTIONS

′	L Sin	d	L Tan	c d	L Ctn	L Cos	d		Proportional parts
0	9.74 756	19	9.82 899	27	0.17 101	9.91 857	8	60	
1	9.74 775	19	9.82 926	27	0.17 074	9.91 849	9	59	
2	9.74 794	18	9.82 953	27	0.17 047	9.91 840	8	58	
3	9.74 812	19	9.82 980	28	0.17 020	9.91 832	9	57	
4	9.74 831	19	9.83 008	27	0.16 992	9.91 823	8	56	
5	9.74 850	18	9.83 035	27	0.16 965	9.91 815	9	55	″ 28 27 26
6	9.74 868	19	9.83 062	27	0.16 938	9.91 806	8	54	
7	9.74 887	19	9.83 089	28	0.16 911	9.91 798	8	53	1 0.5 0.4 0.4
8	9.74 906	18	9.83 117	27	0.16 883	9.91 789	8	52	2 0.9 0.9 0.9
9	9.74 924	19	9.83 144	27	0.16 856	9.91 781	9	51	3 1.4 1.4 1.3
10	9.74 943	18	9.83 171	27	0.16 829	9.91 772	9	50	4 1.9 1.8 1.7
11	9.74 961	19	9.83 198	27	0.16 802	9.91 763	8	49	5 2.3 2.2 2.2
12	9.74 980	19	9.83 225	27	0.16 775	9.91 755	9	48	6 2.8 2.7 2.6
13	9.74 999	18	9.83 252	28	0.16 748	9.91 746	8	47	7 3.3 3.2 3.0
14	9.75 017	19	9.83 280	27	0.16 720	9.91 738	9	46	8 3.7 3.6 3.5
15	9.75 036	18	9.83 307	27	0.16 693	9.91 729	9	45	9 4.2 4.0 3.9
16	9.75 054	19	9.83 334	27	0.16 666	9.91 720	8	44	10 4.7 4.5 4.3
17	9.75 073	18	9.83 361	27	0.16 639	9.91 712	9	43	20 9.3 9.0 8.7
18	9.75 091	19	9.83 388	27	0.16 612	9.91 703	8	42	30 14.0 13.5 13.0
19	9.75 110	18	9.83 415	27	0.16 585	9.91 695	9	41	40 18.7 18.0 17.3
20	9.75 128	19	9.83 442	28	0.16 558	9.91 686	9	40	50 23.3 22.5 21.7
21	9.75 147	18	9.83 470	27	0.16 530	9.91 677	8	39	
22	9.75 165	19	9.83 497	27	0.16 503	9.91 669	9	38	
23	9.75 184	18	9.83 524	27	0.16 476	9.91 660	9	37	″ 19 18
24	9.75 202	19	9.83 551	27	0.16 449	9.91 651	8	36	
25	9.75 221	18	9.83 578	27	0.16 422	9.91 643	9	35	1 0.3 0.3
26	9.75 239	19	9.83 605	27	0.16 395	9.91 634	9	34	2 0.6 0.6
27	9.75 258	18	9.83 632	27	0.16 368	9.91 625	8	33	3 1.0 0.9
28	9.75 276	18	9.83 659	27	0.16 341	9.91 617	9	32	4 1.3 1.2
29	9.75 294	19	9.83 686	27	0.16 314	9.91 608	9	31	
30	9.75 313	18	9.83 713	27	0.16 287	9.91 599	8	30	5 1.6 1.5
31	9.75 331	19	9.83 740	28	0.16 260	9.91 591	9	29	6 1.9 1.8
32	9.75 350	18	9.83 768	27	0.16 232	9.91 582	9	28	7 2.2 2.1
33	9.75 368	18	9.83 795	27	0.16 205	9.91 573	8	27	8 2.5 2.4
34	9.75 386	19	9.83 822	27	0.16 178	9.91 565	9	26	9 2.8 2.7
35	9.75 405	18	9.83 849	27	0.16 151	9.91 556	9	25	10 3.2 3.0
36	9.75 423	18	9.83 876	27	0.16 124	9.91 547	9	24	20 6.3 6.0
37	9.75 441	18	9.83 903	27	0.16 097	9.91 538	8	23	30 9.5 9.0
38	9.75 459	19	9.83 930	27	0.16 070	9.91 530	9	22	40 12.7 12.0
39	9.75 478	18	9.83 957	27	0.16 043	9.91 521	9	21	50 15.8 15.0
40	9.75 496	18	9.83 984	27	0.16 016	9.91 512	8	20	
41	9.75 514	19	9.84 011	27	0.15 989	9.91 504	9	19	″ 9 8
42	9.75 533	18	9.84 038	27	0.15 962	9.91 495	9	18	
43	9.75 551	18	9.84 065	27	0.15 935	9.91 486	9	17	1 0.2 0.1
44	9.75 569	18	9.84 092	27	0.15 908	9.91 477	8	16	2 0.3 0.3
45	9.75 587	18	9.84 119	27	0.15 881	9.91 469	9	15	3 0.4 0.4
46	9.75 605	19	9.84 146	27	0.15 854	9.91 460	9	14	4 0.6 0.5
47	9.75 624	18	9.84 173	27	0.15 827	9.91 451	9	13	5 0.8 0.7
48	9.75 642	18	9.84 200	27	0.15 800	9.91 442	9	12	6 0.9 0.8
49	9.75 660	18	9.84 227	27	0.15 773	9.91 433	8	11	7 1.0 0.9
50	9.75 678	18	9.84 254	26	0.15 746	9.91 425	9	10	8 1.2 1.1
51	9.75 696	18	9.84 280	27	0.15 720	9.91 416	9	9	9 1.4 1.2
52	9.75 714	19	9.84 307	27	0.15 693	9.91 407	9	8	10 1.5 1.3
53	9.75 733	18	9.84 334	27	0.15 666	9.91 398	9	7	20 3.0 2.7
54	9.75 751	18	9.84 361	27	0.15 639	9.91 389	8	6	30 4.5 4.0
55	9.75 769	18	9.84 388	27	0.15 612	9.91 381	9	5	40 6.0 5.3
56	9.75 787	18	9.84 415	27	0.15 585	9.91 372	9	4	50 7.5 6.7
57	9.75 805	18	9.84 442	27	0.15 558	9.91 363	9	3	
58	9.75 823	18	9.84 469	27	0.15 531	9.91 354	9	2	
59	9.75 841	18	9.84 496	27	0.15 504	9.91 345	9	1	
60	9.75 859		9.84 523		0.15 477	9.91 336		0	
	L Cos	d	L Ctn	c d	L Tan	L Sin	d	′	Proportional parts

35°—LOGARITHMS OF TRIGONOMETRIC FUNCTIONS

′	L Sin	d	L Tan	c d	L Ctn	L Cos	d		Proportional parts			
0	9.75 859	8	9.84 523	27	0.15 477	9.91 336	8	60				
1	9.75 877	18	9.84 550	26	0.15 450	9.91 328	9	59				
2	9.75 895	18	9.84 576	27	0.15 424	9.91 319	9	58				
3	9.75 913	18	9.84 603	27	0.15 397	9.91 310	9	57				
4	9.75 931	18	9.84 630	27	0.15 370	9.91 301	9	56				
5	9.75 949	18	9.84 657	27	0.15 343	9.91 292	9	55	″	27	26	18
6	9.75 967	18	9.84 684	27	0.15 316	9.91 283	9	54				
7	9.75 985	18	9.84 711	27	0.15 289	9.91 274	8	53				
8	9.76 003	18	9.84 738	26	0.15 262	9.91 266	9	52	1	0.4	0.4	0.3
9	9.76 021	18	9.84 764	27	0.15 236	9.91 257	9	51	2	0.9	0.9	0.6
									3	1.4	1.3	0.9
10	9.76 039	18	9.84 791	27	0.15 209	9.91 248	9	50	4	1.8	1.7	1.2
11	9.76 057	18	9.84 818	27	0.15 182	9.91 239	9	49				
12	9.76 075	18	9.84 845	27	0.15 155	9.91 230	9	48	5	2.2	2.2	1.5
13	9.76 093	18	9.84 872	27	0.15 128	9.91 221	9	47	6	2.7	2.6	1.8
14	9.76 111	18	9.84 899	26	0.15 101	9.91 212	9	46	7	3.2	3.0	2.1
									8	3.6	3.5	2.4
15	9.76 129	17	9.84 925	27	0.15 075	9.91 203	9	45	9	4.0	3.9	2.7
16	9.76 146	18	9.84 952	27	0.15 048	9.91 194	9	44				
17	9.76 164	18	9.84 979	27	0.15 021	9.91 185	9	43	10	4.5	4.3	3.0
18	9.76 182	18	9.85 006	27	0.14 994	9.91 176	9	42	20	9.0	8.7	6.0
19	9.76 200	18	9.85 033	26	0.14 967	9.91 167	9	41	30	13.5	13.0	9.0
									40	18.0	17.3	12.0
20	9.76 218	18	9.85 059	27	0.14 941	9.91 158	9	40	50	22.5	21.7	15.0
21	9.76 236	17	9.85 086	27	0.14 914	9.91 149	9	39				
22	9.76 253	18	9.85 113	27	0.14 887	9.91 141	8	38				
23	9.76 271	18	9.85 140	26	0.14 860	9.91 132	9	37				
24	9.76 289	18	9.85 166	27	0.14 834	9.91 123	9	36	″	17	10	
25	9.76 307	17	9.85 193	27	0.14 807	9.91 114	9	35	1	0.3	0.2	
26	9.76 324	18	9.85 220	27	0.14 780	9.91 105	9	34	2	0.6	0.3	
27	9.76 342	18	9.85 247	26	0.14 753	9.91 096	9	33	3	0.8	0.5	
28	9.76 360	18	9.85 273	27	0.14 727	9.91 087	9	32	4	1.1	0.7	
29	9.76 378	17	9.85 300	27	0.14 700	9.91 078	9	31				
									5	1.4	0.8	
30	9.76 395	18	9.85 327	27	0.14 673	9.91 069	9	30	6	1.7	1.0	
31	9.76 413	18	9.85 354	26	0.14 646	9.91 060	9	29	7	2.0	1.2	
32	9.76 431	17	9.85 380	27	0.14 620	9.91 051	9	28	8	2.3	1.3	
33	9.76 448	18	9.85 407	27	0.14 593	9.91 042	9	27	9	2.6	1.5	
34	9.76 466	18	9.85 434	26	0.14 566	9.91 033	10	26				
									10	2.8	1.7	
35	9.76 484	17	9.85 460	27	0.14 540	9.91 023	9	25	20	5.7	3.3	
36	9.76 501	18	9.85 487	27	0.14 513	9.91 014	9	24	30	8.5	5.0	
37	9.76 519	18	9.85 514	26	0.14 486	9.91 005	9	23	40	11.3	6.7	
38	9.76 537	17	9.85 540	27	0.14 460	9.90 996	9	22	50	14.2	8.3	
39	9.76 554	18	9.85 567	27	0.14 433	9.90 987	9	21				
40	9.76 572	18	9.85 594	26	0.14 406	9.90 978	9	20				
41	9.76 590	17	9.85 620	27	0.14 380	9.90 969	9	19	″	9	8	
42	9.76 607	18	9.85 647	27	0.14 353	9.90 960	9	18				
43	9.76 625	17	9.85 674	26	0.14 326	9.90 951	9	17	1	0.2	0.1	
44	9.76 642	18	9.85 700	27	0.14 300	9.90 942	9	16	2	0.3	0.3	
									3	0.4	0.4	
45	9.76 660	17	9.85 727	27	0.14 273	9.90 933	9	15	4	0.6	0.5	
46	9.76 677	18	9.85 754	26	0.14 246	9.90 924	9	14				
47	9.76 695	17	9.85 780	27	0.14 220	9.90 915	9	13	5	0.8	0.7	
48	9.76 712	18	9.85 807	27	0.14 193	9.90 906	10	12	6	0.9	0.8	
49	9.76 730	17	9.85 834	26	0.14 166	9.90 896	9	11	7	1.0	0.9	
									8	1.2	1.1	
50	9.76 747	18	9.85 860	27	0.14 140	9.90 887	9	10	9	1.4	1.2	
51	9.76 765	17	9.85 887	26	0.14 113	9.90 878	9	9				
52	9.76 782	18	9.85 913	27	0.14 087	9.90 869	9	8	10	1.5	1.3	
53	9.76 800	17	9.85 940	27	0.14 060	9.90 860	9	7	20	3.0	2.7	
54	9.76 817	18	9.85 967	26	0.14 033	9.90 851	9	6	30	4.5	4.0	
									40	6.0	5.3	
55	9.76 835	17	9.85 993	27	0.14 007	9.90 842	10	5	50	7.5	6.7	
56	9.76 852	18	9.86 020	26	0.13 980	9.90 832	9	4				
57	9.76 870	17	9.86 046	27	0.13 954	9.90 823	9	3				
58	9.76 887	17	9.86 073	27	0.13 927	9.90 814	9	2				
59	9.76 904	18	9.86 100	26	0.13 900	9.90 805	9	1				
60	9.76 922		9.86 126		0.13 874	9.90 796		0				
—	L Cos	d	L Ctn	c d	L Tan	L Sin	d	′	Proportional parts			

54°

Table IV   Page 155

36°—LOGARITHMS OF TRIGONOMETRIC FUNCTIONS

′	L Sin	d	L Tan	c d	L Ctn	L Cos	d	
0	9.76 922	17	9.86 126	27	0.13 874	9.90 796	9	60
1	9.76 939	18	9.86 153	26	0.13 847	9.90 787	10	59
2	9.76 957	17	9.86 179	27	0.13 821	9.90 777	9	58
3	9.76 974	17	9.86 206	26	0.13 794	9.90 768	9	57
4	9.76 991	18	9.86 232	27	0.13 768	9.90 759	9	56
5	9.77 009	17	9.86 259	26	0.13 741	9.90 750	10	55
6	9.77 026	17	9.86 285	27	0.13 715	9.90 741	10	54
7	9.77 043	18	9.86 312	26	0.13 688	9.90 731	9	53
8	9.77 061	17	9.86 338	27	0.13 662	9.90 722	9	52
9	9.77 078	17	9.86 365	27	0.13 635	9.90 713	9	51
10	9.77 095	17	9.86 392	26	0.13 608	9.90 704	10	50
11	9.77 112	18	9.86 418	27	0.13 582	9.90 694	9	49
12	9.77 130	17	9.86 445	26	0.13 555	9.90 685	9	48
13	9.77 147	17	9.86 471	27	0.13 529	9.90 676	9	47
14	9.77 164	17	9.86 498	26	0.13 502	9.90 667	10	46
15	9.77 181	18	9.86 524	27	0.13 476	9.90 657	9	45
16	9.77 199	17	9.86 551	26	0.13 449	9.90 648	9	44
17	9.77 216	17	9.86 577	26	0.13 423	9.90 639	9	43
18	9.77 233	17	9.86 603	27	0.13 397	9.90 630	10	42
19	9.77 250	18	9.86 630	26	0.13 370	9.90 620	9	41
20	9.77 268	17	9.86 656	27	0.13 344	9.90 611	9	40
21	9.77 285	17	9.86 683	26	0.13 317	9.90 602	10	39
22	9.77 302	17	9.86 709	27	0.13 291	9.90 592	9	38
23	9.77 319	17	9.86 736	26	0.13 264	9.90 583	9	37
24	9.77 336	17	9.86 762	27	0.13 238	9.90 574	9	36
25	9.77 353	17	9.86 789	26	0.13 211	9.90 565	10	35
26	9.77 370	17	9.86 815	27	0.13 185	9.90 555	9	34
27	9.77 387	18	9.86 842	26	0.13 158	9.90 546	9	33
28	9.77 405	17	9.86 868	26	0.13 132	9.90 537	10	32
29	9.77 422	17	9.86 894	27	0.13 106	9.90 527	9	31
30	9.77 439	17	9.86 921	26	0.13 079	9.90 518	9	30
31	9.77 456	17	9.86 947	27	0.13 053	9.90 509	10	29
32	9.77 473	17	9.86 974	26	0.13 026	9.90 499	9	28
33	9.77 490	17	9.87 000	27	0.13 000	9.90 490	10	27
34	9.77 507	17	9.87 027	26	0.12 973	9.90 480	9	26
35	9.77 524	17	9.87 053	26	0.12 947	9.90 471	9	25
36	9.77 541	17	9.87 079	27	0.12 921	9.90 462	10	24
37	9.77 558	17	9.87 106	26	0.12 894	9.90 452	9	23
38	9.77 575	17	9.87 132	26	0.12 868	9.90 443	9	22
39	9.77 592	17	9.87 158	27	0.12 842	9.90 434	10	21
40	9.77 609	17	9.87 185	26	0.12 815	9.90 424	9	20
41	9.77 626	17	9.87 211	27	0.12 789	9.90 415	10	19
42	9.77 643	17	9.87 238	26	0.12 762	9.90 405	10	18
43	9.77 660	17	9.87 264	26	0.12 736	9.90 396	9	17
44	9.77 677	17	9.87 290	27	0.12 710	9.90 386	9	16
45	9.77 694	17	9.87 317	26	0.12 683	9.90 377	9	15
46	9.77 711	17	9.87 343	26	0.12 657	9.90 368	10	14
47	9.77 728	16	9.87 369	27	0.12 631	9.90 358	9	13
48	9.77 744	17	9.87 396	26	0.12 604	9.90 349	10	12
49	9.77 761	17	9.87 422	26	0.12 578	9.90 339	9	11
50	9.77 778	17	9.87 448	27	0.12 552	9.90 330	10	10
51	9.77 795	17	9.87 475	26	0.12 525	9.90 320	9	9
52	9.77 812	17	9.87 501	26	0.12 499	9.90 311	10	8
53	9.77 829	17	9.87 527	27	0.12 473	9.90 301	9	7
54	9.77 846	16	9.87 554	26	0.12 446	9.90 292	10	6
55	9.77 862	17	9.87 580	26	0.12 420	9.90 282	9	5
56	9.77 879	17	9.87 606	27	0.12 394	9.90 273	10	4
57	9.77 896	17	9.87 633	26	0.12 367	9.90 263	9	3
58	9.77 913	17	9.87 659	26	0.12 341	9.90 254	10	2
59	9.77 930	16	9.87 685	26	0.12 315	9.90 244	9	1
60	9.77 946		9.87 711		0.12 289	9.90 235		0
	L Cos	d	L Ctn	c d	L Tan	L Sin	d	′

Proportional parts

″	27	26
1	0.4	0.4
2	0.9	0.9
3	1.4	1.3
4	1.8	1.7
5	2.2	2.2
6	2.7	2.6
7	3.2	3.0
8	3.6	3.5
9	4.0	3.9
10	4.5	4.3
20	9.0	8.7
30	13.5	13.0
40	18.0	17.3
50	22.5	21.7

″	18	17	16
1	0.3	0.3	0.3
2	0.6	0.6	0.5
3	0.9	0.8	0.8
4	1.2	1.1	1.1
5	1.5	1.4	1.3
6	1.8	1.7	1.6
7	2.1	2.0	1.9
8	2.4	2.3	2.1
9	2.7	2.6	2.4
10	3.0	2.8	2.7
20	6.0	5.7	5.3
30	9.0	8.5	8.0
40	12.0	11.3	10.7
50	15.0	14.2	13.3

″	10	9
1	0.2	0.2
2	0.3	0.3
3	0.5	0.4
4	0.7	0.6
5	0.8	0.8
6	1.0	0.9
7	1.2	1.0
8	1.3	1.2
9	1.5	1.4
10	1.7	1.5
20	3.3	3.0
30	5.0	4.5
40	6.7	6.0
50	8.3	7.5

Proportional parts

37°—LOGARITHMS OF TRIGONOMETRIC FUNCTIONS

′	L Sin	d	L Tan	c d	L Ctn	L Cos	d	′
0	9.77 946	17	9.87 711	27	0.12 289	9.90 235	10	60
1	9.77 963	17	9.87 738	26	0.12 262	9.90 225	9	59
2	9.77 980	17	9.87 764	26	0.12 236	9.90 216	10	58
3	9.77 997	16	9.87 790	27	0.12 210	9.90 206	9	57
4	9.78 013	17	9.87 817	26	0.12 183	9.90 197	10	56
5	9.78 030	17	9.87 843	26	0.12 157	9.90 187	9	55
6	9.78 047	16	9.87 869	26	0.12 131	9.90 178	10	54
7	9.78 063	17	9.87 895	27	0.12 105	9.90 168	9	53
8	9.78 080	17	9.87 922	26	0.12 078	9.90 159	10	52
9	9.78 097	16	9.87 948	26	0.12 052	9.90 149	10	51
10	9.78 113	17	9.87 974	26	0.12 026	9.90 139	9	50
11	9.78 130	17	9.88 000	27	0.12 000	9.90 130	10	49
12	9.78 147	16	9.88 027	26	0.11 973	9.90 120	9	48
13	9.78 163	17	9.88 053	26	0.11 947	9.90 111	10	47
14	9.78 180	17	9.88 079	26	0.11 921	9.90 101	10	46
15	9.78 197	16	9.88 105	26	0.11 895	9.90 091	9	45
16	9.78 213	17	9.88 131	27	0.11 869	9.90 082	10	44
17	9.78 230	16	9.88 158	26	0.11 842	9.90 072	9	43
18	9.78 246	17	9.88 184	26	0.11 816	9.90 063	10	42
19	9.78 263	17	9.88 210	26	0.11 790	9.90 053	10	41
20	9.78 280	16	9.88 236	26	0.11 764	9.90 043	9	40
21	9.78 296	17	9.88 262	27	0.11 738	9.90 034	10	39
22	9.78 313	16	9.88 289	26	0.11 711	9.90 024	10	38
23	9.78 329	17	9.88 315	26	0.11 685	9.90 014	9	37
24	9.78 346	16	9.88 341	26	0.11 659	9.90 005	10	36
25	9.78 362	17	9.88 367	26	0.11 633	9.89 995	10	35
26	9.78 379	16	9.88 393	27	0.11 607	9.89 985	9	34
27	9.78 395	17	9.88 420	26	0.11 580	9.89 976	10	33
28	9.78 412	16	9.88 446	26	0.11 554	9.89 966	10	32
29	9.78 428	17	9.88 472	26	0.11 528	9.89 956	9	31
30	9.78 445	16	9.88 498	26	0.11 502	9.89 947	10	30
31	9.78 461	17	9.88 524	26	0.11 476	9.89 937	10	29
32	9.78 478	16	9.88 550	27	0.11 450	9.89 927	9	28
33	9.78 494	16	9.88 577	26	0.11 423	9.89 918	10	27
34	9.78 510	17	9.88 603	26	0.11 397	9.89 908	10	26
35	9.78 527	16	9.88 629	26	0.11 371	9.89 898	10	25
36	9.78 543	17	9.88 655	26	0.11 345	9.89 888	9	24
37	9.78 560	16	9.88 681	26	0.11 319	9.89 879	10	23
38	9.78 576	16	9.88 707	26	0.11 293	9.89 869	10	22
39	9.78 592	17	9.88 733	26	0.11 267	9.89 859	10	21
40	9.78 609	16	9.88 759	27	0.11 241	9.89 849	9	20
41	9.78 625	17	9.88 786	26	0.11 214	9.89 840	10	19
42	9.78 642	16	9.88 812	26	0.11 188	9.89 830	10	18
43	9.78 658	16	9.88 838	26	0.11 162	9.89 820	10	17
44	9.78 674	17	9.88 864	26	0.11 136	9.89 810	9	16
45	9.78 691	16	9.88 890	26	0.11 110	9.89 801	10	15
46	9.78 707	16	9.88 916	26	0.11 084	9.89 791	10	14
47	9.78 723	16	9.88 942	26	0.11 058	9.89 781	10	13
48	9.78 739	17	9.88 968	26	0.11 032	9.89 771	10	12
49	9.78 756	16	9.88 994	26	0.11 006	9.89 761	9	11
50	9.78 772	16	9.89 020	26	0.10 980	9.89 752	10	10
51	9.78 788	17	9.89 046	27	0.10 954	9.89 742	10	9
52	9.78 805	16	9.89 073	26	0.10 927	9.89 732	10	8
53	9.78 821	16	9.89 099	26	0.10 901	9.89 722	10	7
54	9.78 837	16	9.89 125	26	0.10 875	9.89 712	10	6
55	9.78 853	16	9.89 151	26	0.10 849	9.89 702	9	5
56	9.78 869	17	9.89 177	26	0.10 823	9.89 693	10	4
57	9.78 886	16	9.89 203	26	0.10 797	9.89 683	10	3
58	9.78 902	16	9.89 229	26	0.10 771	9.89 673	10	2
59	9.78 918	16	9.89 255	26	0.10 745	9.89 663	10	1
60	9.78 934		9.89 281		0.10 719	9.89 653		0
	L Cos	d	L Ctn	c d	L Tan	L Sin	d	′

Proportional parts

″	27	26
1	0.4	0.4
2	0.9	0.9
3	1.4	1.3
4	1.8	1.7
5	2.2	2.2
6	2.7	2.6
7	3.2	3.0
8	3.6	3.5
9	4.0	3.9
10	4.5	4.3
20	9.0	8.7
30	13.5	13.0
40	18.0	17.3
50	22.5	21.7

″	17	16
1	0.3	0.3
2	0.6	0.5
3	0.8	0.8
4	1.1	1.1
5	1.4	1.3
6	1.7	1.6
7	2.0	1.9
8	2.3	2.1
9	2.6	2.4
10	2.8	2.7
20	5.7	5.3
30	8.5	8.0
40	11.3	10.7
50	14.2	13.3

″	10	9
1	0.2	0.2
2	0.3	0.3
3	0.5	0.4
4	0.7	0.6
5	0.8	0.8
6	1.0	0.9
7	1.2	1.0
8	1.3	1.2
9	1.5	1.4
10	1.7	1.5
20	3.3	3.0
30	5.0	4.5
40	6.7	6.0
50	8.3	7.5

Proportional parts

52°

Table IV   **Page 157**

38°—LOGARITHMS OF TRIGONOMETRIC FUNCTIONS

′	L Sin	d	L Tan	c d	L Ctn	L Cos	d	
0	9.78 934	16	9.89 281	26	0.10 719	9.89 653	10	60
1	9.78 950	17	9.89 307	26	0.10 693	9.89 643	10	59
2	9.78 967	16	9.89 333	26	0.10 667	9.89 633	9	58
3	9.78 983	16	9.89 359	26	0.10 641	9.89 624	10	57
4	9.78 999	16	9.89 385	26	0.10 615	9.89 614	10	56
5	9.79 015	16	9.89 411	26	0.10 589	9.89 604	10	55
6	9.79 031	16	9.89 437	26	0.10 563	9.89 594	10	54
7	9.79 047	16	9.89 463	26	0.10 537	9.89 584	10	53
8	9.79 063	16	9.89 489	26	0.10 511	9.89 574	10	52
9	9.79 079	16	9.89 515	26	0.10 485	9.89 564	10	51
10	9.79 095	16	9.89 541	26	0.10 459	9.89 554	10	50
11	9.79 111	17	9.89 567	26	0.10 433	9.89 544	10	49
12	9.79 128	16	9.89 593	26	0.10 407	9.89 534	10	48
13	9.79 144	16	9.89 619	26	0.10 381	9.89 524	10	47
14	9.79 160	16	9.89 645	26	0.10 355	9.89 514	10	46
15	9.79 176	16	9.89 671	26	0.10 329	9.89 504	9	45
16	9.79 192	16	9.89 697	26	0.10 303	9.89 495	10	44
17	9.79 208	16	9.89 723	26	0.10 277	9.89 485	10	43
18	9.79 224	16	9.89 749	26	0.10 251	9.89 475	10	42
19	9.79 240	16	9.89 775	26	0.10 225	9.89 465	10	41
20	9.79 256	16	9.89 801	26	0.10 199	9.89 455	10	40
21	9.79 272	16	9.89 827	26	0.10 173	9.89 445	10	39
22	9.79 288	16	9.89 853	26	0.10 147	9.89 435	10	38
23	9.79 304	15	9.89 879	26	0.10 121	9.89 425	10	37
24	9.79 319	16	9.89 905	26	0.10 095	9.89 415	10	36
25	9.79 335	16	9.89 931	26	0.10 069	9.89 405	10	35
26	9.79 351	16	9.89 957	26	0.10 043	9.89 395	10	34
27	9.79 367	16	9.89 983	26	0.10 017	9.89 385	10	33
28	9.79 383	16	9.90 009	26	0.09 991	9.89 375	11	32
29	9.79 399	16	9.90 035	26	0.09 965	9.89 364	10	31
30	9.79 415	16	9.90 061	25	0.09 939	9.89 354	10	30
31	9.79 431	16	9.90 086	26	0.09 914	9.89 344	10	29
32	9.79 447	16	9.90 112	26	0.09 888	9.89 334	10	28
33	9.79 463	15	9.90 138	26	0.09 862	9.89 324	10	27
34	9.79 478	16	9.90 164	26	0.09 836	9.89 314	10	26
35	9.79 494	16	9.90 190	26	0.09 810	9.89 304	10	25
36	9.79 510	16	9.90 216	26	0.09 784	9.89 294	10	24
37	9.79 526	16	9.90 242	26	0.09 758	9.89 284	10	23
38	9.79 542	16	9.90 268	26	0.09 732	9.89 274	10	22
39	9.79 558	15	9.90 294	26	0.09 706	9.89 264	10	21
40	9.79 573	16	9.90 320	26	0.09 680	9.89 254	10	20
41	9.79 589	16	9.90 346	25	0.09 654	9.89 244	11	19
42	9.79 605	16	9.90 371	26	0.09 629	9.89 233	10	18
43	9.79 621	15	9.90 397	26	0.09 603	9.89 223	10	17
44	9.79 636	16	9.90 423	26	0.09 577	9.89 213	10	16
45	9.79 652	16	9.90 449	26	0.09 551	9.89 203	10	15
46	9.79 668	16	9.90 475	26	0.09 525	9.89 193	10	14
47	9.79 684	15	9.90 501	26	0.09 499	9.89 183	10	13
48	9.79 699	16	9.90 527	26	0.09 473	9.89 173	11	12
49	9.79 715	16	9.90 553	25	0.09 447	9.89 162	11	11
50	9.79 731	15	9.90 578	26	0.09 422	9.89 152	10	10
51	9.79 746	16	9.90 604	26	0.09 396	9.89 142	10	9
52	9.79 762	16	9.90 630	26	0.09 370	9.89 132	10	8
53	9.79 778	15	9.90 656	26	0.09 344	9.89 122	10	7
54	9.79 793	16	9.90 682	26	0.09 318	9.89 112	11	6
55	9.79 809	16	9.90 708	26	0.09 292	9.89 101	10	5
56	9.79 825	15	9.90 734	25	0.09 266	9.89 091	10	4
57	9.79 840	16	9.90 759	26	0.09 241	9.89 081	10	3
58	9.79 856	16	9.90 785	26	0.09 215	9.89 071	11	2
59	9.79 872	15	9.90 811	26	0.09 189	9.89 060	10	1
60	9.79 887		9.90 837		0.09 163	9.89 050		0

| | L Cos | d | L Ctn | c d | L Tan | L Sin | d | ′ |

Proportional parts

″	26	25
1	0.4	0.4
2	0.9	0.8
3	1.3	1.2
4	1.7	1.7
5	2.2	2.1
6	2.6	2.5
7	3.0	2.9
8	3.5	3.3
9	3.9	3.8
10	4.3	4.2
20	8.7	8.3
30	13.0	12.5
40	17.3	16.7
50	21.7	20.8

″	17	16	15
1	0.3	0.3	0.2
2	0.6	0.5	0.5
3	0.8	0.8	0.8
4	1.1	1.1	1.0
5	1.4	1.3	1.2
6	1.7	1.6	1.5
7	2.0	1.9	1.8
8	2.3	2.1	2.0
9	2.6	2.4	2.2
10	2.8	2.7	2.5
20	5.7	5.3	5.0
30	8.5	8.0	7.5
40	11.3	10.7	10.0
50	14.2	13.3	12.5

″	11	10	9
1	0.2	0.2	0.2
2	0.4	0.3	0.3
3	0.6	0.5	0.4
4	0.7	0.7	0.6
5	0.9	0.8	0.8
6	1.1	1.0	0.9
7	1.3	1.2	1.0
8	1.5	1.3	1.2
9	1.6	1.5	1.4
10	1.8	1.7	1.5
20	3.7	3.3	3.0
30	5.5	5.0	4.5
40	7.3	6.7	6.0
50	9.2	8.3	7.5

Proportional parts

51°

39°—LOGARITHMS OF TRIGONOMETRIC FUNCTIONS

′	L Sin	d	L Tan	c d	L Ctn	L Cos	d	
0	9.79 887	16	9.90 837	26	0.09 163	9.89 050	10	60
1	9.79 903	15	9.90 863	26	0.09 137	9.89 040	10	59
2	9.79 918	16	9.90 889	25	0.09 111	9.89 030	10	58
3	9.79 934	16	9.90 914	26	0.09 086	9.89 020	11	57
4	9.79 950	15	9.90 940	26	0.09 060	9.89 009	10	56
5	9.79 965	16	9.90 966	26	0.09 034	9.88 999	10	55
6	9.79 981	15	9.90 992	26	0.09 008	9.88 989	10	54
7	9.79 996	16	9.91 018	25	0.08 982	9.88 978	11	53
8	9.80 012	15	9.91 043	26	0.08 957	9.88 968	10	52
9	9.80 027	16	9.91 069	26	0.08 931	9.88 958	10	51
10	9.80 043	15	9.91 095	26	0.08 905	9.88 948	11	50
11	9.80 058	16	9.91 121	26	0.08 879	9.88 937	10	49
12	9.80 074	15	9.91 147	25	0.08 853	9.88 927	10	48
13	9.80 089	16	9.91 172	26	0.08 828	9.88 917	11	47
14	9.80 105	15	9.91 198	26	0.08 802	9.88 906	10	46
15	9.80 120	16	9.91 224	26	0.08 776	9.88 896	10	45
16	9.80 136	15	9.91 250	26	0.08 750	9.88 886	11	44
17	9.80 151	15	9.91 276	25	0.08 724	9.88 875	10	43
18	9.80 166	16	9.91 301	26	0.08 699	9.88 865	10	42
19	9.80 182	15	9.91 327	26	0.08 673	9.88 855	11	41
20	9.80 197	16	9.91 353	26	0.08 647	9.88 844	10	40
21	9.80 213	15	9.91 379	25	0.08 621	9.88 834	10	39
22	9.80 228	16	9.91 404	26	0.08 596	9.88 824	11	38
23	9.80 244	15	9.91 430	26	0.08 570	9.88 813	10	37
24	9.80 259	15	9.91 456	26	0.08 544	9.88 803	10	36
25	9.80 274	16	9.91 482	25	0.08 518	9.88 793	11	35
26	9.80 290	15	9.91 507	26	0.08 493	9.88 782	10	34
27	9.80 305	15	9.91 533	26	0.08 467	9.88 772	11	33
28	9.80 320	16	9.91 559	26	0.08 441	9.88 761	10	32
29	9.80 336	15	9.91 585	25	0.08 415	9.88 751	10	31
30	9.80 351	15	9.91 610	26	0.08 390	9.88 741	11	30
31	9.80 366	16	9.91 636	26	0.08 364	9.88 730	10	29
32	9.80 382	15	9.91 662	26	0.08 338	9.88 720	11	28
33	9.80 397	15	9.91 688	25	0.08 312	9.88 709	10	27
34	9.80 412	16	9.91 713	26	0.08 287	9.88 699	11	26
35	9.80 428	15	9.91 739	26	0.08 261	9.88 688	10	25
36	9.80 443	15	9.91 765	26	0.08 235	9.88 678	10	24
37	9.80 458	15	9.91 791	25	0.08 209	9.88 668	11	23
38	9.80 473	16	9.91 816	26	0.08 184	9.88 657	10	22
39	9.80 489	15	9.91 842	26	0.08 158	9.88 647	11	21
40	9.80 504	15	9.91 868	25	0.08 132	9.88 636	10	20
41	9.80 519	15	9.91 893	26	0.08 107	9.88 626	11	19
42	9.80 534	16	9.91 919	26	0.08 081	9.88 615	10	18
43	9.80 550	15	9.91 945	26	0.03 055	9.88 605	11	17
44	9.80 565	15	9.91 971	25	0.08 029	9.88 594	10	16
45	9.80 580	15	9.91 996	26	0.08 004	9.88 584	11	15
46	9.80 595	15	9.92 022	26	0.07 978	9.88 573	10	14
47	9.80 610	15	9.92 048	25	0.07 952	9.88 563	11	13
48	9.80 625	16	9.92 073	26	0.07 927	9.88 552	10	12
49	9.80 641	15	9.92 099	26	0.07 901	9.88 542	11	11
50	9.80 656	15	9.92 125	25	0.07 875	9.88 531	10	10
51	9.80 671	15	9.92 150	26	0.07 850	9.88 521	11	9
52	9.80 686	15	9.92 176	26	0.07 824	9.88 510	11	8
53	9.80 701	15	9.92 202	26	0.07 798	9.88 499	10	7
54	9.80 716	15	9.92 227	26	0.07 773	9.88 489	11	6
55	9.80 731	15	9.92 253	26	0.07 747	9.88 478	10	5
56	9.80 746	16	9.92 279	25	0.07 721	9.88 468	11	4
57	9.80 762	15	9.92 304	26	0.07 696	9.88 457	10	3
58	9.80 777	15	9.92 330	26	0.07 670	9.88 447	11	2
59	9.80 792	15	9.92 356	25	0.07 644	9.88 436	11	1
60	9.80 807		9.92 381		0.07 619	9.88 425		0
	L Cos	d	L Ctn	c d	L Tan	L Sin	d	′

Proportional parts

″	26	25
1	0.4	0.4
2	0.9	0.8
3	1.3	1.2
4	1.7	1.7
5	2.2	2.1
6	2.6	2.5
7	3.0	2.9
8	3.5	3.3
9	3.9	3.8
10	4.3	4.2
20	8.7	8.3
30	13.0	12.5
40	17.3	16.7
50	21.7	20.8

″	16	15
1	0.3	0.2
2	0.5	0.5
3	0.8	0.8
4	1.1	1.0
5	1.3	1.2
6	1.6	1.5
7	1.9	1.8
8	2.1	2.0
9	2.4	2.2
10	2.7	2.5
20	5.3	5.0
30	8.0	7.5
40	10.7	10.0
50	13.3	12.5

″	11	10
1	0.2	0.2
2	0.4	0.3
3	0.6	0.5
4	0.7	0.7
5	0.9	0.8
6	1.1	1.0
7	1.3	1.2
8	1.5	1.3
9	1.6	1.5
10	1.8	1.7
20	3.7	3.3
30	5.5	5.0
40	7.3	6.7
50	9.2	8.3

Proportional parts

50°

Table IV Page 159
40°—LOGARITHMS OF TRIGONOMETRIC FUNCTIONS

′	L Sin	d	L Tan	c d	L Ctn	L Cos	d		Proportional parts		
0	9.80 807	15	9.92 381	26	0.07 619	9.88 425	10	60			
1	9.80 822	15	9.92 407	26	0.07 593	9.88 415	11	59			
2	9.80 837	15	9.92 433	25	0.07 567	9.88 404	10	58			
3	9.80 852	15	9.92 458	26	0.07 542	9.88 394	11	57			
4	9.80 867	15	9.92 484	26	0.07 516	9.88 383	11	56		″	26	25
5	9.80 882	15	9.92 510	25	0.07 490	9.88 372	10	55	1	0.4	0.4
6	9.80 897	15	9.92 535	26	0.07 465	9.88 362	11	54	2	0.9	0.8
7	9.80 912	15	9.92 561	26	0.07 439	9.88 351	11	53	3	1.3	1.2
8	9.80 927	15	9.92 587	25	0.07 413	9.88 340	10	52	4	1.7	1.7
9	9.80 942	15	9.92 612	26	0.07 388	9.88 330	11	51			
									5	2.2	2.1
10	9.80 957	15	9.92 638	25	0.07 362	9.88 319	11	50	6	2.6	2.5
11	9.80 972	15	9.92 663	26	0.07 337	9.88 308	10	49	7	3.0	2.9
12	9.80 987	15	9.92 689	26	0.07 311	9.88 298	11	48	8	3.5	3.3
13	9.81 002	15	9.92 715	25	0.07 285	9.88 287	11	47	9	3.9	3.8
14	9.81 017	15	9.92 740	26	0.07 260	9.88 276	10	46			
									10	4.3	4.2
15	9.81 032	15	9.92 766	26	0.07 234	9.88 266	11	45	20	8.7	8.3
16	9.81 047	14	9.92 792	25	0.07 208	9.88 255	11	44	30	13.0	12.5
17	9.81 061	15	9.92 817	26	0.07 183	9.88 244	10	43	40	17.3	16.7
18	9.81 076	15	9.92 843	25	0.07 157	9.88 234	11	42	50	21.7	20.8
19	9.81 091	15	9.92 868	26	0.07 132	9.88 223	11	41			
20	9.81 106	15	9.92 894	26	0.07 106	9.88 212	11	40			
21	9.81 121	15	9.92 920	25	0.07 080	9.88 201	10	39		″	15	14
22	9.81 136	15	9.92 945	26	0.07 055	9.88 191	11	38			
23	9.81 151	15	9.92 971	25	0.07 029	9.88 180	11	37	1	0.2	0.2
24	9.81 166	14	9.92 996	26	0.07 004	9.88 169	11	36	2	0.5	0.5
									3	0.8	0.7
25	9.81 180	15	9.93 022	26	0.06 978	9.88 158	10	35	4	1.0	0.9
26	9.81 195	15	9.93 048	25	0.06 952	9.88 148	11	34			
27	9.81 210	15	9.93 073	26	0.06 927	9.88 137	11	33	5	1.2	1.2
28	9.81 225	15	9.93 099	25	0.06 901	9.88 126	11	32	6	1.5	1.4
29	9.81 240	14	9.93 124	26	0.06 876	9.88 115	10	31	7	1.8	1.6
									8	2.0	1.9
30	9.81 254	15	9.93 150	25	0.06 850	9.88 105	11	30	9	2.2	2.1
31	9.81 269	15	9.93 175	26	0.06 825	9.88 094	11	29			
32	9.81 284	15	9.93 201	26	0.06 799	9.88 083	11	28	10	2.5	2.3
33	9.81 299	15	9.93 227	25	0.06 773	9.88 072	11	27	20	5.0	4.7
34	9.81 314	14	9.93 252	26	0.06 748	9.88 061	10	26	30	7.5	7.0
									40	10.0	9.3
35	9.81 328	15	9.93 278	25	0.06 722	9.88 051	11	25	50	12.5	11.7
36	9.81 343	15	9.93 303	26	0.06 697	9.88 040	11	24			
37	9.81 358	14	9.93 329	25	0.06 671	9.88 029	11	23			
38	9.81 372	15	9.93 354	26	0.06 646	9.88 018	11	22			
39	9.81 387	15	9.93 380	26	0.06 620	9.88 007	11	21		″	11	10
40	9.81 402	15	9.93 406	25	0.06 594	9.87 996	11	20	1	0.2	0.2
41	9.81 417	14	9.93 431	26	0.06 569	9.87 985	10	19	2	0.4	0.3
42	9.81 431	15	9.93 457	25	0.06 543	9.87 975	11	18	3	0.6	0.5
43	9.81 446	15	9.93 482	26	0.06 518	9.87 964	11	17	4	0.7	0.7
44	9.81 461	14	9.93 508	25	0.06 492	9.87 953	11	16			
									5	0.9	0.8
45	9.81 475	15	9.93 533	26	0.06 467	9.87 942	11	15	6	1.1	1.0
46	9.81 490	15	9.93 559	25	0.06 441	9.87 931	11	14	7	1.3	1.2
47	9.81 505	14	9.93 584	26	0.06 416	9.87 920	11	13	8	1.5	1.3
48	9.81 519	15	9.93 610	26	0.06 390	9.87 909	11	12	9	1.6	1.5
49	9.81 534	15	9.93 636	25	0.06 364	9.87 898	11	11			
									10	1.8	1.7
50	9.81 549	14	9.93 661	26	0.06 339	9.87 887	10	10	20	3.7	3.3
51	9.81 563	15	9.93 687	25	0.06 313	9.87 877	11	9	30	5.5	5.0
52	9.81 578	14	9.93 712	26	0.06 288	9.87 866	11	8	40	7.3	6.7
53	9.81 592	15	9.93 738	25	0.06 262	9.87 855	11	7	50	9.2	8.3
54	9.81 607	15	9.93 763	26	0.06 237	9.87 844	11	6			
55	9.81 622	14	9.93 789	25	0.06 211	9.87 833	11	5			
56	9.81 636	15	9.93 814	26	0.06 186	9.87 822	11	4			
57	9.81 651	14	9.93 840	25	0.06 160	9.87 811	11	3			
58	9.81 665	15	9.93 865	26	0.06 135	9.87 800	11	2			
59	9.81 680	14	9.93 891	25	0.06 109	9.87 789	11	1			
60	9.81 694		9.93 916		0.06 084	9.87 778		0			
—	L Cos	d	L Ctn	c d	L Tan	L Sin	d	′	Proportional parts		

41°—LOGARITHMS OF TRIGONOMETRIC FUNCTIONS

′	L Sin	d	L Tan	c d	L Ctn	L Cos	d	
0	9.81 694	15	9.93 916	26	0.06 084	9.87 778	11	60
1	9.81 709	14	9.93 942	25	0.06 058	9.87 767	11	59
2	9.81 723	15	9.93 967	26	0.06 033	9.87 756	11	58
3	9.81 738	14	9.93 993	25	0.06 007	9.87 745	11	57
4	9.81 752	15	9.94 018	26	0.05 982	9.87 734	11	56
5	9.81 767	14	9.94 044	25	0.05 956	9.87 723	11	55
6	9.81 781	15	9.94 069	26	0.05 931	9.87 712	11	54
7	9.81 796	14	9.94 095	25	0.05 905	9.87 701	11	53
8	9.81 810	15	9.94 120	26	0.05 880	9.87 690	11	52
9	9.81 825	14	9.94 146	25	0.05 854	9.87 679	11	51
10	9.81 839	15	9.94 171	26	0.05 829	9.87 668	11	50
11	9.81 854	14	9.94 197	25	0.05 803	9.87 657	11	49
12	9.81 868	14	9.94 222	26	0.05 778	9.87 646	11	48
13	9.81 882	15	9.94 248	25	0.05 752	9.87 635	11	47
14	9.81 897	14	9.94 273	26	0.05 727	9.87 624	11	46
15	9.81 911	15	9.94 299	25	0.05 701	9.87 613	12	45
16	9.81 926	14	9.94 324	26	0.05 676	9.87 601	11	44
17	9.81 940	15	9.94 350	25	0.05 650	9.87 590	11	43
18	9.81 955	14	9.94 375	26	0.05 625	9.87 579	11	42
19	9.81 969	14	9.94 401	25	0.05 599	9.87 568	11	41
20	9.81 983	15	9.94 426	26	0.05 574	9.87 557	11	40
21	9.81 998	14	9.94 452	25	0.05 548	9.87 546	11	39
22	9.82 012	14	9.94 477	26	0.05 523	9.87 535	11	38
23	9.82 026	15	9.94 503	25	0.05 497	9.87 524	11	37
24	9.82 041	14	9.94 528	26	0.05 472	9.87 513	12	36
25	9.82 055	14	9.94 554	25	0.05 446	9.87 501	11	35
26	9.82 069	15	9.94 579	25	0.05 421	9.87 490	11	34
27	9.82 084	14	9.94 604	26	0.05 396	9.87 479	11	33
28	9.82 098	14	9.94 630	25	0.05 370	9.87 468	11	32
29	9.82 112	14	9.94 655	26	0.05 345	9.87 457	11	31
30	9.82 126	15	9.94 681	25	0.05 319	9.87 446	12	30
31	9.82 141	14	9.94 706	26	0.05 294	9.87 434	11	29
32	9.82 155	14	9.94 732	25	0.05 268	9.87 423	11	28
33	9.82 169	15	9.94 757	26	0.05 243	9.87 412	11	27
34	9.82 184	14	9.94 783	25	0.05 217	9.87 401	11	26
35	9.82 198	14	9.94 808	26	0.05 192	9.87 390	12	25
36	9.82 212	14	9.94 834	25	0.05 166	9.87 378	11	24
37	9.82 226	14	9.94 859	25	0.05 141	9.87 367	11	23
38	9.82 240	15	9.94 884	26	0.05 116	9.87 356	11	22
39	9.82 255	14	9.94 910	25	0.05 090	9.87 345	11	21
40	9.82 269	14	9.94 935	26	0.05 065	9.87 334	12	20
41	9.82 283	14	9.94 961	25	0.05 039	9.87 322	11	19
42	9.82 297	14	9.94 986	26	0.05 014	9.87 311	11	18
43	9.82 311	15	9.95 012	25	0.04 988	9.87 300	12	17
44	9.82 326	14	9.95 037	25	0.04 963	9.87 288	11	16
45	9.82 340	14	9.95 062	26	0.04 938	9.87 277	11	15
46	9.82 354	14	9.95 088	25	0.04 912	9.87 266	11	14
47	9.82 368	14	9.95 113	26	0.04 887	9.87 255	12	13
48	9.82 382	14	9.95 139	25	0.04 861	9.87 243	11	12
49	9.82 396	14	9.95 164	26	0.04 836	9.87 232	11	11
50	9.82 410	14	9.95 190	25	0.04 810	9.87 221	12	10
51	9.82 424	15	9.95 215	25	0.04 785	9.87 209	11	9
52	9.82 439	14	9.95 240	26	0.04 760	9.87 198	11	8
53	9.82 453	14	9.95 266	25	0.04 734	9.87 187	12	7
54	9.82 467	14	9.95 291	26	0.04 709	9.87 175	11	6
55	9.82 481	14	9.95 317	25	0.04 683	9.87 164	11	5
56	9.82 495	14	9.95 342	26	0.04 658	9.87 153	12	4
57	9.82 509	14	9.95 368	25	0.04 632	9.87 141	11	3
58	9.82 523	14	9.95 393	25	0.04 607	9.87 130	11	2
59	9.82 537	14	9.95 418	26	0.04 582	9.87 119	12	1
60	9.82 551		9.95 444		0.04 556	9.87 107		0
	L Cos	d	L Ctn	c d	L Tan	L Sin	d	′

Proportional parts

″	26	25
1	0.4	0.4
2	0.9	0.8
3	1.3	1.2
4	1.7	1.7
5	2.2	2.1
6	2.6	2.5
7	3.0	2.9
8	3.5	3.3
9	3.9	3.8
10	4.3	4.2
20	8.7	8.3
30	13.0	12.5
40	17.3	16.7
50	21.7	20.8

″	15	14
1	0.2	0.2
2	0.5	0.5
3	0.8	0.7
4	1.0	0.9
5	1.2	1.2
6	1.5	1.4
7	1.8	1.6
8	2.0	1.9
9	2.2	2.1
10	2.5	2.3
20	5.0	4.7
30	7.5	7.0
40	10.0	9.3
50	12.5	11.7

″	12	11
1	0.2	0.2
2	0.4	0.4
3	0.6	0.6
4	0.8	0.7
5	1.0	0.9
6	1.2	1.1
7	1.4	1.3
8	1.6	1.5
9	1.8	1.6
10	2.0	1.8
20	4.0	3.7
30	6.0	5.5
40	8.0	7.3
50	10.0	9.2

Proportional parts

48°

Table IV   *Page 161*

42°—LOGARITHMS OF TRIGONOMETRIC FUNCTIONS

′	L Sin	d	L Tan	c d	L Ctn	L Cos	d		Proportional parts		
0	9.82 551	14	9.95 444	25	0.04 556	9.87 107	11	60			
1	9.82 565	14	9.95 469	26	0.04 531	9.87 096	11	59			
2	9.82 579	14	9.95 495	25	0.04 505	9.87 085	12	58			
3	9.82 593	14	9.95 520	25	0.04 480	9.87 073	11	57			
4	9.82 607	14	9.95 545	26	0.04 455	9.87 062	12	56	″	26	25
5	9.82 621	14	9.95 571	25	0.04 429	9.87 050	11	55			
6	9.82 635	14	9.95 596	26	0.04 404	9.87 039	11	54	1	0.4	0.4
7	9.82 649	14	9.95 622	25	0.04 378	9.87 028	12	53	2	0.9	0.8
8	9.82 663	14	9.95 647	25	0.04 353	9.87 016	11	52	3	1.3	1.2
9	9.82 677	14	9.95 672	26	0.04 328	9.87 005	12	51	4	1.7	1.7
10	9.82 691	14	9.95 698	25	0.04 302	9.86 993	11	50	5	2.2	2.1
11	9.82 705	14	9.95 723	25	0.04 277	9.86 982	12	49	6	2.6	2.5
12	9.82 719	14	9.95 748	26	0.04 252	9.86 970	11	48	7	3.0	2.9
13	9.82 733	14	9.95 774	25	0.04 226	9.86 959	12	47	8	3.5	3.3
14	9.82 747	14	9.95 799	26	0.04 201	9.86 947	11	46	9	3.9	3.8
15	9.82 761	14	9.95 825	25	0.04 175	9.86 936	12	45	10	4.3	4.2
16	9.82 775	13	9.95 850	25	0.04 150	9.86 924	11	44	20	8.7	8.3
17	9.82 788	14	9.95 875	26	0.04 125	9.86 913	11	43	30	13.0	12.5
18	9.82 802	14	9.95 901	25	0.04 099	9.86 902	12	42	40	17.3	16.7
19	9.82 816	14	9.95 926	26	0.04 074	9.86 890	11	41	50	21.7	20.8
20	9.82 830	14	9.95 952	25	0.04 048	9.86 879	12	40			
21	9.82 844	14	9.95 977	25	0.04 023	9.86 867	12	39			
22	9.82 858	14	9.96 002	26	0.03 998	9.86 855	11	38	″	14	13
23	9.82 872	13	9.96 028	25	0.03 972	9.86 844	12	37			
24	9.82 885	14	9.96 053	25	0.03 947	9.86 832	11	36	1	0.2	0.2
25	9.82 899	14	9.96 078	26	0.03 922	9.86 821	12	35	2	0.5	0.4
26	9.82 913	14	9.96 104	25	0.03 896	9.86 809	11	34	3	0.7	0.6
27	9.82 927	14	9.96 129	26	0.03 871	9.86 798	12	33	4	0.9	0.9
28	9.82 941	14	9.96 155	25	0.03 845	9.86 786	11	32	5	1.2	1.1
29	9.82 955	13	9.96 180	25	0.03 820	9.86 775	12	31	6	1.4	1.3
30	9.82 968	14	9.96 205	26	0.03 795	9.86 763	11	30	7	1.6	1.5
31	9.82 982	14	9.96 231	25	0.03 769	9.86 752	12	29	8	1.9	1.7
32	9.82 996	14	9.96 256	25	0.03 744	9.86 740	12	28	9	2.1	2.0
33	9.83 010	13	9.96 281	26	0.03 719	9.86 728	11	27	10	2.3	2.2
34	9.83 023	14	9.96 307	25	0.03 693	9.86 717	12	26	20	4.7	4.3
35	9.83 037	14	9.96 332	25	0.03 668	9.86 705	11	25	30	7.0	6.5
36	9.83 051	14	9.96 357	26	0.03 643	9.86 694	12	24	40	9.3	8.7
37	9.83 065	13	9.96 383	25	0.03 617	9.86 682	12	23	50	11.7	10.8
38	9.83 078	14	9.96 408	25	0.03 592	9.86 670	11	22			
39	9.83 092	14	9.96 433	26	0.03 567	9.86 659	12	21			
40	9.83 106	14	9.96 459	25	0.03 541	9.86 647	12	20	″	12	11
41	9.83 120	13	9.96 484	26	0.03 516	9.86 635	11	19	1	0.2	0.2
42	9.83 133	14	9.96 510	25	0.03 490	9.86 624	12	18	2	0.4	0.4
43	9.83 147	14	9.96 535	25	0.03 465	9.86 612	12	17	3	0.6	0.6
44	9.83 161	13	9.96 560	26	0.03 440	9.86 600	11	16	4	0.8	0.7
45	9.83 174	14	9.96 586	25	0.03 414	9.86 589	12	15	5	1.0	0.9
46	9.83 188	14	9.96 611	25	0.03 389	9.86 577	12	14	6	1.2	1.1
47	9.83 202	13	9.96 636	26	0.03 364	9.86 565	11	13	7	1.4	1.3
48	9.83 215	14	9.96 662	25	0.03 338	9.86 554	12	12	8	1.6	1.5
49	9.83 229	13	9.96 687	25	0.03 313	9.86 542	12	11	9	1.8	1.6
50	9.83 242	14	9.96 712	26	0.03 288	9.86 530	12	10	10	2.0	1.8
51	9.83 256	14	9.96 738	25	0.03 262	9.86 518	11	9	20	4.0	3.7
52	9.83 270	13	9.96 763	25	0.03 237	9.86 507	12	8	30	6.0	5.5
53	9.83 283	14	9.96 788	26	0.03 212	9.86 495	12	7	40	8.0	7.3
54	9.83 297	13	9.96 814	25	0.03 186	9.86 483	11	6	50	10.0	9.2
55	9.83 310	14	9.96 839	25	0.03 161	9.86 472	12	5			
56	9.83 324	14	9.96 864	26	0.03 136	9.86 460	12	4			
57	9.83 338	13	9.96 890	25	0.03 110	9.86 448	12	3			
58	9.83 351	14	9.96 915	25	0.03 085	9.86 436	11	2			
59	9.83 365	13	9.96 940	26	0.03 060	9.86 425	12	1			
60	9.83 378		9.96 966		0.03 034	9.86 413		0			
′	L Cos	d	L Ctn	c d	L Tan	L Sin	d	′	Proportional parts		

43°—LOGARITHMS OF TRIGONOMETRIC FUNCTIONS

'	L Sin	d	L Tan	c d	L Ctn	L Cos	d	'	Proportional parts		
0	9.83 378	14	9.96 966	25	0.03 034	9.86 413	12	60			
1	9.83 392	13	9.96 991	25	0.03 009	9.86 401	12	59			
2	9.83 405	14	9.97 016	26	0.02 984	9.86 389	12	58			
3	9.83 419	13	9.97 042	25	0.02 958	9.86 377	11	57			
4	9.83 432	14	9.97 067	25	0.02 933	9.86 366	12	56			
5	9.83 446	13	9.97 092	26	0.02 908	9.86 354	12	55	''	26	25
6	9.83 459	14	9.97 118	25	0.02 882	9.86 342	12	54			
7	9.83 473	13	9.97 143	25	0.02 857	9.86 330	12	53	1	0.4	0.4
8	9.83 486	14	9.97 168	25	0.02 832	9.86 318	12	52	2	0.9	0.8
9	9.83 500	13	9.97 193	26	0.02 807	9.86 306	11	51	3	1.3	1.2
									4	1.7	1.7
10	9.83 513	14	9.97 219	25	0.02 781	9.86 295	12	50			
11	9.83 527	13	9.97 244	25	0.02 756	9.86 283	12	49	5	2.2	2.1
12	9.83 540	14	9.97 269	26	0.02 731	9.86 271	12	48	6	2.6	2.5
13	9.83 554	13	9.97 295	25	0.02 705	9.86 259	12	47	7	3.0	2.9
14	9.83 567	14	9.97 320	25	0.02 680	9.86 247	12	46	8	3.5	3.3
									9	3.9	3.8
15	9.83 581	13	9.97 345	26	0.02 655	9.86 235	12	45			
16	9.83 594	14	9.97 371	25	0.02 629	9.86 223	12	44	10	4.3	4.2
17	9.83 608	13	9.97 396	25	0.02 604	9.86 211	11	43	20	8.7	8.3
18	9.83 621	13	9.97 421	26	0.02 579	9.86 200	12	42	30	13.0	12.5
19	9.83 634	14	9.97 447	25	0.02 553	9.86 188	12	41	40	17.3	16.7
									50	21.7	20.8
20	9.83 648	13	9.97 472	25	0.02 528	9.86 176	12	40			
21	9.83 661	13	9.97 497	26	0.02 503	9.86 164	12	39			
22	9.83 674	14	9.97 523	25	0.02 477	9.86 152	12	38			
23	9.83 688	13	9.97 548	25	0.02 452	9.86 140	12	37	''	14	13
24	9.83 701	14	9.97 573	25	0.02 427	9.86 128	12	36			
									1	0.2	0.2
25	9.83 715	13	9.97 598	26	0.02 402	9.86 116	12	35	2	0.5	0.4
26	9.83 728	13	9.97 624	25	0.02 376	9.86 104	12	34	3	0.7	0.6
27	9.83 741	14	9.97 649	25	0.02 351	9.86 092	12	33	4	0.9	0.9
28	9.83 755	13	9.97 674	26	0.02 326	9.86 080	12	32			
29	9.83 768	13	9.97 700	25	0.02 300	9.86 068	12	31	5	1.2	1.1
									6	1.4	1.3
30	9.83 781	14	9.97 725	25	0.02 275	9.86 056	12	30	7	1.6	1.5
31	9.83 795	13	9.97 750	26	0.02 250	9.86 044	12	29	8	1.9	1.7
32	9.83 808	13	9.97 776	25	0.02 224	9.86 032	12	28	9	2.1	2.0
33	9.83 821	13	9.97 801	25	0.02 199	9.86 020	12	27			
34	9.83 834	14	9.97 826	25	0.02 174	9.86 008	12	26	10	2.3	2.2
									20	4.7	4.3
35	9.83 848	13	9.97 851	26	0.02 149	9.85 996	12	25	30	7.0	6.5
36	9.83 861	13	9.97 877	25	0.02 123	9.85 984	12	24	40	9.3	8.7
37	9.83 874	13	9.97 902	25	0.02 098	9.85 972	12	23	50	11.7	10.8
38	9.83 887	14	9.97 927	26	0.02 073	9.85 960	12	22			
39	9.83 901	13	9.97 953	25	0.02 047	9.85 948	12	21			
40	9.83 914	13	9.97 978	25	0.02 022	9.85 936	12	20	''	12	11
41	9.83 927	13	9.98 003	26	0.01 997	9.85 924	12	19			
42	9.83 940	14	9.98 029	25	0.01 971	9.85 912	12	18	1	0.2	0.2
43	9.83 954	13	9.98 054	25	0.01 946	9.85 900	12	17	2	0.4	0.4
44	9.83 967	13	9.98 079	25	0.01 921	9.85 888	12	16	3	0.6	0.6
									4	0.8	0.7
45	9.83 980	13	9.98 104	26	0.01 896	9.85 876	12	15			
46	9.83 993	13	9.98 130	25	0.01 870	9.85 864	13	14	5	1.0	0.9
47	9.84 006	14	9.98 155	25	0.01 845	9.85 851	12	13	6	1.2	1.1
48	9.84 020	13	9.98 180	26	0.01 820	9.85 839	12	12	7	1.4	1.3
49	9.84 033	13	9.98 206	25	0.01 794	9.85 827	12	11	8	1.6	1.5
									9	1.8	1.6
50	9.84 046	13	9.98 231	25	0.01 769	9.85 815	12	10			
51	9.84 059	13	9.98 256	25	0.01 744	9.85 803	12	9	10	2.0	1.8
52	9.84 072	13	9.98 281	26	0.01 719	9.85 791	12	8	20	4.0	3.7
53	9.84 085	13	9.98 307	25	0.01 693	9.85 779	13	7	30	6.0	5.5
54	9.84 098	14	9.98 332	25	0.01 668	9.85 766	12	6	40	8.0	7.3
									50	10.0	9.2
55	9.84 112	13	9.98 357	26	0.01 643	9.85 754	12	5			
56	9.84 125	13	9.98 383	25	0.01 617	9.85 742	12	4			
57	9.84 138	13	9.98 408	25	0.01 592	9.85 730	12	3			
58	9.84 151	13	9.98 433	25	0.01 567	9.85 718	12	2			
59	9.84 164	13	9.98 458	26	0.01 542	9.85 706	13	1			
60	9.84 177		9.98 484		0.01 516	9.85 693		0			
	L Cos	d	L Ctn	c d	L Tan	L Sin	d	'	Proportional parts		

44°—LOGARITHMS OF TRIGONOMETRIC FUNCTIONS

′	L Sin	d	L Tan	c d	L Ctn	L Cos	d		Proportional parts
0	9.84 177	13	9.98 484	25	0.01 516	9.85 693	12	60	
1	9.84 190	13	9.98 509	25	0.01 491	9.85 681	12	59	
2	9.84 203	13	9.98 534	26	0.01 466	9.85 669	12	58	
3	9.84 216	13	9.98 560	25	0.01 440	9.85 657	12	57	
4	9.84 229	13	9.98 585	25	0.01 415	9.85 645	13	56	
5	9.84 242	13	9.98 610	25	0.01 390	9.85 632	12	55	
6	9.84 255	14	9.98 635	26	0.01 365	9.85 620	12	54	
7	9.84 269	13	9.98 661	25	0.01 339	9.85 608	12	53	
8	9.84 282	13	9.98 686	25	0.01 314	9.85 596	13	52	
9	9.84 295	13	9.98 711	26	0.01 289	9.85 583	12	51	
10	9.84 308	13	9.98 737	25	0.01 263	9.85 571	12	50	
11	9.84 321	13	9.98 762	25	0.01 238	9.85 559	12	49	
12	9.84 334	13	9.98 787	25	0.01 213	9.85 547	13	48	
13	9.84 347	13	9.98 812	26	0.01 188	9.85 534	12	47	
14	9.84 360	13	9.98 838	25	0.01 162	9.85 522	12	46	
									″ 26 25
15	9.84 373	12	9.98 863	25	0.01 137	9.85 510	13	45	1 0.4 0.4
16	9.84 385	13	9.98 888	25	0.01 112	9.85 497	12	44	2 0.9 0.8
17	9.84 398	13	9.98 913	26	0.01 087	9.85 485	12	43	3 1.3 1.2
18	9.84 411	13	9.98 939	25	0.01 061	9.85 473	13	42	4 1.7 1.7
19	9.84 424	13	9.98 964	25	0.01 036	9.85 460	12	41	
									5 2.2 2.1
20	9.84 437	13	9.98 989	26	0.01 011	9.85 448	12	40	6 2.6 2.5
21	9.84 450	13	9.99 015	25	0.00 985	9.85 436	13	39	7 3.0 2.9
22	9.84 463	13	9.99 040	25	0.00 960	9.85 423	12	38	8 3.5 3.3
23	9.84 476	13	9.99 065	25	0.00 935	9.85 411	12	37	9 3.9 3.8
24	9.84 489	13	9.99 090	26	0.00 910	9.85 399	13	36	
									10 4.3 4.2
25	9.84 502	13	9.99 116	25	0.00 884	9.85 386	12	35	20 8.7 8.3
26	9.84 515	13	9.99 141	25	0.00 859	9.85 374	13	34	30 13.0 12.5
27	9.84 528	12	9.99 166	25	0.00 834	9.85 361	12	33	40 17.3 16.7
28	9.84 540	13	9.99 191	26	0.00 809	9.85 349	12	32	50 21.7 20.8
29	9.84 553	13	9.99 217	25	0.00 783	9.85 337	13	31	
30	9.84 566	13	9.99 242	25	0.00 758	9.85 324	12	30	
31	9.84 579	13	9.99 267	26	0.00 733	9.85 312	13	29	
32	9.84 592	13	9.99 293	25	0.00 707	9.85 299	12	28	″ 14 13 12
33	9.84 605	13	9.99 318	25	0.00 682	9.85 287	13	27	
34	9.84 618	12	9.99 343	25	0.00 657	9.85 274	12	26	1 0.2 0.2 0.2
									2 0.5 0.4 0.4
35	9.84 630	13	9.99 368	26	0.00 632	9.85 262	12	25	3 0.7 0.6 0.6
36	9.84 643	13	9.99 394	25	0.00 606	9.85 250	13	24	4 0.9 0.9 0.8
37	9.84 656	13	9.99 419	25	0.00 581	9.85 237	12	23	
38	9.84 669	13	9.99 444	25	0.00 556	9.85 225	13	22	5 1.2 1.1 1.0
39	9.84 682	12	9.99 469	26	0.00 531	9.85 212	12	21	6 1.4 1.3 1.2
									7 1.6 1.5 1.4
40	9.84 694	13	9.99 495	25	0.00 505	9.85 200	13	20	8 1.9 1.7 1.6
41	9.84 707	13	9.99 520	25	0.00 480	9.85 187	12	19	9 2.1 2.0 1.8
42	9.84 720	13	9.99 545	25	0.00 455	9.85 175	13	18	
43	9.84 733	12	9.99 570	26	0.00 430	9.85 162	12	17	10 2.3 2.2 2.0
44	9.84 745	13	9.99 596	25	0.00 404	9.85 150	13	16	20 4.7 4.3 4.0
									30 7.0 6.5 6.0
45	9.84 758	13	9.99 621	25	0.00 379	9.85 137	12	15	40 9.3 8.7 8.0
46	9.84 771	13	9.99 646	26	0.00 354	9.85 125	13	14	50 11.7 10.8 10.0
47	9.84 784	12	9.99 672	25	0.00 328	9.85 112	12	13	
48	9.84 796	13	9.99 697	25	0.00 303	9.85 100	13	12	
49	9.84 809	13	9.99 722	25	0.00 278	9.85 087	13	11	
50	9.84 822	13	9.99 747	26	0.00 253	9.85 074	12	10	
51	9.84 835	12	9.99 773	25	0.00 227	9.85 062	13	9	
52	9.84 847	13	9.99 798	25	0.00 202	9.85 049	12	8	
53	9.84 860	13	9.99 823	25	0.00 177	9.85 037	13	7	
54	9.84 873	12	9.99 848	26	0.00 152	9.85 024	12	6	
55	9.84 885	13	9.99 874	25	0.00 126	9.85 012	13	5	
56	9.84 898	13	9.99 899	25	0.00 101	9.84 999	13	4	
57	9.84 911	12	9.99 924	25	0.00 076	9.84 986	12	3	
58	9.84 923	13	9.99 949	26	0.00 051	9.84 974	13	2	
59	9.84 936	13	9.99 975	25	0.00 025	9.84 961	12	1	
60	9.84 949		0.00 000		0.00 000	9.84 949		0	
	L Cos	d	L Ctn	c d	L Tan	L Sin	d	′	Proportional parts

Table V

NATURAL TRIGONOMETRIC FUNCTIONS

0°				179°		1°				178°	
'	**Sin**	**Tan**	**Ctn**	**Cos**		**'**	**Sin**	**Tan**	**Ctn**	**Cos**	
0	.00000	.00000	———	1.0000	60	0	.01745	.01746	57.290	.99985	60
1	.00029	.00029	3437.7	1.0000	59	1	.01774	.01775	56.351	.99984	59
2	.00058	.00058	1718.9	1.0000	58	2	.01803	.01804	55.442	.99984	58
3	.00087	.00087	1145.9	1.0000	57	3	.01832	.01833	54.561	.99983	57
4	.00116	.00116	859.44	1.0000	56	4	.01862	.01862	53.709	.99983	56
5	.00145	.00145	687.55	1.0000	55	5	.01891	.01891	52.882	.99982	55
6	.00175	.00175	572.96	1.0000	54	6	.01920	.01920	52.081	.99982	54
7	.00204	.00204	491.11	1.0000	53	7	.01949	.01949	51.303	.99981	53
8	.00233	.00233	429.72	1.0000	52	8	.01978	.01978	50.549	.99980	52
9	.00262	.00262	381.97	1.0000	51	9	.02007	.02007	49.816	.99980	51
10	.00291	.00291	343.77	1.0000	50	10	.02036	.02036	49.104	.99979	50
11	.00320	.00320	312.52	.99999	49	11	.02065	.02066	48.412	.99979	49
12	.00349	.00349	286.48	.99999	48	12	.02094	.02095	47.740	.99978	48
13	.00378	.00378	264.44	.99999	47	13	.02123	.02124	47.085	.99977	47
14	.00407	.00407	245.55	.99999	46	14	.02152	.02153	46.449	.99977	46
15	.00436	.00436	229.18	.99999	45	15	.02181	.02182	45.829	.99976	45
16	.00465	.00465	214.86	.99999	44	16	.02211	.02211	45.226	.99976	44
17	.00495	.00495	202.22	.99999	43	17	.02240	.02240	44.639	.99975	43
18	.00524	.00524	190.98	.99999	42	18	.02269	.02269	44.066	.99974	42
19	.00553	.00553	180.93	.99998	41	19	.02298	.02298	43.508	.99974	41
20	.00582	.00582	171.89	.99998	40	20	.02327	.02328	42.964	.99973	40
21	.00611	.00611	163.70	.99998	39	21	.02356	.02357	42.433	.99972	39
22	.00640	.00640	156.26	.99998	38	22	.02385	.02386	41.916	.99972	38
23	.00669	.00669	149.47	.99998	37	23	.02414	.02415	41.411	.99971	37
24	.00698	.00698	143.24	.99998	36	24	.02443	.02444	40.917	.99970	36
25	.00727	.00727	137.51	.99997	35	25	.02472	.02473	40.436	.99969	35
26	.00756	.00756	132.22	.99997	34	26	.02501	.02502	39.965	.99969	34
27	.00785	.00785	127.32	.99997	33	27	.02530	.02531	39.506	.99968	33
28	.00814	.00815	122.77	.99997	32	28	.02560	.02560	39.057	.99967	32
29	.00844	.00844	118.54	.99996	31	29	.02589	.02589	38.618	.99966	31
30	.00873	.00873	114.59	.99996	30	30	.02618	.02619	38.188	.99966	30
31	.00902	.00902	110.89	.99996	29	31	.02647	.02648	37.769	.99965	29
32	.00931	.00931	107.43	.99996	28	32	.02676	.02677	37.358	.99964	28
33	.00960	.00960	104.17	.99995	27	33	.02705	.02706	36.956	.99963	27
34	.00989	.00989	101.11	.99995	26	34	.02734	.02735	36.563	.99963	26
35	.01018	.01018	98.218	.99995	25	35	.02763	.02764	36.178	.99962	25
36	.01047	.01047	95.489	.99995	24	36	.02792	.02793	35.801	.99961	24
37	.01076	.01076	92.908	.99994	23	37	.02821	.02822	35.431	.99960	23
38	.01105	.01105	90.463	.99994	22	38	.02850	.02851	35.070	.99959	22
39	.01134	.01135	88.144	.99994	21	39	.02879	.02881	34.715	.99959	21
40	.01164	.01164	85.940	.99993	20	40	.02908	.02910	34.368	.99958	20
41	.01193	.01193	83.844	.99993	19	41	.02938	.02939	34.027	.99957	19
42	.01222	.01222	81.847	.99993	18	42	.02967	.02968	33.694	.99956	18
43	.01251	.01251	79.943	.99992	17	43	.02996	.02997	33.366	.99955	17
44	.01280	.01280	78.126	.99992	16	44	.03025	.03026	33.045	.99954	16
45	.01309	.01309	76.390	.99991	15	45	.03054	.03055	32.730	.99953	15
46	.01338	.01338	74.729	.99991	14	46	.03083	.03084	32.421	.99952	14
47	.01367	.01367	73.139	.99991	13	47	.03112	.03114	32.118	.99952	13
48	.01396	.01396	71.615	.99990	12	48	.03141	.03143	31.821	.99951	12
49	.01425	.01425	70.153	.99990	11	49	.03170	.03172	31.528	.99950	11
50	.01454	.01455	68.750	.99989	10	50	.03199	.03201	31.242	.99949	10
51	.01483	.01484	67.402	.99989	9	51	.03228	.03230	30.960	.99948	9
52	.01513	.01513	66.105	.99989	8	52	.03257	.03259	30.683	.99947	8
53	.01542	.01542	64.858	.99988	7	53	.03286	.03288	30.412	.99946	7
54	.01571	.01571	63.657	.99988	6	54	.03316	.03317	30.145	.99945	6
55	.01600	.01600	62.499	.99987	5	55	.03345	.03346	29.882	.99944	5
56	.01629	.01629	61.383	.99987	4	56	.03374	.03376	29.624	.99943	4
57	.01658	.01658	60.306	.99986	3	57	.03403	.03405	29.371	.99942	3
58	.01687	.01687	59.266	.99986	2	58	.03432	.03434	29.122	.99941	2
59	.01716	.01716	58.261	.99985	1	59	.03461	.03463	28.877	.99940	1
60	.01745	.01746	57.290	.99985	0	60	.03490	.03492	28.636	.99939	0
	Cos	**Ctn**	**Tan**	**Sin**	**'**		**Cos**	**Ctn**	**Tan**	**Sin**	**'**

| 90° | | | | 89° | | 91° | | | | 88° | |

Table V **NATURAL TRIGONOMETRIC FUNCTIONS** *Page 165*

2°   **177°**   **3°**   **176°**

′	Sin	Tan	Ctn	Cos		′	Sin	Tan	Ctn	Cos	
0	.03490	.03492	28.636	.99939	60	0	.05234	.05241	19.081	.99863	60
1	.03519	.03521	28.399	.99938	59	1	.05263	.05270	18.976	.99861	59
2	.03548	.03550	28.166	.99937	58	2	.05292	.05299	18.871	.99860	58
3	.03577	.03579	27.937	.99936	57	3	.05321	.05328	18.768	.99858	57
4	.03606	.03609	27.712	.99935	56	4	.05350	.05357	18.666	.99857	56
5	.03635	.03638	27.490	.99934	55	5	.05379	.05387	18.564	.99855	55
6	.03664	.03667	27.271	.99933	54	6	.05408	.05416	18.464	.99854	54
7	.03693	.03696	27.057	.99932	53	7	.05437	.05445	18.366	.99852	53
8	.03723	.03725	26.845	.99931	52	8	.05466	.05474	18.268	.99851	52
9	.03752	.03754	26.637	.99930	51	9	.05495	.05503	18.171	.99849	51
10	.03781	.03783	26.432	.99929	50	10	.05524	.05533	18.075	.99847	50
11	.03810	.03812	26.230	.99927	49	11	.05553	.05562	17.980	.99846	49
12	.03839	.03842	26.031	.99926	48	12	.05582	.05591	17.886	.99844	48
13	.03868	.03871	25.835	.99925	47	13	.05611	.05620	17.793	.99842	47
14	.03897	.03900	25.642	.99924	46	14	.05640	.05649	17.702	.99841	46
15	.03926	.03929	25.452	.99923	45	15	.05669	.05678	17.611	.99839	45
16	.03955	.03958	25.264	.99922	44	16	.05698	.05708	17.521	.99838	44
17	.03984	.03987	25.080	.99921	43	17	.05727	.05737	17.431	.99836	43
18	.04013	.04016	24.898	.99919	42	18	.05756	.05766	17.343	.99834	42
19	.04042	.04046	24.719	.99918	41	19	.05785	.05795	17.256	.99833	41
20	.04071	.04075	24.542	.99917	40	20	.05814	.05824	17.169	.99831	40
21	.04104	.04104	24.368	.99916	39	21	.05844	.05854	17.084	.99829	39
22	.04129	.04133	24.196	.99915	38	22	.05873	.05883	16.999	.99827	38
23	.04159	.04162	24.026	.99913	37	23	.05902	.05912	16.915	.99826	37
24	.04188	.04191	23.859	.99912	36	24	.05931	.05941	16.832	.99824	36
25	.04217	.04220	23.695	.99911	35	25	.05960	.05970	16.750	.99822	35
26	.04246	.04250	23.532	.99910	34	26	.05989	.05999	16.668	.99821	34
27	.04275	.04279	23.372	.99909	33	27	.06018	.06029	16.587	.99819	33
28	.04304	.04308	23.214	.99907	32	28	.06047	.06058	16.507	.99817	32
29	.04333	.04337	23.058	.99906	31	29	.06076	.06087	16.428	.99815	31
30	.04362	.04366	22.904	.99905	30	30	.06105	.06116	16.350	.99813	30
31	.04391	.04395	22.752	.99904	29	31	.06134	.06145	16.272	.99812	29
32	.04420	.04424	22.602	.99902	28	32	.06163	.06175	16.195	.99810	28
33	.04449	.04454	22.454	.99901	27	33	.06192	.06204	16.119	.99808	27
34	.04478	.04483	22.308	.99900	26	34	.06221	.06233	16.043	.99806	26
35	.04507	.04512	22.164	.99898	25	35	.06250	.06262	15.969	.99804	25
36	.04536	.04541	22.022	.99897	24	36	.06279	.06291	15.895	.99803	24
37	.04565	.04570	21.881	.99896	23	37	.06308	.06321	15.821	.99801	23
38	.04594	.04599	21.743	.99894	22	38	.06337	.06350	15.748	.99799	22
39	.04623	.04628	21.606	.99893	21	39	.06366	.06379	15.676	.99797	21
40	.04653	.04658	21.470	.99892	20	40	.06395	.06408	15.605	.99795	20
41	.04682	.04687	21.337	.99890	19	41	.06424	.06438	15.534	.99793	19
42	.04711	.04716	21.205	.99889	18	42	.06453	.06467	15.464	.99792	18
43	.04740	.04745	21.075	.99888	17	43	.06482	.06496	15.394	.99790	17
44	.04769	.04774	20.946	.99886	16	44	.06511	.06525	15.325	.99788	16
45	.04798	.04803	20.819	.99885	15	45	.06540	.06554	15.257	.99786	15
46	.04827	.04833	20.693	.99883	14	46	.06569	.06584	15.189	.99784	14
47	.04856	.04862	20.569	.99882	13	47	.06598	.06613	15.122	.99782	13
48	.04885	.04891	20.446	.99881	12	48	.06627	.06642	15.056	.99780	12
49	.04914	.04920	20.325	.99879	11	49	.06656	.06671	14.990	.99778	11
50	.04943	.04949	20.206	.99878	10	50	.06685	.06700	14.924	.99776	10
51	.04972	.04978	20.087	.99876	9	51	.06714	.06730	14.860	.99774	9
52	.05001	.05007	19.970	.99875	8	52	.06743	.06759	14.795	.99772	8
53	.05030	.05037	19.855	.99873	7	53	.06773	.06788	14.732	.99770	7
54	.05059	.05066	19.740	.99872	6	54	.06802	.06817	14.669	.99768	6
55	.05088	.05095	19.627	.99870	5	55	.06831	.06847	14.606	.99766	5
56	.05117	.05124	19.516	.99869	4	56	.06860	.06876	14.544	.99764	4
57	.05146	.05153	19.405	.99867	3	57	.06889	.06905	14.482	.99762	3
58	.05175	.05182	19.296	.99866	2	58	.06918	.06934	14.421	.99760	2
59	.05205	.05212	19.188	.99864	1	59	.06947	.06963	14.361	.99758	1
60	.05234	.05241	19.081	.99863	0	60	.06976	.06993	14.301	.99756	0
	Cos	Ctn	Tan	Sin	′		Cos	Ctn	Tan	Sin	′

NATURAL TRIGONOMETRIC FUNCTIONS

4°			175°			5°			174°

′	Sin	Tan	Ctn	Cos		′	Sin	Tan	Ctn	Cos	
0	.06976	.06993	14.301	.99756	60	0	.08716	.08749	11.430	.99619	60
1	.07005	.07022	14.241	.99754	59	1	.08745	.08778	11.392	.99617	59
2	.07034	.07051	14.182	.99752	58	2	.08774	.08807	11.354	.99614	58
3	.07063	.07080	14.124	.99750	57	3	.08803	.08837	11.316	.99612	57
4	.07092	.07110	14.065	.99748	56	4	.08831	.08866	11.279	.99609	56
5	.07121	.07139	14.008	.99746	55	5	.08860	.08895	11.242	.99607	55
6	.07150	.07168	13.951	.99744	54	6	.08889	.08925	11.205	.99604	54
7	.07179	.07197	13.894	.99742	53	7	.08918	.08954	11.168	.99602	53
8	.07208	.07227	13.838	.99740	52	8	.08947	.08983	11.132	.99599	52
9	.07237	.07256	13.782	.99738	51	9	.08976	.09013	11.095	.99596	51
10	.07266	.07285	13.727	.99736	50	10	.09005	.09042	11.059	.99594	50
11	.07295	.07314	13.672	.99734	49	11	.09034	.09071	11.024	.99591	49
12	.07324	.07344	13.617	.99731	48	12	.09063	.09101	10.988	.99588	48
13	.07353	.07373	13.563	.99729	47	13	.09092	.09130	10.953	.99586	47
14	.07382	.07402	13.510	.99727	46	14	.09121	.09159	10.918	.99583	46
15	.07411	.07431	13.457	.99725	45	15	.09150	.09189	10.883	.99580	45
16	.07440	.07461	13.404	.99723	44	16	.09179	.09218	10.848	.99578	44
17	.07469	.07490	13.352	.99721	43	17	.09208	.09247	10.814	.99575	43
18	.07498	.07519	13.300	.99719	42	18	.09237	.09277	10.780	.99572	42
19	.07527	.07548	13.248	.99716	41	19	.09266	.09306	10.746	.99570	41
20	.07556	.07578	13.197	.99714	40	20	.09295	.09335	10.712	.99567	40
21	.07585	.07607	13.146	.99712	39	21	.09324	.09365	10.678	.99564	39
22	.07614	.07636	13.096	.99710	38	22	.09353	.09394	10.645	.99562	38
23	.07643	.07665	13.046	.99708	37	23	.09382	.09423	10.612	.99559	37
24	.07672	.07695	12.996	.99705	36	24	.09411	.09453	10.579	.99556	36
25	.07701	.07724	12.947	.99703	35	25	.09440	.09482	10.546	.99553	35
26	.07730	.07753	12.898	.99701	34	26	.09469	.09511	10.514	.99551	34
27	.07759	.07782	12.850	.99699	33	27	.09498	.09541	10.481	.99548	33
28	.07788	.07812	12.801	.99696	32	28	.09527	.09570	10.449	.99545	32
29	.07817	.07841	12.754	.99694	31	29	.09556	.09600	10.417	.99542	31
30	.07846	.07870	12.706	.99692	30	30	.09585	.09629	10.385	.99540	30
31	.07875	.07899	12.659	.99689	29	31	.09614	.09658	10.354	.99537	29
32	.07904	.07929	12.612	.99687	28	32	.09642	.09688	10.322	.99534	28
33	.07933	.07958	12.566	.99685	27	33	.09671	.09717	10.291	.99531	27
34	.07962	.07987	12.520	.99683	26	34	.09700	.09746	10.260	.99528	26
35	.07991	.08017	12.474	.99680	25	35	.09729	.09776	10.229	.99526	25
36	.08020	.08046	12.429	.99678	24	36	.09758	.09805	10.199	.99523	24
37	.08049	.08075	12.384	.99676	23	37	.09787	.09834	10.168	.99520	23
38	.08078	.08104	12.339	.99673	22	38	.09816	.09864	10.138	.99517	22
39	.08107	.08134	12.295	.99671	21	39	.09845	.09893	10.108	.99514	21
40	.08136	.08163	12.251	.99668	20	40	.09874	.09923	10.078	.99511	20
41	.08165	.08192	12.207	.99666	19	41	.09903	.09952	10.048	.99508	19
42	.08194	.08221	12.163	.99664	18	42	.09932	.09981	10.019	.99506	18
43	.08223	.08251	12.120	.99661	17	43	.09961	.10011	9.9893	.99503	17
44	.08252	.08280	12.077	.99659	16	44	.09990	.10040	9.9601	.99500	16
45	.08281	.08309	12.035	.99657	15	45	.10019	.10069	9.9310	.99497	15
46	.08310	.08339	11.992	.99654	14	46	.10048	.10099	9.9021	.99494	14
47	.08339	.08368	11.950	.99652	13	47	.10077	.10128	9.8734	.99491	13
48	.08368	.08397	11.909	.99649	12	48	.10106	.10158	9.8448	.99488	12
49	.08397	.08427	11.867	.99647	11	49	.10135	.10187	9.8164	.99485	11
50	.08426	.08456	11.826	.99644	10	50	.10164	.10216	9.7882	.99482	10
51	.08455	.08485	11.785	.99642	9	51	.10192	.10246	9.7601	.99479	9
52	.08484	.08514	11.745	.99639	8	52	.10221	.10275	9.7322	.99476	8
53	.08513	.08544	11.705	.99637	7	53	.10250	.10305	9.7044	.99473	7
54	.08542	.08573	11.664	.99635	6	54	.10279	.10334	9.6768	.99470	6
55	.08571	.08602	11.625	.99632	5	55	.10308	.10363	9.6493	.99467	5
56	.08600	.08632	11.585	.99630	4	56	.10337	.10393	9.6220	.99464	4
57	.08629	.08661	11.546	.99627	3	57	.10366	.10422	9.5949	.99461	3
58	.08658	.08690	11.507	.99625	2	58	.10395	.10452	9.5679	.99458	2
59	.08687	.08720	11.468	.99622	1	59	.10424	.10481	9.5411	.99455	1
60	.08716	.08749	11.430	.99619	0	60	.10453	.10510	9.5144	.99452	0
	Cos	Ctn	Tan	Sin	′		Cos	Ctn	Tan	Sin	′

94°			85°			95°			84°

Table V NATURAL TRIGONOMETRIC FUNCTIONS Page 167

6° 173° 7° 172°

′	Sin	Tan	Ctn	Cos		′	Sin	Tan	Ctn	Cos	
0	.10453	.10510	9.5144	.99452	60	0	.12187	.12278	8.1443	.99255	60
1	.10482	.10540	9.4878	.99449	59	1	.12216	.12308	8.1248	.99251	59
2	.10511	.10569	9.4614	.99446	58	2	.12245	.12338	8.1054	.99248	58
3	.10540	.10599	9.4352	.99443	57	3	.12274	.12367	8.0860	.99244	57
4	.10569	.10628	9.4090	.99440	56	4	.12302	.12397	8.0667	.99240	56
5	.10597	.10657	9.3831	.99437	55	5	.12331	.12426	8.0476	.99237	55
6	.10626	.10687	9.3572	.99434	54	6	.12360	.12456	8.0285	.99233	54
7	.10655	.10716	9.3315	.99431	53	7	.12389	.12485	8.0095	.99230	53
8	.10684	.10746	9.3060	.99428	52	8	.12418	.12515	7.9906	.99226	52
9	.10713	.10775	9.2806	.99424	51	9	.12447	.12544	7.9718	.99222	51
10	.10742	.10805	9.2553	.99421	50	10	.12476	.12574	7.9530	.99219	50
11	.10771	.10834	9.2302	.99418	49	11	.12504	.12603	7.9344	.99215	49
12	.10800	.10863	9.2052	.99415	48	12	.12533	.12633	7.9158	.99211	48
13	.10829	.10893	9.1803	.99412	47	13	.12562	.12662	7.8973	.99208	47
14	.10858	.10922	9.1555	.99409	46	14	.12591	.12692	7.8789	.99204	46
15	.10887	.10952	9.1309	.99406	45	15	.12620	.12722	7.8606	.99200	45
16	.10916	.10981	9.1065	.99402	44	16	.12649	.12751	7.8424	.99197	44
17	.10945	.11011	9.0821	.99399	43	17	.12678	.12781	7.8243	.99193	43
18	.10973	.11040	9.0579	.99396	42	18	.12706	.12810	7.8062	.99189	42
19	.11002	.11070	9.0338	.99393	41	19	.12735	.12840	7.7882	.99186	41
20	.11031	.11099	9.0098	.99390	40	20	.12764	.12869	7.7704	.99182	40
21	.11060	.11128	8.9860	.99386	39	21	.12793	.12899	7.7525	.99178	39
22	.11089	.11158	8.9623	.99383	38	22	.12822	.12929	7.7348	.99175	38
23	.11118	.11187	8.9387	.99380	37	23	.12851	.12958	7.7171	.99171	37
24	.11147	.11217	8.9152	.99377	36	24	.12880	.12988	7.6996	.99167	36
25	.11176	.11246	8.8919	.99374	35	25	.12908	.13017	7.6821	.99163	35
26	.11205	.11276	8.8686	.99370	34	26	.12937	.13047	7.6647	.99160	34
27	.11234	.11305	8.8455	.99367	33	27	.12966	.13076	7.6473	.99156	33
28	.11263	.11335	8.8225	.99364	32	28	.12995	.13106	7.6301	.99152	32
29	.11291	.11364	8.7996	.99360	31	29	.13024	.13136	7.6129	.99148	31
30	.11320	.11394	8.7769	.99357	30	30	.13053	.13165	7.5958	.99144	30
31	.11349	.11423	8.7542	.99354	29	31	.13081	.13195	7.5787	.99141	29
32	.11378	.11452	8.7317	.99351	28	32	.13110	.13224	7.5618	.99137	28
33	.11407	.11482	8.7093	.99347	27	33	.13139	.13254	7.5449	.99133	27
34	.11436	.11511	8.6870	.99344	26	34	.13168	.13284	7.5281	.99129	26
35	.11465	.11541	8.6648	.99341	25	35	.13197	.13313	7.5113	.99125	25
36	.11494	.11570	8.6427	.99337	24	36	.13226	.13343	7.4947	.99122	24
37	.11523	.11600	8.6208	.99334	23	37	.13254	.13372	7.4781	.99118	23
38	.11552	.11629	8.5989	.99331	22	38	.13283	.13402	7.4615	.99114	22
39	.11580	.11659	8.5772	.99327	21	39	.13312	.13432	7.4451	.99110	21
40	.11609	.11688	8.5555	.99324	20	40	.13341	.13461	7.4287	.99106	20
41	.11638	.11718	8.5340	.99320	19	41	.13370	.13491	7.4124	.99102	19
42	.11667	.11747	8.5126	.99317	18	42	.13399	.13521	7.3962	.99098	18
43	.11696	.11777	8.4913	.99314	17	43	.13427	.13550	7.3800	.99094	17
44	.11725	.11806	8.4701	.99310	16	44	.13456	.13580	7.3639	.99091	16
45	.11754	.11836	8.4490	.99307	15	45	.13485	.13609	7.3479	.99087	15
46	.11783	.11865	8.4280	.99303	14	46	.13514	.13639	7.3319	.99083	14
47	.11812	.11895	8.4071	.99300	13	47	.13543	.13669	7.3160	.99079	13
48	.11840	.11924	8.3863	.99297	12	48	.13572	.13698	7.3002	.99075	12
49	.11869	.11954	8.3656	.99293	11	49	.13600	.13728	7.2844	.99071	11
50	.11898	.11983	8.3450	.99290	10	50	.13629	.13758	7.2687	.99067	10
51	.11927	.12013	8.3245	.99286	9	51	.13658	.13787	7.2531	.99063	9
52	.11956	.12042	8.3041	.99283	8	52	.13687	.13817	7.2375	.99059	8
53	.11985	.12072	8.2838	.99279	7	53	.13716	.13846	7.2220	.99055	7
54	.12014	.12101	8.2636	.99276	6	54	.13744	.13876	7.2066	.99051	6
55	.12043	.12131	8.2434	.99272	5	55	.13773	.13906	7.1912	.99047	5
56	.12071	.12160	8.2234	.99269	4	56	.13802	.13935	7.1759	.99043	4
57	.12100	.12190	8.2035	.99265	3	57	.13831	.13965	7.1607	.99039	3
58	.12129	.12219	8.1837	.99262	2	58	.13860	.13995	7.1455	.99035	2
59	.12158	.12249	8.1640	.99258	1	59	.13889	.14024	7.1304	.99031	1
60	.12187	.12278	8.1443	.99255	0	60	.13917	.14054	7.1154	.99027	0
	Cos	Ctn	Tan	Sin	′		Cos	Ctn	Tan	Sin	′

′	Sin	Tan	Ctn	Cos		′	Sin	Tan	Ctn	Cos	
0	.13917	.14054	7.1154	.99027	60	0	.15643	.15838	6.3138	.98769	60
1	.13946	.14084	7.1004	.99023	59	1	.15672	.15868	6.3019	.98764	59
2	.13975	.14113	7.0855	.99019	58	2	.15701	.15898	6.2901	.98760	58
3	.14004	.14143	7.0706	.99015	57	3	.15730	.15928	6.2783	.98755	57
4	.14033	.14173	7.0558	.99011	56	4	.15758	.15958	6.2666	.98751	56
5	.14061	.14202	7.0410	.99006	55	5	.15787	.15988	6.2549	.98746	55
6	.14090	.14232	7.0264	.99002	54	6	.15816	.16017	6.2432	.98741	54
7	.14119	.14262	7.0117	.98998	53	7	.15845	.16047	6.2316	.98737	53
8	.14148	.14291	6.9972	.98994	52	8	.15873	.16077	6.2200	.98732	52
9	.14177	.14321	6.9827	.98990	51	9	.15902	.16107	6.2085	.98728	51
10	.14205	.14351	6.9682	.98986	50	10	.15931	.16137	6.1970	.98723	50
11	.14234	.14381	6.9538	.98982	49	11	.15959	.16167	6.1856	.98718	49
12	.14263	.14410	6.9395	.98978	48	12	.15988	.16196	6.1742	.98714	48
13	.14292	.14440	6.9252	.98973	47	13	.16017	.16226	6.1628	.98709	47
14	.14320	.14470	6.9110	.98969	46	14	.16046	.16256	6.1515	.98704	46
15	.14349	.14499	6.8969	.98965	45	15	.16074	.16286	6.1402	.98700	45
16	.14378	.14529	6.8828	.98961	44	16	.16103	.16316	6.1290	.98695	44
17	.14407	.14559	6.8687	.98957	43	17	.16132	.16346	6.1178	.98690	43
18	.14436	.14588	6.8548	.98953	42	18	.16160	.16376	6.1066	.98686	42
19	.14464	.14618	6.8408	.98948	41	19	.16189	.16405	6.0955	.98681	41
20	.14493	.14648	6.8269	.98944	40	20	.16218	.16435	6.0844	.98676	40
21	.14522	.14678	6.8131	.98940	39	21	.16246	.16465	6.0734	.98671	39
22	.14551	.14707	6.7994	.98936	38	22	.16275	.16495	6.0624	.98667	38
23	.14580	.14737	6.7856	.98931	37	23	.16304	.16525	6.0514	.98662	37
24	.14608	.14767	6.7720	.98927	36	24	.16333	.16555	6.0405	.98657	36
25	.14637	.14796	6.7584	.98923	35	25	.16361	.16585	6.0296	.98652	35
26	.14666	.14826	6.7448	.98919	34	26	.16390	.16615	6.0188	.98648	34
27	.14695	.14856	6.7313	.98914	33	27	.16419	.16645	6.0080	.98643	33
28	.14723	.14886	6.7179	.98910	32	28	.16447	.16674	5.9972	.98638	32
29	.14752	.14915	6.7045	.98906	31	29	.16476	.16704	5.9865	.98633	31
30	.14781	.14945	6.6912	.98902	30	30	.16505	.16734	5.9758	.98629	30
31	.14810	.14975	6.6779	.98897	29	31	.16533	.16764	5.9651	.98624	29
32	.14838	.15005	6.6646	.98893	28	32	.16562	.16794	5.9545	.98619	28
33	.14867	.15034	6.6514	.98889	27	33	.16591	.16824	5.9439	.98614	27
34	.14896	.15064	6.6383	.98884	26	34	.16620	.16854	5.9333	.98609	26
35	.14925	.15094	6.6252	.98880	25	35	.16648	.16884	5.9228	.98604	25
36	.14954	.15124	6.6122	.98876	24	36	.16677	.16914	5.9124	.98600	24
37	.14982	.15153	6.5992	.98871	23	37	.16706	.16944	5.9019	.98595	23
38	.15011	.15183	6.5863	.98867	22	38	.16734	.16974	5.8915	.98590	22
39	.15040	.15213	6.5734	.98863	21	39	.16763	.17004	5.8811	.98585	21
40	.15069	.15243	6.5606	.98858	20	40	.16792	.17033	5.8708	.98580	20
41	.15097	.15272	6.5478	.98854	19	41	.16820	.17063	5.8605	.98575	19
42	.15126	.15302	6.5350	.98849	18	42	.16849	.17093	5.8502	.98570	18
43	.15155	.15332	6.5223	.98845	17	43	.16878	.17123	5.8400	.98565	17
44	.15184	.15362	6.5097	.98841	16	44	.16906	.17153	5.8298	.98561	16
45	.15212	.15391	6.4971	.98836	15	45	.16935	.17183	5.8197	.98556	15
46	.15241	.15421	6.4846	.98832	14	46	.16964	.17213	5.8095	.98551	14
47	.15270	.15451	6.4721	.98827	13	47	.16992	.17243	5.7994	.98546	13
48	.15299	.15481	6.4596	.98823	12	48	.17021	.17273	5.7894	.98541	12
49	.15327	.15511	6.4472	.98818	11	49	.17050	.17303	5.7794	.98536	11
50	.15356	.15540	6.4348	.98814	10	50	.17078	.17333	5.7694	.98531	10
51	.15385	.15570	6.4225	.98809	9	51	.17107	.17363	5.7594	.98526	9
52	.15414	.15600	6.4103	.98805	8	52	.17136	.17393	5.7495	.98521	8
53	.15442	.15630	6.3980	.98800	7	53	.17164	.17423	5.7396	.98516	7
54	.15471	.15660	6.3859	.98796	6	54	.17193	.17453	5.7297	.98511	6
55	.15500	.15689	6.3737	.98791	5	55	.17222	.17483	5.7199	.98506	5
56	.15529	.15719	6.3617	.98787	4	56	.17250	.17513	5.7101	.98501	4
57	.15557	.15749	6.3496	.98782	3	57	.17279	.17543	5.7004	.98496	3
58	.15586	.15779	6.3376	.98778	2	58	.17308	.17573	5.6906	.98491	2
59	.15615	.15809	6.3257	.98773	1	59	.17336	.17603	5.6809	.98486	1
60	.15643	.15838	6.3138	.98769	0	60	.17365	.17633	5.6713	.98481	0
	Cos	Ctn	Tan	Sin	′		Cos	Ctn	Tan	Sin	′

′	Sin	Tan	Ctn	Cos		′	Sin	Tan	Ctn	Cos	
0	.17365	.17633	5.6713	.98481	60	0	.19081	.19438	5.1446	.98163	60
1	.17393	.17663	5.6617	.98476	59	1	.19109	.19468	5.1366	.98157	59
2	.17422	.17693	5.6521	.98471	58	2	.19138	.19498	5.1286	.98152	58
3	.17451	.17723	5.6425	.98466	57	3	.19167	.19529	5.1207	.98146	57
4	.17479	.17753	5.6329	.98461	56	4	.19195	.19559	5.1128	.98140	56
5	.17508	.17783	5.6234	.98455	55	5	.19224	.19589	5.1049	.98135	55
6	.17537	.17813	5.6140	.98450	54	6	.19252	.19619	5.0970	.98129	54
7	.17565	.17843	5.6045	.98445	53	7	.19281	.19649	5.0892	.98124	53
8	.17594	.17873	5.5951	.98440	52	8	.19309	.19680	5.0814	.98118	52
9	.17623	.17903	5.5857	.98435	51	9	.19338	.19710	5.0736	.98112	51
10	.17651	.17933	5.5764	.98430	50	10	.19366	.19740	5.0658	.98107	50
11	.17680	.17963	5.5671	.98425	49	11	.19395	.19770	5.0581	.98101	49
12	.17708	.17993	5.5578	.98420	48	12	.19423	.19801	5.0504	.98096	48
13	.17737	.18023	5.5485	.98414	47	13	.19452	.19831	5.0427	.98090	47
14	.17766	.18053	5.5393	.98409	46	14	.19481	.19861	5.0350	.98084	46
15	.17794	.18083	5.5301	.98404	45	15	.19509	.19891	5.0273	.98079	45
16	.17823	.18113	5.5209	.98399	44	16	.19538	.19921	5.0197	.98073	44
17	.17852	.18143	5.5118	.98394	43	17	.19566	.19952	5.0121	.98067	43
18	.17880	.18173	5.5026	.98389	42	18	.19595	.19982	5.0045	.98061	42
19	.17909	.18203	5.4936	.98383	41	19	.19623	.20012	4.9969	.98056	41
20	.17937	.18233	5.4845	.98378	40	20	.19652	.20042	4.9894	.98050	40
21	.17966	.18263	5.4755	.98373	39	21	.19680	.20073	4.9819	.98044	39
22	.17995	.18293	5.4665	.98368	38	22	.19709	.20103	4.9744	.98039	38
23	.18023	.18323	5.4575	.98362	37	23	.19737	.20133	4.9669	.98033	37
24	.18052	.18353	5.4486	.98357	36	24	.19766	.20164	4.9594	.98027	36
25	.18081	.18384	5.4397	.98352	35	25	.19794	.20194	4.9520	.98021	35
26	.18109	.18414	5.4308	.98347	34	26	.19823	.20224	4.9446	.98016	34
27	.18138	.18444	5.4219	.98341	33	27	.19851	.20254	4.9372	.98010	33
28	.18166	.18474	5.4131	.98336	32	28	.19880	.20285	4.9298	.98004	32
29	.18195	.18504	5.4043	.98331	31	29	.19908	.20315	4.9225	.97998	31
30	.18224	.18534	5.3955	.98325	30	30	.19937	.20345	4.9152	.97992	30
31	.18252	.18564	5.3868	.98320	29	31	.19965	.20376	4.9078	.97987	29
32	.18281	.18594	5.3781	.98315	28	32	.19994	.20406	4.9006	.97981	28
33	.18309	.18624	5.3694	.98310	27	33	.20022	.20436	4.8933	.97975	27
34	.18338	.18654	5.3607	.98304	26	34	.20051	.20466	4.8860	.97969	26
35	.18367	.18684	5.3521	.98299	25	35	.20079	.20497	4.8788	.97963	25
36	.18395	.18714	5.3435	.98294	24	36	.20108	.20527	4.8716	.97958	24
37	.18424	.18745	5.3349	.98288	23	37	.20136	.20557	4.8644	.97952	23
38	.18452	.18775	5.3263	.98283	22	38	.20165	.20588	4.8573	.97946	22
39	.18481	.18805	5.3178	.98277	21	39	.20193	.20618	4.8501	.97940	21
40	.18509	.18835	5.3093	.98272	20	40	.20222	.20648	4.8430	.97934	20
41	.18538	.18865	5.3008	.98267	19	41	.20250	.20679	4.8359	.97928	19
42	.18567	.18895	5.2924	.98261	18	42	.20279	.20709	4.8288	.97922	18
43	.18595	.18925	5.2839	.98256	17	43	.20307	.20739	4.8218	.97916	17
44	.18624	.18955	5.2755	.98250	16	44	.20336	.20770	4.8147	.97910	16
45	.18652	.18986	5.2672	.98245	15	45	.20364	.20800	4.8077	.97905	15
46	.18681	.19016	5.2588	.98240	14	46	.20393	.20830	4.8007	.97899	14
47	.18710	.19046	5.2505	.98234	13	47	.20421	.20861	4.7937	.97893	13
48	.18738	.19076	5.2422	.98229	12	48	.20450	.20891	4.7867	.97887	12
49	.18767	.19106	5.2339	.98223	11	49	.20478	.20921	4.7798	.97881	11
50	.18795	.19136	5.2257	.98218	10	50	.20507	.20952	4.7729	.97875	10
51	.18824	.19166	5.2174	.98212	9	51	.20535	.20982	4.7659	.97869	9
52	.18852	.19197	5.2092	.98207	8	52	.20563	.21013	4.7591	.97863	8
53	.18881	.19227	5.2011	.98201	7	53	.20592	.21043	4.7522	.97857	7
54	.18910	.19257	5.1929	.98196	6	54	.20620	.21073	4.7453	.97851	6
55	.18938	.19287	5.1848	.98190	5	55	.20649	.21104	4.7385	.97845	5
56	.18967	.19317	5.1767	.98185	4	56	.20677	.21134	4.7317	.97839	4
57	.18995	.19347	5.1686	.98179	3	57	.20706	.21164	4.7249	.97833	3
58	.19024	.19378	5.1606	.98174	2	58	.20734	.21195	4.7181	.97827	2
59	.19052	.19408	5.1526	.98168	1	59	.20763	.21225	4.7114	.97821	1
60	.19081	.19438	5.1446	.98163	0	60	.20791	.21256	4.7046	.97815	0
	Cos	Ctn	Tan	Sin	′		Cos	Ctn	Tan	Sin	′

′	Sin	Tan	Ctn	Cos		′	Sin	Tan	Ctn	Cos	
0	.20791	.21256	4.7046	.97815	60	0	.22495	.23087	4.3315	.97437	60
1	.20820	.21286	4.6979	.97809	59	1	.22523	.23117	4.3257	.97430	59
2	.20848	.21316	4.6912	.97803	58	2	.22552	.23148	4.3200	.97424	58
3	.20877	.21347	4.6845	.97797	57	3	.22580	.23179	4.3143	.97417	57
4	.20905	.21377	4.6779	.97791	56	4	.22608	.23209	4.3086	.97411	56
5	.20933	.21408	4.6712	.97784	55	5	.22637	.23240	4.3029	.97404	55
6	.20962	.21438	4.6646	.97778	54	6	.22665	.23271	4.2972	.97398	54
7	.20990	.21469	4.6580	.97772	53	7	.22693	.23301	4.2916	.97391	53
8	.21019	.21499	4.6514	.97766	52	8	.22722	.23332	4.2859	.97384	52
9	.21047	.21529	4.6448	.97760	51	9	.22750	.23363	4.2803	.97378	51
10	.21076	.21560	4.6382	.97754	50	10	.22778	.23393	4.2747	.97371	50
11	.21104	.21590	4.6317	.97748	49	11	.22807	.23424	4.2691	.97365	49
12	.21132	.21621	4.6252	.97742	48	12	.22835	.23455	4.2635	.97358	48
13	.21161	.21651	4.6187	.97735	47	13	.22863	.23485	4.2580	.97351	47
14	.21189	.21682	4.6122	.97729	46	14	.22892	.23516	4.2524	.97345	46
15	.21218	.21712	4.6057	.97723	45	15	.22920	.23547	4.2468	.97338	45
16	.21246	.21743	4.5993	.97717	44	16	.22948	.23578	4.2413	.97331	44
17	.21275	.21773	4.5928	.97711	43	17	.22977	.23608	4.2358	.97325	43
18	.21303	.21804	4.5864	.97705	42	18	.23005	.23639	4.2303	.97318	42
19	.21331	.21834	4.5800	.97698	41	19	.23033	.23670	4.2248	.97311	41
20	.21360	.21864	4.5736	.97692	40	20	.23062	.23700	4.2193	.97304	40
21	.21388	.21895	4.5673	.97686	39	21	.23090	.23731	4.2139	.97298	39
22	.21417	.21925	4.5609	.97680	38	22	.23118	.23762	4.2084	.97291	38
23	.21445	.21956	4.5546	.97673	37	23	.23146	.23793	4.2030	.97284	37
24	.21474	.21986	4.5483	.97667	36	24	.23175	.23823	4.1976	.97278	36
25	.21502	.22017	4.5420	.97661	35	25	.23203	.23854	4.1922	.97271	35
26	.21530	.22047	4.5357	.97655	34	26	.23231	.23885	4.1868	.97264	34
27	.21559	.22078	4.5294	.97648	33	27	.23260	.23916	4.1814	.97257	33
28	.21587	.22108	4.5232	.97642	32	28	.23288	.23946	4.1760	.97251	32
29	.21616	.22139	4.5169	.97636	31	29	.23316	.23977	4.1706	.97244	31
30	.21644	.22169	4.5107	.97630	30	30	.23345	.24008	4.1653	.97237	30
31	.21672	.22200	4.5045	.97623	29	31	.23373	.24039	4.1600	.97230	29
32	.21701	.22231	4.4983	.97617	28	32	.23401	.24069	4.1547	.97223	28
33	.21729	.22261	4.4922	.97611	27	33	.23429	.24100	4.1493	.97217	27
34	.21758	.22292	4.4860	.97604	26	34	.23458	.24131	4.1441	.97210	26
35	.21786	.22322	4.4799	.97598	25	35	.23486	.24162	4.1388	.97203	25
36	.21814	.22353	4.4737	.97592	24	36	.23514	.24193	4.1335	.97196	24
37	.21843	.22383	4.4676	.97585	23	37	.23542	.24223	4.1282	.97189	23
38	.21871	.22414	4.4615	.97579	22	38	.23571	.24254	4.1230	.97182	22
39	.21899	.22444	4.4555	.97573	21	39	.23599	.24285	4.1178	.97176	21
40	.21928	.22475	4.4494	.97566	20	40	.23627	.24316	4.1126	.97169	20
41	.21956	.22505	4.4434	.97560	19	41	.23656	.24347	4.1074	.97162	19
42	.21985	.22536	4.4373	.97553	18	42	.23684	.24377	4.1022	.97155	18
43	.22013	.22567	4.4313	.97547	17	43	.23712	.24408	4.0970	.97148	17
44	.22041	.22597	4.4253	.97541	16	44	.23740	.24439	4.0918	.97141	16
45	.22070	.22628	4.4194	.97534	15	45	.23769	.24470	4.0867	.97134	15
46	.22098	.22658	4.4134	.97528	14	46	.23797	.24501	4.0815	.97127	14
47	.22126	.22689	4.4075	.97521	13	47	.23825	.24532	4.0764	.97120	13
48	.22155	.22719	4.4015	.97515	12	48	.23853	.24562	4.0713	.97113	12
49	.22183	.22750	4.3956	.97508	11	49	.23882	.24593	4.0662	.97106	11
50	.22212	.22781	4.3897	.97502	10	50	.23910	.24624	4.0611	.97100	10
51	.22240	.22811	4•3838	.97496	9	51	.23938	.24655	4.0560	.97093	9
52	.22268	.22842	4.3779	.97489	8	52	.23966	.24686	4.0509	.97086	8
53	.22297	.22872	4.3721	.97483	7	53	.23995	.24717	4.0459	.97079	7
54	.22325	.22903	4.3662	.97476	6	54	.24023	.24747	4.0408	.97072	6
55	.22353	.22934	4.3604	.97470	5	55	.24051	.24778	4.0358	.97065	5
56	.22382	.22964	4.3546	.97463	4	56	.24079	.24809	4.0308	.97058	4
57	.22410	.22995	4.3488	.97457	3	57	.24108	.24840	4.0257	.97051	3
58	.22438	.23026	4.3430	.97450	2	58	.24136	.24871	4.0207	.97044	2
59	.22467	.23056	4.3372	.97444	1	59	.24164	.24902	4.0158	.97037	1
60	.22495	.23087	4.3315	.97437	0	60	.24192	.24933	4.0108	.97030	0
	Cos	Ctn	Tan	Sin	′		Cos	Ctn	Tan	Sin	′

Table V NATURAL TRIGONOMETRIC FUNCTIONS Page 171

14° 165° 15° 164°

′	Sin	Tan	Ctn	Cos		′	Sin	Tan	Ctn	Cos	
0	.24192	.24933	4.0108	.97030	60	0	.25882	.26795	3.7321	.96593	60
1	.24220	.24964	4.0058	.97023	59	1	.25910	.26826	3.7277	.96585	59
2	.24249	.24995	4.0009	.97015	58	2	.25938	.26857	3.7234	.96578	58
3	.24277	.25026	3.9959	.97008	57	3	.25966	.26888	3.7191	.96570	57
4	.24305	.25056	3.9910	.97001	56	4	.25994	.26920	3.7148	.96562	56
5	.24333	.25087	3.9861	.96994	55	5	.26022	.26951	3.7105	.96555	55
6	.24362	.25118	3.9812	.96987	54	6	.26050	.26982	3.7062	.96547	54
7	.24390	.25149	3.9763	.96980	53	7	.26079	.27013	3.7019	.96540	53
8	.24418	.25180	3.9714	.96973	52	8	.26107	.27044	3.6976	.96532	52
9	.24446	.25211	3.9665	.96966	51	9	.26135	.27076	3.6933	.96524	51
10	.24474	.25242	3.9617	.96959	50	10	.26163	.27107	3.6891	.96517	50
11	.24503	.25273	3.9568	.96952	49	11	.26191	.27138	3.6848	.96509	49
12	.24531	.25304	3.9520	.96945	48	12	.26219	.27169	3.6806	.96502	48
13	.24559	.25335	3.9471	.96937	47	13	.26247	.27201	3.6764	.96494	47
14	.24587	.25366	3.9423	.96930	46	14	.26275	.27232	3.6722	.96486	46
15	.24615	.25397	3.9375	.96923	45	15	.26303	.27263	3.6680	.96479	45
16	.24644	.25428	3.9327	.96916	44	16	.26331	.27294	3.6638	.96471	44
17	.24672	.25459	3.9279	.96909	43	17	.26359	.27326	3.6596	.96463	43
18	.24700	.25490	3.9232	.96902	42	18	.26387	.27357	3.6554	.96456	42
19	.24728	.25521	3.9184	.96894	41	19	.26415	.27388	3.6512	.96448	41
20	.24756	.25552	3.9136	.96887	40	20	.26443	.27419	3.6470	.96440	40
21	.24784	.25583	3.9089	.96880	39	21	.26471	.27451	3.6429	.96433	39
22	.24813	.25614	3.9042	.96873	38	22	.26500	.27482	3.6387	.96425	38
23	.24841	.25645	3.8995	.96866	37	23	.26528	.27513	3.6346	.96417	37
24	.24869	.25676	3.8947	.96858	36	24	.26556	.27545	3.6305	.96410	36
25	.24897	.25707	3.8900	.96851	35	25	.26584	.27576	3.6264	.96402	35
26	.24925	.25738	3.8854	.96844	34	26	.26612	.27607	3.6222	.96394	34
27	.24954	.25769	3.8807	.96837	33	27	.26640	.27638	3.6181	.96386	33
28	.24982	.25800	3.8760	.96829	32	28	.26668	.27670	3.6140	.96379	32
29	.25010	.25831	3.8714	.96822	31	29	.26696	.27701	3.6100	.96371	31
30	.25038	.25862	3.8667	.96815	30	30	.26724	.27732	3.6059	.96363	30
31	.25066	.25893	3.8621	.96807	29	31	.26752	.27764	3.6018	.96355	29
32	.25094	.25924	3.8575	.96800	28	32	.26780	.27795	3.5978	.96347	28
33	.25122	.25955	3.8528	.96793	27	33	.26808	.27826	3.5937	.96340	27
34	.25151	.25986	3.8482	.96786	26	34	.26836	.27858	3.5897	.96332	26
35	.25179	.26017	3.8436	.96778	25	35	.26864	.27889	3.5856	.96324	25
36	.25207	.26048	3.8391	.96771	24	36	.26892	.27921	3.5816	.96316	24
37	.25235	.26079	3.8345	.96764	23	37	.26920	.27952	3.5776	.96308	23
38	.25263	.26110	3.8299	.96756	22	38	.26948	.27983	3.5736	.96301	22
39	.25291	.26141	3.8254	.96749	21	39	.26976	.28015	3.5696	.96293	21
40	.25320	.26172	3.8208	.96742	20	40	.27004	.28046	3.5656	.96285	20
41	.25348	.26203	3.8163	.96734	19	41	.27032	.28077	3.5616	.96277	19
42	.25376	.26235	3.8118	.96727	18	42	.27060	.28109	3.5576	.96269	18
43	.25404	.26266	3.8073	.96719	17	43	.27088	.28140	3.5536	.96261	17
44	.25432	.26297	3.8028	.96712	16	44	.27116	.28172	3.5497	.96253	16
45	.25460	.26328	3.7983	.96705	15	45	.27144	.28203	3.5457	.96246	15
46	.25488	.26359	3.7938	.96697	14	46	.27172	.28234	3.5418	.96238	14
47	.25516	.26390	3.7893	.96690	13	47	.27200	.28266	3.5379	.96230	13
48	.25545	.26421	3.7848	.96682	12	48	.27228	.28297	3.5339	.96222	12
49	.25573	.26452	3.7804	.96675	11	49	.27256	.28329	3.5300	.96214	11
50	.25601	.26483	3.7760	.96667	10	50	.27284	.28360	3.5261	.96206	10
51	.25629	.26515	3.7715	.96660	9	51	.27312	.28391	3.5222	.96198	9
52	.25657	.26546	3.7671	.96653	8	52	.27340	.28423	3.5183	.96190	8
53	.25685	.26577	3.7627	.96645	7	53	.27368	.28454	3.5144	.96182	7
54	.25713	.26608	3.7583	.96638	6	54	.27396	.28486	3.5105	.96174	6
55	.25741	.26639	3.7539	.96630	5	55	.27424	.28517	3.5067	.96166	5
56	.25769	.26670	3.7495	.96623	4	56	.27452	.28549	3.5028	.96158	4
57	.25798	.26701	3.7451	.96615	3	57	.27480	.28580	3.4989	.96150	3
58	.25826	.26733	3.7408	.96608	2	58	.27508	.28612	3.4951	.96142	2
59	.25854	.26764	3.7364	.96600	1	59	.27536	.28643	3.4912	.96134	1
60	.25882	.26795	3.7321	.96593	0	60	.27564	.28675	3.4874	.96126	0
	Cos	Ctn	Tan	Sin	′		Cos	Ctn	Tan	Sin	′

′	Sin	Tan	Ctn	Cos	
0	.27564	.28675	3.4874	.96126	60
1	.27592	.28706	3.4836	.96118	59
2	.27620	.28738	3.4798	.96110	58
3	.27648	.28769	3.4760	.96102	57
4	.27676	.28801	3.4722	.96094	56
5	.27704	.28832	3.4684	.96086	55
6	.27731	.28864	3.4646	.96078	54
7	.27759	.28895	3.4608	.96070	53
8	.27787	.28927	3.4570	.96062	52
9	.27815	.28958	3.4533	.96054	51
10	.27843	.28990	3.4495	.96046	50
11	.27871	.29021	3.4458	.96037	49
12	.27899	.29053	3.4420	.96029	48
13	.27927	.29084	3.4383	.96021	47
14	.27955	.29116	3.4346	.96013	46
15	.27983	.29147	3.4308	.96005	45
16	.28011	.29179	3.4271	.95997	44
17	.28039	.29210	3.4234	.95989	43
18	.28067	.29242	3.4197	.95981	42
19	.28095	.29274	3.4160	.95972	41
20	.28123	.29305	3.4124	.95964	40
21	.28150	.29337	3.4087	.95956	39
22	.28178	.29368	3.4050	.95948	38
23	.28206	.29400	3.4014	.95940	37
24	.28234	.29432	3.3977	.95931	36
25	.28262	.29463	3.3941	.95923	35
26	.28290	.29495	3.3904	.95915	34
27	.28318	.29526	3.3868	.95907	33
28	.28346	.29558	3.3832	.95898	32
29	.28374	.29590	3.3796	.95890	31
30	.28402	.29621	3.3759	.95882	30
31	.28429	.29653	3.3723	.95874	29
32	.28457	.29685	3.3687	.95865	28
33	.28485	.29716	3.3652	.95857	27
34	.28513	.29748	3.3616	.95849	26
35	.28541	.29780	3.3580	.95841	25
36	.28569	.29811	3.3544	.95832	24
37	.28597	.29843	3.3509	.95824	23
38	.28625	.29875	3.3473	.95816	22
39	.28652	.29906	3.3438	.95807	21
40	.28680	.29938	3.3402	.95799	20
41	.28708	.29970	3.3367	.95791	19
42	.28736	.30001	3.3332	.95782	18
43	.28764	.30033	3.3297	.95774	17
44	.28792	.30065	3.3261	.95766	16
45	.28820	.30097	3.3226	.95757	15
46	.28847	.30128	3.3191	.95749	14
47	.28875	.30160	3.3156	.95740	13
48	.28903	.30192	3.3122	.95732	12
49	.28931	.30224	3.3087	.95724	11
50	.28959	.30255	3.3052	.95715	10
51	.28987	.30287	3.3017	.95707	9
52	.29015	.30319	3.2983	.95698	8
53	.29042	.30351	3.2948	.95690	7
54	.29070	.30382	3.2914	.95681	6
55	.29098	.30414	3.2879	.95673	5
56	.29126	.30446	3.2845	.95664	4
57	.29154	.30478	3.2811	.95656	3
58	.29182	.30509	3.2777	.95647	2
59	.29209	.30541	3.2743	.95639	1
60	.29237	.30573	3.2709	.95630	0
	Cos	Ctn	Tan	Sin	′

′	Sin	Tan	Ctn	Cos	
0	.29237	.30573	3.2709	.95630	60
1	.29265	.30605	3.2675	.95622	59
2	.29293	.30637	3.2641	.95613	58
3	.29321	.30669	3.2607	.95605	57
4	.29348	.30700	3.2573	.95596	56
5	.29376	.30732	3.2539	.95588	55
6	.29404	.30764	3.2506	.95579	54
7	.29432	.30796	3.2472	.95571	53
8	.29460	.30828	3.2438	.95562	52
9	.29487	.30860	3.2405	.95554	51
10	.29515	.30891	3.2371	.95545	50
11	.29543	.30923	3.2338	.95536	49
12	.29571	.30955	3.2305	.95528	48
13	.29599	.30987	3.2272	.95519	47
14	.29626	.31019	3.2238	.95511	46
15	.29654	.31051	3.2205	.95502	45
16	.29682	.31083	3.2172	.95493	44
17	.29710	.31115	3.2139	.95485	43
18	.29737	.31147	3.2106	.95476	42
19	.29765	.31178	3.2073	.95467	41
20	.29793	.31210	3.2041	.95459	40
21	.29821	.31242	3.2008	.95450	39
22	.29849	.31274	3.1975	.95441	38
23	.29876	.31306	3.1943	.95433	37
24	.29904	.31338	3.1910	.95424	36
25	.29932	.31370	3.1878	.95415	35
26	.29960	.31402	3.1845	.95407	34
27	.29987	.31434	3.1813	.95398	33
28	.30015	.31466	3.1780	.95389	32
29	.30043	.31498	3.1748	.95380	31
30	.30071	.31530	3.1716	.95372	30
31	.30098	.31562	3.1684	.95363	29
32	.30126	.31594	3.1652	.95354	28
33	.30154	.31626	3.1620	.95345	27
34	.30182	.31658	3.1588	.95337	26
35	.30209	.31690	3.1556	.95328	25
36	.30237	.31722	3.1524	.95319	24
37	.30265	.31754	3.1492	.95310	23
38	.30292	.31786	3.1460	.95301	22
39	.30320	.31818	3.1429	.95293	21
40	.30348	.31850	3.1397	.95284	20
41	.30376	.31882	3.1366	.95275	19
42	.30403	.31914	3.1334	.95266	18
43	.30431	.31946	3.1303	.95257	17
44	.30459	.31978	3.1271	.95248	16
45	.30486	.32010	3.1240	.95240	15
46	.30514	.32042	3.1209	.95231	14
47	.30542	.32074	3.1178	.95222	13
48	.30570	.32106	3.1146	.95213	12
49	.30597	.32139	3.1115	.95204	11
50	.30625	.32171	3.1084	.95195	10
51	.30653	.32203	3.1053	.95186	9
52	.30680	.32235	3.1022	.95177	8
53	.30708	.32267	3.0991	.95168	7
54	.30736	.32299	3.0961	.95159	6
55	.30763	.32331	3.0930	.95150	5
56	.30791	.32363	3.0899	.95142	4
57	.30819	.32396	3.0868	.95133	3
58	.30846	.32428	3.0838	.95124	2
59	.30874	.32460	3.0807	.95115	1
60	.30902	.32492	3.0777	.95106	0
	Cos	Ctn	Tan	Sin	′

18°   161°   19°   160°

′	Sin	Tan	Ctn	Cos		′	Sin	Tan	Ctn	Cos	
0	.30902	.32492	3.0777	.95106	60	0	.32557	.34433	2.9042	.94552	60
1	.30929	.32524	3.0746	.95097	59	1	.32584	.34465	2.9015	.94542	59
2	.30957	.32556	3.0716	.95088	58	2	.32612	.34498	2.8987	.94533	58
3	.30985	.32588	3.0686	.95079	57	3	.32639	.34530	2.8960	.94523	57
4	.31012	.32621	3.0655	.95070	56	4	.32667	.34563	2.8933	.94514	56
5	.31040	.32653	3.0625	.95061	55	5	.32694	.34596	2.8905	.94504	55
6	.31068	.32685	3.0595	.95052	54	6	.32722	.34628	2.8878	.94495	54
7	.31095	.32717	3.0565	.95043	53	7	.32749	.34661	2.8851	.94485	53
8	.31123	.32749	3.0535	.95033	52	8	.32777	.34693	2.8824	.94476	52
9	.31151	.32782	3.0505	.95024	51	9	.32804	.34726	2.8797	.94466	51
10	.31178	.32814	3.0475	.95015	50	10	.32832	.34758	2.8770	.94457	50
11	.31206	.32846	3.0445	.95006	49	11	.32859	.34791	2.8743	.94447	49
12	.31233	.32878	3.0415	.94997	48	12	.32887	.34824	2.8716	.94438	48
13	.31261	.32911	3.0385	.94988	47	13	.32914	.34856	2.8689	.94428	47
14	.31289	.32943	3.0356	.94979	46	14	.32942	.34889	2.8662	.94418	46
15	.31316	.32975	3.0326	.94970	45	15	.32969	.34922	2.8636	.94409	45
16	.31344	.33007	3.0296	.94961	44	16	.32997	.34954	2.8609	.94399	44
17	.31372	.33040	3.0267	.94952	43	17	.33024	.34987	2.8582	.94390	43
18	.31399	.33072	3.0237	.94943	42	18	.33051	.35020	2.8556	.94380	42
19	.31427	.33104	3.0208	.94933	41	19	.33079	.35052	2.8529	.94370	41
20	.31454	.33136	3.0178	.94924	40	20	.33106	.35085	2.8502	.94361	40
21	.31482	.33169	3.0149	.94915	39	21	.33134	.35118	2.8476	.94351	39
22	.31510	.33201	3.0120	.94906	38	22	.33161	.35150	2.8449	.94342	38
23	.31537	.33233	3.0090	.94897	37	23	.33189	.35183	2.8423	.94332	37
24	.31565	.33266	3.0061	.94888	36	24	.33216	.35216	2.8397	.94322	36
25	.31593	.33298	3.0032	.94878	35	25	.33244	.35248	2.8370	.94313	35
26	.31620	.33330	3.0003	.94869	34	26	.33271	.35281	2.8344	.94303	34
27	.31648	.33363	2.9974	.94860	33	27	.33298	.35314	2.8318	.94293	33
28	.31675	.33395	2.9945	.94851	32	28	.33326	.35346	2.8291	.94284	32
29	.31703	.33427	2.9916	.94842	31	29	.33353	.35379	2.8265	.94274	31
30	.31730	.33460	2.9887	.94832	30	30	.33381	.35412	2.8239	.94264	30
31	.31758	.33492	2.9858	.94823	29	31	.33408	.35445	2.8213	.94254	29
32	.31786	.33524	2.9829	.94814	28	32	.33436	.35477	2.8187	.94245	28
33	.31813	.33557	2.9800	.94805	27	33	.33463	.35510	2.8161	.94235	27
34	.31841	.33589	2.9772	.94795	26	34	.33490	.35543	2.8135	.94225	26
35	.31868	.33621	2.9743	.94786	25	35	.33518	.35576	2.8109	.94215	25
36	.31896	.33654	2.9714	.94777	24	36	.33545	.35608	2.8083	.94206	24
37	.31923	.33686	2.9686	.94768	23	37	.33573	.35641	2.8057	.94196	23
38	.31951	.33718	2.9657	.94758	22	38	.33600	.35674	2.8032	.94186	22
39	.31979	.33751	2.9629	.94749	21	39	.33627	.35707	2.8006	.94176	21
40	.32006	.33783	2.9600	.94740	20	40	.33655	.35740	2.7980	.94167	20
41	.32034	.33816	2.9572	.94730	19	41	.33682	.35772	2.7955	.94157	19
42	.32061	.33848	2.9544	.94721	18	42	.33710	.35805	2.7929	.94147	18
43	.32089	.33881	2.9515	.94712	17	43	.33737	.35838	2.7903	.94137	17
44	.32116	.33913	2.9487	.94702	16	44	.33764	.35871	2.7878	.94127	16
45	.32144	.33945	2.9459	.94693	15	45	.33792	.35904	2.7852	.94118	15
46	.32171	.33978	2.9431	.94684	14	46	.33819	.35937	2.7827	.94108	14
47	.32199	.34010	2.9403	.94674	13	47	.33846	.35969	2.7801	.94098	13
48	.32227	.34043	2.9375	.94665	12	48	.33874	.36002	2.7776	.94088	12
49	.32254	.34075	2.9347	.94656	11	49	.33901	.36035	2.7751	.94078	11
50	.32282	.34108	2.9319	.94646	10	50	.33929	.36068	2.7725	.94068	10
51	.32309	.34140	2.9291	.94637	9	51	.33956	.36101	2.7700	.94058	9
52	.32337	.34173	2.9263	.94627	8	52	.33983	.36134	2.7675	.94049	8
53	.32364	.34205	2.9235	.94618	7	53	.34011	.36167	2.7650	.94039	7
54	.32392	.34238	2.9208	.94609	6	54	.34038	.36199	2.7625	.94029	6
55	.32419	.34270	2.9180	.94599	5	55	.34065	.36232	2.7600	.94019	5
56	.32447	.34303	2.9152	.94590	4	56	.34093	.36265	2.7575	.94009	4
57	.32474	.34335	2.9125	.94580	3	57	.34120	.36298	2.7550	.93999	3
58	.32502	.34368	2.9097	.94571	2	58	.34147	.36331	2.7525	.93989	2
59	.32529	.34400	2.9070	.94561	1	59	.34175	.36364	2.7500	.93979	1
60	.32557	.34433	2.9042	.94552	0	60	.34202	.36397	2.7475	.93969	0
	Cos	Ctn	Tan	Sin	′		Cos	Ctn	Tan	Sin	′

20°   159°   21°   158°

′	Sin	Tan	Ctn	Cos	
0	.34202	.36397	2.7475	.93969	60
1	.34229	.36430	2.7450	.93959	69
2	.34257	.36463	2.7425	.93949	58
3	.34284	.36496	2.7400	.93939	57
4	.34311	.36529	2.7376	.93929	56
5	.34339	.36562	2.7351	.93919	55
6	.34366	.36595	2.7326	.93909	54
7	.34393	.36628	2.7302	.93899	53
8	.34421	.36661	2.7277	.93889	52
9	.34448	.36694	2.7253	.93879	51
10	.34475	.36727	2.7228	.93869	50
11	.34503	.36760	2.7204	.93859	49
12	.34530	.36793	2.7179	.93849	48
13	.34557	.36826	2.7155	.93839	47
14	.34584	.36859	2.7130	.93829	46
15	.34612	.36892	2.7106	.93819	45
16	.34639	.36925	2.7082	.93809	44
17	.34666	.36958	2.7058	.93799	43
18	.34694	.36991	2.7034	.93789	42
19	.34721	.37024	2.7009	.93779	41
20	.34748	.37057	2.6985	.93769	40
21	.34775	.37090	2.6961	.93759	39
22	.34803	.37123	2.6937	.93748	38
23	.34830	.37157	2.6913	.93738	37
24	.34857	.37190	2.6889	.93728	36
25	.34884	.37223	2.6865	.93718	35
26	.34912	.37256	2.6841	.93708	34
27	.34939	.37289	2.6818	.93698	33
28	.34966	.37322	2.6794	.93688	32
29	.34993	.37355	2.6770	.93677	31
30	.35021	.37388	2.6746	.93667	30
31	.35048	.37422	2.6723	.93657	29
32	.35075	.37455	2.6699	.93647	28
33	.35102	.37488	2.6675	.93637	27
34	.35130	.37521	2.6652	.93626	26
35	.35157	.37554	2.6628	.93616	25
36	.35184	.37588	2.6605	.93606	24
37	.35211	.37621	2.6581	.93596	23
38	.35239	.37654	2.6558	.93585	22
39	.35266	.37687	2.6534	.93575	21
40	.35293	.37720	2.6511	.93565	20
41	.35320	.37754	2.6488	.93555	19
42	.35347	.37787	2.6464	.93544	18
43	.35375	.37820	2.6441	.93534	17
44	.35402	.37853	2.6418	.93524	16
45	.35429	.37887	2.6395	.93514	15
46	.35456	.37920	2.6371	.93503	14
47	.35484	.37953	2.6348	.93493	13
48	.35511	.37986	2.6325	.93483	12
49	.35538	.38020	2.6302	.93472	11
50	.35565	.38053	2.6279	.93462	10
51	.35592	.38086	2.6256	.93452	9
52	.35619	.38120	2.6233	.93441	8
53	.35647	.38153	2.6210	.93431	7
54	.35674	.38186	2.6187	.93420	6
55	.35701	.38220	2.6165	.93410	5
56	.35728	.38253	2.6142	.93400	4
57	.35755	.38286	2.6119	.93389	3
58	.35782	.38320	2.6096	.93379	2
59	.35810	.38353	2.6074	.93368	1
60	.35837	.38386	2.6051	.93358	0
	Cos	Ctn	Tan	Sin	′

110°   69°

′	Sin	Tan	Ctn	Cos	
0	.35837	.38386	2.6051	.93358	60
1	.35864	.38420	2.6028	.93348	59
2	.35891	.38453	2.6006	.93337	58
3	.35918	.38487	2.5983	.93327	57
4	.35945	.38520	2.5961	.93316	56
5	.35973	.38553	2.5938	.93306	55
6	.36000	.38587	2.5916	.93295	54
7	.36027	.38620	2.5893	.93285	53
8	.36054	.38654	2.5871	.93274	52
9	.36081	.38687	2.5848	.93264	51
10	.36108	.38721	2.5826	.93253	50
11	.36135	.38754	2.5804	.93243	49
12	.36162	.38787	2.5782	.93232	48
13	.36190	.38821	2.5759	.93222	47
14	.36217	.38854	2.5737	.93211	46
15	.36244	.38888	2.5715	.93201	45
16	.36271	.38921	2.5693	.93190	44
17	.36298	.38955	2.5671	.93180	43
18	.36325	.38988	2.5649	.93169	42
19	.36352	.39022	2.5627	.93159	41
20	.36379	.39055	2.5605	.93148	40
21	.36406	.39089	2.5583	.93137	39
22	.36434	.39122	2.5561	.93127	38
23	.36461	.39156	2.5539	.93116	37
24	.36488	.39190	2.5517	.93106	36
25	.36515	.39223	2.5495	.93095	35
26	.36542	.39257	2.5473	.93084	34
27	.36569	.39290	2.5452	.93074	33
28	.36596	.39324	2.5430	.93063	32
29	.36623	.39357	2.5408	.93052	31
30	.36650	.39391	2.5386	.93042	30
31	.36677	.39425	2.5365	.93031	29
32	.36704	.39458	2.5343	.93020	28
33	.36731	.39492	2.5322	.93010	27
34	.36758	.39526	2.5300	.92999	26
35	.36785	.39559	2.5279	.92988	25
36	.36812	.39593	2.5257	.92978	24
37	.36839	.39626	2.5236	.92967	23
38	.36867	.39660	2.5214	.92956	22
39	.36894	.39694	2.5193	.92945	21
40	.36921	.39727	2.5172	.92935	20
41	.36948	.39761	2.5150	.92924	19
42	.36975	.39795	2.5129	.92913	18
43	.37002	.39829	2.5108	.92902	17
44	.37029	.39862	2.5086	.92892	16
45	.37056	.39896	2.5065	.92881	15
46	.37083	.39930	2.5044	.92870	14
47	.37110	.39963	2.5023	.92859	13
48	.37137	.39997	2.5002	.92849	12
49	.37164	.40031	2.4981	.92838	11
50	.37191	.40065	2.4960	.92827	10
51	.37218	.40098	2.4939	.92816	9
52	.37245	.40132	2.4918	.92805	8
53	.37272	.40166	2.4897	.92794	7
54	.37299	.40200	2.4876	.92784	6
55	.37326	.40234	2.4855	.92773	5
56	.37353	.40267	2.4834	.92762	4
57	.37380	.40301	2.4813	.92751	3
58	.37407	.40335	2.4792	.92740	2
59	.37434	.40369	2.4772	.92729	1
60	.37461	.40403	2.4751	.92718	0
	Cos	Ctn	Tan	Sin	′

111°   68°

Table V NATURAL TRIGONOMETRIC FUNCTIONS *Page 175*

22°   157°   23°   156°

′	Sin	Tan	Ctn	Cos		′	Sin	Tan	Ctn	Cos	
0	.37461	.40403	2.4751	.92718	60	0	.39073	.42447	2.3559	.92050	60
1	.37488	.40436	2.4730	.92707	59	1	.39100	.42482	2.3539	.92039	59
2	.37515	.40470	2.4709	.92697	58	2	.39127	.42516	2.3520	.92028	58
3	.37542	.40504	2.4689	.92686	57	3	.39153	.42551	2.3501	.92016	57
4	.37569	.40538	2.4668	.92675	56	4	.39180	.42585	2.3483	.92005	56
5	.37595	.40572	2.4648	.92664	55	5	.39207	.42619	2.3464	.91994	55
6	.37622	.40606	2.4627	.92653	54	6	.39234	.42654	2.3445	.91982	54
7	.37649	.40640	2.4606	.92642	53	7	.39260	.42688	2.3426	.91971	53
8	.37676	.40674	2.4586	.92631	52	8	.39287	.42722	2.3407	.91959	52
9	.37703	.40707	2.4566	.92620	51	9	.39314	.42757	2.3388	.91948	51
10	.37730	.40741	2.4545	.92609	50	10	.39341	.42791	2.3369	.91936	50
11	.37757	.40775	2.4525	.92598	49	11	.39367	.42826	2.3351	.91925	49
12	.37784	.40809	2.4504	.92587	48	12	.39394	.42860	2.3332	.91914	48
13	.37811	.40843	2.4484	.92576	47	13	.39421	.42894	2.3313	.91902	47
14	.37838	.40877	2.4464	.92565	46	14	.39448	.42929	2.3294	.91891	46
15	.37865	.40911	2.4443	.92554	45	15	.39474	.42963	2.3276	.91879	45
16	.37892	.40945	2.4423	.92543	44	16	.39501	.42998	2.3257	.91868	44
17	.37919	.40979	2.4403	.92532	43	17	.39528	.43032	2.3238	.91856	43
18	.37946	.41013	2.4383	.92521	42	18	.39555	.43067	2.3220	.91845	42
19	.37973	.41047	2.4362	.92510	41	19	.39581	.43101	2.3201	.91833	41
20	.37999	.41081	2.4342	.92499	40	20	.39608	.43136	2.3183	.91822	40
21	.38026	.41115	2.4322	.92488	39	21	.39635	.43170	2.3164	.91810	39
22	.38053	.41149	2.4302	.92477	38	22	.39661	.43205	2.3146	.91799	38
23	.38080	.41183	2.4282	.92466	37	23	.39688	.43239	2.3127	.91787	37
24	.38107	.41217	2.4262	.92455	36	24	.39715	.43274	2.3109	.91775	36
25	.38134	.41251	2.4242	.92444	35	25	.39741	.43308	2.3090	.91764	35
26	.38161	.41285	2.4222	.92432	34	26	.39768	.43343	2.3072	.91752	34
27	.38188	.41319	2.4202	.92421	33	27	.39795	.43378	2.3053	.91741	33
28	.38215	.41353	2.4182	.92410	32	28	.39822	.43412	2.3035	.91729	32
29	.38241	.41387	2.4162	.92399	31	29	.39848	.43447	2.3017	.91718	31
30	.38268	.41421	2.4142	.92388	30	30	.39875	.43481	2.2998	.91706	30
31	.38295	.41455	2.4122	.92377	29	31	.39902	.43516	2.2980	.91694	29
32	.38322	.41490	2.4102	.92366	28	32	.39928	.43550	2.2962	.91683	28
33	.38349	.41524	2.4083	.92355	27	33	.39955	.43585	2.2944	.91671	27
34	.38376	.41558	2.4063	.92343	26	34	.39982	.43620	2.2925	.91660	26
35	.38403	.41592	2.4043	.92332	25	35	.40008	.43654	2.2907	.91648	25
36	.38430	.41626	2.4023	.92321	24	36	.40035	.43689	2.2889	.91636	24
37	.38456	.41660	2.4004	.92310	23	37	.40062	.43724	2.2871	.91625	23
38	.38483	.41694	2.3984	.92299	22	38	.40088	.43758	2.2853	.91613	22
39	.38510	.41728	2.3964	.92287	21	39	.40115	.43793	2.2835	.91601	21
40	.38537	.41763	2.3945	.92276	20	40	.40141	.43828	2.2817	.91590	20
41	.38564	.41797	2.3925	.92265	19	41	.40168	.43862	2.2799	.91578	19
42	.38591	.41831	2.3906	.92254	18	42	.40195	.43897	2.2781	.91566	18
43	.38617	.41865	2.3886	.92243	17	43	.40221	.43932	2.2763	.91555	17
44	.38644	.41899	2.3867	.92231	16	44	.40248	.43966	2.2745	.91543	16
45	.38671	.41933	2.3847	.92220	15	45	.40275	.44001	2.2727	.91531	15
46	.38698	.41968	2.3828	.92209	14	46	.40301	.44036	2.2709	.91519	14
47	.38725	.42002	2.3808	.92198	13	47	.40328	.44071	2.2691	.91508	13
48	.38752	.42036	2.3789	.92186	12	48	.40355	.44105	2.2673	.91496	12
49	.38778	.42070	2.3770	.92175	11	49	.40381	.44140	2.2655	.91484	11
50	.38805	.42105	2.3750	.92164	10	50	.40408	.44175	2.2637	.91472	10
51	.38832	.42139	2.3731	.92152	9	51	.40434	.44210	2.2620	.91461	9
52	.38859	.42173	2.3712	.92141	8	52	.40461	.44244	2.2602	.91449	8
53	.38886	.42207	2.3693	.92130	7	53	.40488	.44279	2.2584	.91437	7
54	.38912	.42242	2.3673	.92119	6	54	.40514	.44314	2.2566	.91425	6
55	.38939	.42276	2.3654	.92107	5	55	.40541	.44349	2.2549	.91414	5
56	.38966	.42310	2.3635	.92096	4	56	.40567	.44384	2.2531	.91402	4
57	.38993	.42345	2.3616	.92085	3	57	.40594	.44418	2.2513	.91390	3
58	.39020	.42379	2.3597	.92073	2	58	.40621	.44453	2.2496	.91378	2
59	.39046	.42413	2.3578	.92062	1	59	.40647	.44488	2.2478	.91366	1
60	.39073	.42447	2.3559	.92050	0	60	.40674	.44523	2.2460	.91355	0
	Cos	Ctn	Tan	Sin	′		Cos	Ctn	Tan	Sin	′

′	Sin	Tan	Ctn	Cos		′	Sin	Tan	Ctn	Cos	
0	.40674	.44523	2.2460	.91355	60	0	.42262	.46631	2.1445	.90631	60
1	.40700	.44558	2.2443	.91343	59	1	.42288	.46666	2.1429	.90618	59
2	.40727	.44593	2.2425	.91331	58	2	.42315	.46702	2.1413	.90606	58
3	.40753	.44627	2.2408	.91319	57	3	.42341	.46737	2.1396	.90594	57
4	.40780	.44662	2.2390	.91307	56	4	.42367	.46772	2.1380	.90582	56
5	.40806	.44697	2.2373	.91295	55	5	.42394	.46808	2.1364	.90569	55
6	.40833	.44732	2.2355	.91283	54	6	.42420	.46843	2.1348	.90557	54
7	.40860	.44767	2.2338	.91272	53	7	.42446	.46879	2.1332	.90545	53
8	.40886	.44802	2.2320	.91260	52	8	.42473	.46914	2.1315	.90532	52
9	.40913	.44837	2.2303	.91248	51	9	.42499	.46950	2.1299	.90520	51
10	.40939	.44872	2.2286	.91236	50	10	.42525	.46985	2.1283	.90507	50
11	.40966	.44907	2.2268	.91224	49	11	.42552	.47021	2.1267	.90495	49
12	.40992	.44942	2.2251	.91212	48	12	.42578	.47056	2.1251	.90483	48
13	.41019	.44977	2.2234	.91200	47	13	.42604	.47092	2.1235	.90470	47
14	.41045	.45012	2.2216	.91188	46	14	.42631	.47128	2.1219	.90458	46
15	.41072	.45047	2.2199	.91176	45	15	.42657	.47163	2.1203	.90446	45
16	.41098	.45082	2.2182	.91164	44	16	.42683	.47199	2.1187	.90433	44
17	.41125	.45117	2.2165	.91152	43	17	.42709	.47234	2.1171	.90421	43
18	.41151	.45152	2.2148	.91140	42	18	.42736	.47270	2.1155	.90408	42
19	.41178	.45187	2.2130	.91128	41	19	.42762	.47305	2.1139	.90396	41
20	.41204	.45222	2.2113	.91116	40	20	.42788	.47341	2.1123	.90383	40
21	.41231	.45257	2.2096	.91104	39	21	.42815	.47377	2.1107	.90371	39
22	.41257	.45292	2.2079	.91092	38	22	.42841	.47412	2.1092	.90358	38
23	.41284	.45327	2.2062	.91080	37	23	.42867	.47448	2.1076	.90346	37
24	.41310	.45362	2.2045	.91068	36	24	.42894	.47483	2.1060	.90334	36
25	.41337	.45397	2.2028	.91056	35	25	.42920	.47519	2.1044	.90321	35
26	.41363	.45432	2.2011	.91044	34	26	.42946	.47555	2.1028	.90309	34
27	.41390	.45467	2.1994	.91032	33	27	.42972	.47590	2.1013	.90296	33
28	.41416	.45502	2.1977	.91020	32	28	.42999	.47626	2.0997	.90284	32
29	.41443	.45538	2.1960	.91008	31	29	.43025	.47662	2.0981	.90271	31
30	.41469	.45573	2.1943	.90996	30	30	.43051	.47698	2.0965	.90259	30
31	.41496	.45608	2.1926	.90984	29	31	.43077	.47733	2.0950	.90246	29
32	.41522	.45643	2.1909	.90972	28	32	.43104	.47769	2.0934	.90233	28
33	.41549	.45678	2.1892	.90960	27	33	.43130	.47805	2.0918	.90221	27
34	.41575	.45713	2.1876	.90948	26	34	.43156	.47840	2.0903	.90208	26
35	.41602	.45748	2.1859	.90936	25	35	.43182	.47876	2.0887	.90196	25
36	.41628	.45784	2.1842	.90924	24	36	.43209	.47912	2.0872	.90183	24
37	.41655	.45819	2.1825	.90911	23	37	.43235	.47948	2.0856	.90171	23
38	.41681	.45854	2.1808	.90899	22	38	.43261	.47984	2.0840	.90158	22
39	.41707	.45889	2.1792	.90887	21	39	.43287	.48019	2.0825	.90146	21
40	.41734	.45924	2.1775	.90875	20	40	.43313	.48055	2.0809	.90133	20
41	.41760	.45960	2.1758	.90863	19	41	.43340	.48091	2.0794	.90120	19
42	.41787	.45995	2.1742	.90851	18	42	.43366	.48127	2.0778	.90108	18
43	.41813	.46030	2.1725	.90839	17	43	.43392	.48163	2.0763	.90095	17
44	.41840	.46065	2.1708	.90826	16	44	.43418	.48198	2.0748	.90082	16
45	.41866	.46101	2.1692	.90814	15	45	.43445	.48234	2.0732	.90070	15
46	.41892	.46136	2.1675	.90802	14	46	.43471	.48270	2.0717	.90057	14
47	.41919	.46171	2.1659	.90790	13	47	.43497	.48306	2.0701	.90045	13
48	.41945	.46206	2.1642	.90778	12	48	.43523	.48342	2.0686	.90032	12
49	.41972	.46242	2.1625	.90766	11	49	.43549	.48378	2.0671	.90019	11
50	.41998	.46277	2.1609	.90753	10	50	.43575	.48414	2.0655	.90007	10
51	.42024	.46312	2.1592	.90741	9	51	.43602	.48450	2.0640	.89994	9
52	.42051	.46348	2.1576	.90729	8	52	.43628	.48486	2.0625	.89981	8
53	.42077	.46383	2.1560	.90717	7	53	.43654	.48521	2.0609	.89968	7
54	.42104	.46418	2.1543	.90704	6	54	.43680	.48557	2.0594	.89956	6
55	.42130	.46454	2.1527	.90692	5	55	.43706	.48593	2.0579	.89943	5
56	.42156	.46489	2.1510	.90680	4	56	.43733	.48629	2.0564	.89930	4
57	.42183	.46525	2.1494	.90668	3	57	.43759	.48665	2.0549	.89918	3
58	.42209	.46560	2.1478	.90655	2	58	.43785	.48701	2.0533	.89905	2
59	.42235	.46595	2.1461	.90643	1	59	.43811	.48737	2.0518	.89892	1
60	.42262	.46631	2.1445	.90631	0	60	.43837	.48773	2.0503	.89879	0
	Cos	Ctn	Tan	Sin	′		Cos	Ctn	Tan	Sin	′

Table V NATURAL TRIGONOMETRIC FUNCTIONS *Page 177*

26° 153° 27° 152°

′	Sin	Tan	Ctn	Cos		′	Sin	Tan	Ctn	Cos	
0	.43837	.48773	2.0503	.89879	60	0	.45399	.50953	1.9626	.89101	60
1	.43863	.48809	2.0488	.89867	59	1	.45425	.50989	1.9612	.89087	59
2	.43889	.48845	2.0473	.89854	58	2	.45451	.51026	1.9598	.89074	58
3	.43916	.48881	2.0458	.89841	57	3	.45477	.51063	1.9584	.89061	57
4	.43942	.48917	2.0443	.89828	56	4	.45503	.51099	1.9570	.89048	56
5	.43968	.48953	2.0428	.89816	55	5	.45529	.51136	1.9556	.89035	55
6	.43994	.48989	2.0413	.89803	54	6	.45554	.51173	1.9542	.89021	54
7	.44020	.49026	2.0398	.89790	53	7	.45580	.51209	1.9528	.89008	53
8	.44046	.49062	2.0383	.89777	52	8	.45606	.51246	1.9514	.88995	52
9	.44072	.49098	2.0368	.89764	51	9	.45632	.51283	1.9500	.88981	51
10	.44098	.49134	2.0353	.89752	50	10	.45658	.51319	1.9486	.88968	50
11	.44124	.49170	2.0338	.89739	49	11	.45684	.51356	1.9472	.88955	49
12	.44151	.49206	2.0323	.89726	48	12	.45710	.51393	1.9458	.88942	48
13	.44177	.49242	2.0308	.89713	47	13	.45736	.51430	1.9444	.88928	47
14	.44203	.49278	2.0293	.89700	46	14	.45762	.51467	1.9430	.88915	46
15	.44229	.49315	2.0278	.89687	45	15	.45787	.51503	1.9416	.88902	45
16	.44255	.49351	2.0263	.89674	44	16	.45813	.51540	1.9402	.88888	44
17	.44281	.49387	2.0248	.89662	43	17	.45839	.51577	1.9388	.88875	43
18	.44307	.49423	2.0233	.89649	42	18	.45865	.51614	1.9375	.88862	42
19	.44333	.49459	2.0219	.89636	41	19	.45891	.51651	1.9361	.88848	41
20	.44359	.49495	2.0204	.89623	40	20	.45917	.51688	1.9347	.88835	40
21	.44385	.49532	2.0189	.89610	39	21	.45942	.51724	1.9333	.88822	39
22	.44411	.49568	2.0174	.89597	38	22	.45968	.51761	1.9319	.88808	38
23	.44437	.49604	2.0160	.89584	37	23	.45994	.51798	1.9306	.88795	37
24	.44464	.49640	2.0145	.89571	36	24	.46020	.51835	1.9292	.88782	36
25	.44490	.49677	2.0130	.89558	35	25	.46046	.51872	1.9278	.88768	35
26	.44516	.49713	2.0115	.89545	34	26	.46072	.51909	1.9265	.88755	34
27	.44542	.49749	2.0101	.89532	33	27	.46097	.51946	1.9251	.88741	33
28	.44568	.49786	2.0086	.89519	32	28	.46123	.51983	1.9237	.88728	32
29	.44594	.49822	2.0072	.89506	31	29	.46149	.52020	1.9223	.88715	31
30	.44620	.49858	2.0057	.89493	30	30	.46175	.52057	1.9210	.88701	30
31	.44646	.49894	2.0042	.89480	29	31	.46201	.52094	1.9196	.88688	29
32	.44672	.49931	2.0028	.89467	28	32	.46226	.52131	1.9183	.88674	28
33	.44698	.49967	2.0013	.89454	27	33	.46252	.52168	1.9169	.88661	27
34	.44724	.50004	1.9999	.89441	26	34	.46278	.52205	1.9155	.88647	26
35	.44750	.50040	1.9984	.89428	25	35	.46304	.52242	1.9142	.88634	25
36	.44776	.50076	1.9970	.89415	24	36	.46330	.52279	1.9128	.88620	24
37	.44802	.50113	1.9955	.89402	23	37	.46355	.52316	1.9115	.88607	23
38	.44828	.50149	1.9941	.89389	22	38	.46381	.52353	1.9101	.88593	22
39	.44854	.50185	1.9926	.89376	21	39	.46407	.52390	1.9088	.88580	21
40	.44880	.50222	1.9912	.89363	20	40	.46433	.52427	1.9074	.88566	20
41	.44906	.50258	1.9897	.89350	19	41	.46458	.52464	1.9061	.88553	19
42	.44932	.50295	1.9883	.89337	18	42	.46484	.52501	1.9047	.88539	18
43	.44958	.50331	1.9868	.89324	17	43	.46510	.52538	1.9034	.88526	17
44	.44984	.50368	1.9854	.89311	16	44	.46536	.52575	1.9020	.88512	16
45	.45010	.50404	1.9840	.89298	15	45	.46561	.52613	1.9007	.88499	15
46	.45036	.50441	1.9825	.89285	14	46	.46587	.52650	1.8993	.88485	14
47	.45062	.50477	1.9811	.89272	13	47	.46613	.52687	1.8980	.88472	13
48	.45088	.50514	1.9797	.89259	12	48	.46639	.52724	1.8967	.88458	12
49	.45114	.50550	1.9782	.89245	11	49	.46664	.52761	1.8953	.88445	11
50	.45140	.50587	1.9768	.89232	10	50	.46690	.52798	1.8940	.88431	10
51	.45166	.50623	1.9754	.89219	9	51	.46716	.52836	1.8927	.88417	9
52	.45192	.50660	1.9740	.89206	8	52	.46742	.52873	1.8913	.88404	8
53	.45218	.50696	1.9725	.89193	7	53	.46767	.52910	1.8900	.88390	7
54	.45243	.50733	1.9711	.89180	6	54	.46793	.52947	1.8887	.88377	6
55	.45269	.50769	1.9697	.89167	5	55	.46819	.52985	1.8873	.88363	5
56	.45295	.50806	1.9683	.89153	4	56	.46844	.53022	1.8860	.88349	4
57	.45321	.50843	1.9669	.89140	3	57	.46870	.53059	1.8847	.88336	3
58	.45347	.50879	1.9654	.89127	2	58	.46896	.53096	1.8834	.88322	2
59	.45373	.50916	1.9640	.89114	1	59	.46921	.53134	1.8820	.88308	1
60	.45399	.50953	1.9626	.89101	0	60	.46947	.53171	1.8807	.88295	0
	Cos	Ctn	Tan	Sin	′		Cos	Ctn	Tan	Sin	′

NATURAL TRIGONOMETRIC FUNCTIONS

′	Sin	Tan	Ctn	Cos		′	Sin	Tan	Ctn	Cos	
0	.46947	.53171	1.8807	.88295	60	0	.48481	.55431	1.8040	.87462	60
1	.46973	.53208	1.8794	.88281	59	1	.48506	.55469	1.8028	.87448	59
2	.46999	.53246	1.8781	.88267	58	2	.48532	.55507	1.8016	.87434	58
3	.47024	.53283	1.8768	.88254	57	3	.48557	.55545	1.8003	.87420	57
4	.47050	.53320	1.8755	.88240	56	4	.48583	.55583	1.7991	.87406	56
5	.47076	.53358	1.8741	.88226	55	5	.48608	.55621	1.7979	.87391	55
6	.47101	.53395	1.8728	.88213	54	6	.48634	.55659	1.7966	.87377	54
7	.47127	.53432	1.8715	.88199	53	7	.48659	.55697	1.7954	.87363	53
8	.47153	.53470	1.8702	.88185	52	8	.48684	.55736	1.7942	.87349	52
9	.47178	.53507	1.8689	.88172	51	9	.48710	.55774	1.7930	.87335	51
10	.47204	.53545	1.8676	.88158	50	10	.48735	.55812	1.7917	.87321	50
11	.47229	.53582	1.8663	.88144	49	11	.48761	.55850	1.7905	.87306	49
12	.47255	.53620	1.8650	.88130	48	12	.48786	.55888	1.7893	.87292	48
13	.47281	.53657	1.8637	.88117	47	13	.48811	.55926	1.7881	.87278	47
14	.47306	.53694	1.8624	.88103	46	14	.48837	.55964	1.7868	.87264	46
15	.47332	.53732	1.8611	.88089	45	15	.48862	.56003	1.7856	.87250	45
16	.47358	.53769	1.8598	.88075	44	16	.48888	.56041	1.7844	.87235	44
17	.47383	.53807	1.8585	.88062	43	17	.48913	.56079	1.7832	.87221	43
18	.47409	.53844	1.8572	.88048	42	18	.48938	.56117	1.7820	.87207	42
19	.47434	.53882	1.8559	.88034	41	19	.48964	.56156	1.7808	.87193	41
20	.47460	.53920	1.8546	.88020	40	20	.48989	.56194	1.7796	.87178	40
21	.47486	.53957	1.8533	.88006	39	21	.49014	.56232	1.7783	.87164	39
22	.47511	.53995	1.8520	.87993	38	22	.49040	.56270	1.7771	.87150	38
23	.47537	.54032	1.8507	.87979	37	23	.49065	.56309	1.7759	.87136	37
24	.47562	.54070	1.8495	.87965	36	24	.49090	.56347	1.7747	.87121	36
25	.47588	.54107	1.8482	.87951	35	25	.49116	.56385	1.7735	.87107	35
26	.47614	.54145	1.8469	.87937	34	26	.49141	.56424	1.7723	.87093	34
27	.47639	.54183	1.8456	.87923	33	27	.49166	.56462	1.7711	.87079	33
28	.47665	.54220	1.8443	.87909	32	28	.49192	.56501	1.7699	.87064	32
29	.47690	.54258	1.8430	.87896	31	29	.49217	.56539	1.7687	.87050	31
30	.47716	.54296	1.8418	.87882	30	30	.49242	.56577	1.7675	.87036	30
31	.47741	.54333	1.8405	.87868	29	31	.49268	.56616	1.7663	.87021	29
32	.47767	.54371	1.8392	.87854	28	32	.49293	.56654	1.7651	.87007	28
33	.47793	.54409	1.8379	.87840	27	33	.49318	.56693	1.7639	.86993	27
34	.47818	.54446	1.8367	.87826	26	34	.49344	.56731	1.7627	.86978	26
35	.47844	.54484	1.8354	.87812	25	35	.49369	.56769	1.7615	.86964	25
36	.47869	.54522	1.8341	.87798	24	36	.49394	.56808	1.7603	.86949	24
37	.47895	.54560	1.8329	.87784	23	37	.49419	.56846	1.7591	.86935	23
38	.47920	.54597	1.8316	.87770	22	38	.49445	.56885	1.7579	.86921	22
39	.47946	.54635	1.8303	.87756	21	39	.49470	.56923	1.7567	.86906	21
40	.47971	.54673	1.8291	.87743	20	40	.49495	.56962	1.7556	.86892	20
41	.47997	.54711	1.8278	.87729	19	41	.49521	.57000	1.7544	.86878	19
42	.48022	.54748	1.8265	.87715	18	42	.49546	.57039	1.7532	.86863	18
43	.48048	.54786	1.8253	.87701	17	43	.49571	.57078	1.7520	.86849	17
44	.48073	.54824	1.8240	.87687	16	44	.49596	.57116	1.7508	.86834	16
45	.48099	.54862	1.8228	.87673	15	45	.49622	.57155	1.7496	.86820	15
46	.48124	.54900	1.8215	.87659	14	46	.49647	.57193	1.7485	.86805	14
47	.48150	.54938	1.8202	.87645	13	47	.49672	.57232	1.7473	.86791	13
48	.48175	.54975	1.8190	.87631	12	48	.49697	.57271	1.7461	.86777	12
49	.48201	.55013	1.8177	.87617	11	49	.49723	.57309	1.7449	.86762	11
50	.48226	.55051	1.8165	.87603	10	50	.49748	.57348	1.7437	.86748	10
51	.48252	.55089	1.8152	.87589	9	51	.49773	.57386	1.7426	.86733	9
52	.48277	.55127	1.8140	.87575	8	52	.49798	.57425	1.7414	.86719	8
53	.48303	.55165	1.8127	.87561	7	53	.49824	.57464	1.7402	.86704	7
54	.48328	.55203	1.8115	.87546	6	54	.49849	.57503	1.7391	.86690	6
55	.48354	.55241	1.8103	.87532	5	55	.49874	.57541	1.7379	.86675	5
56	.48379	.55279	1.8090	.87518	4	56	.49899	.57580	1.7367	.86661	4
57	.48405	.55317	1.8078	.87504	3	57	.49924	.57619	1.7355	.86646	3
58	.48430	.55355	1.8065	.87490	2	58	.49950	.57657	1.7344	.86632	2
59	.48456	.55393	1.8053	.87476	1	59	.49975	.57696	1.7332	.86617	1
60	.48481	.55431	1.8040	.87462	0	60	.50000	.57735	1.7321	.86603	0
	Cos	Ctn	Tan	Sin	′		Cos	Ctn	Tan	Sin	′

Table V   NATURAL TRIGONOMETRIC FUNCTIONS   Page 179
30°   149°   31°   148°

′	Sin	Tan	Ctn	Cos		′	Sin	Tan	Ctn	Cos	
0	.50000	.57735	1.7321	.86603	60	0	.51504	.60086	1.6643	.85717	60
1	.50025	.57774	1.7309	.86588	59	1	.51529	.60126	1.6632	.85702	59
2	.50050	.57813	1.7297	.86573	58	2	.51554	.60165	1.6621	.85687	58
3	.50076	.57851	1.7286	.86559	57	3	.51579	.60205	1.6610	.85672	57
4	.50101	.57890	1.7274	.86544	56	4	.51604	.60245	1.6599	.85657	56
5	.50126	.57929	1.7262	.86530	55	5	.51628	.60284	1.6588	.85642	55
6	.50151	.57968	1.7251	.86515	54	6	.51653	.60324	1.6577	.85627	54
7	.50176	.58007	1.7239	.86501	53	7	.51678	.60364	1.6566	.85612	53
8	.50201	.58046	1.7228	.86486	52	8	.51703	.60403	1.6555	.85597	52
9	.50227	.58085	1.7216	.86471	51	9	.51728	.60443	1.6545	.85582	51
10	.50252	.58124	1.7205	.86457	50	10	.51753	.60483	1.6534	.85567	50
11	.50277	.58162	1.7193	.86442	49	11	.51778	.60522	1.6523	.85551	49
12	.50302	.58201	1.7182	.86427	48	12	.51803	.60562	1.6512	.85536	48
13	.50327	.58240	1.7170	.86413	47	13	.51828	.60602	1.6501	.85521	47
14	.50352	.58279	1.7159	.86398	46	14	.51852	.60642	1.6490	.85506	46
15	.50377	.58318	1.7147	.86384	45	15	.51877	.60681	1.6479	.85491	45
16	.50403	.58357	1.7136	.86369	44	16	.51902	.60721	1.6469	.85476	44
17	.50428	.58396	1.7124	.86354	43	17	.51927	.60761	1.6458	.85461	43
18	.50453	.58435	1.7113	.86340	42	18	.51952	.60801	1.6447	.85446	42
19	.50478	.58474	1.7102	.86325	41	19	.51977	.60841	1.6436	.85431	41
20	.50503	.58513	1.7090	.86310	40	20	.52002	.60881	1.6426	.85416	40
21	.50528	.58552	1.7079	.86295	39	21	.52026	.60921	1.6415	.85401	39
22	.50553	.58591	1.7067	.86281	38	22	.52051	.60960	1.6404	.85385	38
23	.50578	.58631	1.7056	.86266	37	23	.52076	.61000	1.6393	.85370	37
24	.50603	.58670	1.7045	.86251	36	24	.52101	.61040	1.6383	.85355	36
25	.50628	.58709	1.7033	.86237	35	25	.52126	.61080	1.6372	.85340	35
26	.50654	.58748	1.7022	.86222	34	26	.52151	.61120	1.6361	.85325	34
27	.50679	.58787	1.7011	.86207	33	27	.52175	.61160	1.6351	.85310	33
28	.50704	.58826	1.6999	.86192	32	28	.52200	.61200	1.6340	.85294	32
29	.50729	.58865	1.6988	.86178	31	29	.52225	.61240	1.6329	.85279	31
30	.50754	.58905	1.6977	.86163	30	30	.52250	.61280	1.6319	.85264	30
31	.50779	.58944	1.6965	.86148	29	31	.52275	.61320	1.6308	.85249	29
32	.50804	.58983	1.6954	.86133	28	32	.52299	.61360	1.6297	.85234	28
33	.50829	.59022	1.6943	.86119	27	33	.52324	.61400	1.6287	.85218	27
34	.50854	.59061	1.6932	.86104	26	34	.52349	.61440	1.6276	.85203	26
35	.50879	.59101	1.6920	.86089	25	35	.52374	.61480	1.6265	.85188	25
36	.50904	.59140	1.6909	.86074	24	36	.52399	.61520	1.6255	.85173	24
37	.50929	.59179	1.6898	.86059	23	37	.52423	.61561	1.6244	.85157	23
38	.50954	.59218	1.6887	.86045	22	38	.52448	.61601	1.6234	.85142	22
39	.50979	.59258	1.6875	.86030	21	39	.52473	.61641	1.6223	.85127	21
40	.51004	.59297	1.6864	.86015	20	40	.52498	.61681	1.6212	.85112	20
41	.51029	.59336	1.6853	.86000	19	41	.52522	.61721	1.6202	.85096	19
42	.51054	.59376	1.6842	.85985	18	42	.52547	.61761	1.6191	.85081	18
43	.51079	.59415	1.6831	.85970	17	43	.52572	.61801	1.6181	.85066	17
44	.51104	.59454	1.6820	.85956	16	44	.52597	.61842	1.6170	.85051	16
45	.51129	.59494	1.6808	.85941	15	45	.52621	.61882	1.6160	.85035	15
46	.51154	.59533	1.6797	.85926	14	46	.52646	.61922	1.6149	.85020	14
47	.51179	.59573	1.6786	.85911	13	47	.52671	.61962	1.6139	.85005	13
48	.51204	.59612	1.6775	.85896	12	48	.52696	.62003	1.6128	.84989	12
49	.51229	.59651	1.6764	.85881	11	49	.52720	.62043	1.6118	.84974	11
50	.51254	.59691	1.6753	.85866	10	50	.52745	.62083	1.6107	.84959	10
51	.51279	.59730	1.6742	.85851	9	51	.52770	.62124	1.6097	.84943	9
52	.51304	.59770	1.6731	.85836	8	52	.52794	.62164	1.6087	.84928	8
53	.51329	.59809	1.6720	.85821	7	53	.52819	.62204	1.6076	.84913	7
54	.51354	.59849	1.6709	.85806	6	54	.52844	.62245	1.6066	.84897	6
55	.51379	.59888	1.6698	.85792	5	55	.52869	.62285	1.6055	.84882	5
56	.51404	.59928	1.6687	.85777	4	56	.52893	.62325	1.6045	.84866	4
57	.51429	.59967	1.6676	.85762	3	57	.52918	.62366	1.6034	.84851	3
58	.51454	.60007	1.6665	.85747	2	58	.52943	.62406	1.6024	.84836	2
59	.51479	.60046	1.6654	.85732	1	59	.52967	.62446	1.6014	.84820	1
60	.51504	.60086	1.6643	.85717	0	60	.52992	.62487	1.6003	.84805	0
	Cos	Ctn	Tan	Sin	′		Cos	Ctn	Tan	Sin	′

′	Sin	Tan	Ctn	Cos		′	Sin	Tan	Ctn	Cos	
0	.52992	.62487	1.6003	.84805	60	0	.54464	.64941	1.5399	.83867	60
1	.53017	.62527	1.5993	.84789	59	1	.54488	.64982	1.5389	.83851	59
2	.53041	.62568	1.5983	.84774	58	2	.54513	.65024	1.5379	.83835	58
3	.53066	.62608	1.5972	.84759	57	3	.54537	.65065	1.5369	.83819	57
4	.53091	.62649	1.5962	.84743	56	4	.54561	.65106	1.5359	.83804	56
5	.53115	.62689	1.5952	.84728	55	5	.54586	.65148	1.5350	.83788	55
6	.53140	.62730	1.5941	.84712	54	6	.54610	.65189	1.5340	.83772	54
7	.53164	.62770	1.5931	.84697	53	7	.54635	.65231	1.5330	.83756	53
8	.53189	.62811	1.5921	.84681	52	8	.54659	.65272	1.5320	.83740	52
9	.53214	.62852	1.5911	.84666	51	9	.54683	.65314	1.5311	.83724	51
10	.53238	.62892	1.5900	.84650	50	10	.54708	.65355	1.5301	.83708	50
11	.53263	.62933	1.5890	.84635	49	11	.54732	.65397	1.5291	.83692	49
12	.53288	.62973	1.5880	.84619	48	12	.54756	.65438	1.5282	.83676	48
13	.53312	.63014	1.5869	.84604	47	13	.54781	.65480	1.5272	.83660	47
14	.53337	.63055	1.5859	.84588	46	14	.54805	.65521	1.5262	.83645	46
15	.53361	.63095	1.5849	.84573	45	15	.54829	.65563	1.5253	.83629	45
16	.53386	.63136	1.5839	.84557	44	16	.54854	.65604	1.5243	.83613	44
17	.53411	.63177	1.5829	.84542	43	17	.54878	.65646	1.5233	.83597	43
18	.53435	.63217	1.5818	.84526	42	18	.54902	.65688	1.5224	.83581	42
19	.53460	.63258	1.5808	.84511	41	19	.54927	.65729	1.5214	.83565	41
20	.53484	.63299	1.5798	.84495	40	20	.54951	.65771	1.5204	.83549	40
21	.53509	.63340	1.5788	.84480	39	21	.54975	.65813	1.5195	.83533	39
22	.53534	.63380	1.5778	.84464	38	22	.54999	.65854	1.5185	.83517	38
23	.53558	.63421	1.5768	.84448	37	23	.55024	.65896	1.5175	.83501	37
24	.53583	.63462	1.5757	.84433	36	24	.55048	.65938	1.5166	.83485	36
25	.53607	.63503	1.5747	.84417	35	25	.55072	.65980	1.5156	.83469	35
26	.53632	.63544	1.5737	.84402	34	26	.55097	.66021	1.5147	.83453	34
27	.53656	.63584	1.5727	.84386	33	27	.55121	.66063	1.5137	.83437	33
28	.53681	.63625	1.5717	.84370	32	28	.55145	.66105	1.5127	.83421	32
29	.53705	.63666	1.5707	.84355	31	29	.55169	.66147	1.5118	.83405	31
30	.53730	.63707	1.5697	.84339	30	30	.55194	.66189	1.5108	.83389	30
31	.53754	.63748	1.5687	.84324	29	31	.55218	.66230	1.5099	.83373	29
32	.53779	.63789	1.5677	.84308	28	32	.55242	.66272	1.5089	.83356	28
33	.53804	.63830	1.5667	.84292	27	33	.55266	.66314	1.5080	.83340	27
34	.53828	.63871	1.5657	.84277	26	34	.55291	.66356	1.5070	.83324	26
35	.53853	.63912	1.5647	.84261	25	35	.55315	.66398	1.5061	.83308	25
36	.53877	.63953	1.5637	.84245	24	36	.55339	.66440	1.5051	.83292	24
37	.53902	.63994	1.5627	.84230	23	37	.55363	.66482	1.5042	.83276	23
38	.53926	.64035	1.5617	.84214	22	38	.55388	.66524	1.5032	.83260	22
39	.53951	.64076	1.5607	.84198	21	39	.55412	.66566	1.5023	.83244	21
40	.53975	.64117	1.5597	.84182	20	40	.55436	.66608	1.5013	.83228	20
41	.54000	.64158	1.5587	.84167	19	41	.55460	.66650	1.5004	.83212	19
42	.54024	.64199	1.5577	.84151	18	42	.55484	.66692	1.4994	.83195	18
43	.54049	.64240	1.5567	.84135	17	43	.55509	.66734	1.4985	.83179	17
44	.54073	.64281	1.5557	.84120	16	44	.55533	.66776	1.4975	.83163	16
45	.54097	.64322	1.5547	.84104	15	45	.55557	.66818	1.4966	.83147	15
46	.54122	.64363	1.5537	.84088	14	46	.55581	.66860	1.4957	.83131	14
47	.54146	.64404	1.5527	.84072	13	47	.55605	.66902	1.4947	.83115	13
48	.54171	.64446	1.5517	.84057	12	48	.55630	.66944	1.4938	.83098	12
49	.54195	.64487	1.5507	.84041	11	49	.55654	.66986	1.4928	.83082	11
50	.54220	.64528	1.5497	.84025	10	50	.55678	.67028	1.4919	.83066	10
51	.54244	.64569	1.5487	.84009	9	51	.55702	.67071	1.4910	.83050	9
52	.54269	.64610	1.5477	.83994	8	52	.55726	.67113	1.4900	.83034	8
53	.54293	.64652	1.5468	.83978	7	53	.55750	.67155	1.4891	.83017	7
54	.54317	.64693	1.5458	.83962	6	54	.55775	.67197	1.4882	.83001	6
55	.54342	.64734	1.5448	.83946	5	55	.55799	.67239	1.4872	.82985	5
56	.54366	.64775	1.5438	.83930	4	56	.55823	.67282	1.4863	.82969	4
57	.54391	.64817	1.5428	.83915	3	57	.55847	.67324	1.4854	.82953	3
58	.54415	.64858	1.5418	.83899	2	58	.55871	.67366	1.4844	.82936	2
59	.54440	.64899	1.5408	.83883	1	59	.55895	.67409	1.4835	.82920	1
60	.54464	.64941	1.5399	.83867	0	60	.55919	.67451	1.4826	.82904	0
	Cos	Ctn	Tan	Sin	′		Cos	Ctn	Tan	Sin	′

′	Sin	Tan	Ctn	Cos		′	Sin	Tan	Ctn	Cos	
0	.55919	.67451	1.4826	.82904	60	0	.57358	.70021	1.4281	.81915	60
1	.55943	.67493	1.4816	.82887	59	1	.57381	.70064	1.4273	.81899	59
2	.55968	.67536	1.4807	.82871	58	2	.57405	.70107	1.4264	.81882	58
3	.55992	.67578	1.4798	.82855	57	3	.57429	.70151	1.4255	.81865	57
4	.56016	.67620	1.4788	.82839	56	4	.57453	.70194	1.4246	.81848	56
5	.56040	.67663	1.4779	.82822	55	5	.57477	.70238	1.4237	.81832	55
6	.56064	.67705	1.4770	.82806	54	6	.57501	.70281	1.4229	.81815	54
7	.56088	.67748	1.4761	.82790	53	7	.57524	.70325	1.4220	.81798	53
8	.56112	.67790	1.4751	.82773	52	8	.57548	.70368	1.4211	.81782	52
9	.56136	.67832	1.4742	.82757	51	9	.57572	.70412	1.4202	.81765	51
10	.56160	.67875	1.4733	.82741	50	10	.57596	.70455	1.4193	.81748	50
11	.56184	.67917	1.4724	.82724	49	11	.57619	.70499	1.4185	.81731	49
12	.56208	.67960	1.4715	.82708	48	12	.57643	.70542	1.4176	.81714	48
13	.56232	.68002	1.4705	.82692	47	13	.57667	.70586	1.4167	.81698	47
14	.56256	.68045	1.4696	.82675	46	14	.57691	.70629	1.4158	.81681	46
15	.56280	.68088	1.4687	.82659	45	15	.57715	.70673	1.4150	.81664	45
16	.56305	.68130	1.4678	.82643	44	16	.57738	.70717	1.4141	.81647	44
17	.56329	.68173	1.4669	.82626	43	17	.57762	.70760	1.4132	.81631	43
18	.56353	.68215	1.4659	.82610	42	18	.57786	.70804	1.4124	.81614	42
19	.56377	.68258	1.4650	.82593	41	19	.57810	.70848	1.4115	.81597	41
20	.56401	.68301	1.4641	.82577	40	20	.57833	.70891	1.4106	.81580	40
21	.56425	.68343	1.4632	.82561	39	21	.57857	.70935	1.4097	.81563	39
22	.56449	.68386	1.4623	.82544	38	22	.57881	.70979	1.4089	.81546	38
23	.56473	.68429	1.4614	.82528	37	23	.57904	.71023	1.4080	.81530	37
24	.56497	.68471	1.4605	.82511	36	24	.57928	.71066	1.4071	.81513	36
25	.56521	.68514	1.4596	.82495	35	25	.57952	.71110	1.4063	.81496	35
26	.56545	.68557	1.4586	.82478	34	26	.57976	.71154	1.4054	.81479	34
27	.56569	.68600	1.4577	.82462	33	27	.57999	.71198	1.4045	.81462	33
28	.56593	.68642	1.4568	.82446	32	28	.58023	.71242	1.4037	.81445	32
29	.56617	.68685	1.4559	.82429	31	29	.58047	.71285	1.4028	.81428	31
30	.56641	.68728	1.4550	.82413	30	30	.58070	.71329	1.4019	.81412	30
31	.56665	.68771	1.4541	.82396	29	31	.58094	.71373	1.4011	.81395	29
32	.56689	.68814	1.4532	.82380	28	32	.58118	.71417	1.4002	.81378	28
33	.56713	.68857	1.4523	.82363	27	33	.58141	.71461	1.3994	.81361	27
34	.56736	.68900	1.4514	.82347	26	34	.58165	.71505	1.3985	.81344	26
35	.56760	.68942	1.4505	.82330	25	35	.58189	.71549	1.3976	.81327	25
36	.56784	.68985	1.4496	.82314	24	36	.58212	.71593	1.3968	.81310	24
37	.56808	.69028	1.4487	.82297	23	37	.58236	.71637	1.3959	.81293	23
38	.56832	.69071	1.4478	.82281	22	38	.58260	.71681	1.3951	.81276	22
39	.56856	.69114	1.4469	.82264	21	39	.58283	.71725	1.3942	.81259	21
40	.56880	.69157	1.4460	.82248	20	40	.58307	.71769	1.3934	.81242	20
41	.56904	.69200	1.4451	.82231	19	41	.58330	.71813	1.3925	.81225	19
42	.56928	.69243	1.4442	.82214	18	42	.58354	.71857	1.3916	.81208	18
43	.56952	.69286	1.4433	.82198	17	43	.58378	.71901	1.3908	.81191	17
44	.56976	.69329	1.4424	.82181	16	44	.58401	.71946	1.3899	.81174	16
45	.57000	.69372	1.4415	.82165	15	45	.58425	.71990	1.3891	.81157	15
46	.57024	.69416	1.4406	.82148	14	46	.58449	.72034	1.3882	.81140	14
47	.57047	.69459	1.4397	.82132	13	47	.58472	.72078	1.3874	.81123	13
48	.57071	.69502	1.4388	.82115	12	48	.58496	.72122	1.3865	.81106	12
49	.57095	.69545	1.4379	.82098	11	49	.58519	.72167	1.3857	.81089	11
50	.57119	.69588	1.4370	.82082	10	50	.58543	.72211	1.3848	.81072	10
51	.57143	.69631	1.4361	.82065	9	51	.58567	.72255	1.3840	.81055	9
52	.57167	.69675	1.4352	.82048	8	52	.58590	.72299	1.3831	.81038	8
53	.57191	.69718	1.4344	.82032	7	53	.58614	.72344	1.3823	.81021	7
54	.57215	.69761	1.4335	.82015	6	54	.58637	.72388	1.3814	.81004	6
55	.57238	.69804	1.4326	.81999	5	55	.58661	.72432	1.3806	.80987	5
56	.57262	.69847	1.4317	.81982	4	56	.58684	.72477	1.3798	.80970	4
57	.57286	.69891	1.4308	.81965	3	57	.58708	.72521	1.3789	.80953	3
58	.57310	.69934	1.4299	.81949	2	58	.58731	.72565	1.3781	.80936	2
59	.57334	.69977	1.4290	.81932	1	59	.58755	.72610	1.3772	.80919	1
60	.57358	.70021	1.4281	.81915	0	60	.58779	.72654	1.3764	.80902	0
	Cos	Ctn	Tan	Sin	′		Cos	Ctn	Tan	Sin	′

36°   143°   37°   142°

′	Sin	Tan	Ctn	Cos			′	Sin	Tan	Ctn	Cos	
0	.58779	.72654	1.3764	.80902	60		0	.60182	.75355	1.3270	.79864	60
1	.58802	.72699	1.3755	.80885	59		1	.60205	.75401	1.3262	.79846	59
2	.58826	.72743	1.3747	.80867	58		2	.60228	.75447	1.3254	.79829	58
3	.58849	.72788	1.3739	.80850	57		3	.60251	.75492	1.3246	.79811	57
4	.58873	.72832	1.3730	.80833	56		4	.60274	.75538	1.3238	.79793	56
5	.58896	.72877	1.3722	.80816	55		5	.60298	.75584	1.3230	.79776	55
6	.58920	.72921	1.3713	.80799	54		6	.60321	.75629	1.3222	.79758	54
7	.58943	.72966	1.3705	.80782	53		7	.60344	.75675	1.3214	.79741	53
8	.58967	.73010	1.3697	.80765	52		8	.60367	.75721	1.3206	.79723	52
9	.58990	.73055	1.3688	.80748	51		9	.60390	.75767	1.3198	.79706	51
10	.59014	.73100	1.3680	.80730	50		10	.60414	.75812	1.3190	.79688	50
11	.59037	.73144	1.3672	.80713	49		11	.60437	.75858	1.3182	.79671	49
12	.59061	.73189	1.3663	.80696	48		12	.60460	.75904	1.3175	.79653	48
13	.59084	.73234	1.3655	.80679	47		13	.60483	.75950	1.3167	.79635	47
14	.59108	.73278	1.3647	.80662	46		14	.60506	.75996	1.3159	.79618	46
15	.59131	.73323	1.3638	.80644	45		15	.60529	.76042	1.3151	.79600	45
16	.59154	.73368	1.3630	.80627	44		16	.60553	.76088	1.3143	.79583	44
17	.59178	.73413	1.3622	.80610	43		17	.60576	.76134	1.3135	.79565	43
18	.59201	.73457	1.3613	.80593	42		18	.60599	.76180	1.3127	.79547	42
19	.59225	.73502	1.3605	.80576	41		19	.60622	.76226	1.3119	.79530	41
20	.59248	.73547	1.3597	.80558	40		20	.60645	.76272	1.3111	.79512	40
21	.59272	.73592	1.3588	.80541	39		21	.60668	.76318	1.3103	.79494	39
22	.59295	.73637	1.3580	.80524	38		22	.60691	.76364	1.3095	.79477	38
23	.59318	.73681	1.3572	.80507	37		23	.60714	.76410	1.3087	.79459	37
24	.59342	.73726	1.3564	.80489	36		24	.60738	.76456	1.3079	.79441	36
25	.59365	.73771	1.3555	.80472	35		25	.60761	.76502	1.3072	.79424	35
26	.59389	.73816	1.3547	.80455	34		26	.60784	.76548	1.3064	.79406	34
27	.59412	.73861	1.3539	.80438	33		27	.60807	.76594	1.3056	.79388	33
28	.59436	.73906	1.3531	.80420	32		28	.60830	.76640	1.3048	.79371	32
29	.59459	.73951	1.3522	.80403	31		29	.60853	.76686	1.3040	.79353	31
30	.59482	.73996	1.3514	.80386	30		30	.60876	.76733	1.3032	.79335	30
31	.59506	.74041	1.3506	.80368	29		31	.60899	.76779	1.3024	.79318	29
32	.59529	.74086	1.3498	.80351	28		32	.60922	.76825	1.3017	.79300	28
33	.59552	.74131	1.3490	.80334	27		33	.60945	.76871	1.3009	.79282	27
34	.59576	.74176	1.3481	.80316	26		34	.60968	.76918	1.3001	.79264	26
35	.59599	.74221	1.3473	.80299	25		35	.60991	.76964	1.2993	.79247	25
36	.59622	.74267	1.3465	.80282	24		36	.61015	.77010	1.2985	.79229	24
37	.59646	.74312	1.3457	.80264	23		37	.61038	.77057	1.2977	.79211	23
38	.59669	.74357	1.3449	.80247	22		38	.61061	.77103	1.2970	.79193	22
39	.59693	.74402	1.3440	.80230	21		39	.61084	.77149	1.2962	.79176	21
40	.59716	.74447	1.3432	.80212	20		40	.61107	.77196	1.2954	.79158	20
41	.59739	.74492	1.3424	.80195	19		41	.61130	.77242	1.2946	.79140	19
42	.59763	.74538	1.3416	.80178	18		42	.61153	.77289	1.2938	.79122	18
43	.59786	.74583	1.3408	.80160	17		43	.61176	.77335	1.2931	.79105	17
44	.59809	.74628	1.3400	.80143	16		44	.61199	.77382	1.2923	.79087	16
45	.59832	.74674	1.3392	.80125	15		45	.61222	.77428	1.2915	.79069	15
46	.59856	.74719	1.3384	.80108	14		46	.61245	.77475	1.2907	.79051	14
47	.59879	.74764	1.3375	.80091	13		47	.61268	.77521	1.2900	.79033	13
48	.59902	.74810	1.3367	.80073	12		48	.61291	.77568	1.2892	.79016	12
49	.59926	.74855	1.3359	.80056	11		49	.61314	.77615	1.2884	.78998	11
50	.59949	.74900	1.3351	.80038	10		50	.61337	.77661	1.2876	.78980	10
51	.59972	.74946	1.3343	.80021	9		51	.61360	.77708	1.2869	.78962	9
52	.59995	.74991	1.3335	.80003	8		52	.61383	.77754	1.2861	.78944	8
53	.60019	.75037	1.3327	.79986	7		53	.61406	.77801	1.2853	.78926	7
54	.60042	.75082	1.3319	.79968	6		54	.61429	.77848	1.2846	.78908	6
55	.60065	.75128	1.3311	.79951	5		55	.61451	.77895	1.2838	.78891	5
56	.60089	.75173	1.3303	.79934	4		56	.61474	.77941	1.2830	.78873	4
57	.60112	.75219	1.3295	.79916	3		57	.61497	.77988	1.2822	.78855	3
58	.60135	.75264	1.3287	.79899	2		58	.61520	.78035	1.2815	.78837	2
59	.60158	.75310	1.3278	.79881	1		59	.61543	.78082	1.2807	.78819	1
60	.60182	.75355	1.3270	.79864	0		60	.61566	.78129	1.2799	.78801	0
	Cos	Ctn	Tan	Sin	′			Cos	Ctn	Tan	Sin	′

126°   53°   127°   52°

Table V **NATURAL TRIGONOMETRIC FUNCTIONS** *Page 183*

38° 141° 39° 140°

′	Sin	Tan	Ctn	Cos			′	Sin	Tan	Ctn	Cos	
0	.61566	.78129	1.2799	.78801	60		0	.62932	.80978	1.2349	.77715	60
1	.61589	.78175	1.2792	.78783	59		1	.62955	.81027	1.2342	.77696	59
2	.61612	.78222	1.2784	.78765	58		2	.62977	.81075	1.2334	.77678	58
3	.61635	.78269	1.2776	.78747	57		3	.63000	.81123	1.2327	.77660	57
4	.61658	.78316	1.2769	.78729	56		4	.63022	.81171	1.2320	.77641	56
5	.61681	.78363	1.2761	.78711	55		5	.63045	.81220	1.2312	.77623	55
6	.61704	.78410	1.2753	.78694	54		6	.63068	.81268	1.2305	.77605	54
7	.61726	.78457	1.2746	.78676	53		7	.63090	.81316	1.2298	.77586	53
8	.61749	.78504	1.2738	.78658	52		8	.63113	.81364	1.2290	.77568	52
9	.61772	.78551	1.2731	.78640	51		9	.63135	.81413	1.2283	.77550	51
10	.61795	.78598	1.2723	.78622	50		10	.63158	.81461	1.2276	.77531	50
11	.61818	.78645	1.2715	.78604	49		11	.63180	.81510	1.2268	.77513	49
12	.61841	.78692	1.2708	.78586	48		12	.63203	.81558	1.2261	.77494	48
13	.61864	.78739	1.2700	.78568	47		13	.63225	.81606	1.2254	.77476	47
14	.61887	.78786	1.2693	.78550	46		14	.63248	.81655	1.2247	.77458	46
15	.61909	.78834	1.2685	.78532	45		15	.63271	.81703	1.2239	.77439	45
16	.61932	.78881	1.2677	.78514	44		16	.63293	.81752	1.2232	.77421	44
17	.61955	.78928	1.2670	.78496	43		17	.63316	.81800	1.2225	.77402	43
18	.61978	.78975	1.2662	.78478	42		18	.63338	.81849	1.2218	.77384	42
19	.62001	.79022	1.2655	.78460	41		19	.63361	.81898	1.2210	.77366	41
20	.62024	.79070	1.2647	.78442	40		20	.63383	.81946	1.2203	.77347	40
21	.62046	.79117	1.2640	.78424	39		21	.63406	.81995	1.2196	.77329	39
22	.62069	.79164	1.2632	.78405	38		22	.63428	.82044	1.2189	.77310	38
23	.62092	.79212	1.2624	.78387	37		23	.63451	.82092	1.2181	.77292	37
24	.62115	.79259	1.2617	.78369	36		24	.63473	.82141	1.2174	.77273	36
25	.62138	.79306	1.2609	.78351	35		25	.63496	.82190	1.2167	.77255	35
26	.62160	.79354	1.2602	.78333	34		26	.63518	.82238	1.2160	.77236	34
27	.62183	.79401	1.2594	.78315	33		27	.63540	.82287	1.2153	.77218	33
28	.62206	.79449	1.2587	.78297	32		28	.63563	.82336	1.2145	.77199	32
29	.62229	.79496	1.2579	.78279	31		29	.63585	.82385	1.2138	.77181	31
30	.62251	.79544	1.2572	.78261	30		30	.63608	.82434	1.2131	.77162	30
31	.62274	.79591	1.2564	.78243	29		31	.63630	.82483	1.2124	.77144	29
32	.62297	.79639	1.2557	.78225	28		32	.63653	.82531	1.2117	.77125	28
33	.62320	.79686	1.2549	.78206	27		33	.63675	.82580	1.2109	.77107	27
34	.62342	.79734	1.2542	.78188	26		34	.63698	.82629	1.2102	.77088	26
35	.62365	.79781	1.2534	.78170	25		35	.63720	.82678	1.2095	.77070	25
36	.62388	.79829	1.2527	.78152	24		36	.63742	.82727	1.2088	.77051	24
37	.62411	.79877	1.2519	.78134	23		37	.63765	.82776	1.2081	.77033	23
38	.62433	.79924	1.2512	.78116	22		38	.63787	.82825	1.2074	.77014	22
39	.62456	.79972	1.2504	.78098	21		39	.63810	.82874	1.2066	.76996	21
40	.62479	.80020	1.2497	.78079	20		40	.63832	.82923	1.2059	.76977	20
41	.62502	.80067	1.2489	.78061	19		41	.63854	.82972	1.2052	.76959	19
42	.62524	.80115	1.2482	.78043	18		42	.63877	.83022	1.2045	.76940	18
43	.62547	.80163	1.2475	.78025	17		43	.63899	.83071	1.2038	.76921	17
44	.62570	.80211	1.2467	.78007	16		44	.63922	.83120	1.2031	.76903	16
45	.62592	.80258	1.2460	.77988	15		45	.63944	.83169	1.2024	.76884	15
46	.62615	.80306	1.2452	.77970	14		46	.63966	.83218	1.2017	.76866	14
47	.62638	.80354	1.2445	.77952	13		47	.63989	.83268	1.2009	.76847	13
48	.62660	.80402	1.2437	.77934	12		48	.64011	.83317	1.2002	.76828	12
49	.62683	.80450	1.2430	.77916	11		49	.64033	.83366	1.1995	.76810	11
50	.62706	.80498	1.2423	.77897	10		50	.64056	.83415	1.1988	.76791	10
51	.62728	.80546	1.2415	.77879	9		51	.64078	.83465	1.1981	.76772	9
52	.62751	.80594	1.2408	.77861	8		52	.64100	.83514	1.1974	.76754	8
53	.62774	.80642	1.2401	.77843	7		53	.64123	.83564	1.1967	.76735	7
54	.62796	.80690	1.2393	.77824	6		54	.64145	.83613	1.1960	.76717	6
55	.62819	.80738	1.2386	.77806	5		55	.64167	.83662	1.1953	.76698	5
56	.62842	.80786	1.2378	.77788	4		56	.64190	.83712	1.1946	.76679	4
57	.62864	.80834	1.2371	.77769	3		57	.64212	.83761	1.1939	.76661	3
58	.62887	.80882	1.2364	.77751	2		58	.64234	.83811	1.1932	.76642	2
59	.62909	.80930	1.2356	.77733	1		59	.64256	.83860	1.1925	.76623	1
60	.62932	.80978	1.2349	.77715	0		60	.64279	.83910	1.1918	.76604	0
	Cos	Ctn	Tan	Sin	′			Cos	Ctn	Tan	Sin	′

′	Sin	Tan	Ctn	Cos			′	Sin	Tan	Ctn	Cos	
0	.64279	.83910	1.1918	.76604	60		0	.65606	.86929	1.1504	.75471	60
1	.64301	.83960	1.1910	.76586	59		1	.65628	.86980	1.1497	.75452	59
2	.64323	.84009	1.1903	.76567	58		2	.65650	.87031	1.1490	.75433	58
3	.64346	.84059	1.1896	.76548	57		3	.65672	.87082	1.1483	.75414	57
4	.64368	.84108	1.1889	.76530	56		4	.65694	.87133	1.1477	.75395	56
5	.64390	.84158	1.1882	.76511	55		5	.65716	.87184	1.1470	.75375	55
6	.64412	.84208	1.1875	.76492	54		6	.65738	.87236	1.1463	.75356	54
7	.64435	.84258	1.1868	.76473	53		7	.65759	.87287	1.1456	.75337	53
8	.64457	.84307	1.1861	.76455	52		8	.65781	.87338	1.1450	.75318	52
9	.64479	.84357	1.1854	.76436	51		9	.65803	.87389	1.1443	.75299	51
10	.64501	.84407	1.1847	.76417	50		10	.65825	.87441	1.1436	.75280	50
11	.64524	.84457	1.1840	.76398	49		11	.65847	.87492	1.1430	.75261	49
12	.64546	.84507	1.1833	.76380	48		12	.65869	.87543	1.1423	.75241	48
13	.64568	.84556	1.1826	.76361	47		13	.65891	.87595	1.1416	.75222	47
14	.64590	.84606	1.1819	.76342	46		14	.65913	.87646	1.1410	.75203	46
15	.64612	.84656	1.1812	.76323	45		15	.65935	.87698	1.1403	.75184	45
16	.64635	.84706	1.1806	.76304	44		16	.65956	.87749	1.1396	.75165	44
17	.64657	.84756	1.1799	.76286	43		17	.65978	.87801	1.1389	.75146	43
18	.64679	.84806	1.1792	.76267	42		18	.66000	.87852	1.1383	.75126	42
19	.64701	.84856	1.1785	.76248	41		19	.66022	.87904	1.1376	.75107	41
20	.64723	.84906	1.1778	.76229	40		20	.66044	.87955	1.1369	.75088	40
21	.64746	.84956	1.1771	.76210	39		21	.66066	.88007	1.1363	.75069	39
22	.64768	.85006	1.1764	.76192	38		22	.66088	.88059	1.1356	.75050	38
23	.64790	.85057	1.1757	.76173	37		23	.66109	.88110	1.1349	.75030	37
24	.64812	.85107	1.1750	.76154	36		24	.66131	.88162	1.1343	.75011	36
25	.64834	.85157	1.1743	.76135	35		25	.66153	.88214	1.1336	.74992	35
26	.64856	.85207	1.1736	.76116	34		26	.66175	.88265	1.1329	.74973	34
27	.64878	.85257	1.1729	.76097	33		27	.66197	.88317	1.1323	.74953	33
28	.64901	.85308	1.1722	.76078	32		28	.66218	.88369	1.1316	.74934	32
29	.64923	.85358	1.1715	.76059	31		29	.66240	.88421	1.1310	.74915	31
30	.64945	.85408	1.1708	.76041	30		30	.66262	.88473	1.1303	.74896	30
31	.64967	.85458	1.1702	.76022	29		31	.66284	.88524	1.1296	.74876	29
32	.64989	.85509	1.1695	.76003	28		32	.66306	.88576	1.1290	.74857	28
33	.65011	.85559	1.1688	.75984	27		33	.66327	.88628	1.1283	.74838	27
34	.65033	.85609	1.1681	.75965	26		34	.66349	.88680	1.1276	.74818	26
35	.65055	.85660	1.1674	.75946	25		35	.66371	.88732	1.1270	.74799	25
36	.65077	.85710	1.1667	.75927	24		36	.66393	.88784	1.1263	.74780	24
37	.65100	.85761	1.1660	.75908	23		37	.66414	.88836	1.1257	.74760	23
38	.65122	.85811	1.1653	.75889	22		38	.66436	.88888	1.1250	.74741	22
39	.65144	.85862	1.1647	.75870	21		39	.66458	.88940	1.1243	.74722	21
40	.65166	.85912	1.1640	.75851	20		40	.66480	.88992	1.1237	.74703	20
41	.65188	.85963	1.1633	.75832	19		41	.66501	.89045	1.1230	.74683	19
42	.65210	.86014	1.1626	.75813	18		42	.66523	.89097	1.1224	.74664	18
43	.65232	.86064	1.1619	.75794	17		43	.66545	.89149	1.1217	.74644	17
44	.65254	.86115	1.1612	.75775	16		44	.66566	.89201	1.1211	.74625	16
45	.65276	.86166	1.1606	.75756	15		45	.66588	.89253	1.1204	.74606	15
46	.65298	.86216	1.1599	.75738	14		46	.66610	.89306	1.1197	.74586	14
47	.65320	.86267	1.1592	.75719	13		47	.66632	.89358	1.1191	.74567	13
48	.65342	.86318	1.1585	.75700	12		48	.66653	.89410	1.1184	.74548	12
49	.65364	.86368	1.1578	.75680	11		49	.66675	.89463	1.1178	.74528	11
50	.65386	.86419	1.1571	.75661	10		50	.66697	.89515	1.1171	.74509	10
51	.65408	.86470	1.1565	.75642	9		51	.66718	.89567	1.1165	.74489	9
52	.65430	.86521	1.1558	.75623	8		52	.66740	.89620	1.1158	.74470	8
53	.65452	.86572	1.1551	.75604	7		53	.66762	.89672	1.1152	.74451	7
54	.65474	.86623	1.1544	.75585	6		54	.66783	.89725	1.1145	.74431	6
55	.65496	.86674	1.1538	.75566	5		55	.66805	.89777	1.1139	.74412	5
56	.65518	.86725	1.1531	.75547	4		56	.66827	.89830	1.1132	.74392	4
57	.65540	.86776	1.1524	.75528	3		57	.66848	.89883	1.1126	.74373	3
58	.65562	.86827	1.1517	.75509	2		58	.66870	.89935	1.1119	.74353	2
59	.65584	.86878	1.1510	.75490	1		59	.66891	.89988	1.1113	.74334	1
60	.65606	.86929	1.1504	.75471	0		60	.66913	.90040	1.1106	.74314	0
	Cos	Ctn	Tan	Sin	′			Cos	Ctn	Tan	Sin	′

′	Sin	Tan	Ctn	Cos		′	Sin	Tan	Ctn	Cos	
0	.66913	.90040	1.1106	.74314	60	0	.68200	.93252	1.0724	.73135	60
1	.66935	.90093	1.1100	.74295	59	1	.68221	.93306	1.0717	.73116	59
2	.66956	.90146	1.1093	.74276	58	2	.68242	.93360	1.0711	.73096	58
3	.66978	.90199	1.1087	.74256	57	3	.68264	.93415	1.0705	.73076	57
4	.66999	.90251	1.1080	.74237	56	4	.68285	.93469	1.0699	.73056	56
5	.67021	.90304	1.1074	.74217	55	5	.68306	.93524	1.0692	.73036	55
6	.67043	.90357	1.1067	.74198	54	6	.68327	.93578	1.0686	.73016	54
7	.67064	.90410	1.1061	.74178	53	7	.68349	.93633	1.0680	.72996	53
8	.67086	.90463	1.1054	.74159	52	8	.68370	.93688	1.0674	.72976	52
9	.67107	.90516	1.1048	.74139	51	9	.68391	.93742	1.0668	.72957	51
10	.67129	.90569	1.1041	.74120	50	10	.68412	.93797	1.0661	.72937	50
11	.67151	.90621	1.1035	.74100	49	11	.68434	.93852	1.0655	.72917	49
12	.67172	.90674	1.1028	.74080	48	12	.68455	.93906	1.0649	.72897	48
13	.67194	.90727	1.1022	.74061	47	13	.68476	.93961	1.0643	.72877	47
14	.67215	.90781	1.1016	.74041	46	14	.68497	.94016	1.0637	.72857	46
15	.67237	.90834	1.1009	.74022	45	15	.68518	.94071	1.0630	.72837	45
16	.67258	.90887	1.1003	.74002	44	16	.68539	.94125	1.0624	.72817	44
17	.67280	.90940	1.0996	.73983	43	17	.68561	.94180	1.0618	.72797	43
18	.67301	.90993	1.0990	.73963	42	18	.68582	.94235	1.0612	.72777	42
19	.67323	.91046	1.0983	.73944	41	19	.68603	.94290	1.0606	.72757	41
20	.67344	.91099	1.0977	.73924	40	20	.68624	.94345	1.0599	.72737	40
21	.67366	.91153	1.0971	.73904	39	21	.68645	.94400	1.0593	.72717	39
22	.67387	.91206	1.0964	.73885	38	22	.68666	.94455	1.0587	.72697	38
23	.67409	.91259	1.0958	.73865	37	23	.68688	.94510	1.0581	.72677	37
24	.67430	.91313	1.0951	.73846	36	24	.68709	.94565	1.0575	.72657	36
25	.67452	.91366	1.0945	.73826	35	25	.68730	.94620	1.0569	.72637	35
26	.67473	.91419	1.0939	.73806	34	26	.68751	.94676	1.0562	.72617	34
27	.67495	.91473	1.0932	.73787	33	27	.68772	.94731	1.0556	.72597	33
28	.67516	.91526	1.0926	.73767	32	28	.68793	.94786	1.0550	.72577	32
29	.67538	.91580	1.0919	.73747	31	29	.68814	.94841	1.0544	.72557	31
30	.67559	.91633	1.0913	.73728	30	30	.68835	.94896	1.0538	.72537	30
31	.67580	.91687	1.0907	.73708	29	31	.68857	.94952	1.0532	.72517	29
32	.67602	.91740	1.0900	.73688	28	32	.68878	.95007	1.0526	.72497	28
33	.67623	.91794	1.0894	.73669	27	33	.68899	.95062	1.0519	.72477	27
34	.67645	.91847	1.0888	.73649	26	34	.68920	.95118	1.0513	.72457	26
35	.67666	.91901	1.0881	.73629	25	35	.68941	.95173	1.0507	.72437	25
36	.67688	.91955	1.0875	.73610	24	36	.68962	.95229	1.0501	.72417	24
37	.67709	.92008	1.0869	.73590	23	37	.68983	.95284	1.0495	.72397	23
38	.67730	.92062	1.0862	.73570	22	38	.69004	.95340	1.0489	.72377	22
39	.67752	.92116	1.0856	.73551	21	39	.69025	.95395	1.0483	.72357	21
40	.67773	.92170	1.0850	.73531	20	40	.69046	.95451	1.0477	.72337	20
41	.67795	.92224	1.0843	.73511	19	41	.69067	.95506	1.0470	.72317	19
42	.67816	.92277	1.0837	.73491	18	42	.69088	.95562	1 0464	.72297	18
43	.67837	.92331	1.0831	.73472	17	43	.69109	.95618	1.0458	.72277	17
44	.67859	.92385	1.0824	.73452	16	44	.69130	.95673	1.0452	.72257	16
45	.67880	.92439	1.0818	.73432	15	45	.69151	.95729	1.0446	.72236	15
46	.67901	.92493	1.0812	.73413	14	46	.69172	.95785	1.0440	.72216	14
47	.67923	.92547	1.0805	.73393	13	47	.69193	.95841	1.0434	.72196	13
48	.67944	.92601	1.0799	.73373	12	48	.69214	.95897	1.0428	.72176	12
49	.67965	.92655	1.0793	.73353	11	49	.69235	.95952	1.0422	.72156	11
50	.67987	.92709	1.0786	.73333	10	50	.69256	.96008	1.0416	.72136	10
51	.68008	.92763	1.0780	.73314	9	51	.69277	.96064	1.0410	.72116	9
52	.68029	.92817	1.0774	.73294	8	52	.69298	.96120	1.0404	.72095	8
53	.68051	.92872	1.0768	.73274	7	53	.69319	.96176	1.0398	.72075	7
54	.68072	.92926	1.0761	.73254	6	54	.69340	.96232	1.0392	.72055	6
55	.68093	.92980	1.0755	.73234	5	55	.69361	.96288	1.0385	.72035	5
56	.68115	.93034	1.0749	.73215	4	56	.69382	.96344	1.0379	.72015	4
57	.68136	.93088	1.0742	.73195	3	57	.69403	.96400	1.0373	.71995	3
58	.68157	.93143	1.0736	.73175	2	58	.69424	.96457	1.0367	.71974	2
59	.68179	.93197	1.0730	.73155	1	59	.69445	.96513	1.0361	.71954	1
60	.68200	.93252	1.0724	.73135	0	60	.69466	.96569	1.0355	.71934	0
	Cos	Ctn	Tan	Sin	′		Cos	Ctn	Tan	Sin	′

′	Sin	Tan	Ctn	Cos	
0	.69466	.96569	1.0355	.71934	60
1	.69487	.96625	1.0349	.71914	59
2	.69508	.96681	1.0343	.71894	58
3	.69529	.96738	1.0337	.71873	57
4	.69549	.96794	1.0331	.71853	56
5	.69570	.96850	1.0325	.71833	55
6	.69591	.96907	1.0319	.71813	54
7	.69612	.96963	1.0313	.71792	53
8	.69633	.97020	1.0307	.71772	52
9	.69654	.97076	1.0301	.71752	51
10	.69675	.97133	1.0295	.71732	50
11	.69696	.97189	1.0289	.71711	49
12	.69717	.97246	1.0283	.71691	48
13	.69737	.97302	1.0277	.71671	47
14	.69758	.97359	1.0271	.71650	46
15	.69779	.97416	1.0265	.71630	45
16	.69800	.97472	1.0259	.71610	44
17	.69821	.97529	1.0253	.71590	43
18	.69842	.97586	1.0247	.71569	42
19	.69862	.97643	1.0241	.71549	41
20	.69883	.97700	1.0235	.71529	40
21	.69904	.97756	1.0230	.71508	39
22	.69925	.97813	1.0224	.71488	38
23	.69946	.97870	1.0218	.71468	37
24	.69966	.97927	1.0212	.71447	36
25	.69987	.97984	1.0206	.71427	35
26	.70008	.98041	1.0200	.71407	34
27	.70029	.98098	1.0194	.71386	33
28	.70049	.98155	1.0188	.71366	32
29	.70070	.98213	1.0182	.71345	31
30	.70091	.98270	1.0176	.71325	30
31	.70112	.98327	1.0170	.71305	29
32	.70132	.98384	1.0164	.71284	28
33	.70153	.98441	1.0158	.71264	27
34	.70174	.98499	1.0152	.71243	26
35	.70195	.98556	1.0147	.71223	25
36	.70215	.98613	1.0141	.71203	24
37	.70236	.98671	1.0135	.71182	23
38	.70257	.98728	1.0129	.71162	22
39	.70277	.98786	1.0123	.71141	21
40	.70298	.98843	1.0117	.71121	20
41	.70319	.98901	1.0111	.71100	19
42	.70339	.98958	1.0105	.71080	18
43	.70360	.99016	1.0099	.71059	17
44	.70381	.99073	1.0094	.71039	16
45	.70401	.99131	1.0088	.71019	15
46	.70422	.99189	1.0082	.70998	14
47	.70443	.99247	1.0076	.70978	13
48	.70463	.99304	1.0070	.70957	12
49	.70484	.99362	1.0064	.70937	11
50	.70505	.99420	1.0058	.70916	10
51	.70525	.99478	1.0052	.70896	9
52	.70546	.99536	1.0047	.70875	8
53	.70567	.99594	1.0041	.70855	7
54	.70587	.99652	1.0035	.70834	6
55	.70608	.99710	1.0029	.70813	5
56	.70628	.99768	1.0023	.70793	4
57	.70649	.99826	1.0017	.70772	3
58	.70670	.99884	1.0012	.70752	2
59	.70690	.99942	1.0006	.70731	1
60	.70711	1.0000	1.0000	.70711	0
	Cos	Ctn	Tan	Sin	′

Table VI

DECIMAL EQUIVALENTS
OF COMMON FRACTIONS

	1/64 = 0.015625
1/32 = 2/64 =	.03125
	3/64 = .046875
1/16 = 2/32 = 4/64 =	.0625
	5/64 = .078125
3/32 = 6/64 =	.09375
	7/64 = .109375
1/8 = 4/32 = 8/64 =	0.125
	9/64 = .140625
5/32 = 10/64 =	.15625
	11/64 = .171875
3/16 = 6/32 = 12/64 =	.1875
	13/64 = .203125
7/32 = 14/64 =	.21875
	15/64 = .234375
1/4 = 8/32 = 16/64 =	0.25
	17/64 = .265625
9/32 = 18/64 =	.28125
	19/64 = .296875
5/16 = 10/32 = 20/64 =	.3125
	21/64 = .328125
11/32 = 22/64 =	.34375
	23/64 = .359375
3/8 = 12/32 = 24/64 =	0.375
	25/64 = .390625
13/32 = 26/64 =	.40625
	27/64 = .421875
7/16 = 14/32 = 28/64 =	.4375
	29/64 = .453125
15/32 = 30/64 =	.46875
	31/64 = .484375
1/2 = 16/32 = 32/64 =	0.50
	33/64 = .515625
17/32 = 34/64 =	.53125
	35/64 = .546875
9/16 = 18/32 = 36/64 =	.5625
	37/64 = .578125
19/32 = 38/64 =	.59375
	39/64 = .609375
5/8 = 20/32 = 40/64 =	0.625
	41/64 = .640625
21/32 = 42/64 =	.65625
	43/64 = .671875
11/16 = 22/32 = 44/64 =	.6875
	45/64 = .703125
23/32 = 46/64 =	.71875
	47/64 = .734375
3/4 = 24/32 = 48/64 =	0.75
	49/64 = .765625
25/32 = 50/64 =	.78125
	51/64 = .796875
13/16 = 26/32 = 52/64 =	.8125
	53/64 = .828125
27/32 = 54/64 =	.84375
	55/64 = .859375
7/8 = 28/32 = 56/64 =	0.875
	57/64 = .890625
29/32 = 58/64 =	.90625
	59/64 = .921875
15/16 = 30/32 = 60/64 =	.9375
	61/64 = .953125
31/32 = 62/64 =	.96875
	63/64 = .984375

Table VII   **Table VII**   *Page 187*

MINUTES AND SECONDS TO DECIMAL PARTS OF A DEGREE

MINUTES AND SECONDS TO DECIMAL PARTS OF A DEGREE				DECIMAL PARTS OF A DEGREE TO MINUTES AND SECONDS					
Min.	Degrees	Sec.	Degrees	Deg.	'	''	Deg.	'	''
0	0.00000	0	0.00000	0.00	0	00	0.60	36	00
1	.01667	1	.00028	.01	0	36	.61	36	36
2	.03333	2	.00055	.02	1	12	.62	37	12
3	.05000	3	.00083	.03	1	48	.63	37	48
4	.06667	4	.00111	.04	2	24	.64	38	24
5	.08333	5	.00139	.05	3	00	.65	39	00
6	.10000	6	.00167	.06	3	36	.66	39	36
7	.11667	7	.00194	.07	4	12	.67	40	12
8	.13333	8	.00222	.08	4	48	.68	40	48
9	.15000	9	.00250	.09	5	24	.69	41	24
10	0.16667	10	0.00278	0.10	6	00	0.70	42	00
11	.18333	11	.00305	.11	6	36	.71	42	36
12	.20000	12	.00333	.12	7	12	.72	43	12
13	.21667	13	.00361	.13	7	48	.73	43	48
14	.23333	14	.00389	.14	8	24	.74	44	24
15	.25000	15	.00417	.15	9	00	.75	45	00
16	.26667	16	.00444	.16	9	36	.76	45	36
17	.28333	17	.00472	.17	10	12	.77	46	12
18	.30000	18	.00500	.18	10	48	.78	46	48
19	.31667	19	.00527	.19	11	24	.79	47	24
20	0.33333	20	0.00556	0.20	12	00	0.80	48	00
21	.35000	21	.00583	.21	12	36	.81	48	36
22	.36667	22	.00611	.22	13	12	.82	49	12
23	.38333	23	.00639	.23	13	48	.83	49	48
24	.40000	24	.00667	.24	14	24	.84	50	24
25	.41667	25	.00694	.25	15	00	.85	51	00
26	.43333	26	.00722	.26	15	36	.86	51	36
27	.45000	27	.00750	.27	16	12	.87	52	12
28	.46667	28	.00778	.28	16	48	.88	52	48
29	.48333	29	.00805	.29	17	24	.89	53	24
30	0.50000	30	0.00833	0.30	18	00	0.90	54	00
31	.51667	31	.00861	.31	18	36	.91	54	36
32	.53333	32	.00889	.32	19	12	.92	55	12
33	.55000	33	.00916	.33	19	48	.93	55	48
34	.56667	34	.00944	.34	20	24	.94	56	24
35	.58333	35	.00972	.35	21	00	.95	57	00
36	.60000	36	.01000	.36	21	36	.96	57	36
37	.61667	37	.01028	.37	22	12	.97	58	12
38	.63333	38	.01055	.38	22	48	.98	58	48
39	.65000	39	.01083	.39	23	24	.99	59	24
40	0.66667	40	0.01111	0.40	24	00	1.00	60	00
41	.68333	41	.01139	.41	24	36	—	—	—
42	.70000	42	.01167	.42	25	12			
43	.71666	43	.01194	.43	25	48			
44	.73333	44	.01222	.44	26	24	Deg.		Sec.
45	.75000	45	.01250	.45	27	00	0.000		0.0
46	.76667	46	.01278	.46	27	36	.001		3.6
47	.78333	47	.01305	.47	28	12	.002		7.2
48	.80000	48	.01333	.48	28	48	.003		10.8
49	.81667	49	.01361	.49	29	24	.004		14.4
50	0.83333	50	0.01389	0.50	30	00	.005		18.0
51	.85000	51	.01416	.51	30	36	.006		21.6
52	.86667	52	.01444	.52	31	12	.007		25.2
53	.88333	53	.01472	.53	31	48	.008		28.8
54	.90000	54	.01500	.54	32	24	.009		32.4
55	.91667	55	.01527	.55	33	00	0.010		36.0
56	.93333	56	.01555	.56	33	36			
57	.95000	57	.01583	.57	34	12			
58	.96667	58	.01611	.58	34	48			
59	.98333	59	.01639	.59	35	24			
60	1.00000	60	0.01667	0.60	36				

Table VIII

NATURAL TRIGONOMETRIC FUNCTIONS FOR DECIMAL FRACTIONS OF A DEGREE

Deg.	Sin	Tan	Ctn	Cos		Deg.	Sin	Tan	Ctn	Cos	
0.0	.00000	.00000	∞	1.00000	90.0	6.0	.10453	.10510	9.5144	.99452	84.0
.1	.00175	.00175	572.96	1.00000	.9	.1	.10626	.10687	9.3572	.99434	.9
.2	.00349	.00349	286.48	0.99999	.8	.2	.10800	.10863	9.2052	.99415	.8
.3	.00524	.00524	190.98	.99999	.7	.3	.10973	.11040	9.0579	.99396	.7
.4	.00698	.00698	143.24	.99998	.6	.4	.11147	.11217	8.9152	.99377	.6
.5	.00873	.00873	114.59	.99996	.5	.5	.11320	.11394	8.7769	.99357	.5
.6	.01047	.01047	95.489	.99995	.4	.6	.11494	.11570	8.6427	.99337	.4
.7	.01222	.01222	81.847	.99993	.3	.7	.11667	.11747	8.5126	.99317	.3
.8	.01396	.01396	71.615	.99990	.2	.8	.11840	.11924	8.3863	.99297	.2
.9	.01571	.01571	63.657	.99988	.1	.9	.12014	.12101	8.2636	.99276	.1
1.0	.01745	.01746	57.290	.99985	89.0	7.0	.12187	.12278	8.1443	.99255	83.0
.1	.01920	.01920	52.081	.99982	.9	.1	.12360	.12456	8.0285	.99233	.9
.2	.02094	.02095	47.740	.99978	.8	.2	.12533	.12633	7.9158	.99211	.8
.3	.02269	.02269	44.066	.99974	.7	.3	.12706	.12810	7.8062	.99189	.7
.4	.02443	.02444	40.917	.99970	.6	.4	.12880	.12988	7.6996	.99167	.6
.5	.02618	.02619	38.188	.99966	.5	.5	.13053	.13165	7.5958	.99144	.5
.6	.02792	.02793	35.801	.99961	.4	.6	.13226	.13343	7.4947	.99122	.4
.7	.02967	.02968	33.694	.99956	.3	.7	.13399	.13521	7.3962	.99098	.3
.8	.03141	.03143	31.821	.99951	.2	.8	.13572	.13698	7.3002	.99075	.2
.9	.03316	.03317	30.145	.99945	.1	.9	.13744	.13876	7.2066	.99051	.1
2.0	.03490	.03492	28.636	.99939	88.0	8.0	.13917	.14054	7.1154	.99027	82.0
.1	.03664	.03667	27.271	.99933	.9	.1	.14090	.14232	7.0264	.99002	.9
.2	.03839	.03842	26.031	.99926	.8	.2	.14263	.14410	6.9395	.98978	.8
.3	.04013	.04016	24.898	.99919	.7	.3	.14436	.14588	6.8548	.98953	.7
.4	.04188	.04191	23.859	.99912	.6	.4	.14608	.14767	6.7720	.98927	.6
.5	.04362	.04366	22.904	.99905	.5	.5	.14781	.14945	6.6912	.98902	.5
.6	.04536	.04541	22.022	.99897	.4	.6	.14954	.15124	6.6122	.98876	.4
.7	.04711	.04716	21.205	.99889	.3	.7	.15126	.15302	6.5350	.98849	.3
.8	.04885	.04891	20.446	.99881	.2	.8	.15299	.15481	6.4596	.98823	.2
.9	.05059	.05066	19.740	.99872	.1	.9	.15471	.15660	6.3859	.98796	.1
3.0	.05234	.05241	19.081	.99863	87.0	9.0	.15643	.15838	6.3138	.98769	81.0
.1	.05408	.05416	18.464	.99854	.9	.1	.15816	.16017	6.2432	.98741	.9
.2	.05582	.05591	17.886	.99844	.8	.2	.15988	.16196	6.1742	.98714	.8
.3	.05756	.05766	17.343	.99834	.7	.3	.16160	.16376	6.1066	.98686	.7
.4	.05931	.05941	16.832	.99824	.6	.4	.16333	.16555	6.0405	.98657	.6
.5	.06105	.06116	16.350	.99813	.5	.5	.16505	.16734	5.9758	.98629	.5
.6	.06279	.06291	15.895	.99803	.4	.6	.16677	.16914	5.9124	.98600	.4
.7	.06453	.06467	15.464	.99792	.3	.7	.16849	.17093	5.8502	.98570	.3
.8	.06627	.06642	15.056	.99780	.2	.8	.17021	.17273	5.7894	.98541	.2
.9	.06802	.06817	14.669	.99768	.1	.9	.17193	.17453	5.7297	.98511	.1
4.0	.06976	.06993	14.301	.99756	86.0	10.0	.17365	.17633	5.6713	.98481	80.0
.1	.07150	.07168	13.951	.99744	.9	.1	.17537	.17813	5.6140	.98450	.9
.2	.07324	.07344	13.617	.99731	.8	.2	.17708	.17993	5.5578	.98420	.8
.3	.07498	.07519	13.300	.99719	.7	.3	.17880	.18173	5.5026	.98389	.7
.4	.07672	.07695	12.996	.99705	.6	.4	.18052	.18353	5.4486	.98357	.6
.5	.07846	.07870	12.706	.99692	.5	.5	.18224	.18534	5.3955	.98325	.5
.6	.08020	.08046	12.429	.99678	.4	.6	.18395	.18714	5.3435	.98294	.4
.7	.08194	.08221	12.163	.99664	.3	.7	.18567	.18895	5.2924	.98261	.3
.8	.08368	.08397	11.909	.99649	.2	.8	.18738	.19076	5.2422	.98229	.2
.9	.08542	.08573	11.664	.99635	.1	.9	.18910	.19257	5.1929	.98196	.1
5.0	.08716	.08749	11.430	.99619	85.0	11.0	.19081	.19438	5.1446	.98163	79.0
.1	.08889	.08925	11.205	.99604	.9	.1	.19252	.19619	5.0970	.98129	.9
.2	.09063	.09101	10.988	.99588	.8	.2	.19423	.19801	5.0504	.98096	.8
.3	.09237	.09277	10.780	.99572	.7	.3	.19595	.19982	5.0045	.98061	.7
.4	.09411	.09453	10.579	.99556	.6	.4	.19766	.20164	4.9594	.98027	.6
.5	.09585	.09629	10.385	.99540	.5	.5	.19937	.20345	4.9152	.97992	.5
.6	.09758	.09805	10.199	.99523	.4	.6	.20108	.20527	4.8716	.97958	.4
.7	.09932	.09981	10.019	.99506	.3	.7	.20279	.20709	4.8288	.97922	.3
.8	.10106	.10158	9.8448	.99488	.2	.8	.20450	.20891	4.7867	.97887	.2
.9	.10279	.10334	9.6768	.99470	.1	.9	.20620	.21073	4.7453	.97851	.1
6.0	.10453	.10510	9.5144	.99452	84.0	12.0	.20791	.21256	4.7046	.97815	78.0
	Cos	Ctn	Tan	Sin	Deg.		Cos	Ctn	Tan	Sin	Deg.

Table VIII   Page 189

NATURAL TRIGONOMETRIC FUNCTIONS FOR DECIMAL FRACTIONS OF A DEGREE

Deg.	Sin	Tan	Ctn	Cos	
12.0	.20791	.21256	4.7046	.97815	78.0
.1	.20962	.21438	4.6646	.97778	.9
.2	.21132	.21621	4.6252	.97742	.8
.3	.21303	.21804	4.5864	.97705	.7
.4	.21474	.21986	4.5483	.97667	.6
.5	.21644	.22169	4.5107	.97630	.5
.6	.21814	.22353	4.4737	.97592	.4
.7	.21985	.22536	4.4373	.97553	.3
.8	.22155	.22719	4.4015	.97515	.2
.9	.22325	.22903	4.3662	.97476	.1
13.0	.22495	.23087	4.3315	.97437	77.0
.1	.22665	.23271	4.2972	.97398	.9
.2	.22835	.23455	4.2635	.97358	.8
.3	.23005	.23639	4.2303	.97318	.7
.4	.23175	.23823	4.1976	.97278	.6
.5	.23345	.24008	4.1653	.97237	.5
.6	.23514	.24193	4.1335	.97196	.4
.7	.23684	.24377	4.1022	.97155	.3
.8	.23853	.24562	4.0713	.97113	.2
.9	.24023	.24747	4.0408	.97072	.1
14.0	.24192	.24933	4.0108	.97030	76.0
.1	.24362	.25118	3.9812	.96987	.9
.2	.24531	.25304	3.9520	.96945	.8
.3	.24700	.25490	3.9232	.96902	.7
.4	.24869	.25676	3.8947	.96858	.6
.5	.25038	.25862	3.8667	.96815	.5
.6	.25207	.26048	3.8391	.96771	.4
.7	.25376	.26235	3.8118	.96727	.3
.8	.25545	.26421	3.7848	.96682	.2
.9	.25713	.26608	3.7583	.96638	.1
15.0	.25882	.26795	3.7321	.96593	75.0
.1	.26050	.26982	3.7062	.96547	.9
.2	.26219	.27169	3.6806	.96502	.8
.3	.26387	.27357	3.6554	.96456	.7
.4	.26556	.27545	3.6305	.96410	.6
.5	.26724	.27732	3.6059	.96363	.5
.6	.26892	.27921	3.5816	.96316	.4
.7	.27060	.28109	3.5576	.96269	.3
.8	.27228	.28297	3.5339	.96222	.2
.9	.27396	.28486	3.5105	.96174	.1
16.0	.27564	.28675	3.4874	.96126	74.0
.1	.27731	.28864	3.4646	.96078	.9
.2	.27899	.29053	3.4420	.96029	.8
.3	.28067	.29242	3.4197	.95981	.7
.4	.28234	.29432	3.3977	.95931	.6
.5	.28402	.29621	3.3759	.95882	.5
.6	.28569	.29811	3.3544	.95832	.4
.7	.28736	.30001	3.3332	.95782	.3
.8	.28903	.30192	3.3122	.95732	.2
.9	.29070	.30382	3.2914	.95681	.1
17.0	.29237	.30578	3.2709	.95630	73.0
.1	.29404	.30764	3.2506	.95579	.9
.2	.29571	.30955	3.2305	.95528	.8
.3	.29737	.31147	3.2106	.95476	.7
.4	.29904	.31338	3.1910	.95424	.6
.5	.30071	.31530	3.1716	.95372	.5
.6	.30237	.31722	3.1524	.95319	.4
.7	.30403	.31914	3.1334	.95266	.3
.8	.30570	.32106	3.1146	.95213	.2
.9	.30736	.32299	3.0961	.95159	.1
18.0	.30902	.32492	3.0777	.95106	72.0
	Cos	Ctn	Tan	Sin	Deg.

Deg.	Sin	Tan	Ctn	Cos	
18.0	.30902	.32492	3.0777	.95106	72.0
.1	.31068	.32685	3.0595	.95052	.9
.2	.31233	.32878	3 0415	.94997	.8
.3	.31399	.33072	3.0237	.94943	.7
.4	.31565	.33266	3.0061	.94888	.6
.5	.31730	.33460	2.9887	.94832	.5
.6	.31896	.33654	2.9714	.94777	.4
.7	.32061	.33848	2.9544	.94721	.3
.8	.32227	.34043	2.9375	.94665	.2
.9	.32392	.34238	2.9208	.94609	.1
19.0	.32557	.34433	2.9042	.94552	71.0
.1	.32722	.34628	2.8878	.94495	.9
.2	.32887	.34824	2.8716	.94438	.8
.3	.33051	.35020	2.8556	.94380	.7
.4	.33216	.35216	2.8397	.94322	.6
.5	.33381	.35412	2.8239	.94264	.5
.6	.33545	.35608	2.8083	.94206	.4
.7	.33710	.35805	2.7929	.94147	.3
.8	.33874	.36002	2.7776	.94088	.2
.9	.34038	.36199	2.7625	.94029	.1
20.0	.34202	.36397	2.7475	.93969	70.0
.1	.34366	.36595	2.7326	.93909	.9
.2	.34530	.36793	2.7179	.93849	.8
.3	.34694	.36991	2.7034	.93789	.7
.4	.34857	.37190	2.6889	.93728	.6
.5	.35021	.37388	2.6746	.93667	.5
.6	.35184	.37588	2.6605	.93606	.4
.7	.35347	.37787	2.6464	.93544	.3
.8	.35511	.37986	2.6325	.93483	.2
.9	.35674	.38186	2.6187	.93420	.1
21.0	.35837	.38386	2.6051	.93358	69.0
.1	.36000	.38587	2.5916	.93295	.9
.2	.36162	.38787	2.5782	.93232	.8
.3	.36325	.38988	2.5649	.93169	.7
.4	.36488	.39190	2.5517	.93106	.6
.5	.36650	.39391	2.5386	.93042	.5
.6	.36812	.39593	2.5257	.92978	.4
.7	.36975	.39795	2.5129	.92913	.3
.8	.37137	.39997	2.5002	.92849	.2
.9	.37299	.40200	2.4876	.92784	.1
22.0	.37461	.40403	2.4751	.92718	68.0
.1	.37622	.40606	2.4627	.92653	.9
.2	.37784	.40809	2.4504	.92587	.8
.3	.37946	.41013	2.4383	.92521	.7
.4	.38107	.41217	2.4262	.92455	.6
.5	.38268	.41421	2.4142	.92388	.5
.6	.38430	.41626	2.4023	.92321	.4
.7	.38591	.41831	2.3906	.92254	.3
.8	.38752	.42036	2.3789	.92186	.2
.9	.38912	.42242	2.3673	.92119	.1
23.0	.39073	.42447	2.3559	.92050	67.0
.1	.39234	.42654	2.3445	.91982	.9
.2	.39394	.42860	2.3332	.91914	.8
.3	.39555	.43067	2.3220	.91845	.7
.4	.39715	.43274	2.3109	.91775	.6
.5	.39875	.43481	2.2998	.91706	.5
.6	.40035	.43689	2.2889	.91636	.4
.7	.40195	.43897	2.2781	.91566	.3
.8	.40355	.44105	2.2673	.91496	.2
.9	.40514	.44314	2.2566	.91425	.1
24.0	.40674	.44523	2.2460	.91355	66.0
	Cos	Ctn	Tan	Sin	Deg.

NATURAL TRIGONOMETRIC FUNCTIONS FOR DECIMAL FRACTIONS OF A DEGREE

Deg.	Sin	Tan	Ctn	Cos	
24.0	.40674	.44523	2.2460	.91355	66.0
.1	.40833	.44732	2.2355	.91283	.9
.2	.40992	.44942	2.2251	.91212	.8
.3	.41151	.45152	2.2148	.91140	.7
.4	.41310	.45362	2.2045	.91068	.6
.5	.41469	.45573	2.1943	.90996	.5
.6	.41628	.45784	2.1842	.90924	.4
.7	.41787	.45995	2.1742	.90851	.3
.8	.41945	.46206	2.1642	.90778	.2
.9	.42104	.46418	2.1543	.90704	.1
25.0	.42262	.46631	2.1445	.90631	65.0
.1	.42420	.46843	2.1348	.90557	.9
.2	.42578	.47056	2.1251	.90483	.8
.3	.42736	.47270	2.1155	.90408	.7
.4	.42894	.47483	2.1060	.90334	.6
.5	.43051	.47698	2.0965	.90259	.5
.6	.43209	.47912	2.0872	.90183	.4
.7	.43366	.48127	2.0778	.90108	.3
.8	.43523	.48342	2.0686	.90032	.2
.9	.43680	.48557	2.0594	.89956	.1
26.0	.43837	.48773	2.0503	.89879	64.0
.1	.43994	.48989	2.0413	.89803	.9
.2	.44151	.49206	2.0323	.89726	.8
.3	.44307	.49423	2.0233	.89649	.7
.4	.44464	.49640	2.0145	.89571	.6
.5	.44620	.49858	2.0057	.89493	.5
.6	.44776	.50076	1.9970	.89415	.4
.7	.44932	.50295	1.9883	.89337	.3
.8	.45088	.50514	1.9797	.89259	.2
.9	.45243	.50733	1.9711	.89180	.1
27.0	.45399	.50953	1.9626	.89101	63.0
.1	.45554	.51173	1.9542	.89021	.9
.2	.45710	.51393	1.9458	.88942	.8
.3	.45865	.51614	1.9375	.88862	.7
.4	.46020	.51835	1.9292	.88782	.6
.5	.46175	.52057	1.9210	.88701	.5
.6	.46330	.52279	1.9128	.88620	.4
.7	.46484	.52501	1.9047	.88539	.3
.8	.46639	.52724	1.8967	.88458	.2
.9	.46793	.52947	1.8887	.88377	.1
28.0	.46947	.53171	1.8807	.88295	62.0
.1	.47101	.53395	1.8728	.88213	.9
.2	.47255	.53620	1.8650	.88130	.8
.3	.47409	.53844	1.8572	.88048	.7
.4	.47562	.54070	1.8495	.87965	.6
.5	.47716	.54296	1.8418	.87882	.5
.6	.47869	.54522	1.8341	.87798	.4
.7	.48022	.54748	1.8265	.87715	.3
.8	.48175	.54975	1.8190	.87631	.2
.9	.48328	.55203	1.8115	.87546	.1
29.0	.48481	.55431	1.8040	.87462	61.0
.1	.48634	.55659	1.7966	.87377	.9
.2	.48786	.55888	1.7893	.87292	.8
.3	.48938	.56117	1.7820	.87207	.7
.4	.49090	.56347	1.7747	.87121	.6
.5	.49242	.56577	1.7675	.87036	.5
.6	.49394	.56808	1.7603	.86949	.4
.7	.49546	.57039	1.7532	.86863	.3
.8	.49697	.57271	1.7461	.86777	.2
.9	.49849	.57503	1.7391	.86690	.1
30.0	.50000	.57735	1.7321	.86603	60.0
	Cos	Ctn	Tan	Sin	Deg.

Deg.	Sin	Tan	Ctn	Cos	
30.0	.50000	.57735	1.7321	.86603	60.0
.1	.50151	.57968	1.7251	.86515	.9
.2	.50302	.58201	1.7182	.86427	.8
.3	.50453	.58435	1.7113	.86340	.7
.4	.50603	.58670	1.7045	.86251	.6
.5	.50754	.58905	1.6977	.86163	.5
.6	.50904	.59140	1.6909	.86074	.4
.7	.51054	.59376	1.6842	.85985	.3
.8	.51204	.59612	1.6775	.85896	.2
.9	.51354	.59849	1.6709	.85806	.1
31.0	.51504	.60086	1.6643	.85717	59.0
.1	.51653	.60324	1.6577	.85627	.9
.2	.51803	.60562	1.6512	.85536	.8
.3	.51952	.60801	1.6447	.85446	.7
.4	.52101	.61040	1.6383	.85355	.6
.5	.52250	.61280	1.6319	.85264	.5
.6	.52399	.61520	1.6255	.85173	.4
.7	.52547	.61761	1.6191	.85081	.3
.8	.52696	.62003	1.6128	.84989	.2
.9	.52844	.62245	1.6066	.84897	.1
32.0	.52992	.62487	1.6003	.84805	58.0
.1	.53140	.62730	1.5941	.84712	.9
.2	.53288	.62973	1.5880	.84619	.8
.3	.53435	.63217	1.5818	.84526	.7
.4	.53583	.63462	1.5757	.84433	.6
.5	.53730	.63707	1.5697	.84339	.5
.6	.53877	.63953	1.5637	.84245	.4
.7	.54024	.64199	1.5577	.84151	.3
.8	.54171	.64446	1.5517	.84057	.2
.9	.54317	.64693	1.5458	.83962	.1
33.0	.54464	.64941	1.5399	.83867	57.0
.1	.54610	.65189	1.5340	.83772	.9
.2	.54756	.65438	1.5282	.83676	.8
.3	.54902	.65688	1.5224	.83581	.7
.4	.55048	.65938	1.5166	.83485	.6
.5	.55194	.66189	1.5108	.83389	.5
.6	.55339	.66440	1.5051	.83292	.4
.7	.55484	.66692	1.4994	.83195	.3
.8	.55630	.66944	1.4938	.83098	.2
.9	.55775	.67197	1.4882	.83001	.1
34.0	.55919	.67451	1.4826	.82904	56.0
.1	.56064	.67705	1.4770	.82806	.9
.2	.56208	.67960	1.4715	.82708	.8
.3	.56353	.68215	1.4659	.82610	.7
.4	.56497	.68471	1.4605	.82511	.6
.5	.56641	.68728	1.4550	.82413	.5
.6	.56784	.68985	1.4496	.82314	.4
.7	.56928	.69243	1.4442	.82214	.3
.8	.57071	.69502	1.4388	.82115	.2
.9	.57215	.69761	1.4335	.82015	.1
35.0	.57358	.70021	1.4281	.81915	55.0
.1	.57501	.70281	1.4229	.81815	.9
.2	.57643	.70542	1.4176	.81714	.8
.3	.57786	.70804	1.4124	.81614	.7
.4	.57928	.71066	1.4071	.81513	.6
.5	.58070	.71329	1.4019	.81412	.5
.6	.58212	.71593	1.3968	.81310	.4
.7	.58354	.71857	1.3916	.81208	.3
.8	.58496	.72122	1.3865	.81106	.2
.9	.58637	.72388	1.3814	.81004	.1
36.0	.58779	.72654	1.3764	.80902	54.0
	Cos	Ctn	Tan	Sin	Deg.

Table VIII   Page 191

NATURAL TRIGONOMETRIC FUNCTIONS FOR DECIMAL
FRACTIONS OF A DEGREE

Deg.	Sin	Tan	Ctn	Cos		Deg.	Sin	Tan	Ctn	Cos	
36.0	.58779	.72654	1.3764	.80902	54.0	40.5	.64945	.85408	1.1708	.76041	49.5
.1	.58920	.72921	1.3713	.80799	.9	.6	.65077	.85710	1.1667	.75927	.4
.2	.59061	.73189	1.3663	.80696	.8	.7	.65210	.86014	1.1626	.75813	.3
.3	.59201	.73457	1.3613	.80593	.7	.8	.65342	.86318	1.1585	.75700	.2
.4	.59342	.73726	1.3564	.80489	.6	.9	.65474	.86623	1.1544	.75585	.1
.5	.59482	.73996	1.3514	.80386	.5	41.0	.65606	.86929	1.1504	.75471	49.0
.6	.59622	.74267	1.3465	.80282	.4	.1	.65738	.87236	1.1463	.75356	9
.7	.59763	.74538	1.3416	.80178	.3	.2	.65869	.87543	1.1423	.75241	.8
.8	.59902	.74810	1.3367	.80073	.2	.3	.66000	.87852	1.1383	.75126	.7
.9	.60042	.75082	1.3319	.79968	.1	.4	.66131	.88162	1.1343	.75011	.6
37.0	.60182	.75355	1.3270	.79864	53.0	.5	.66262	.88473	1.1303	.74896	.5
.1	.60321	.75629	1.3222	.79758	.9	.6	.66393	.88784	1.1263	.74780	.4
.2	.60460	.75904	1.3175	.79653	.8	.7	.66523	.89097	1.1224	.74664	.3
.3	.60599	.76180	1.3127	.79547	.7	.8	.66653	.89410	1.1184	.74548	.2
.4	.60738	.76456	1.3079	.79441	.6	.9	.66783	.89725	1.1145	.74431	.1
.5	.60876	.76733	1.3032	.79335	.5	42.0	.66913	.90040	1.1106	.74314	48.0
.6	.61015	.77010	1.2985	.79229	.4	.1	.67043	.90357	1.1067	.74198	.9
.7	.61153	.77289	1.2938	.79122	.3	.2	.67172	.90674	1.1028	.74080	.8
.8	.61291	.77568	1.2892	.79016	.2	.3	.67301	.90993	1.0990	.73963	.7
.9	.61429	.77848	1.2846	.78908	.1	.4	.67430	.91313	1.0951	.73846	.6
38.0	.61566	.78129	1.2799	.78801	52.0	.5	.67559	.91633	1.0913	.73728	.5
.1	.61704	.78410	1.2753	.78694	.9	.6	.67688	.91955	1.0875	.73610	.4
.2	.61841	.78692	1.2708	.78586	.8	.7	.67816	.92277	1.0837	.73491	.3
.3	.61978	.78975	1.2662	.78478	.7	.8	.67944	.92601	1.0799	.73373	.2
.4	.62115	.79259	1.2617	.78369	.6	.9	.68072	.92926	1.0761	.73254	.1
.5	.62251	.79544	1.2572	.78261	.5	43.0	.68200	.93252	1.0724	.73135	47.0
.6	.62388	.79829	1.2527	.78152	.4	.1	.68327	.93578	1.0686	.73016	.9
.7	.62524	.80115	1.2482	.78043	.3	.2	.68455	.93906	1.0649	.72897	.8
.8	.62660	.80402	1.2437	.77934	.2	.3	.68582	.94235	1.0612	.72777	.7
.9	.62796	.80690	1.2393	.77824	.1	.4	.68709	.94565	1.0575	.72657	.6
39.0	.62932	.80978	1.2349	.77715	51.0	.5	.68835	.94896	1.0538	.72537	.5
.1	.63068	.81268	1.2305	.77605	.9	.6	.68962	.95229	1.0501	.72417	.4
.2	.63203	.81558	1.2261	.77494	.8	.7	.69088	.95562	1.0464	.72297	.3
.3	.63338	.81849	1.2218	.77384	.7	.8	.69214	.95897	1.0428	.72176	.2
.4	.63473	.82141	1.2174	.77273	.6	.9	.69340	.96232	1.0392	.72055	.1
.5	.63608	.82434	1.2131	.77162	.5	44.0	.69466	.96569	1.0355	.71934	46.0
.6	.63742	.82727	1.2088	.77051	.4	.1	.69591	.96907	1.0319	.71813	.9
.7	.63877	.83022	1.2045	.76940	.3	.2	.69717	.97246	1.0283	.71691	.8
.8	.64011	.83317	1.2002	.76828	.2	.3	.69842	.97586	1.0247	.71569	.7
.9	.64145	.83613	1.1960	.76717	.1	.4	.69966	.97927	1.0212	.71447	.6
40.0	.64279	.83910	1.1918	.76604	50.0	.5	.70091	.98270	1.0176	.71325	.5
.1	.64412	.84208	1.1875	.76492	.9	.6	.70215	.98613	1.0141	.71203	.4
.2	.64546	.84507	1.1833	.76380	.8	.7	.70339	.98958	1.0105	.71080	.3
.3	.64679	.84806	1.1792	.76267	.7	.8	.70463	.99304	1.0070	.70957	.2
.4	.64812	.85107	1.1750	.76154	.6	.9	.70587	.99652	1.0035	.70834	.1
40.5	.64945	.85408	1.1708	.76041	49.5	45.0	.70711	1.00000	1.0000	.70711	45.0
	Cos	Ctn	Tan	Sin	Deg.		Cos	Ctn	Tan	Sin	Deg.

Table IX

LOGARITHMS OF TRIGONOMETRIC FUNCTIONS IN RADIAN MEASURE

Rad	L Sin	L Tan	L Ctn	L Cos	Rad	L Sin	L Tan	L Ctn	L Cos
.00	.....	.....	.....	10.0000	.50	9.6807	9.7374	0.2626	9.9433
.01	8.0000	8.0000	2.0000	.0000	.51	.6886	.7477	.2523	.9409
.02	.3010	.3011	1.6989	9.9999	.52	.6963	.7578	.2422	.9384
.03	.4771	.4773	.5227	.9998	.53	.7037	.7678	.2322	.9359
.04	.6019	.6023	.3977	.9997	.54	.7111	.7777	.2223	.9333
.05	8.6988	8.6993	1.3007	9.9995	.55	9.7182	9.7875	0.2125	9.9307
.06	.7779	.7787	.2213	.9992	.56	.7252	.7972	.2028	.9280
.07	.8447	.8458	.1542	.9989	.57	.7321	.8068	.1932	.9253
.08	.9026	.9040	.0960	.9986	.58	.7388	.8164	.1836	.9224
.09	.9537	.9554	.0446	.9982	.59	.7454	.8258	.1742	.9196
.10	8.9993	9.0015	0.9985	9.9978	.60	9.7518	9.8351	0.1649	9.9166
.11	9.0405	.0431	.9569	.9974	.61	.7581	.8444	.1556	.9136
.12	.0781	.0813	.9187	.9969	.62	.7642	.8536	.1464	.9106
.13	.1127	.1164	.8836	.9963	.63	.7702	.8628	.1372	.9074
.14	.1447	.1490	.8510	.9957	.64	.7761	.8719	.1281	.9042
.15	9.1745	9.1794	0.8206	9.9951	.65	9.7819	9.8809	0.1191	9.9010
.16	.2023	.2078	.7922	.9944	.66	.7875	.8899	.1101	.8976
.17	.2284	.2347	.7653	.9937	.67	.7931	.8989	.1011	.8942
.18	.2529	.2600	.7400	.9929	.68	.7985	.9078	.0922	.8907
.19	.2761	.2840	.7160	.9921	.69	.8038	.9166	.0834	.8872
.20	9.2981	9.3069	0.6931	9.9913	.70	9.8090	9.9255	0.0745	9.8836
.21	.3190	.3287	.6713	.9904	.71	.8141	.9343	.0657	.8799
.22	.3389	.3495	.6505	.9894	.72	.8191	.9430	.0570	.8761
.23	.3579	.3695	.6305	.9884	.73	.8240	.9518	.0482	.8723
.24	.3760	.3887	.6113	.9874	.74	.8288	.9605	.0395	.8683
.25	9.3934	9.4071	0.5929	9.9863	.75	9.8336	9.9692	0.0308	9.8643
.26	.4101	.4249	.5751	.9852	.76	.8382	.9779	.0221	.8602
.27	.4261	.4421	.5579	.9840	.77	.8427	.9866	.0134	.8561
.28	.4415	.4587	.5413	.9827	.78	.8471	.9953	.0047	.8518
.29	.4563	.4748	.5252	.9815	.79	.8515	0.0040	9.9960	.8475
.30	9.4706	9.4904	0.5096	9.9802	.80	9.8557	0.0127	9.9873	9.8431
.31	.4844	.5056	.4944	.9788	.81	.8599	.0214	.9786	.8385
.32	.4977	.5203	.4797	.9774	.82	.8640	.0301	.9699	.8339
.33	.5106	.5347	.4653	.9759	.83	.8680	.0388	.9612	.8292
.34	.5231	.5487	.4513	.9744	.84	.8719	.0475	.9525	.8244
.35	9.5352	9.5623	0.4377	9.9728	.85	9.8758	0.0563	9.9437	9.8195
.36	.5469	.5757	.4243	.9712	.86	.8796	.0650	.9350	.8145
.37	.5582	.5887	.4113	.9696	.87	.8833	.0738	.9262	.8094
.38	.5693	.6014	.3986	.9679	.88	.8869	.0827	.9173	.8042
.39	.5800	.6139	.3861	.9661	.89	.8905	.0915	.9085	.7989
.40	9.5904	9.6261	0.3739	9.9643	.90	9.8939	0.1004	9.8996	9.7935
.41	.6005	.6381	.3619	.9624	.91	.8974	.1094	.8906	.7880
.42	.6104	.6499	.3501	.9605	.92	.9007	.1184	.8816	.7823
.43	.6200	.6615	.3385	.9585	.93	.9040	.1274	.8726	.7766
.44	.6293	.6728	.3272	.9565	.94	.9072	.1365	.8635	.7707
.45	9.6385	9.6840	0.3160	9.9545	.95	9.9103	0.1456	9.8544	9.7647
.46	.6473	.6950	.3050	.9523	.96	.9134	.1548	.8452	.7585
.47	.6560	.7058	.2942	.9502	.97	.9164	.1641	.8359	.7523
.48	.6644	.7165	.2835	.9479	.98	.9193	.1735	.8265	.7459
.49	.6727	.7270	.2730	.9456	.99	.9222	.1829	.8171	.7393
.50	9.6807	9.7374	0.2626	9.9433	1.00	9.9250	0.1924	9.8076	9.7326

Table X   *Page 193*

LOGARITHMS OF TRIGONOMETRIC FUNCTIONS IN RADIAN MEASURE

Rad	L Sin	L Tan	L Ctn	L Cos	Rad	L Sin	L Tan	L Ctn	L Cos
1.00	9.9250	0.1924	9.8076	9.7326	1.30	9.9839	0.5566	9.4434	9.4273
1.01	.9278	.2020	.7980	.7258	1.31	.9851	.5737	.4263	.4114
1.02	.9305	.2117	.7883	.7188	1.32	.9862	.5914	.4086	.3948
1.03	.9331	.2215	.7785	.7117	1.33	.9873	.6098	.3902	.3774
1.04	.9357	.2314	.7686	.7043	1.34	.9883	.6290	.3710	.3594
1.05	9.9382	0.2414	9.7586	9.6969	1.35	9.9893	0.6489	9.3511	9.3405
1.06	.9407	.2515	.7485	.6892	1.36	.9903	.6696	.3304	.3206
1.07	.9431	.2617	.7383	.6814	1.37	.9912	.6914	.3086	.2998
1.08	.9454	.2721	.7279	.6733	1.38	.9920	.7141	.2859	.2779
1.09	.9477	.2826	.7174	.6651	1.39	.9929	.7380	.2620	.2548
1.10	9.9500	0.2933	9.7067	9.6567	1.40	9.9936	0.7633	9.2367	9.2304
1.11	.9522	.3041	.6959	.6480	1.41	.9944	.7900	.2100	.2044
1.12	.9543	.3151	.6849	.6392	1.42	.9950	.8183	.1817	.1767
1.13	.9564	.3263	.6737	.6301	1.43	.9957	.8485	.1515	.1472
1.14	.9584	.3376	.6624	.6208	1.44	.9963	.8809	.1191	.1154
1.15	9.9604	0.3492	9.6508	9.6112	1.45	9.9968	0.9158	9.0842	9.0810
1.16	.9623	.3609	.6391	.6013	1.46	.9973	.9537	.0463	.0436
1.17	.9641	.3729	.6271	.5912	1.47	.9978	.9951	.0049	.0027
1.18	.9660	.3851	.6149	.5808	1.48	.9982	1.0407	8.9593	8.9575
1.19	.9677	.3976	.6024	.5701	1.49	.9986	.0917	.9083	.9069
1.20	9.9694	0.4103	9.5897	9.5591	1.50	9.9989	1.1493	8.8507	8.8496
1.21	.9711	.4233	.5767	.5478	1.51	.9992	.2156	.7844	.7836
1.22	.9727	.4366	.5634	.5361	1.52	.9994	.2938	.7062	.7056
1.23	.9743	.4502	.5498	.5241	1.53	.9996	.3891	.6109	.6105
1.24	.9758	.4642	.5358	.5116	1.54	.9998	.5114	.4886	.4884
1.25	9.9773	0.4785	9.5215	9.4988	1.55	9.9999	1.6820	8.3180	8.3180
1.26	.9787	.4932	.5068	.4855	1.56	0.0000	1.9667	8.0333	8.0333
1.27	.9800	.5083	.4917	.4717	1.57	0.0000	3.0989	6.9011	6.9011
1.28	.9814	.5239	.4761	.4575	1.58	0.0000	3.0360n	7.9640n	7.9640n
1.29	.9826	.5400	.4600	.4427	1.59	9.9999	2.7166n	8.2834n	8.2834n
1.30	9.9839	0.5566	9.4434	9.4273	1.60	9.9998	1.5344n	9.4656n	8.4654n

$$1 \ \text{radian} \ = \ 57°17'44''.806 \ = \ 57°.2957795$$
$$1° \ = \ .01745329 \ \text{radians}$$

Table X

DEGREES, MINUTES AND SECONDS TO RADIANS

Deg	Rad	Min	Rad	Sec	Rad
1	0.01745 33	1	0.00029 09	1	0.00000 48
2	0.03490 66	2	0.00058 18	2	0.00000 97
3	0.05235 99	3	0.00087 27	3	0.00001 45
4	0.06981 32	4	0.00116 36	4	0.00001 94
5	0.08726 65	5	0.00145 44	5	0.00002 42
6	0.10471 98	6	0.00174 53	6	0.00002 91
7	0.12217 30	7	0.00203 62	7	0.00003 39
8	0.13962 63	8	0.00232 71	8	0.00003 88
9	0.15707 96	9	0.00261 80	9	0.00004 36
10	0.17453 29	10	0.00290 89	10	0.00004 85
20	0.34906 59	20	0.00581 78	20	0.00009 70
30	0.52359 88	30	0.00872 66	30	0.00014 54
40	0.69813 17	40	0.01163 55	40	0.00019 39
50	0.87266 46	50	0.01454 44	50	0.00024 24
60	1.04719 76	60	0.01745 33	60	0.00029 09
70	1.22173 05				
80	1.39626 34				
90	1.57079 63				

Table XI

TRIGONOMETRIC FUNCTIONS IN RADIAN MEASURE

Rad	Sin	Tan	Ctn	Cos	Rad	Sin	Tan	Ctn	Cos
.00	.0000	.0000	......	1.0000	.50	.4794	.5463	1.830	.8776
.01	.0100	.0100	99.997	1.0000	.51	.4882	.5594	1.788	.8727
.02	.0200	.0200	49.993	.9998	.52	.4969	.5726	1.747	.8678
.03	.0300	.0300	33.323	.9996	.53	.5055	.5859	1.707	.8628
.04	.0400	.0400	24.987	.9992	.54	.5141	.5994	1.668	.8577
.05	.0500	.0500	19.983	.9988	.55	.5227	.6131	1.631	.8525
.06	.0600	.0601	16.647	.9982	.56	.5312	.6269	1.595	.8473
.07	.0699	.0701	14.262	.9976	.57	.5396	.6410	1.560	.8419
.08	.0799	.0802	12.473	.9968	.58	.5480	.6552	1.526	.8365
.09	.0899	.0902	11.081	.9960	.59	.5564	.6696	1.494	.8309
.10	.0998	.1003	9.967	.9950	.60	.5646	.6841	1.462	.8253
.11	.1098	.1104	9.054	.9940	.61	.5729	.6989	1.431	.8196
.12	.1197	.1206	8.293	.9928	.62	.5810	.7139	1.401	.8139
.13	.1296	.1307	7.649	.9916	.63	.5891	.7291	1.372	.8080
.14	.1395	.1409	7.096	.9902	.64	.5972	.7445	1.343	.8021
.15	.1494	.1511	6.617	.9888	.65	.6052	.7602	1.315	.7961
.16	.1593	.1614	6.197	.9872	.66	.6131	.7761	1.288	.7900
.17	.1692	.1717	5.826	.9856	.67	.6210	.7923	1.262	.7838
.18	.1790	.1820	5.495	.9838	.68	.6288	.8087	1.237	.7776
.19	.1889	.1923	5.200	.9820	.69	.6365	.8253	1.212	.7712
.20	.1987	.2027	4.933	.9801	.70	.6442	.8423	1.187	.7648
.21	.2085	.2131	4.692	.9780	.71	.6518	.8595	1.163	.7584
.22	.2182	.2236	4.472	.9759	.72	.6594	.8771	1.140	.7518
.23	.2280	.2341	4.271	.9737	.73	.6669	.8949	1.117	.7452
.24	.2377	.2447	4.086	.9713	.74	.6743	.9131	1.095	.7385
.25	.2474	.2553	3.916	.9689	.75	.6816	.9316	1.073	.7317
.26	.2571	.2660	3.759	.9664	.76	.6889	.9505	1.052	.7248
.27	.2667	.2768	3.613	.9638	.77	.6961	.9697	1.031	.7179
.28	.2764	.2876	3.478	.9611	.78	.7033	.9893	1.011	.7109
.29	.2860	.2984	3.351	.9582	.79	.7104	1.009	.9908	.7038
.30	.2955	.3093	3.233	.9553	.80	.7174	1.030	.9712	.6967
.31	.3051	.3203	3.122	.9523	.81	.7243	1.050	.9520	.6895
.32	.3146	.3314	3.018	.9492	.82	.7311	1.072	.9331	.6822
.33	.3240	.3425	2.920	.9460	.83	.7379	1.093	.9146	.6749
.34	.3335	.3537	2.827	.9428	.84	.7446	1.116	.8964	.6675
.35	.3429	.3650	2.740	.9394	.85	.7513	1.138	.8785	.6600
.36	.3523	.3764	2.657	.9359	.86	.7578	1.162	.8609	.6524
.37	.3616	.3879	2.578	.9323	.87	.7643	1.185	.8437	.6448
.38	.3709	.3994	2.504	.9287	.88	.7707	1.210	.8267	.6372
.39	.3802	.4111	2.433	.9249	.89	.7771	1.235	.8100	.6294
.40	.3894	.4228	2.365	.9211	.90	.7833	1.260	.7936	.6216
.41	.3986	.4346	2.301	.9171	.91	.7895	1.286	.7774	.6137
.42	.4078	.4466	2.239	.9131	.92	.7956	1.313	.7615	.6058
.43	.4169	.4586	2.180	.9090	.93	.8016	1.341	.7458	.5978
.44	.4259	.4708	2.124	.9048	.94	.8076	1.369	.7303	.5898
.45	.4350	.4831	2.070	.9004	.95	.8134	1.398	.7151	.5817
.46	.4439	.4954	2.018	.8961	.96	.8192	1.428	.7001	.5735
.47	.4529	.5080	1.969	.8916	.97	.8249	1.459	.6853	.5653
.48	.4618	.5206	1.921	.8870	.98	.8305	1.491	.6707	.5570
.49	.4706	.5334	1.875	.8823	.99	.8360	1.524	.6563	.5487
.50	.4794	.5463	1.830	.8776	1.00	.8415	1.557	.6421	.5403

Table XII   *Page 195*

TRIGONOMETRIC FUNCTIONS IN RADIAN MEASURE

Rad	Sin	Tan	Ctn	Cos	Rad	Sin	Tan	Ctn	Cos
1.00	.8415	1.557	.6421	.5403	1.30	.9636	3.602	.2776	.2675
1.01	.8468	1.592	.6281	.5319	1.31	.9662	3.747	.2669	.2579
1.02	.8521	1.628	.6142	.5234	1.32	.9687	3.903	.2562	.2482
1.03	.8573	1.665	.6005	.5148	1.33	.9711	4.072	.2456	.2385
1.04	.8624	1.704	.5870	.5062	1.34	.9735	4.256	.2350	.2288
1.05	.8674	1.743	.5736	.4976	1.35	.9757	4.455	.2245	.2190
1.06	.8724	1.784	.5604	.4889	1.36	.9779	4.673	.2140	.2092
1.07	.8772	1.827	.5473	.4801	1.37	.9799	4.913	.2035	.1994
1.08	.8820	1.871	.5344	.4713	1.38	.9819	5.177	.1931	.1896
1.09	.8866	1.917	.5216	.4625	1.39	.9837	5.471	.1828	.1798
1.10	.8912	1.965	.5090	.4536	1.40	.9854	5.798	.1725	.1700
1.11	.8957	2.014	.4964	.4447	1.41	.9871	6.165	.1622	.1601
1.12	.9001	2.066	.4840	.4357	1.42	.9887	6.581	.1519	.1502
1.13	.9044	2.120	.4718	.4267	1.43	.9901	7.055	.1417	.1403
1.14	.9086	2.176	.4596	.4176	1.44	.9915	7.602	.1315	.1304
1.15	.9128	2.234	.4475	.4085	1.45	.9927	8.238	.1214	.1205
1.16	.9168	2.296	.4356	.3993	1.46	.9939	8.989	.1113	.1106
1.17	.9208	2.360	.4237	.3902	1.47	.9949	9.887	.1011	.1006
1.18	.9246	2.427	.4120	.3809	1.48	.9959	10.983	.0910	.0907
1.19	.9284	2.498	.4003	.3717	1.49	.9967	12.350	.0810	.0807
1.20	.9320	2.572	.3888	.3624	1.50	.9975	14.101	.0709	.0707
1.21	.9356	2.650	.3773	.3530	1.51	.9982	16.428	.0609	.0608
1.22	.9391	2.733	.3659	.3436	1.52	.9987	19.670	.0508	.0508
1.23	.9425	2.820	.3546	.3342	1.53	.9992	24.498	.0408	.0408
1.24	.9458	2.912	.3434	.3248	1.54	.9995	32.461	.0308	.0308
1.25	.9490	3.010	.3323	.3153	1.55	.9998	48.078	.0208	.0208
1.26	.9521	3.113	.3212	.3058	1.56	.9999	92.620	.0108	.0108
1.27	.9551	3.224	.3102	.2963	1.57	1.0000	1255.8	.0008	.0008
1.28	.9580	3.341	.2993	.2867	1.58	1.0000	−108.65	−.0092	−.0092
1.29	.9608	3.467	.2884	.2771	1.59	.9998	−52.067	−.0192	−.0192
1.30	.9636	3.602	.2776	.2675	1.60	.9996	−34.233	−.0292	−.0292

π radians = 180° $\qquad$ π = 3.14159265
1 radian = 57°17′44″ .806 = 57°.2957795
3600″ = 60′ = 1° = .01745329 radian

Table XII

RADIANS TO DEGREES, MINUTES AND SECONDS

	Radians	Tenths	Hundredths	Thousandths	Ten-thousandths
1	57°17′44″.8	5°43′46″.5	0°34′22″.6	0° 3′26″.3	0°0′20″.6
2	114°35′29″.6	11°27′33″.0	1° 8′45″.3	0° 6′52″.5	0°0′41″.3
3	171°53′14″.4	17°11′19″.4	1°43′07″.9	0°10′18″.8	0°1′01″.9
4	229°10′59″.2	22°55′05″.9	2°17′30″.6	0°13′45″.1	0°1′22″.5
5	286°28′44″.0	28°38′52″.4	2°51′53″.2	0°17′11″.3	0°1′43″.1
6	343°46′28″.8	34°22′38″.9	3°26′15″.9	0°20′37″.6	0°2′03″.8
7	401° 4′13″.6	40° 6′25″.4	4° 0′38″.5	0°24′03″.9	0°2′24″.4
8	458°21′58″.4	45°50′11″.8	4°35′01″.2	0°27′30″.1	0°2′45″.0
9	515°39′43″.3	51°33′58″.3	5° 9′23″.8	0°30′56″.4	0°3′05″.6

Table XIII

POWERS, ROOTS, RECIPROCALS, CIRCUMFERENCES, AND AREAS OF CIRCLES

n	n^2	n^3	$\sqrt{n}$	$\sqrt[3]{n}$	$1000/n$	Circum. of circle πn	Area of circle $\frac{1}{4}\pi n^2$
1	1	1	1.0000	1.00000	1000.00	3.14159	0.79
2	4	8	1.4142	1.25992	500.00	6.28319	3.14
3	9	27	1.7321	1.44225	333.33	9.42478	7.07
4	16	64	2.0000	1.58740	250.00	12.5664	12.57
5	25	125	2.2361	1.70998	200.00	15.7080	19.64
6	36	216	2.4495	1.81712	166.67	18.8496	28.27
7	49	343	2.6458	1.91293	142.86	21.9911	38.49
8	64	512	2.8284	2.00000	125.00	25.1327	50.27
9	81	729	3.0000	2.08008	111.11	28.2743	63.62
10	100	1 000	3.1623	2.15443	100.0000	31.4159	78.5
11	121	1 331	3.3166	2.22398	90.9091	34.5575	95.0
12	144	1 728	3.4641	2.28943	83.3333	37.6991	113.1
13	169	2 197	3.6056	2.35133	76.9231	40.8407	132.7
14	196	2 744	3.7417	2.41014	71.4286	43.9823	153.9
15	225	3 375	3.8730	2.46621	66.6667	47.1239	176.7
16	256	4 096	4.0000	2.51984	62.5000	50.2655	201.1
17	289	4 913	4.1231	2.57128	58.8235	53.4071	227.0
18	324	5 832	4.2426	2.62074	55.5556	56.5487	254.5
19	361	6 859	4.3589	2.66840	52.6316	59.6903	283.5
20	400	8 000	4.4721	2.71442	50.0000	62.8319	314.2
21	441	9 261	4.5826	2.75892	47.6190	65.9734	346.4
22	484	10 648	4.6904	2.80204	45.4545	69.1150	380.1
23	529	12 167	4.7958	2.84387	43.4783	72.2566	415.5
24	576	13 824	4.8990	2.88450	41.6667	75.3982	452.4
25	625	15 625	5.0000	2.92402	40.0000	78.5398	490.9
26	676	17 576	5.0990	2.96250	38.4615	81.6814	530.9
27	729	19 683	5.1962	3.00000	37.0370	84.8230	572.6
28	784	21 952	5.2915	3.03659	35.7143	87.9646	615.8
29	841	24 389	5.3852	3.07232	34.4828	91.1062	660.5
30	900	27 000	5.4772	3.10723	33.3333	94.2478	706.9
31	961	29 791	5.5678	3.14138	32.2581	97.3894	754.8
32	1 024	32 768	5.6569	3.17480	31.2500	100.531	804.3
33	1 089	35 937	5.7446	3.20753	30.3030	103.673	855.3
34	1 156	39 304	5.8310	3.23961	29.4118	106.814	907.9
35	1 225	42 875	5.9161	3.27107	28.5714	109.956	962.1
36	1 296	46 656	6.0000	3.30193	27.7778	113.097	1017.9
37	1 369	50 653	6.0828	3.33222	27.0270	116.239	1075.2
38	1 444	54 872	6.1644	3.36198	26.3158	119.381	1134.1
39	1 521	59 319	6.2450	3.39121	25.6410	122.522	1194.6
40	1 600	64 000	6.3246	3.41995	25.0000	125.664	1256.6
41	1 681	68 921	6.4031	3.44822	24.3902	128.805	1320.3
42	1 764	74 088	6.4807	3.47603	23.8095	131.947	1385.4
43	1 849	79 507	6.5574	3.50340	23.2558	135.088	1452.2
44	1 936	85 184	6.6332	3.53035	22.7273	138.230	1520.5
45	2 025	91 125	6.7082	3.55689	22.2222	141.372	1590.4
46	2 116	97 336	6.7823	3.58305	21.7391	144.513	1661.9
47	2 209	103 823	6.8557	3.60883	21.2766	147.655	1734.9
48	2 304	110 592	6.9282	3.63424	20.8333	150.796	1809.6
49	2 401	117 649	7.0000	3.65931	20.4082	153.938	1885.7

Table XIII *Page 197*

POWERS, ROOTS, RECIPROCALS, CIRCUMFERENCES, AND AREAS OF CIRCLES

n	n^2	n^3	$\sqrt{n}$	$\sqrt[3]{n}$	$1000/n$	Circum. of Circle πn	Area of circle $\frac{1}{4}\pi n^2$
50	2 500	125 000	7.0711	3.68403	20.0000	157.080	1963.5
51	2 601	132 651	7.1414	3.70843	19.6078	160.221	2042.8
52	2 704	140 608	7.2111	3.73251	19.2308	163.363	2123.7
53	2 809	148 877	7.2801	3.75629	18.8679	166.504	2206.2
54	2 916	157 464	7.3485	3.77976	18.5185	169.646	2290.2
55	3 025	166 375	7.4162	3.80295	18.1818	172.788	2375.8
56	3 136	175 616	7.4833	3.82586	17.8571	175.929	2463.0
57	3 249	185 193	7.5498	3.84850	17.5439	179.071	2551.8
58	3 364	195 112	7.6158	3.87088	17.2414	182.212	2642.1
59	3 481	205 379	7.6811	3.89300	16.9492	185.354	2734.0
60	3 600	216 000	7.7460	3.91487	16.6667	188.496	2827.4
61	3 721	226 981	7.8102	3.93650	16.3934	191.637	2922.5
62	3 844	238 328	7.8740	3.95789	16.1290	194.779	3019.1
63	3 969	250 047	7.9373	3.97906	15.8730	197.920	3117.3
64	4 096	262 144	8.0000	4.00000	15.6250	201.062	3217.0
65	4 225	274 625	8.0623	4.02073	15.3846	204.204	3318.3
66	4 356	287 496	8.1240	4.04124	15.1515	207.345	3421.2
67	4 489	300 763	8.1854	4.06155	14.9254	210.487	3525.7
68	4 624	314 432	8.2462	4.08166	14.7059	213.628	3631.7
69	4 761	328 509	8.3066	4.10157	14.4928	216.770	3739.3
70	4 900	343 000	8.3666	4.12129	14.2857	219.911	3848.5
71	5 041	357 911	8.4261	4.14082	14.0845	223.053	3959.2
72	5 184	373 248	8.4853	4.16017	13.8889	226.195	4071.5
73	5 329	389 017	8.5440	4.17934	13.6986	229.336	4185.4
74	5 476	405 224	8.6023	4.19834	13.5135	232.478	4300.8
75	5 625	421 875	8.6603	4.21716	13.3333	235.619	4417.9
76	5 776	438 976	8.7178	4.23582	13.1579	238.761	4536.5
77	5 929	456 533	8.7750	4.25432	12.9870	241.903	4656.6
78	6 084	474 552	8.8318	4.27266	12.8205	245.044	4778.4
79	6 241	493 039	8.8882	4.29084	12.6582	248.186	4901.7
80	6 400	512 000	8.9443	4.30887	12.5000	251.327	5026.6
81	6 561	531 441	9.0000	4.32675	12.3457	254.469	5153.0
82	6 724	551 368	9.0554	4.34448	12.1951	257.611	5281.0
83	6 889	571 787	9.1104	4.36207	12.0482	260.752	5410.6
84	7 056	592 704	9.1652	4.37952	11.9048	263.894	5541.8
85	7 225	614 125	9.2195	4.39683	11.7647	267.035	5674.5
86	7 396	636 056	9.2736	4.41400	11.6279	270.177	5808.8
87	7 569	658 503	9.3274	4.43105	11.4943	273.319	5944.7
88	7 744	681 472	9.3808	4.44796	11.3636	276.460	6082.1
89	7 921	704 969	9.4340	4.46475	11.2360	279.602	6221.1
90	8 100	729 000	9.4868	4.48140	11.1111	282.743	6361.7
91	8 281	753 571	9.5394	4.49794	10.9890	285.885	6503.9
92	8 464	778 688	9.5917	4.51436	10.8696	289.027	6647.6
93	8 649	804 357	9.6437	4.53065	10.7527	292.168	6792.9
94	8 836	830 584	9.6954	4.54684	10.6383	295.310	6939.8
95	9 025	857 375	9.7468	4.56290	10.5263	298.451	7088.2
96	9 216	884 736	9.7980	4.57886	10.4167	301.593	7238.2
97	9 409	912 673	9.8489	4.59470	10.3093	304.734	7389.8
98	9 604	941 192	9.8995	4.61044	10.2041	307.876	7543.0
99	9 801	970 299	9.9499	4.62607	10.1010	311.018	7697.7

POWERS, ROOTS, RECIPROCALS, CIRCUMFERENCES, AND AREAS OF CIRCLES

n	n^2	n^3	$\sqrt{n}$	$\sqrt[3]{n}$	$1000/n$	Circum. of circle πn	Area of circle $\frac{1}{4}\pi n^2$
100	10 000	1 000 000	10.0000	4.64159	10.00000	314.159	7854.0
101	10 201	1 030 301	10.0499	4.65701	9.90099	317.301	8011.9
102	10 404	1 061 208	10.0995	4.67233	9.80392	320.442	8171.3
103	10 609	1 092 727	10.1489	4.68755	9.70874	323.584	8332.3
104	10 816	1 124 864	10.1980	4.70267	9.61538	326.726	8494.9
105	11 025	1 157 625	10.2470	4.71769	9.52381	329.867	8659.0
106	11 236	1 191 016	10.2956	4.73262	9.43396	333.009	8824.7
107	11 449	1 225 043	10.3441	4.74746	9.34579	336.150	8992.0
108	11 664	1 259 712	10.3923	4.76220	9.25926	339.292	9160.9
109	11 881	1 295 029	10.4403	4.77686	9.17431	342.434	9331.3
110	12 100	1 331 000	10.4881	4.79142	9.09091	345.575	9503.3
111	12 321	1 367 631	10.5357	4.80590	9.00901	348.717	9676.9
112	12 544	1 404 928	10.5830	4.82028	8.92857	351.858	9852.0
113	12 769	1 442 897	10.6301	4.83459	8.84956	355.000	10028.8
114	12 996	1 481 544	10.6771	4.84881	8.77193	358.142	10207.0
115	13 225	1 520 875	10.7238	4.86294	8.69565	361.283	10386.9
116	13 456	1 560 896	10.7703	4.87700	8.62069	364.425	10568.3
117	13 689	1 601 613	10.8167	4.89097	8.54701	367.566	10751.3
118	13 924	1 643 032	10.8628	4.90487	8.47458	370.708	10935.9
119	14 161	1 685 159	10.9087	4.91868	8.40336	373.850	11122.0
120	14 400	1 728 000	10.9545	4.93242	8.33333	376.991	11309.7
121	14 641	1 771 561	11.0000	4.94609	8.26446	380.133	11499.0
122	14 884	1 815 848	11.0454	4.95968	8.19672	383.274	11689.9
123	15 129	1 860 867	11.0905	4.97319	8.13008	386.416	11882.3
124	15 376	1 906 624	11.1355	4.98663	8.06452	389.557	12076.3
125	15 625	1 953 125	11.1803	5.00000	8.00000	392.699	12271.8
126	15 876	2 000 376	11.2250	5.01330	7.93651	395.841	12469.0
127	16 129	2 048 383	11.2694	5.02653	7.87402	398.982	12667.7
128	16 384	2 097 152	11.3137	5.03968	7.81250	402.124	12868.0
129	16 641	2 146 689	11.3578	5.05277	7.75194	405.265	13069.8
130	16 900	2 197 000	11.4018	5.06580	7.69231	408.407	13273.2
131	17 161	2 248 091	11.4455	5.07875	7.63359	411.549	13478.2
132	17 424	2 299 968	11.4891	5.09164	7.57576	414.690	13684.8
133	17 689	2 352 637	11.5326	5.10447	7.51880	417.832	13892.9
134	17 956	2 406 104	11.5758	5.11723	7.46269	420.973	14102.6
135	18 225	2 460 375	11.6190	5.12993	7.40741	424.115	14313.9
136	18 496	2 515 456	11.6619	5.14256	7.35294	427.257	14526.7
137	18 769	2 571 353	11.7047	5.15514	7.29927	430.398	14741.1
138	19 044	2 628 072	11.7473	5.16765	7.24638	433.540	14957.1
139	19 321	2 685 619	11.7898	5.18010	7.19424	436.681	15174.7
140	19 600	2 744 000	11.8322	5.19249	7.14286	439.823	15393.8
141	19 881	2 803 221	11.8743	5.20483	7.09220	442.965	15614.5
142	20 164	2 863 288	11.9164	5.21710	7.04225	446.106	15836.8
143	20 449	2 924 207	11.9583	5.22932	6.99301	449.248	16060.6
144	20 736	2 985 984	12.0000	5.24148	6.94444	452.389	16286.0
145	21 025	3 048 625	12.0416	5.25359	6.89655	455.531	16513.0
146	21 316	3 112 136	12.0830	5.26564	6.84932	458.673	16741.5
147	21 609	3 176 523	12.1244	5.27763	6.80272	461.814	16971.7
148	21 904	3 241 792	12.1655	5.28957	6.75676	464.956	17203.4
149	22 201	3 307 949	12.2066	5.30146	6.71141	468.097	17436.6

Table XIII Page 199

POWERS, ROOTS, RECIPROCALS, CIRCUMFERENCES, AND AREAS OF CIRCLES

n	n^2	n^3	$\sqrt{n}$	$\sqrt[3]{n}$	$1000/n$	Circum. of circle πn	Area of circle $\frac{1}{4}\pi n^2$
150	22 500	3 375 000	12.2474	5.31329	6.66667	471.239	17671.5
151	22 801	3 442 951	12.2882	5.32507	6.62252	474.380	17907.9
152	23 104	3 511 808	12.3288	5.33680	6.57895	477.522	18145.8
153	23 409	3 581 577	12.3693	5.34848	6.53595	480.664	18385.4
154	23 716	3 652 264	12.4097	5.36011	6.49351	483.805	18626.5
155	24 025	3 723 875	12.4499	5.37169	6.45161	486.947	18869.2
156	24 336	3 796 416	12.4900	5.38321	6.41026	490.088	19113.4
157	24 649	3 869 893	12.5300	5.39469	6.36943	493.230	19359.3
158	24 964	3 944 312	12.5698	5.40612	6.32911	496.372	19606.7
159	25 281	4 019 679	12.6095	5.41750	6.28931	499.513	19855.7
160	25 600	4 096 000	12.6491	5.42884	6.25000	502.655	20106.2
161	25 921	4 173 281	12.6886	5.44012	6.21118	505.796	20358.3
162	26 244	4 251 528	12.7279	5.45136	6.17284	508.938	20612.0
163	26 569	4 330 747	12.7671	5.46256	6.13497	512.080	20867.2
164	26 896	4 410 944	12.8062	5.47370	6.09756	515.221	21124.1
165	27 225	4 492 125	12.8452	5.48481	6.06061	518.363	21382.5
166	27 556	4 574 296	12.8841	5.49586	6.02410	521.504	21642.4
167	27 889	4 657 463	12.9228	5.50688	5.98802	524.646	21904.0
168	28 224	4 741 632	12.9615	5.51785	5.95238	527.788	22167.1
169	28 561	4 826 809	13.0000	5.52877	5.91716	530.929	22431.8
170	28 900	4 913 000	13.0384	5.53966	5.88235	534.071	22698.0
171	29 241	5 000 211	13.0767	5.55050	5.84795	537.212	22965.8
172	29 584	5 088 448	13.1149	5.56130	5.81395	540.354	23235.2
173	29 929	5 177 717	13.1529	5.57205	5.78035	543.496	23506.2
174	30 276	5 268 024	13.1909	5.58277	5.74713	546.637	23778.7
175	30 625	5 359 375	13.2288	5.59344	5.71429	549.779	24052.8
176	30 976	5 451 776	13.2665	5.60408	5.68182	552.920	24328.5
177	31 329	5 545 233	13.3041	5.61467	5.64972	556.062	24605.7
178	31 684	5 639 752	13.3417	5.62523	5.61798	559.203	24884.6
179	32 041	5 735 339	13.3791	5.63574	5.58659	562.345	25164.9
180	32 400	5 832 000	13.4164	5.64622	5.55556	565.487	25446.9
181	32 761	5 929 741	13.4536	5.65665	5.52486	568.628	25730.4
182	33 124	6 028 568	13.4907	5.66705	5.49451	571.770	26015.5
183	33 489	6 128 487	13.5277	5.67741	5.46448	574.911	26302.2
184	33 856	6 229 504	13.5647	5.68773	5.43478	578.053	26590.4
185	34 225	6 331 625	13.6015	5.69802	5.40541	581.195	26880.3
186	34 596	6 434 856	13.6382	5.70827	5.37634	584.336	27171.6
187	34 969	6 539 203	13.6748	5.71848	5.34759	587.478	27464.6
188	35 344	6 644 672	13.7113	5.72865	5.31915	590.619	27759.1
189	35 721	6 751 269	13.7477	5.73879	5.29101	593.761	28055.2
190	36 100	6 859 000	13.7840	5.74890	5.26316	596.903	28352.9
191	36 481	6 967 871	13.8203	5.75897	5.23560	600.044	28652.1
192	36 864	7 077 888	13.8564	5.76900	5.20833	603.186	28952.9
193	37 249	7 189 057	13.8924	5.77900	5.18135	606.327	29255.3
194	37 636	7 301 384	13.9284	5.78896	5.15464	609.469	29559.2
195	38 025	7 414 875	13.9642	5.79889	5.12821	612.611	29864.8
196	38 416	7 529 536	14.0000	5.80879	5.10204	615.752	30171.9
197	38 809	7 645 373	14.0357	5.81865	5.07614	618.894	30480.5
198	39 204	7 762 392	14.0712	5.82848	5.05051	622.035	30790.7
199	39 601	7 880 599	14.1067	5.83827	5.02513	625.177	31102.6

POWERS, ROOTS, RECIPROCALS, CIRCUMFERENCES, AND AREAS OF CIRCLES

n	n^2	n^3	$\sqrt{n}$	$\sqrt[3]{n}$	$1000/n$	Circum. of circle πn	Area of circle $\frac{1}{4}\pi n^2$
200	40 000	8 000 000	14.1421	5.84804	5.00000	628.319	31415.9
201	40 401	8 120 601	14.1774	5.85777	4.97512	631.460	31730.9
202	40 804	8 242 408	14.2127	5.86746	4.95050	634.602	32047.4
203	41 209	8 365 427	14.2478	5.87713	4.92611	637.743	32365.5
204	41 616	8 489 664	14.2829	5.88677	4.90196	640.885	32685.1
205	42 025	8 615 125	14.3178	5.89637	4.87805	644.026	33006.4
206	42 436	8 741 816	14.3527	5.90594	4.85437	647.168	33329.2
207	42 849	8 869 743	14.3875	5.91548	4.83092	650.310	33653.5
208	43 264	8 998 912	14.4222	5.92499	4.80769	653.451	33979.5
209	43 681	9 129 329	14.4568	5.93447	4.78469	656.593	34307.0
210	44 100	9 261 000	14.4914	5.94392	4.76190	659.734	34636.1
211	44 521	9 393 931	14.5258	5.95334	4.73934	662.876	34966.7
212	44 944	9 528 128	14.5602	5.96273	4.71698	666.018	35298.9
213	45 369	9 663 597	14.5945	5.97209	4.69484	669.159	35632.7
214	45 796	9 800 344	14.6287	5.98142	4.67290	672.301	35968.1
215	46 225	9 938 375	14.6629	5.99073	4.65116	675.442	36305.0
216	46 656	10 077 696	14.6969	6.00000	4.62963	678.584	36643.5
217	47 089	10 218 313	14.7309	6.00925	4.60829	681.726	36983.6
218	47 524	10 360 232	14.7648	6.01846	4.58716	684.867	37325.3
219	47 961	10 503 459	14.7986	6.02765	4.56621	688.009	37668.5
220	48 400	10 648 000	14.8324	6.03681	4.54545	691.150	38013.3
221	48 841	10 793 861	14.8661	6.04594	4.52489	694.292	38359.6
222	49 284	10 941 048	14.8997	6.05505	4.50450	697.434	38707.6
223	49 729	11 089 567	14.9332	6.06413	4.48430	700.575	39057.1
224	50 176	11 239 424	14.9666	6.07318	4.46429	703.717	39408.1
225	50 625	11 390 625	15.0000	6.08220	4.44444	706.858	39760.8
226	51 076	11 543 176	15.0333	6.09120	4.42478	710.000	40115.0
227	51 529	11 697 083	15.0665	6.10017	4.40529	713.142	40470.8
228	51 984	11 852 352	15.0997	6.10911	4.38596	716.283	40828.1
229	52 441	12 008 989	15.1327	6.11803	4.36681	719.425	41187.1
230	52 900	12 167 000	15.1658	6.12693	4.34783	722.566	41547.6
231	53 361	12 326 391	15.1987	6.13579	4.32900	725.708	41909.6
232	53 824	12 487 168	15.2315	6.14463	4.31034	728.849	42273.3
233	54 289	12 649 337	15.2643	6.15345	4.29185	731.991	42638.5
234	54 756	12 812 904	15.2971	6.16224	4.27350	735.133	43005.3
235	55 225	12 977 875	15.3297	6.17101	4.25532	738.274	43373.6
236	55 696	13 144 256	15.3623	6.17975	4.23729	741.416	43743.5
237	56 169	13 312 053	15.3948	6.18846	4.21941	744.557	44115.0
238	56 644	13 481 272	15.4272	6.19715	4.20168	747.699	44488.1
239	57 121	13 651 919	15.4596	6.20582	4.18410	750.841	44862.7
240	57 600	13 824 000	15.4919	6.21447	4.16667	753.982	45238.9
241	58 081	13 997 521	15.5242	6.22308	4.14938	757.124	45616.7
242	58 564	14 172 488	15.5563	6.23168	4.13223	760.265	45996.1
243	59 049	14 348 907	15.5885	6.24025	4.11523	763.407	46377.0
244	59 536	14 526 784	15.6205	6.24880	4.09836	766.549	46759.5
245	60 025	14 706 125	15.6525	6.25732	4.08163	769.690	47143.5
246	60 516	14 886 936	15.6844	6.26583	4.06504	772.832	47529.2
247	61 009	15 069 223	15.7162	6.27431	4.04858	775.973	47916.4
248	61 504	15 252 992	15.7480	6.28276	4.03226	779.115	48305.1
249	62 001	15 438 249	15.7797	6.29119	4.01606	782.257	48695.5

Table XIII

Page 201

POWERS, ROOTS, RECIPROCALS, CIRCUMFERENCES, AND AREAS OF CIRCLES

n	n^2	n^3	$\sqrt{n}$	$\sqrt[3]{n}$	$1000/n$	Circum. of Circle πn	Area of circle $\frac{1}{4}\pi n^2$
250	62 500	15 625 000	15.8114	6.29961	4.00000	785.398	49087.4
251	63 001	15 813 251	15.8430	6.30799	3.98406	788.540	49480.9
252	63 504	16 003 008	15.8745	6.31636	3.96825	791.681	49875.9
253	64 009	16 194 277	15.9060	6.32470	3.95257	794.823	50272.6
254	64 516	16 387 064	15.9374	6.33303	3.93701	797.965	50670.7
255	65 025	16 581 375	15.9687	6.34133	3.92157	801.106	51070.5
256	65 536	16 777 216	16.0000	6.34960	3.90625	804.248	51471.9
257	66 049	16 974 593	16.0312	6.35786	3.89105	807.389	51874.8
258	66 564	17 173 512	16.0624	6.36610	3.87597	810.531	52279.2
259	67 081	17 373 979	16.0935	6.37431	3.86100	813.672	52685.3
260	67 600	17 576 000	16.1245	6.38250	3.84615	816.814	53092.9
261	68 121	17 779 581	16.1555	6.39068	3.83142	819.956	53502.1
262	68.644	17 984 728	16.1864	6.39883	3.81679	823.097	53912.9
263	69 169	18 191 447	16.2173	6.40696	3.80228	826.239	54325.2
264	69 696	18 399 744	16.2481	6.41507	3.78788	829.380	54739.1
265	70 225	18 609 625	16.2788	6.42316	3.77358	832.522	55154.6
266	70 756	18 821 096	16.3095	6.43123	3.75940	835.664	55571.6
267	71 289	19 034 163	16.3401	6.43928	3.74532	838.805	55990.3
268	71 824	19 248 832	16.3707	6.44731	3.73134	841.947	56410.4
269	72 361	19 465 109	16.4012	6.45531	3.71747	845.088	56832.2
270	72 900	19 683 000	16.4317	6.46330	3.70370	848.230	57255.5
271	73 441	19 902 511	16.4621	6.47127	3.69004	851.372	57680.4
272	73 984	20 123 648	16.4924	6.47922	3.67647	854.513	58106.9
273	74 529	20 346 417	16.5227	6.48715	3.66300	857.655	58534.9
274	75 076	20 570 824	16.5529	5.49507	3.64964	860.796	58964.6
275	75 625	20 796 875	16.5831	6.50296	3.63636	863.938	59395.7
276	76 176	21 024 576	16.6132	6.51083	3.62319	867.080	59828.5
277	76 729	21 253 933	16.6433	6.51868	3.61011	870.221	60262.8
278	77 284	21 484 952	16.6733	6.52652	3.59712	873.363	60698.7
279	77 841	21 717 639	16.7033	6.53434	3.58423	876.504	61136.2
280	78 400	21 952 000	16 7332	6.54213	3.57143	879.646	61575.2
281	78 961	22 188 041	16.7631	6.54991	3.55872	882.788	62015.8
282	79 524	22 425 768	16.7929	6.55767	3.54610	885.929	62458.0
283	80 089	22 665 187	16.8226	6.56541	3.53357	889.071	62901.8
284	80 656	22 906 304	16.8523	6.57314	3.52113	892.212	63347.1
285	81 225	23 149 125	16.8819	6.58084	3.50877	895.354	63794.0
286	81 796	23 393 656	16.9115	6.58853	3.49650	898.495	64242.4
287	82 369	23 639 903	16.9411	6.59620	3.48432	901.637	64692.5
288	82 944	23 887 872	16.9706	6.60385	3.47222	904.779	65144.1
289	83 521	24 137 569	17.0000	6.61149	3.46021	907.920	65597.2
290	84 100	24 389 000	17.0294	6.61911	3.44828	911.062	66052.0
291	84 681	24 642 171	17.0587	6.62671	3.43643	914.203	66508.3
292	85 264	24 897 088	17.0880	6.63429	3.42466	917.345	66966.2
293	85 849	25 153 757	17.1172	6.64185	3.41297	920.487	67425.6
294	86 436	25 412 184	17.1464	6.64940	3.40136	923.628	67886.7
295	87 025	25 672 375	17.1756	6.65693	3.38983	926.770	68349.3
296	87 616	25 934 336	17.2047	6.66444	3.37838	929.911	68813.5
297	88 209	26 198 073	17.2337	6.67194	3.36700	933.053	69279.2
298	88 804	26 463 592	17.2627	6.67942	3.35570	936.195	69746.5
299	89 401	26 730 899	17.2916	6.68688	3.34448	939.336	70215.4

POWERS, ROOTS, RECIPROCALS, CIRCUMFERENCES, AND AREAS OF CIRCLES

n	n^2	n^3	$\sqrt{n}$	$\sqrt[3]{n}$	$1000/n$	Circum. of circle πn	Area of circle $\frac{1}{4}\pi n^2$
300	90 000	27 000 000	17.3205	6.69433	3.33333	942.478	70685.8
301	90 601	27 270 901	17.3494	6.70176	3.32226	945.619	71157.9
302	91 204	27 543 608	17.3781	6.70917	3.31126	948.761	71631.5
303	91 809	27 818 127	17.4069	6.71657	3.30033	951.903	72106.6
304	92 416	28 094 464	17.4356	6.72395	3.28947	955.044	72583.4
305	93 025	28 372 625	17.4642	6.73132	3.27869	958.186	73061.7
306	93 636	28 652 616	17.4929	6.73866	3.26797	961.327	73541.5
307	94 249	28 934 443	17.5214	6.74600	3.25733	964.469	74023.0
308	94 864	29 218 112	17.5499	6.75331	3.24675	967.611	74506.0
309	95 481	29 503 629	17.5784	6.76061	3.23625	970.752	74990.6
310	96 100	29 791 000	17.6068	6.76790	3.22581	973.894	75476.8
311	96 721	30 080 231	17.6352	6.77517	3.21543	977.035	75964.5
312	97 344	30 371 328	17.6635	6.78242	3.20513	980.177	76453.8
313	97 969	30 664 297	17.6918	6.78966	3.19489	983.318	76944.7
314	98 596	30 959 144	17.7200	6.79688	3.18471	986.460	77437.1
315	99 225	31 255 875	17.7482	6.80409	3.17460	989.602	77931.1
316	99 856	31 554 496	17.7764	6.81128	3.16456	992.743	78426.7
317	100 489	31 855 013	17.8045	6.81846	3.15457	995.885	78923.9
318	101 124	32 157 432	17.8326	6.82562	3.14465	999.026	79422.6
319	101 761	32 461 759	17.8606	6.83277	3.13480	1002.17	79922.9
320	102 400	32 768 000	17.8885	6.83990	3.12500	1005.31	80424.8
321	103 041	33 076 161	17.9165	6.84702	3.11526	1008.45	80928.2
322	103 684	33 386 248	17.9444	6.85412	3.10559	1011.59	81433.2
323	104 329	33 698 267	17.9722	6.86121	3.09598	1014.73	81939.8
324	104 976	34 012 224	18.0000	6.86829	3.08642	1017.88	82448.0
325	105 625	34 328 125	18.0278	6.87534	3.07692	1021.02	82957.7
326	106 276	34 645 976	18.0555	6.88239	3.06748	1024.16	83469.0
327	106 929	34 965 783	18.0831	6.88942	3.05810	1027.30	83981.8
328	107 584	35 287 552	18.1108	6.89643	3.04878	1030.44	84496.3
329	108 241	35 611 289	18.1384	6.90344	3.03951	1033.58	85012.3
330	108 900	35 937 000	18.1659	6.91042	3.03030	1036.73	85529.9
331	109 561	36 264 691	18.1934	6.91740	3.02115	1039.87	86049.0
332	110 224	36 594 368	18.2209	6.92436	3.01205	1043.01	86569.7
333	110 889	36 926 037	18.2483	6.93130	3.00300	1046.15	87092.0
334	111 556	37 259 704	18.2757	6.93823	2.99401	1049.29	87615.9
335	112 225	37 595 375	18.3030	6.94515	2.98507	1052.43	88141.3
336	112 896	37 933 056	18.3303	6.95205	2.97619	1055.58	88668.3
337	113 569	38 272 753	18.3576	6.95894	2.96736	1058.72	89196.9
338	114 244	38 614 472	18.3848	6.96582	2.95858	1061.86	89727.0
339	114 921	38 958 219	18.4120	6.97268	2.94985	1065.00	90258.7
340	115 600	39 304 000	18.4391	6.97953	2.94118	1068.14	90792.0
341	116 281	39 651 821	18.4662	6.98637	2.93255	1071.28	91326.9
342	116 964	40 001 688	18.4932	6.99319	2.92398	1074.42	91863.3
343	117 649	40 353 607	18.5203	7.00000	2.91545	1077.57	92401.3
344	118 336	40 707 584	18.5472	7.00680	2.90698	1080.71	92940.9
345	119 025	41 063 625	18.5742	7.01358	2.89855	1083.85	93482.0
346	119 716	41 421 736	18.6011	7.02035	2.89017	1086.99	94024.7
347	120 409	41 781 923	18.6279	7.02711	2.88184	1090.13	94569.0
348	121 104	42 144 192	18.6548	7.03385	2.87356	1093.27	95114.9
349	121 801	42 508 549	18.6815	7.04058	2.86533	1096.42	95662.3

Table XIII

Page 203

POWERS, ROOTS, RECIPROCALS, CIRCUMFERENCES, AND AREAS OF CIRCLES

n	n^2	n^3	$\sqrt{n}$	$\sqrt[3]{n}$	$1000/n$	Circum. of circle πn	Area of circle $\frac{1}{4}\pi n^2$
350	122 500	42 875 000	18.7083	7.04730	2.85714	1099.56	96211.3
351	123 201	43 243 551	18.7350	7.05400	2.84900	1102.70	96761.8
352	123 904	43 614 208	18.7617	7.06070	2.84091	1105.84	97314.0
353	124 609	43 986 977	18.7883	7.06738	2.83286	1108.98	97867.7
354	125 316	44 361 864	18.8149	7.07404	2.82486	1112.12	98423.0
355	126 025	44 738 875	18.8414	7.08070	2.81690	1115.27	98979.8
356	126 736	45 118 016	18.8680	7.08734	2.80899	1118.41	99538.2
357	127 449	45 499 293	18.8944	7.09397	2.80112	1121.55	100098.
358	128 164	45 882 712	18.9209	7.10059	2.79330	1124.69	100660.
359	128 881	46 268 279	18.9473	7.10719	2.78552	1127.83	101223.
360	129 600	46 656 000	18.9737	7.11379	2.77778	1130.97	101788.
361	130 321	47 045 881	19.0000	7.12037	2.77008	1134.11	102354.
362	131 044	47 437 928	19.0263	7.12694	2.76243	1137.26	102922.
363	131 769	47 832 147	19.0526	7.13349	2.75482	1140.40	103491.
364	132 496	48 228 544	19.0788	7.14004	2.74725	1143.54	104062.
365	133 225	48 627 125	19.1050	7.14657	2.73973	1146.68	104635.
366	133 956	49 027 896	19.1311	7.15309	2.73224	1149.82	105209.
367	134 689	49 430 863	19.1572	7.15960	2.72480	1152.96	105784.
368	135 424	49 836 032	19.1833	7.16610	2.71739	1156.11	106362.
369	136 161	50 243 409	19.2094	7.17258	2.71003	1159.25	106941.
370	136 900	50 653 000	19.2354	7.17905	2.70270	1162.39	107521.
371	137 641	51 064 811	19.2614	7.18552	2.69542	1165.53	108103.
372	138 384	51 478 848	19.2873	7.19197	2.68817	1168.67	108687.
373	139 129	51 895 117	19.3132	7.19840	2.68097	1171.81	109272.
374	139 876	52 313 624	19.3391	7.20483	2.67380	1174.96	109858.
375	140 625	52 734 375	19.3649	7.21125	2.66667	1178.10	110447.
376	141 376	53 157 376	19.3907	7.21765	2.65957	1181.24	111036.
377	142 129	53 582 633	19.4165	7.22405	2.65252	1184.38	111628.
378	142 884	54 010 152	19.4422	7.23043	2.64550	1187.52	112221.
379	143 641	54 439 939	19.4679	7.23680	2.63852	1190.66	112815.
380	144 400	54 872 000	19.4936	7.24316	2.63158	1193.81	113411.
381	145 161	55 306 341	19.5192	7.24950	2.62467	1196.95	114009.
382	145 924	55 742 968	19.5448	7.25584	2.61780	1200.09	114608.
383	146 689	56 181 887	19.5704	7.26217	2.61097	1203.23	115209.
384	147 456	56 623 104	19.5959	7.26848	2.60417	1206.37	115812.
385	148 225	57 066 625	19.6214	7.27479	2.59740	1209.51	116416.
386	148 996	57 512 456	19.6469	7.28108	2.59067	1212.65	117021.
387	149 769	57 960 603	19.6723	7.28736	2.58398	1215.80	117628.
388	150 544	58 411 072	19.6977	7.29363	2.57732	1218.94	118237.
389	151 321	58 863 869	19.7231	7.29989	2.57069	1222.08	118847.
390	152 100	59 319 000	19.7484	7.30614	2.56410	1225.22	119459.
391	152 881	59 776 471	19.7737	7.31238	2.55754	1228.36	120072.
392	153 664	60 236 288	19.7990	7.31861	2.55102	1231.50	120687.
393	154 449	60 698 457	19.8242	7.32483	2.54453	1234.65	121304.
394	155 236	61 162 984	19.8494	7.33104	2.53807	1237.79	121922.
395	156 025	61 629 875	19.8746	7.33723	2.53165	1240.93	122542.
396	156 816	62 099 136	19.8997	7.34342	2.52525	1244.07	123163.
397	157 609	62 570 773	19.9249	7.34960	2.51889	1247.21	123786.
398	158 404	63 044 792	19.9499	7.35576	2.51256	1250.35	124410.
399	159 201	63 521 199	19.9750	7.36192	2.50627	1253.50	125036.

POWERS, ROOTS, RECIPROCALS, CIRCUMFERENCES,
AND AREAS OF CIRCLES

n	n^2	n^3	$\sqrt{n}$	$\sqrt[3]{n}$	$1000/n$	Circum. of circle πn	Area of circle $\frac{1}{4}\pi n^2$
400	160 000	64 000 000	20.0000	7.36806	2.50000	1256.64	125 664
401	160 801	64 481 201	20.0250	7.37420	2.49377	1259.78	126 293
402	161 604	64 964 808	20.0499	7.38032	2.48756	1262.92	126 923
403	162 409	65 450 827	20.0749	7.38644	2.48139	1266.06	127 556
404	163 216	65 939 264	20.0998	7.39254	2.47525	1269.20	128 190
405	164 025	66 430 125	20.1246	7.39864	2.46914	1272.35	128 825
406	164 836	66 923 416	20.1494	7.40472	2.46305	1275.49	129 462
407	165 649	67 419 143	20.1742	7.41080	2.45700	1278.63	130 100
408	166 464	67 917 312	20.1990	7.41686	2.45098	1281.77	130 741
409	167 281	68 417 929	20.2237	7.42291	2.44499	1284.91	131 382
410	168 100	68 921 000	20.2485	7.42896	2.43902	1288.05	132 025
411	168 921	69 426 531	20.2731	7.43499	2.43309	1291.19	132 670
412	169 744	69 934 528	20.2978	7.44102	2.42718	1294.34	133 317
413	170 569	70 444 997	20.3224	7.44703	2.42131	1297.48	133 965
414	171 396	70 957 944	20.3470	7.45304	2.41546	1300.62	134 614
415	172 225	71 473 375	20.3715	7.45904	2.40964	1303.76	135 265
416	173 056	71 991 296	20.3961	7.46502	2.40385	1306.90	135 918
417	173 889	72 511 713	20.4206	7.47100	2.39808	1310.04	136 572
418	174 724	73 034 632	20.4450	7.47697	2.39234	1313.19	137 228
419	175 561	73 560 059	20.4695	7.48292	2.38663	1316.33	137 885
420	176 400	74 088 000	20.4939	7.48887	2.38095	1319.47	138 544
421	177 241	74 618 461	20.5183	7.49481	2.37530	1322.61	139 205
422	178 084	75 151 448	20.5426	7.50074	2.36967	1325.75	139 867
423	178 929	75 686 967	20.5670	7.50666	2.36407	1328.89	140 531
424	179 776	76 225 024	20.5913	7.51257	2.35849	1332.04	141 196
425	180 625	76 765 625	20.6155	7.51847	2.35294	1335.18	141 863
426	181 476	77 308 776	20.6398	7.52437	2.34742	1338.32	142 531
427	182 329	77 854 483	20.6640	7.53025	2.34192	1341.46	143 201
428	183 184	78 402 752	20.6882	7.53612	2.33645	1344.60	143 872
429	184 041	78 953 589	20.7123	7.54199	2.33100	1347.74	144 545
430	184 900	79 507 000	20.7364	7.54784	2.32558	1350.88	145 220
431	185 761	80 062 991	20.7605	7.55369	2.32019	1354.03	145 896
432	186 624	80 621 568	20.7846	7.55953	2.31481	1357.17	146 574
433	187 489	81 182 737	20.8087	7.56535	2.30947	1360.31	147 254
434	188 356	81 746 504	20.8327	7.57117	2.30415	1363.45	147 934
435	189 225	82 312 875	20.8567	7.57698	2.29885	1366.59	148 617
436	190 096	82 881 856	20.8806	7.58279	2.29358	1369 73	149 301
437	190 969	83 453 453	20.9045	7.58858	2.28833	1372.88	149 987
438	191 844	84 027 672	20.9284	7.59436	2.28311	1376.02	150 674
439	192 721	84 604 519	20.9523	7.60014	2.27790	1379.16	151 363
440	193 600	85 184 000	20.9762	7.60590	2.27273	1382.30	152 053
441	194 481	85 766 121	21.0000	7.61166	2.26757	1385.44	152 745
442	195 364	86 350 888	21.0238	7.61741	2.26244	1388.58	153 439
443	196 249	86 938 307	21.0476	7.62315	2.25734	1391.73	154 134
444	197 136	87 528 384	21.0713	7.62888	2.25225	1394.87	154 830
445	198 025	88 121 125	21.0950	7.63461	2.24719	1398.01	155 528
446	198 916	88 716 536	21.1187	7.64032	2.24215	1401.15	156 228
447	199 809	89 314 623	21.1424	7.64603	2.23714	1404.29	156 930
448	200 704	89 915 392	21.1660	7.65172	2.23214	1407.43	157 633
449	201 601	90 518 849	21.1896	7.65741	2.22717	1410.58	158 337

Table XIII

Page 205

POWERS, ROOTS, RECIPROCALS, CIRCUMFERENCES, AND AREAS OF CIRCLES

n	n^2	n^3	$\sqrt{n}$	$\sqrt[3]{n}$	$1000/n$	Circum. of circle πn	Area of circle $\frac{1}{4}\pi n^2$
450	202 500	91 125 000	21.2132	7.66309	2.22222	1413.72	159 043
451	203 401	91 733 851	21.2368	7.66877	2.21729	1416.86	159 751
452	204 304	92 345 408	21.2603	7.67443	2.21239	1420.00	160 460
453	205 209	92 959 677	21.2838	7.68009	2.20751	1423.14	161 171
454	206 116	93 576 664	21.3073	7.68573	2.20264	1426.28	161 883
455	207 025	94 196 375	21.3307	7.69137	2.19780	1429.42	162 597
456	207 936	94 818 816	21.3542	7.69700	2.19298	1432.57	163 313
457	208 849	95 443 993	21.3776	7.70262	2.18818	1435.71	164 030
458	209 764	96 071 912	21.4009	7.70824	2.18341	1438.85	164 748
459	210 681	96 702 579	21.4243	7.71384	2.17865	1441.99	165 468
460	211 600	97 336 000	21.4476	7.71944	2.17391	1445.13	166 190
461	212 521	97 972 181	21.4709	7.72503	2.16920	1448.27	166 914
462	213 444	98 611 128	21.4942	7.73061	2.16450	1451.42	167 639
463	214 369	99 252 847	21.5174	7.73619	2.15983	1454.56	168 365
464	215 296	99 897 344	21.5407	7.74175	2.15517	1457.70	169 093
465	216 225	100 544 625	21.5639	7.74731	2.15054	1460.84	169 823
466	217 156	101 194 696	21.5870	7.75286	2.14592	1463.98	170 554
467	218 089	101 847 563	21.6102	7.75840	2.14133	1467.12	171 287
468	219 024	102 503 232	21.6333	7.76394	2.13675	1470.27	172 021
469	219 961	103 161 709	21.6564	7.76946	2.13220	1473.41	172 757
470	220 900	103 823 000	21.6795	7.77498	2.12766	1476.55	173 494
471	221 841	104 487 111	21.7025	7.78049	2.12314	1479.69	174 234
472	222 784	105 154 048	21.7256	7.78599	2.11864	1482.83	174 974
473	223 729	105 823 817	21.7486	7.79149	2.11416	1485.97	175 716
474	224 676	106 496 424	21.7715	7.79697	2.10970	1489.11	176 460
475	225 625	107 171 875	21.7945	7.80245	2.10526	1492.26	177 205
476	226 576	107 850 176	21.8174	7.80793	2.10084	1495.40	177 952
477	227 529	108 531 333	21.8403	7.81339	2.09644	1498.54	178 701
478	228 484	109 215 352	21.8632	7.81885	2.09205	1501.68	179 451
479	229 441	109 902 239	21.8861	7.82429	2.08768	1504.82	180 203
480	230 400	110 592 000	21.9089	7.82974	2.08333	1507.96	180 956
481	231 361	111 284 641	21.9317	7.83517	2.07900	1511.11	181 711
482	232 324	111 980 168	21.9545	7.84059	2.07469	1514.25	182 467
483	233 289	112 678 587	21.9773	7.84601	2.07039	1517.39	183 225
484	234 256	113 379 904	22.0000	7.85142	2.06612	1520.53	183 984
485	235 225	114 084 125	22.0227	7.85683	2.06186	1523.67	184 745
486	236 196	114 791 256	22.0454	7.86222	2.05761	1526.81	185 508
487	237 169	115 501 303	22.0681	7.86761	2.05339	1529.96	186 272
488	238 144	116 214 272	22.0907	7.87299	2.04918	1533.10	187 038
489	239 121	116 930 169	22.1133	7.87837	2.04499	1536.24	187 805
490	240 100	117 649 000	22.1359	7.88374	2.04082	1539.38	188 574
491	241 081	118 370 771	22.1585	7.88909	2.03666	1542.52	189 345
492	242 064	119 095 488	22.1811	7.89445	2.03252	1545.66	190 117
493	243 049	119 823 157	22.2036	7.89979	2.02840	1548.81	190 890
494	244 036	120 553 784	22.2261	7.90513	2.02429	1551.95	191 665
495	245 025	121 287 375	22.2486	7.91046	2.02020	1555.09	192 442
496	246 016	122 023 936	22.2711	7.91578	2.01613	1558.23	193 221
497	247 009	122 763 473	22.2935	7.92110	2.01207	1561.37	194 000
498	248 004	123 505 992	22.3159	7.92641	2.00803	1564.51	194 782
499	249 001	124 251 499	22.3383	7.93171	2.00401	1567.65	195 565

POWERS, ROOTS, RECIPROCALS, CIRCUMFERENCES, AND AREAS OF CIRCLES

n	n^2	n^3	$\sqrt{n}$	$\sqrt[3]{n}$	$1000/n$	Circum. of circle πn	Area of circle $\frac{1}{4}\pi n^2$
500	250 000	125 000 000	22.3607	7.93701	2.00000	1570.80	196 350
501	251 001	125 751 501	22.3830	7.94229	1.99601	1573.94	197 136
502	252 004	126 506 008	22.4054	7.94757	1.99203	1577.08	197 923
503	253 009	127 263 527	22.4277	7.95285	1.98807	1580.22	198 713
504	254 016	128 024 064	22.4499	7.95811	1.98413	1583.36	199 504
505	255 025	128 787 625	22.4722	7.96337	1.98020	1586.50	200 296
506	256 036	129 554 216	22.4944	7.96863	1.97628	1589.65	201 090
507	257 049	130 323 843	22.5167	7.97387	1.97239	1592.79	201 886
508	258 064	131 096 512	22.5389	7.97911	1.96850	1595.93	202 683
509	259 081	131 872 229	22.5610	7.98434	1.96464	1599.07	203 482
510	260 100	132 651 000	22.5832	7.98957	1.96078	1602.21	204 282
511	261 121	133 432 831	22.6053	7.99479	1.95695	1605.35	205 084
512	262 144	134 217 728	22.6274	8.00000	1.95312	1608.50	205 887
513	263 169	135 005 697	22.6495	8.00520	1.94932	1611.64	206 692
514	264 196	135 796 744	22.6716	8.01040	1.94553	1614.78	207 499
515	265 225	136 590 875	22.6936	8.01559	1.94175	1617.92	208 307
516	266 256	137 388 096	22.7156	8.02078	1.93798	1621.06	209 117
517	267 289	138 188 413	22.7376	8.02596	1.93424	1624.20	209 928
518	268 324	138 991 832	22.7596	8.03113	1.93050	1627.34	210 741
519	269 361	139 798 359	22.7816	8.03629	1.92678	1630.49	211 556
520	270 400	140 608 000	22.8035	8.04145	1.92308	1633.63	212 372
521	271 441	141 420 761	22.8254	8.04660	1.91939	1636.77	213 189
522	272 484	142 236 648	22.8473	8.05175	1.91571	1639.91	214 008
523	273 529	143 055 667	22.8692	8.05689	1.91205	1643.05	214 829
524	274 576	143 877 824	22.8910	8.06202	1.90840	1646.19	215 651
525	275 625	144 703 125	22.9129	8.06714	1.90476	1649.34	216 475
526	276 676	145 531 576	22.9347	8.07226	1.90114	1652.48	217 301
527	277 729	146 363 183	22.9565	8.07737	1.89753	1655.62	218 128
528	278 784	147 197 952	22.9783	8.08248	1.89394	1658.76	218 956
529	279 841	148 035 889	23.0000	8.08758	1.89036	1661.90	219 787
530	280 900	148 877 000	23.0217	8.09267	1.88679	1665.04	220 618
531	281 961	149 721 291	23.0434	8.09776	1.88324	1668.19	221 452
532	283 024	150 568 768	23.0651	8.10284	1.87970	1671.33	222 287
533	284 089	151 419 437	23.0868	8.10791	1.87617	1674.47	223 123
534	285 156	152 273 304	23.1084	8.11298	1.87266	1677.61	223 961
535	286 225	153 130 375	23.1301	8.11804	1.86916	1680.75	224 801
536	287 296	153 990 656	23.1517	8.12310	1.86567	1683.89	225 642
537	288 369	154 854 153	23.1733	8.12814	1.86220	1687.04	226 484
538	289 444	155 720 872	23.1948	8.13319	1.85874	1690.18	227 329
539	290 521	156 590 819	23.2164	8.13822	1.85529	1693.32	228 175
540	291 600	157 464 000	23.2379	8.14325	1.85185	1696.46	229 022
541	292 681	158 340 421	23.2594	8.14828	1.84843	1699.60	229 871
542	293 764	159 220 088	23.2809	8.15329	1.84502	1702.74	230 722
543	294 849	160 103 007	23.3024	8.15831	1.84162	1705.88	231 574
544	295 936	160 989 184	23.3238	8.16331	1.83824	1709.03	232 428
545	297 025	161 878 625	23.3452	8.16831	1.83486	1712.17	233 283
546	298 116	162 771 336	23.3666	8.17330	1.83150	1715.31	234 140
547	299 209	163 667 323	23.3880	8.17829	1.82815	1718.45	234 998
548	300 304	164 566 592	23.4094	8.18327	1.82482	1721.59	235 858
549	301 401	165 469 149	23.4307	8.18824	1.82149	1724.73	236 720

Table XIII

Page 207

POWERS, ROOTS, RECIPROCALS, CIRCUMFERENCES, AND AREAS OF CIRCLES

n	n^2	n^3	$\sqrt{n}$	$\sqrt[3]{n}$	$1000/n$	Circum. of circle πn	Area of circle $\frac{1}{4}\pi n^2$
550	302 500	166 375 000	23.4521	8.19321	1.81818	1727.88	237 583
551	303 601	167 284 151	23.4734	8.19818	1.81488	1731.02	238 448
552	304 704	168 196 608	23.4947	8.20313	1.81159	1734.16	239 314
553	305 809	169 112 377	23.5160	8.20808	1.80832	1737.30	240 182
554	306 916	170 031 464	23.5372	8.21303	1.80505	1740.44	241 051
555	308 025	170 953 875	23.5584	8.21797	1.80180	1743.58	241 922
556	309 136	171 879 616	23.5797	8.22290	1.79856	1746.73	242 795
557	310 249	172 808 693	23.6008	8.22783	1.79533	1749.87	243 669
558	311 364	173 741 112	23.6220	8.23275	1.79211	1753.01	244 545
559	312 481	174 676 879	23.6432	8.23766	1.78891	1756.15	245 422
560	313 600	175 616 000	23.6643	8.24257	1.78571	1759.29	246 301
561	314 721	176 558 481	23.6854	8.24747	1.78253	1762.43	247 181
562	315 844	177 504 328	23.7065	8.25237	1.77936	1765.58	248 063
563	316 969	178 453 547	23.7276	8.25726	1.77620	1768.72	248 947
564	318 096	179 406 144	23.7487	8.26215	1.77305	1771.86	249 832
565	319 225	180 362 125	23.7697	8.26703	1.76991	1775.00	250 719
566	320 356	181 321 496	23.7908	8.27190	1.76678	1778.14	251 607
567	321 489	182 284 263	23.8118	8.27677	1.76367	1781.28	252 497
568	322 624	183 250 432	23.8328	8.28164	1.76056	1784.42	253 388
569	323 761	184 220 009	23.8537	8.28649	1.75747	1787.57	254 281
570	324 900	185 193 000	23.8747	8.29134	1.75439	1790.71	255 176
571	326 041	186 169 411	23.8956	8.29619	1.75131	1793.85	256 072
572	327 184	187 149 248	23.9165	8.30103	1.74825	1796.99	256 970
573	328 329	188 132 517	23.9374	8.30587	1.74520	1800.13	257 869
574	329 476	189 119 224	23.9583	8.31069	1.74216	1803.27	258 770
575	330 625	190 109 375	23.9792	8.31552	1.73913	1806.42	259 672
576	331 776	191 102 976	24.0000	8.32034	1.73611	1809.56	260 576
577	332 929	192 100 033	24.0208	8.32515	1.73310	1812.70	261 482
578	334 084	193 100 552	24.0416	8.32995	1.73010	1815.84	262 389
579	335 241	194 104 539	24.0624	8.33476	1.72712	1818.98	263 298
580	336 400	195 112 000	24.0832	8.33955	1.72414	1822.12	264 208
581	337 561	196 122 941	24.1039	8.34434	1.72117	1825.27	265 120
582	338 724	197 137 368	24.1247	8.34913	1.71821	1828.41	266 033
583	339 889	198 155 287	24.1454	8.35390	1.71527	1831.55	266 948
584	341 056	199 176 704	24.1661	8.35868	1.71233	1834.69	267 865
585	342 225	200 201 625	24.1868	8.36345	1.70940	1837.83	268 783
586	343 396	201 230 056	24.2074	8.36821	1.70648	1840.97	269 703
587	344 569	202 262 003	24.2281	8.37297	1.70358	1844.11	270 624
588	345 744	203 297 472	24.2487	8.37772	1.70068	1847.26	271 547
589	346 921	204 336 469	24.2693	8.38247	1.69779	1850.40	272 471
590	348 100	205 379 000	24.2899	8.38721	1.69492	1853.54	273 397
591	349 281	206 425 071	24.3105	8.39194	1.69205	1856.68	274 325
592	350 464	207 474 688	24.3311	8.39667	1.68919	1859.82	275 254
593	351 649	208 527 857	24.3516	8.40140	1.68634	1862.96	276 184
594	352 836	209 584 584	24.3721	8.40612	1.68350	1866.11	277 117
595	354 025	210 644 875	24.3926	8.41083	1.68067	1869.25	278 051
596	355 216	211 708 736	24.4131	8.41554	1.67785	1872.39	278 986
597	356 409	212 776 173	24.4336	8.42025	1.67504	1875.53	279 923
598	357 604	213 847 192	24.4540	8.42494	1.67224	1878.67	280 862
599	358 801	214 921 799	24.4745	8.42964	1.66945	1881.81	281 802

POWERS, ROOTS, RECIPROCALS, CIRCUMFERENCES, AND AREAS OF CIRCLES

n	n^2	n^3	$\sqrt{n}$	$\sqrt[3]{n}$	$1000/n$	Circum. of circle πn	Area of circle $\frac{1}{4}\pi n^2$
600	360 000	216 000 000	24.4949	8.43433	1.66667	1884.96	282 743
601	361 201	217 081 801	24.5153	8.43901	1.66389	1888.10	283 687
602	362 404	218 167 208	24.5357	8.44369	1.66113	1891.24	284 631
603	363 609	219 256 227	24.5561	8.44836	1.65837	1894.38	285 578
604	364 816	220 348 864	24.5764	8.45303	1.65563	1897.52	286 526
605	366 025	221 445 125	24.5967	8.45769	1.65289	1900.66	287 475
606	367 236	222 545 016	24.6171	8.46235	1.65017	1903.81	288 426
607	368 449	223 648 543	24.6374	8.46700	1.64745	1906.95	289 379
608	369 664	224 755 712	24.6577	8.47165	1.64474	1910.09	290 333
609	370 881	225 866 529	24.6779	8.47629	1.64204	1913.23	291 289
610	372 100	226 981 000	24.6982	8.48093	1.63934	1916.37	292 247
611	373 321	228 099 131	24.7184	8.48556	1.63666	1919.51	293 206
612	374 544	229 220 928	24.7386	8.49018	1.63399	1922.65	294 166
613	375 769	230 346 397	24.7588	8.49481	1.63132	1925.80	295 128
614	376 996	231 475 544	24.7790	8.49942	1.62866	1928.94	296 092
615	378 225	232 608 375	24.7992	8.50403	1.62602	1932.08	297 057
616	379 456	233 744 896	24.8193	8.50864	1.62338	1935.22	298 024
617	380 689	234 885 113	24.8395	8.51324	1.62075	1938.36	298 992
618	381 924	236 029 032	24.8596	8.51784	1.61812	1941.50	299 962
619	383 161	237 176 659	24.8797	8.52243	1.61551	1944.65	300 934
620	384 400	238 328 000	24.8998	8.52702	1.61290	1947.79	301 907
621	385 641	239 483 061	24.9199	8.53160	1.61031	1950.93	302 882
622	386 884	240 641 848	24.9399	8.53618	1.60772	1954.07	303 858
623	388 129	241 804 367	24.9600	8.54075	1.60514	1957.21	304 836
624	389 376	242 970 624	24.9800	8.54532	1.60256	1960.35	305 815
625	390 625	244 140 625	25.0000	8.54988	1.60000	1963.50	306 796
626	391 876	245 314 376	25.0200	8.55444	1.59744	1966.64	307 779
627	393 129	246 491 883	25.0400	8.55899	1.59490	1969.78	308 763
628	394 384	247 673 152	25.0599	8.56354	1.59236	1972.92	309 748
629	395 641	248 858 189	25.0799	8.56808	1.58983	1976.06	310 736
630	396 900	250 047 000	25.0998	8.57262	1.58730	1979.20	311 725
631	398 161	251 239 591	25.1197	8.57715	1.58479	1982.35	312 715
632	399 424	252 435 968	25.1396	8.58168	1.58228	1985.49	313 707
633	400 689	253 636 137	25.1595	8.58620	1.57978	1988.63	314 700
634	401 956	254 840 104	25.1794	8.59072	1.57729	1991.77	315 696
635	403 225	256 047 875	25.1992	8.59524	1.57480	1994.91	316 692
636	404 496	257 259 456	25.2190	8.59975	1.57233	1998.05	317 690
637	405 769	258 474 853	25.2389	8.60425	1.56986	2001.19	318 690
638	407 044	259 694 072	25.2587	8.60875	1.56740	2004.34	319 692
639	408 321	260 917 119	25.2784	8.61325	1.56495	2007.48	320 695
640	409 600	262 144 000	25.2982	8.61774	1.56250	2010.62	321 699
641	410 881	263 374 721	25.3180	8.62222	1.56006	2013.76	322 705
642	412 164	264 609 288	25.3377	8.62671	1.55763	2016.90	323 713
643	413 449	265 847 707	25.3574	8.63118	1.55521	2020.04	324 722
644	414 736	267 089 984	25.3772	8.63566	1.55280	2023.19	325 733
645	416 025	268 336 125	25.3969	8.64012	1.55039	2026.33	326 745
646	417 316	269 586 136	25.4165	8.64459	1.54799	2029.47	327 759
647	418 609	270 840 023	25.4362	8.64904	1.54560	2032.61	328 775
648	419 904	272 097 792	25.4558	8.65350	1.54321	2035.75	329 792
649	421 201	273 359 449	25.4755	8.65795	1.54083	2038.89	330 810

Table XIII **Page 209**

POWERS, ROOTS, RECIPROCALS, CIRCUMFERENCES,
AND AREAS OF CIRCLES

n	n^2	n^3	$\sqrt{n}$	$\sqrt[3]{n}$	$1000/n$	Circum. of circle πn	Area of circle $\frac{1}{4}\pi n^2$
650	422 500	274 625 000	25.4951	8.66239	1.53846	2042.04	331 831
651	423 801	275 894 451	25.5147	8.66683	1.53610	2045.18	332 853
652	425 104	277 167 808	25.5343	8.67127	1.53374	2048.32	333 876
653	426 409	278 445 077	25.5539	8.67570	1.53139	2051.46	334 901
654	427 716	279 726 264	25.5734	8.68012	1.52905	2054.60	335 927
655	429 025	281 011 375	25.5930	8.68455	1.52672	2057.74	336 955
656	430 336	282 300 416	25.6125	8.68896	1.52439	2060.88	337 985
657	431 649	283 593 393	25.6320	8.69338	1.52207	2064.03	339 016
658	432 964	284 890 312	25.6515	8.69778	1.51976	2067.17	340 049
659	434 281	286 191 179	25.6710	8.70219	1.51745	2070.31	341 084
660	435 600	287 496 000	25.6905	8.70659	1.51515	2073.45	342 119
661	436 921	288 804 781	25.7099	8.71098	1.51286	2076.59	343 157
662	438 244	290 117 528	25.7294	8.71537	1.51057	2079.73	344 196
663	439 569	291 434 247	25.7488	8.71976	1.50830	2082.88	345 237
664	440 896	292 754 944	25.7682	8.72414	1.50602	2086.02	346 279
665	442 225	294 079 625	25.7876	8.72852	1.50376	2089.16	347 323
666	443 556	295 408 296	25.8070	8.73289	1.50150	2092.30	348 368
667	444 889	296 740 963	25.8263	8.73726	1.49925	2095.44	349 415
668	446 224	298 077 632	25.8457	8.74162	1.49701	2098.58	350 464
669	447 561	299 418 309	25.8650	8.74598	1.49477	2101.73	351 514
670	448 900	300 763 000	25.8844	8.75034	1.49254	2104.87	352 565
671	450 241	302 111 711	25.9037	8.75469	1.49031	2108.01	353 618
672	451 584	303 464 448	25.9230	8.75904	1.48810	2111.15	354 673
673	452 929	304 821 217	25.9422	8.76338	1.48588	2114.29	355 730
674	454 276	306 182 024	25.9615	8.76772	1.48368	2117.43	356 788
675	455 625	307 546 875	25.9808	8.77205	1.48148	2120.58	357 847
676	456 976	308 915 776	26.0000	8.77638	1.47929	2123.72	358 908
677	458 329	310 288 733	26.0192	8.78071	1.47710	2126.86	359 971
678	459 684	311 665 752	26.0384	8.78503	1.47493	2130.00	361 035
679	461 041	313 046 839	26.0576	8.78935	1.47275	2133.14	362 101
680	462 400	314 432 000	26.0768	8.79366	1.47059	2136.28	363 168
681	463 761	315 821 241	26.0960	8.79797	1.46843	2139.42	364 237
682	465 124	317 214 568	26.1151	8.80227	1.46628	2142.57	365 308
683	466 489	318 611 987	26.1343	8.80657	1.46413	2145.71	366 380
684	467 856	320 013 504	26.1534	8.81087	1.46199	2148.85	367 453
685	469 225	321 419 125	26.1725	8.81516	1.45985	2151.99	368 528
686	470 596	322 828 856	26.1916	8.81945	1.45773	2155.13	369 605
687	471 969	324 242 703	26.2107	8.82373	1.45560	2158.27	370 684
688	473 344	325 660 672	26.2298	8.82801	1.45349	2161.42	371 764
689	474 721	327 082 769	26.2488	8.83228	1.45138	2164.56	372 845
690	476 100	328 509 000	26.2679	8.83656	1.44928	2167.70	373 928
691	477 481	329 939 371	26.2869	8.84082	1.44718	2170.84	375 013
692	478 864	331 373 888	26.3059	8.84509	1.44509	2173.98	376 099
693	480 249	332 812 557	26.3249	8.84934	1.44300	2177.12	377 187
694	481 636	334 255 384	26.3439	8.85360	1.44092	2180.27	378 276
695	483 025	335 702 375	26.3629	8.85785	1.43885	2183.41	379 367
696	484 416	337 153 536	26.3818	8.86210	1.43678	2186.55	380 459
697	485 809	338 608 873	26.4008	8.86634	1.43472	2189.69	381 554
698	487 204	340 068 392	26.4197	8.87058	1.43266	2192.83	382 649
699	488 601	341 532 099	26.4386	8.87481	1.43062	2195.97	383 746

POWERS, ROOTS, RECIPROCALS, CIRCUMFERENCES, AND AREAS OF CIRCLES

n	n^2	n^3	$\sqrt{n}$	$\sqrt[3]{n}$	$1000/n$	Circum. of circle πn	Area of circle $\frac{1}{4}\pi n^2$
700	490 000	343 000 000	26.4575	8.87904	1.42857	2199.11	384 845
701	491 401	344 472 101	26.4764	8.88327	1.42653	2202.26	385 945
702	492 804	345 948 408	26.4953	8.88749	1.42450	2205.40	387 047
703	494 209	347 428 927	26.5141	8.89171	1.42248	2208.54	388 151
704	495 616	348 913 664	26.5330	8.89592	1.42045	2211.68	389 256
705	497 025	350 402 625	26.5518	8.90013	1.41844	2214.82	390 363
706	498 436	351 895 816	26.5707	8.90434	1.41643	2217.96	391 471
707	499 849	353 393 243	26.5895	8.90854	1.41443	2221.11	392 580
708	501 264	354 894 912	26.6083	8.91274	1.41243	2224.25	393 692
709	502 681	356 400 829	26.6271	8.91693	1.41044	2227.39	394 805
710	504 100	357 911 000	26.6458	8.92112	1.40845	2230.53	395 919
711	505 521	359 425 431	26.6646	8.92531	1.40647	2233.67	397 035
712	506 944	360 944 128	26.6833	8.92949	1.40449	2236.81	398 153
713	508 369	362 467 097	26.7021	8.93367	1.40252	2239.96	399 272
714	509 796	363 994 344	26.7208	8.93784	1.40056	2243.10	400 393
715	511 225	365 525 875	26.7395	8.94201	1.39860	2246.24	401 515
716	512 656	367 061 696	26.7582	8.94618	1.39665	2249.38	402 639
717	514 089	368 601 813	26.7769	8.95034	1.39470	2252.52	403 765
718	515 524	370 146 232	26.7955	8.95450	1.39276	2255.66	404 892
719	516 961	371 694 959	26.8142	8.95866	1.39082	2258.81	406 020
720	518 400	373 248 000	26.8328	8.96281	1.38889	2261.95	407 150
721	519 841	374 805 361	26.8514	8.96696	1.38696	2265.09	408 282
722	521 284	376 367 048	26.8701	8.97110	1.38504	2268.23	409 416
723	522 729	377 933 067	26.8887	8.97524	1.38313	2271.37	410 550
724	524 176	379 503 424	26.9072	8.97938	1.38122	2274.51	411 687
725	525 625	381 078 125	26.9258	8.98351	1.37931	2277.65	412 825
726	527 076	382 657 176	26.9444	8.98764	1.37741	2280.80	413 965
727	528 529	384 240 583	26.9629	8.99176	1.37552	2283.94	415 106
728	529 984	385 828 352	26.9815	8.99588	1.37363	2287.08	416 248
729	531 441	387 420 489	27.0000	9.00000	1.37174	2290.22	417 393
730	532 900	389 017 000	27.0185	9.00411	1.36986	2293.36	418 539
731	534 361	390 617 891	27.0370	9.00822	1.36799	2296.50	419 686
732	535 824	392 223 168	27.0555	9.01233	1.36612	2299.65	420 835
733	537 289	393 832 837	27.0740	9.01643	1.36426	2302.79	421 986
734	538 756	395 446 904	27.0924	9.02053	1.36240	2305.93	423 138
735	540 225	397 065 375	27.1109	9.02462	1.36054	2309.07	424 292
736	541 696	398 688 256	27.1293	9.02871	1.35870	2312.21	425 447
737	543 169	400 315 553	27.1477	9.03280	1.35685	2315.35	426 604
738	544 644	401 947 272	27.1662	9.03689	1.35501	2318.50	427 762
739	546 121	403 583 419	27.1846	9.04097	1.35318	2321.64	428 922
740	547 600	405 224 000	27.2029	9.04504	1.35135	2324.78	430 084
741	549 081	406 869 021	27.2213	9.04911	1.34953	2327.92	431 247
742	550 564	408 518 488	27.2397	9.05318	1.34771	2331.06	432 412
743	552 049	410 172 407	27.2580	9.05725	1.34590	2334.20	433 578
744	553 536	411 830 784	27.2764	9.06131	1.34409	2337.34	434 746
745	555 025	413 493 625	27.2947	9.06537	1.34228	2340.49	435 916
746	556 516	415 160 936	27.3130	9.06942	1.34048	2343.63	437 087
747	558 009	416 832 723	27.3313	9.07347	1.33869	2346.77	438 259
748	559 504	418 508 992	27.3496	9.07752	1.33690	2349.91	439 433
749	561 001	420 189 749	27.3679	9.08156	1.33511	2353.05	440 609

Table XIII   *Page 211*

POWERS, ROOTS, RECIPROCALS, CIRCUMFERENCES, AND AREAS OF CIRCLES

n	n^2	n^3	$\sqrt{n}$	$\sqrt[3]{n}$	$1000/n$	Circum. of circle πn	Area of circle $\frac{1}{4}\pi n^2$
750	562 500	421 875 000	27.3861	9.08560	1.33333	2356.19	441 786
751	564 001	423 564 751	27.4044	9.08964	1.33156	2359.34	442 965
752	565 504	425 259 008	27.4226	9.09367	1.32979	2362.48	444 146
753	567 009	426 957 777	27.4408	9.09770	1.32802	2365.62	445 328
754	568 516	428 661 064	27.4591	9.10173	1.32626	2368.76	446 511
755	570 025	430 368 875	27.4773	9.10575	1.32450	2371.90	447 697
756	571 536	432 081 216	27.4955	9.10977	1.32275	2375.04	448 883
757	573 049	433 798 093	27.5136	9.11378	1.32100	2378.19	450 072
758	574 564	435 519 512	27.5318	9.11779	1.31926	2381.33	451 262
759	576 081	437 245 479	27.5500	9.12180	1.31752	2384.47	452 453
760	577 600	438 976 000	27.5681	9.12581	1.31579	2387.61	453 646
761	579 121	440 711 081	27.5862	9.12981	1.31406	2390.75	454 841
762	580 644	442 450 728	27.6043	9.13380	1.31234	2393.89	456 037
763	582 169	444 194 947	27.6225	9.13780	1.31062	2397.04	457 234
764	583 696	445 943 744	27.6405	9.14179	1.30890	2400.18	458 434
765	585 225	447 697 125	27.6586	9.14577	1.30719	2403.32	459 635
766	586 756	449 455 096	27.6767	9.14976	1.30548	2406.46	460 837
767	588 289	451 217 663	27.6948	9.15374	1.30378	2409.60	462 041
768	589 824	452 984 832	27.7128	9.15771	1.30208	2412.74	463 247
769	591 361	454 756 609	27.7308	9.16169	1.30039	2415.88	464 454
770	592 900	456 533 000	27.7489	9.16566	1.29870	2419.03	465 663
771	594 441	458 314 011	27.7669	9.16962	1.29702	2422.17	466 873
772	595 984	460 099 648	27.7849	9.17359	1.29534	2425.31	468 085
773	597 529	461 889 917	27.8029	9.17754	1.29366	2428.45	469 298
774	599 076	463 684 824	27.8209	9.18150	1.29199	2431.59	470 513
775	600 625	465 484 375	27.8388	9.18545	1.29032	2434.73	471 730
776	602 176	467 288 576	27.8568	9.18940	1.28866	2437.88	472 948
777	603 729	469 097 433	27.8747	9.19335	1.28700	2441.02	474 168
778	605 284	470 910 952	27.8927	9.19729	1.28535	2444.16	475 389
779	606 841	472 729 139	27.9106	9.20123	1.28370	2447.30	476 612
780	608 400	474 552 000	27.9285	9.20516	1.28205	2450.44	477 836
781	609 961	476 379 541	27.9464	9.20910	1.28041	2453.58	479 062
782	611 524	478 211 768	27.9643	9.21302	1.27877	2456.73	480 290
783	613 089	480 048 687	27.9821	9.21695	1.27714	2459.87	481 519
784	614 656	481 890 304	28.0000	9.22087	1.27551	2463.01	482 750
785	616 225	483 736 625	28.0179	9.22479	1.27389	2466.15	483 982
786	617 796	485 587 656	28.0357	9.22871	1.27226	2469.29	485 216
787	619 369	487 443 403	28.0535	9.23262	1.27065	2472.43	486 451
788	620 944	489 303 872	28.0713	9.23653	1.26904	2475.58	487 688
789	622 521	491 169 069	28.0891	9.24043	1.26743	2478.72	488 927
790	624 100	493 039 000	28.1069	9.24434	1.26582	2481.86	490 167
791	625 681	494 913 671	28.1247	9.24823	1.26422	2485.00	491 409
792	627 264	496 793 088	28.1425	9.25213	1.26263	2488.14	492 652
793	628 849	498 677 257	28.1603	9.25602	1.26103	2491.28	493 897
794	630 436	500 566 184	28.1780	9.25991	1.25945	2494.42	495 143
795	632 025	502 459 875	28.1957	9.26380	1.25786	2497.57	496 391
796	633 616	504 358 336	28.2135	9.26768	1.25628	2500.71	497 641
797	635 209	506 261 573	28.2312	9.27156	1.25471	2503.85	498 892
798	636 804	508 169 592	28.2489	9.27544	1.25313	2506.99	500 145
799	638 401	510 082 399	28.2666	9.27931	1.25156	2510.13	501 399

POWERS, ROOTS, RECIPROCALS, CIRCUMFERENCES, AND AREAS OF CIRCLES

n	n^2	n^3	$\sqrt{n}$	$\sqrt[3]{n}$	$1000/n$	Circum. of circle πn	Area of circle $\frac{1}{4}\pi n^2$
800	640 000	512 000 000	28.2843	9.28318	1.25000	2513.27	502 655
801	641 601	513 922 401	28.3019	9.28704	1.24844	2516.42	503 912
802	643 204	515 849 608	28.3196	9.29091	1.24688	2519.56	505 171
803	644 809	517 781 627	28.3373	9.29477	1.24533	2522.70	506 432
804	646 416	519 718 464	28.3549	9.29862	1.24378	2525.84	507 694
805	648 025	521 660 125	28.3725	9.30248	1.24224	2528.98	508 958
806	649 636	523 606 616	28.3901	9.30633	1.24069	2532.12	510 223
807	651 249	525 557 943	28.4077	9.31018	1.23916	2535.27	511 490
808	652 864	527 514 112	28.4253	9.31402	1.23762	2538.41	512 758
809	654 481	529 475 129	28.4429	9.31786	1.23609	2541.55	514 028
810	656 100	531 441 000	28.4605	9.32170	1.23457	2544.69	515 300
811	657 721	533 411 731	28.4781	9.32553	1.23305	2547.83	516 573
812	659 344	535 387 328	28.4956	9.32936	1.23153	2550.97	517 848
813	660 969	537 367 797	28.5132	9.33319	1.23001	2554.11	519 124
814	662 596	539 353 144	28.5307	9.33702	1.22850	2557.26	520 402
815	664 225	541 343 375	28.5482	9.34084	1.22699	2560.40	521 681
816	665 856	543 338 496	28.5657	9.34466	1.22549	2563.54	522 962
817	667 489	545 338 513	28.5832	9.34847	1.22399	2566.68	524 245
818	669 124	547 343 432	28.6007	9.35229	1.22249	2569.82	525 529
819	670 761	549 353 259	28.6182	9.35610	1.22100	2572.96	526 814
820	672 400	551 368 000	28.6356	9.35990	1.21951	2576.11	528 102
821	674 041	553 387 661	28.6531	9.36370	1.21803	2579.25	529 391
822	675 684	555 412 248	28.6705	9.36751	1.21655	2582.39	530 681
823	677 329	557 441 767	28.6880	9.37130	1.21507	2585.53	531 973
824	678 976	559 476 224	28.7054	9.37510	1.21359	2588.67	533 267
825	680 625	561 515 625	28.7228	9.37889	1.21212	2591.81	534 562
826	682 276	563 559 976	28.7402	9.38268	1.21065	2594.96	535 858
827	683 929	565 609 283	28.7576	9.38646	1.20919	2598.10	537 157
828	685 584	567 663 552	28.7750	9.39024	1.20773	2601.24	538 456
829	687 241	569 722 789	28.7924	9.39402	1.20627	2604.38	539 758
830	688 900	571 787 000	28.8097	9.39780	1.20482	2607.52	541 061
831	690 561	573 856 191	28.8271	9.40157	1.20337	2610.66	542 365
832	692 224	575 930 368	28.8444	9.40534	1.20192	2613.81	543 671
833	693 889	578 009 537	28.8617	9.40911	1.20048	2616.95	544 979
834	695 556	580 093 704	28.8791	9.41287	1.19904	2620.09	546 288
835	697 225	582 182 875	28.8964	9.41663	1.19760	2623.23	547 599
836	698 896	584 277 056	28.9137	9.42039	1.19617	2626.37	548 912
837	700 569	586 376 253	28.9310	9.42414	1.19474	2629.51	550 226
838	702 244	588 480 472	28.9482	9.42789	1.19332	2632.65	551 541
839	703 921	590 589 719	28.9655	9.43164	1.19190	2635.80	552 858
840	705 600	592 704 000	28.9828	9.43539	1.19048	2638.94	554 177
841	707 281	594 823 321	29.0000	9.43913	1.18906	2642.08	555 497
842	708 964	596 947 688	29.0172	9.44287	1.18765	2645.22	556 819
843	710 649	599 077 107	29.0345	9.44661	1.18624	2648.36	558 142
844	712 336	601 211 584	29.0517	9.45034	1.18483	2651.50	559 467
845	714 025	603 351 125	29.0689	9.45407	1.18343	2654.65	560 794
846	715 716	605 495 736	29.0861	9.45780	1.18203	2657.79	562 122
847	717 409	607 645 423	29.1033	9.46152	1.18064	2660.93	563 452
848	719 104	609 800 192	29.1204	9.46525	1.17925	2664.07	564 783
849	720 801	611 960 049	29.1376	9.46897	1.17786	2667.21	566 116

Table XIII   *Page 213*

POWERS, ROOTS, RECIPROCALS, CIRCUMFERENCES, AND AREAS OF CIRCLES

n	n^2	n^3	$\sqrt{n}$	$\sqrt[3]{n}$	$1000/n$	Circum. of circle πn	Area of circle $\frac{1}{4}\pi n^2$
850	722 500	614 125 000	29.1548	9.47268	1.17647	2670.35	567 450
851	724 201	616 295 051	29.1719	9.47640	1.17509	2673.50	568 786
852	725 904	618 470 208	29.1890	9.48011	1.17371	2676.64	570 124
853	727 609	620 650 477	29.2062	9.48381	1.17233	2679.78	571 463
854	729 316	622 835 864	29.2233	9.48752	1.17096	2682.92	572 803
855	731 025	625 026 375	29.2404	9.49122	1.16959	2686.06	574 146
856	732 736	627 222 016	29.2575	9.49492	1.16822	2689.20	575 490
857	734 449	629 422 793	29.2746	9.49861	1.16686	2692.34	576 835
858	736 164	631 628 712	29.2916	9.50231	1.16550	2695.49	578 182
859	737 881	633 839 779	29.3087	9.50600	1.16414	2698.63	579 530
860	739 600	636 056 000	29.3258	9.50969	1.16279	2701.77	580 880
861	741 321	638 277 381	29.3428	9.51337	1.16144	2704.91	582 232
862	743 044	640 503 928	29.3598	9.51705	1.16009	2708.05	583 585
863	744 769	642 735 647	29.3769	9.52073	1.15875	2711.19	584 940
864	746 496	644 972 544	29.3939	9.52441	1.15741	2714.34	586 297
865	748 225	647 214 625	29.4109	9.52808	1.15607	2717.48	587 655
866	749 956	649 461 896	29.4279	9.53175	1.15473	2720.62	589 014
867	751 689	651 714 363	29.4449	9.53542	1.15340	2723.76	590 375
868	753 424	653 972 032	29.4618	9.53908	1.15207	2726.90	591 738
869	755 161	656 234 909	29.4788	9.54274	1.15075	2730.04	593 102
870	756 900	658 503 000	29.4958	9.54640	1.14943	2733.19	594 468
871	758 641	660 776 311	29.5127	9.55006	1.14811	2736.33	595 835
872	760 384	663 054 848	29.5296	9.55371	1.14679	2739.47	597 204
873	762 129	665 338 617	29.5466	9.55736	1.14548	2742.61	598 575
874	763 876	667 627 624	29.5635	9.56101	1.14416	2745.75	599 947
875	765 625	669 921 875	29.5804	9.56466	1.14286	2748.89	601 320
876	767 376	672 221 376	29.5973	9.56830	1.14155	2752.04	602 696
877	769 129	674 526 133	29.6142	9.57194	1.14025	2755.18	604 073
878	770 884	676 836 152	29.6311	9.57557	1.13895	2758.32	605 451
879	772 641	679 151 439	29.6479	9.57921	1.13766	2761.46	606 831
880	774 400	681 472 000	29.6648	9.58284	1.13636	2764.60	608 212
881	776 161	683 797 841	29.6816	9.58647	1.13507	2767.74	609 595
882	777 924	686 128 968	29.6985	9.59009	1.13379	2770.88	610 980
883	779 689	688 465 387	29.7153	9.59372	1.13250	2774.03	612 366
884	781 456	690 807 104	29.7321	9.59734	1.13122	2777.17	613 754
885	783 225	693 154 125	29.7489	9.60095	1.12994	2780.31	615 143
886	784 996	695 506 456	29.7658	9.60457	1.12867	2783.45	616 534
887	786 769	697 864 103	29.7825	9.60818	1.12740	2786.59	617 927
888	788 544	700 227 072	29.7993	9.61179	1.12613	2789.73	619 321
889	790 321	702 595 369	29.8161	9.61540	1.12486	2792.88	620 717
890	792 100	704 969 000	29.8329	9.61900	1.12360	2796.02	622 114
891	793 881	707 347 971	29.8496	9.62260	1.12233	2799.16	623 513
892	795 664	709 732 288	29.8664	9.62620	1.12108	2802.30	624 913
893	797 449	712 121 957	29.8831	9.62980	1.11982	2805.44	626 315
894	799 236	714 516 984	29.8998	9.63339	1.11857	2808.58	627 718
895	801 025	716 917 375	29.9166	9.63698	1.11732	2811.73	629 124
896	802 816	719 323 136	29.9333	9.64057	1.11607	2814.87	630 530
897	804 609	721 734 273	29.9500	9.64415	1.11483	2818.01	631 938
898	806 404	724 150 792	29.9666	9.64774	1.11359	2821.15	633 348
899	808 201	726 572 699	29.9833	9.65132	1.11235	2824.29	634 760

POWERS, ROOTS, RECIPROCALS, CIRCUMFERENCES, AND AREAS OF CIRCLES

n	n^2	n^3	$\sqrt{n}$	$\sqrt[3]{n}$	$1000/n$	Circum. of circle πn	Area of circle $\frac{1}{4}\pi n^2$
900	810 000	729 000 000	30.0000	9.65489	1.11111	2827.43	636 173
901	811 801	731 432 701	30.0167	9.65847	1.10988	2830.58	637 587
902	813 604	733 870 808	30.0333	9.66204	1.10865	2833.72	639 003
903	815 409	736 314 327	30.0500	9.66561	1.10742	2836.86	640 421
904	817 216	738 763 264	30.0666	9.66918	1.10619	2840.00	641 840
905	819 025	741 217 625	30.0832	9.67274	1.10497	2843.14	643 261
906	820 836	743 677 416	30.0998	9.67630	1.10375	2846.28	644 683
907	822 649	746 142 643	30.1164	9.67986	1.10254	2849.42	646 107
908	824 464	748 613 312	30.1330	9.68342	1.10132	2852.57	647 533
909	826 281	751 089 429	30.1496	9.68697	1.10011	2855.71	648 960
910	828 100	753 571 000	30.1662	9.69052	1.09890	2858.85	650 388
911	829 921	756 058 031	30.1828	9.69407	1.09769	2861.99	651 818
912	831 744	758 550 528	30.1993	9.69762	1.09649	2865.13	653 250
913	833 569	761 048 497	30.2159	9.70116	1.09529	2868.27	654 684
914	835 396	763 551 944	30.2324	9.70470	1.09409	2871.42	656 118
915	837 225	766 060 875	30.2490	9.70824	1.09290	2874.56	657 555
916	839 056	768 575 296	30.2655	9.71177	1.09170	2877.70	658 993
917	840 889	771 095 213	30.2820	9.71531	1.09051	2880.84	660 433
918	842 724	773 620 632	30.2985	9.71884	1.08932	2883.98	661 874
919	844 561	776 151 559	30.3150	9.72236	1.08814	2887.12	663 317
920	846 400	778 688 000	30.3315	9.72589	1.08696	2890.27	664 761
921	848 241	781 229 961	30.3480	9.72941	1.08578	2893.41	666 207
922	850 084	783 777 448	30.3645	9.73293	1.08460	2896.55	667 654
923	851 929	786 330 467	30.3809	9.73645	1 08342	2899.69	669 103
924	853 776	788 889 024	30.3974	9.73996	1.08225	2902.83	670 554
925	855 625	791 453 125	30.4138	9.74348	1.08108	2905.97	672 006
926	857 476	794 022 776	30.4302	9.74699	1.07991	2909.11	673 460
927	859 329	796 597 983	30.4467	9.75049	1.07875	2912.26	674 915
928	861 184	799 178 752	30.4631	9.75400	1.07759	2915.40	676 372
929	863 041	801 765 089	30.4795	9.75750	1.07643	2918.54	677 831
930	864 900	804 357 000	30.4959	9.76100	1.07527	2921.68	679 291
931	866 761	806 954 491	30.5123	9.76450	1.07411	2924.82	680 753
932	868 624	809 557 568	30.5287	9.76799	1.07296	2927.96	682 216
933	870 489	812 166 237	30.5450	9.77148	1.07181	2931.11	683 680
934	872 356	814 780 504	30.5614	9.77497	1.07066	2934.25	685 147
935	874 225	817 400 375	30.5778	9.77846	1.06952	2937.39	686 615
936	876 096	820 025 856	30.5941	9.78195	1.06838	2940.53	688 084
937	877 969	822 656 953	30.6105	9.78543	1.06724	2943.67	689 555
938	879 844	825 293 672	30.6268	9.78891	1.06610	2946.81	691 028
939	881 721	827 936 019	30.6431	9.79239	1.06496	2949.96	692 502
940	883 600	830 584 000	30.6594	9.79586	1.06383	2953.10	693 978
941	885 481	833 237 621	30.6757	9.79933	1.06270	2956.24	695 455
942	887 364	835 896 888	30.6920	9.80280	1.06157	2959.38	696 934
943	889 249	838 561 807	30.7083	9.80627	1.06045	2962.52	698 415
944	891 136	841 232 384	30.7246	9.80974	1.05932	2965.66	699 897
945	893 025	843 908 625	30.7409	9.81320	1.05820	2968.81	701 380
946	894 916	846 590 536	30.7571	9.81666	1.05708	2971.95	702 865
947	896 809	849 278 123	30.7734	9.82012	1.05597	2975.09	704 352
948	898 704	851 971 392	30.7896	9.82357	1.05485	2978.23	705 840
949	900 601	854 670 349	30.8058	9.82703	1.05374	2981.37	707 330

Table XIII

Page 215

POWERS, ROOTS, RECIPROCALS, CIRCUMFERENCES, AND AREAS OF CIRCLES

n	n^2	n^3	$\sqrt{n}$	$\sqrt[3]{n}$	$1000/n$	Circum. of circle πn	Area of circle $\frac{1}{4}\pi n^2$
950	902 500	857 375 000	30.8221	9.83048	1.05263	2984.51	708 822
951	904 401	860 085 351	30.8383	9.83392	1.05152	2987.65	710 315
952	906 304	862 801 408	30.8545	9.83737	1.05042	2990.80	711 809
953	908 209	865 523 177	30.8707	9.84081	1.04932	2993.94	713 306
954	910 116	868 250 664	30.8869	9.84425	1.04822	2997.08	714 803
955	912 025	870 983 875	30.9031	9.84769	1.04712	3000.22	716 303
956	913 936	873 722 816	30.9192	9.85113	1.04603	3003.36	717 804
957	915 849	876 467 493	30.9354	9.85456	1.04493	3006.50	719 306
958	917 764	879 217 912	30.9516	9.85799	1.04384	3009.65	720 810
959	919 681	881 974 079	30.9677	9.86142	1.04275	3012.79	722 316
960	921 600	884 736 000	30.9839	9.86485	1.04167	3015.93	723 823
961	923 521	887 503 681	31.0000	9.86827	1.04058	3019.07	725 332
962	925 444	890 277 128	31.0161	9.87169	1.03950	3022.21	726 842
963	927 369	893 056 347	31.0322	9.87511	1.03842	3025.35	728 354
964	929 296	895 841 344	31.0483	9.87853	1.03734	3028.50	729 867
965	931 225	898 632 125	31.0644	9.88195	1.03627	3031.64	731 382
966	933 156	901 428 696	31.0805	9.88536	1.03520	3034.78	732 899
967	935 089	904 231 063	31.0966	9.88877	1.03413	3037.92	734 417
968	937 024	907 039 232	31.1127	9.89217	1.03306	3041.06	735 937
969	938 961	909 853 209	31.1288	9.89558	1.03199	3044.20	737 458
970	940 900	912 673 000	31.1448	9.89898	1.03093	3047.34	738 981
971	942 841	915 498 611	31.1609	9.90238	1.02987	3050.49	740 506
972	944 784	918 330 048	31.1769	9.90578	1.02881	3053.63	742 032
973	946 729	921 167 317	31.1929	9.90918	1.02775	3056.77	743 559
974	948 676	924 010 424	31.2090	9.91257	1.02669	3059.91	745 088
975	950 625	926 859 375	31.2250	9.91596	1.02564	3063.05	746 619
976	952 576	929 714 176	31.2410	9.91935	1.02459	3066.19	748 151
977	954 529	932 574 833	31.2570	9.92274	1.02354	3069.34	749 685
978	956 484	935 441 352	31.2730	9.92612	1.02249	3072.48	751 221
979	958 441	938 313 739	31.2890	9.92950	1.02145	3075.62	752 758
980	960 400	941 192 000	31.3050	9.93288	1.02041	3078.76	754 296
981	962 361	944 076 141	31.3209	9.93626	1.01937	3081.90	755 837
982	964 324	946 966 168	31.3369	9.93964	1.01833	3085.04	757 378
983	966 289	949 862 087	31.3528	9.94301	1.01729	3088.19	758 922
984	968 256	952 763 904	31.3688	9.94638	1.01626	3091.33	760 466
985	970 225	955 671 625	31.3847	9.94975	1.01523	3094.47	762 013
986	972 196	958 585 256	31.4006	9.95311	1.01420	3097.61	763 561
987	974 169	961 504 803	31.4166	9.95648	1.01317	3100.75	765 111
988	976 144	964 430 272	31.4325	9.95984	1.01215	3103.89	766 662
989	978 121	967 361 669	31.4484	9.96320	1.01112	3107.04	768 214
990	980 100	970 299 000	31.4643	9.96655	1.01010	3110.18	769 769
991	982 081	973 242 271	31.4802	9.96991	1.00908	3113.32	771 325
992	984 064	976 191 488	31.4960	9.97326	1.00806	3116.46	772 882
993	986 049	979 146 657	31.5119	9.97661	1.00705	3119.60	774 441
994	988 036	982 107 784	31.5278	9.97996	1.00604	3122.74	776 002
995	990 025	985 074 875	31.5436	9.98331	1.00503	3125.88	777 564
996	992 016	988 047 936	31.5595	9.98665	1.00402	3129.03	779 128
997	994 009	991 026 973	31.5753	9.98999	1.00301	3132.17	780 693
998	996 004	994 011 992	31.5911	9.99333	1.00200	3135.31	782 260
999	998 001	997 002 999	31.6070	9.99667	1.00100	3138.45	783 828

athletics , 1 7 3 3 ?

/ /) (

14)

Table XIV

NATURAL LOGARITHMS—0.00 to 5.99

N	L	0	1	2	3	4	5	6	7	8	9
0.0			5.395	6.088	6.493	6.781	7.004	7.187	7.341	7.474	7.592
0.1		7.697	7.793	7.880	7.960	8.034	8.103	8.167	8.228	8.285	8.339
0.2		8.391	8.439	8.486	8.530	8.573	8.614	8.653	8.691	8.727	8.762
0.3		8.796	8.829	8.861	8.891	8.921	8.950	8.978	9.006	9.032	9.058
0.4		9.084	9.108	9.132	9.156	9.179	9.201	9.223	9.245	9.266	9.287
0.5		9.307	9.327	9.346	9.365	9.384	9.402	9.420	9.438	9.455	9.472
0.6		9.489	9.506	9.522	9.538	9.554	9.569	9.584	9.600	9.614	9.629
0.7		9.643	9.658	9.671	9.685	9.699	9.712	9.726	9.739	9.752	9.764
0.8		9.777	9.789	9.802	9.814	9.826	9.837	9.849	9.861	9.872	9.883
0.9		9.895	9.906	9.917	9.927	9.938	9.949	9.959	9.970	9.980	9.990
1.0	0.0	0000	0995	1980	2956	3922	4879	5827	6766	7696	8618
1.1		9531	*0436	*1333	*2222	*3103	*3976	*4842	*5700	*6551	*7395
1.2	0.1	8232	9062	9885	*0701	*1511	*2314	*3111	*3902	*4686	*5464
1.3	0.2	6236	7003	7763	8518	9267	*0010	*0748	*1481	*2208	*2930
1.4	0.3	3647	4359	5066	5767	6464	7156	7844	8526	9204	9878
1.5	0.4	0547	1211	1871	2527	3178	3825	4469	5108	5742	6373
1.6		7000	7623	8243	8858	9470	*0078	*0682	*1282	*1879	*2473
1.7	0.5	3063	3649	4232	4812	5389	5962	6531	7098	7661	8222
1.8		8779	9333	9884	*0432	*0977	*1519	*2058	*2594	*3127	*3658
1.9	0.6	4185	4710	5233	5752	6269	6783	7294	7803	8310	8813
2.0		9315	9813	*0310	*0804	*1295	*1784	*2271	*2755	*3237	*3716
2.1	0.7	4194	4669	5142	5612	6081	6547	7011	7473	7932	8390
2.2		8846	9299	9751	*0200	*0648	*1093	*1536	*1978	*2418	*2855
2.3	0.8	3291	3725	4157	4587	5015	5442	5866	6289	6710	7129
2.4		7547	7963	8377	8789	9200	9609	*0016	*0422	*0826	*1228
2.5	0.9	1629	2028	2426	2822	3216	3609	4001	4391	4779	5166
2.6		5551	5935	6317	6698	7078	7456	7833	8208	8582	8954
2.7		9325	9695	*0063	*0430	*0796	*1160	*1523	*1885	*2245	*2604
2.8	1.0	2962	3318	3674	4028	4380	4732	5082	5431	5779	6126
2.9		6471	6815	7158	7500	7841	8181	8519	8856	9192	9527
3.0		9861	*0194	*0526	*0856	*1186	*1514	*1841	*2168	*2493	*2817
3.1	1.1	3140	3462	3783	4103	4422	4740	5057	5373	5688	6002
3.2		6315	6627	6938	7248	7557	7865	8173	8479	8784	9089
3.3		9392	9695	9996	*0297	*0597	*0896	*1194	*1491	*1788	*2083
3.4	1.2	2378	2671	2964	3256	3547	3837	4127	4415	4703	4990
3.5		5276	5562	5846	6130	6413	6695	6976	7257	7536	7815
3.6		8093	8371	8647	8923	9198	9473	9746	*0019	*0291	*0563
3.7	1.3	0833	1103	1372	1641	1909	2176	2442	2708	2972	3237
3.8		3500	3763	4025	4286	4547	4807	5067	5325	5584	5841
3.9		6098	6354	6609	6864	7118	7372	7624	7877	8128	8379
4.0		8629	8879	9128	9377	9624	9872	*0118	*0364	*0610	*0854
4.1	1.4	1099	1342	1585	1828	2070	2311	2552	2792	3031	3270
4.2		3508	3746	3984	4220	4456	4692	4927	5161	5395	5629
4.3		5862	6094	6326	6557	6787	7018	7247	7476	7705	7933
4.4		8160	8387	8614	8840	9065	9290	9515	9739	9962	*0185
4.5	1.5	0408	0630	0851	1072	1293	1513	1732	1951	2170	2388
4.6		2606	2823	3039	3256	3471	3687	3902	4116	4330	4543
4.7		4756	4969	5181	5393	5604	5814	6025	6235	6444	6653
4.8		6862	7070	7277	7485	7691	7898	8104	8309	8515	8719
4.9		8924	9127	9331	9534	9737	9939	*0141	*0342	*0543	*0744
5.0	1.6	0944	1144	1343	1542	1741	1939	2137	2334	2531	2728
5.1		2924	3120	3315	3511	3705	3900	4094	4287	4481	4673
5.2		4866	5058	5250	5441	5632	5823	6013	6203	6393	6582
5.3		6771	6959	7147	7335	7523	7710	7896	8083	8269	8455
5.4		8640	8825	9010	9194	9378	9562	9745	9928	*0111	*0293
5.5	1.7	0475	0656	0838	1019	1199	1380	1560	1740	1919	2098
5.6		2277	2455	2633	2811	2988	3166	3342	3519	3695	3871
5.7		4047	4222	4397	4572	4746	4920	5094	5267	5440	5613
5.8		5786	5958	6130	6302	6473	6644	6815	6985	7156	7326
5.9		7495	7665	7834	8002	8171	8339	8507	8675	8842	9009
N	L	0	1	2	3	4	5	6	7	8	9

(Take tabular value −10 for rows 0.0 to 0.9)

Table XIV 1.87170 *Page 217*

NATURAL LOGARITHMS—6.00 to 10.09

N	L	0	1	2	3	4	5	6	7	8	9
6.0	1.7	9176	9342	9509	9675	9840	*0006	*0171	*0336	*0500	*0665
6.1	1.8	0829	0993	1156	1319	1482	1645	1808	1970	2132	2294
6.2		2455	2616	2777	2938	3098	3258	3418	3578	3737	3896
6.3		4055	4214	4372	4530	4688	4845	5003	5160	5317	5473
6.4		5630	5786	5942	6097	6253	6408	6563	6718	6872	7026
6.5		7180	7334	7487	7641	7794	7947	8099	8251	8403	8555
6.6		8707	8858	9010	9160	9311	9462	9612	9762	9912	*0061
6.7	1.9	0211	0360	0509	0658	0806	0954	1102	1250	1398	1545
6.8		1692	1839	1986	2132	2279	2425	2571	2716	2862	3007
6.9		3152	3297	3442	3586	3730	3874	4018	4162	4305	4448
7.0		4591	4734	4876	5019	5161	5303	5445	5586	5727	5869
7.1		6009	6150	6291	6431	6571	6711	6851	6991	7130	7269
7.2		7408	7547	7685	7824	7962	8100	8238	8376	8513	8650
7.3		8787	8924	9061	9198	9334	9470	9606	9742	9877	*0013
7.4	2.0	0148	0283	0418	0553	0687	0821	0956	1089	1223	1357
7.5		1490	1624	1757	1890	2022	2155	2287	2419	2551	2683
7.6		2815	2946	3078	3209	3340	3471	3601	3732	3862	3992
7.7		4122	4252	4381	4511	4640	4769	4898	5027	5156	5284
7.8		5412	5540	5668	5796	5924	6051	6179	6306	6433	6560
7.9		6686	6813	6939	7065	7191	7317	7443	7568	7694	7819
8.0		7944	8069	8194	8318	8443	8567	8691	8815	8939	9063
8.1		9186	9310	9433	9556	9679	9802	9924	*0047	*0169	*0291
8.2	2.1	0413	0535	0657	0779	0900	1021	1142	1263	1384	1505
8.3		1626	1746	1866	1986	2106	2226	2346	2465	2585	2704
8.4		2823	2942	3061	3180	3298	3417	3535	3653	3771	3889
8.5		4007	4124	4242	4359	4476	4593	4710	4827	4943	5060
8.6		5176	5292	5409	5524	5640	5756	5871	5987	6102	6217
8.7		6332	6447	6562	6677	6791	6905	7020	7134	7248	7361
8.8		7475	7589	7702	7816	7929	8042	8155	8267	8380	8493
8.9		8605	8717	8830	8942	9054	9165	9277	9389	9500	9611
9.0		9722	9834	9944	*0055	*0166	*0276	*0387	*0497	*0607	*0717
9.1	2.2	0827	0937	1047	1157	1266	1375	1485	1594	1703	1812
9.2		1920	2029	2138	2246	2354	2462	2570	2678	2786	2894
9.3		3001	3109	3216	3324	3431	3538	3645	3751	3858	3965
9.4		4071	4177	4284	4390	4496	4601	4707	4813	4918	5024
9.5		5129	5234	5339	5444	5549	5654	5759	5863	5968	6072
9.6		6176	6280	6384	6488	6592	6696	6799	6903	7006	7109
9.7		7213	7316	7419	7521	7624	7727	7829	7932	8034	8136
9.8		8238	8340	8442	8544	8646	8747	8849	8950	9051	9152
9.9		9253	9354	9455	9556	9657	9757	9858	9958	*0058	*0158
10.0	2.3	0259	0358	0458	0558	0658	0757	0857	0956	1055	1154
N	L	0	1	2	3	4	5	6	7	8	9

NATURAL LOGARITHMS—10 to 99

N	L	0	1	2	3	4	5	6	7	8	9
1	2.30259		39790	48491	56495	63906	70805	77259	83321	89037	94444
2		99573	*04452	*09104	*13549	*17805	*21888	*25810	*29584	*33220	*36730
3	3.40120		43399	46574	49651	52636	55535	58352	61092	63759	66356
4		68888	71357	73767	76120	78419	80666	82864	85015	87120	89182
5		91202	93183	95124	97029	98898	*00733	*02535	*04305	*06044	*07754
6	4.09434		11087	12713	14313	15888	17439	18965	20469	21951	23411
7		24850	26268	27667	29046	30407	31749	33073	34381	35671	36945
8		38203	39445	40672	41884	43082	44265	45435	46591	47734	48864
9		49981	51086	52179	53260	54329	55388	56435	57471	58497	59512

NATURAL LOGARITHMS

100 to 609

N	L	0	1	2	3	4	5	6	7	8	9
10	4.6	0517	1512	2497	3473	4439	5396	6344	7283	8213	9135
11	4.7	0048	0953	1850	2739	3620	4493	5359	6217	7068	7912
12		8749	9579	*0402	*1218	*2028	*2831	*3628	*4419	*5203	*5981
13	4.8	6753	7520	8280	9035	9784	*0527	*1265	*1998	*2725	*3447
14	4.9	4164	4876	5583	6284	6981	7673	8361	9043	9721	*0395
15	5.0	1064	1728	2388	3044	3695	4343	4986	5625	6260	6890
16		7517	8140	8760	9375	9987	*0595	*1199	*1799	*2396	*2990
17	5.1	3580	4166	4749	5329	5906	6479	7048	7615	8178	8739
18		9296	9850	*0401	*0949	*1494	*2036	*2575	*3111	*3644	*4175
19	5.2	4702	5227	5750	6269	6786	7300	7811	8320	8827	9330
20		9832	*0330	*0827	*1321	*1812	*2301	*2788	*3272	*3754	*4233
21	5.3	4711	5186	5659	6129	6598	7064	7528	7990	8450	8907
22		9363	9816	*0268	*0717	*1165	*1610	*2053	*2495	*2935	*3372
23	5.4	3808	4242	4674	5104	5532	5959	6383	6806	7227	7646
24		8064	8480	8894	9306	9717	*0126	*0533	*0939	*1343	*1745
25	5.5	2146	2545	2943	3339	3733	4126	4518	4908	5296	5683
26		6068	6452	6834	7215	7595	7973	8350	8725	9099	9471
27		9842	*0212	*0580	*0947	*1313	*1677	*2040	*2402	*2762	*3121
28	5.6	3479	3835	4191	4545	4897	5249	5599	5948	6296	6643
29		6988	7332	7675	8017	8358	8698	9036	9373	9709	*0044
30	5.7	0378	0711	1043	1373	1703	2031	2359	2685	3010	3334
31		3657	3979	4300	4620	4939	5257	5574	5890	6205	6519
32		6832	7144	7455	7765	8074	8383	8690	8996	9301	9606
33		9909	*0212	*0513	*0814	*1114	*1413	*1711	*2008	*2305	*2600
34	5.8	2895	3188	3481	3773	4064	4354	4644	4932	5220	5507
35		5793	6079	6363	6647	6930	7212	7493	7774	8053	8332
36		8610	8888	9164	9440	9715	9990	*0263	*0536	*0808	*1080
37	5.9	1350	1620	1889	2158	2426	2693	2959	3225	3489	3754
38		4017	4280	4542	4803	5064	5324	5584	5842	6101	6358
39		6615	6871	7126	7381	7635	7889	8141	8394	8645	8896
40		9146	9396	9645	9894	*0141	*0389	*0635	*0881	*1127	*1372
41	6.0	1616	1859	2102	2345	2587	2828	3069	3309	3548	3787
42		4025	4263	4501	4737	4973	5209	5444	5678	5912	6146
43		6379	6611	6843	7074	7304	7535	7764	7993	8222	8450
44		8677	8904	9131	9357	9582	9807	*0032	*0256	*0479	*0702
45	6.1	0925	1147	1368	1589	1810	2030	2249	2468	2687	2905
46		3123	3340	3556	3773	3988	4204	4419	4633	4847	5060
47		5273	5486	5698	5910	6121	6331	6542	6752	6961	7170
48		7379	7587	7794	8002	8208	8415	8621	8826	9032	9236
49		9441	9644	9848	*0051	*0254	*0456	*0658	*0859	*1060	*1261
50	6.2	1461	1661	1860	2059	2258	2456	2654	2851	3048	3245
51		3441	3637	3832	4028	4222	4417	4611	4804	4998	5190
52		5383	5575	5767	5958	6149	6340	6530	6720	6910	7099
53		7288	7476	7664	7852	8040	8227	8413	8600	8786	8972
54		9157	9342	9527	9711	9895	*0079	*0262	*0445	*0628	*0810
55	6.3	0992	1173	1355	1536	1716	1897	2077	2257	2436	2615
56		2794	2972	3150	3328	3505	3683	3859	4036	4212	4388
57		4564	4739	4914	5089	5263	5437	5611	5784	5957	6130
58		6303	6475	6647	6819	6990	7161	7332	7502	7673	7843
59		8012	8182	8351	8519	8688	8856	9024	9192	9359	9526
60		9693	9859	*0026	*0192	*0357	*0523	*0688	*0853	*1017	*1182
N	L	0	1	2	3	4	5	6	7	8	9

Table XIV

Page 219

NATURAL LOGARITHMS

600 to 1109

N	L	0	1	2	3	4		5	6	7	8	9
60	6.3	9693	9859	*0026	*0192	*0357		*0523	*0688	*0853	*1017	*1182
61	6.4	1346	1510	1673	1836	1999		2162	2325	2487	2649	2811
62		2972	3133	3294	3455	3615		3775	3935	4095	4254	4413
63		4572	4731	4889	5047	5205		5362	5520	5677	5834	5990
64		6147	6303	6459	6614	6770		6925	7080	7235	7389	7543
65		7697	7851	8004	8158	8311		8464	8616	8768	8920	9072
66		9224	9375	9527	9677	9828		9979	*0129	*0279	*0429	*0578
67	6.5	0728	0877	1026	1175	1323		1471	1619	1767	1915	2062
68		2209	2356	2503	2649	2796		2942	3088	3233	3379	3524
69		3669	3814	3959	4103	4247		4391	4535	4679	4822	4965
70		5108	5251	5393	5536	5678		5820	5962	6103	6244	6386
71		6526	6667	6808	6948	7088		7228	7368	7508	7647	7786
72		7925	8064	8203	8341	8479		8617	8755	8893	9030	9167
73		9304	9441	9578	9715	9851		9987	*0123	*0259	*0394	*0530
74	6.6	0665	0800	0935	1070	1204		1338	1473	1607	1740	1874
75		2007	2141	2274	2407	2539		2672	2804	2936	3068	3200
76		3332	3463	3595	3726	3857		3988	4118	4249	4379	4509
77		4639	4769	4898	5028	5157		5286	5415	5544	5673	5801
78		5929	6058	6185	6313	6441		6568	6696	6823	6950	7077
79		7203	7330	7456	7582	7708		7834	7960	8085	8211	8336
80		8461	8586	8711	8835	8960		9084	9208	9332	9456	9580
81		9703	9827	9950	*0073	*0196		*0319	*0441	*0564	*0686	*0808
82	6.7	0930	1052	1174	1296	1417		1538	1659	1780	1901	2022
83		2143	2263	2383	2503	2623		2743	2863	2982	3102	3221
84		3340	3459	3578	3697	3815		3934	4052	4170	4288	4406
85		4524	4641	4759	4876	4993		5110	5227	5344	5460	5577
86		5693	5809	5926	6041	6157		6273	6388	6504	6619	6734
87		6849	6964	7079	7194	7308		7422	7537	7651	7765	7878
88		7992	8106	8219	8333	8446		8559	8672	8784	8897	9010
89		9122	9234	9347	9459	9571		9682	9794	9906	*0017	*0128
90	6.8	0239	0351	0461	0572	0683		0793	0904	1014	1124	1235
91		1344	1454	1564	1674	1783		1892	2002	2111	2220	2329
92		2437	2546	2655	2763	2871		2979	3087	3195	3303	3411
93		3518	3626	3733	3841	3948		4055	4162	4268	4375	4482
94		4588	4694	4801	4907	5013		5118	5224	5330	5435	5541
95		5646	5751	5857	5961	6066		6171	6276	6380	6485	6589
96		6693	6797	6901	7005	7109		7213	7316	7420	7523	7626
97		7730	7833	7936	8038	8141		8244	8346	8449	8551	8653
98		8755	8857	8959	9061	9163		9264	9366	9467	9568	9669
99		9770	9871	9972	*0073	*0174		*0274	*0375	*0475	*0575	*0675
100	6.9	0776	0875	0975	1075	1175		1274	1374	1473	1572	1672
101		1771	1870	1968	2067	2166		2264	2363	2461	2560	2658
102		2756	2854	2952	3049	3147		3245	3342	3440	3537	3634
103		3731	3828	3925	4022	4119		4216	4312	4409	4505	4601
104		4698	4794	4890	4986	5081		5177	5273	5368	5464	5559
105		5655	5750	5845	5940	6035		6130	6224	6319	6414	6508
106		6602	6697	6791	6885	6979		7073	7167	7261	7354	7448
107		7541	7635	7728	7821	7915		8008	8101	8193	8286	8379
108		8472	8564	8657	8749	8841		8934	9026	9118	9210	9302
109		9393	9485	9577	9668	9760		9851	9942	*0033	*0125	*0216
110	7.0	0307	0397	0488	0579	0670		0760	0851	0941	1031	1121
N	L	0	1	2	3	4	L	5	6	7	8	9

Table XV

VALUES AND LOGARITHMS OF EXPONENTIAL AND HYPERBOLIC FUNCTIONS

x	e^x		e^{-x}	Sinh x		Cosh x		Tanh x
	Value	Log_{10}	Value	Value	Log_{10}	Value	Log_{10}	Value
0.00	1.0000	.00000	1.00000	0.0000	$-\infty$			.00000
0.01	1.0101	.00434	.99005	0.0100	.00001	1.0000	.00000	.01000
0.02	1.0202	.00869	.98020	0.0200	.30106	1.0001	.00002	.02000
0.03	1.0305	.01303	.97045	0.0300	.47719	1.0002	.00009	.02999
0.04	1.0408	.01737	.96079	0.0400	.60218	1.0005	.00020	.03998
						1.0008	.00035	
0.05	1.0513	.02171	.95123	0.0500	.69915	1.0013	.00054	.04996
0.06	1.0618	.02606	.94176	0.0600	.77841	1.0018	.00078	.05993
0.07	1.0725	.03040	.93239	0.0701	.84545	1.0025	.00106	.06989
0.08	1.0833	.03474	.92312	0.0801	.90355	1.0032	.00139	.07983
0.09	1.0942	.03909	.91393	0.0901	.95483	1.0041	.00176	.08976
0.10	1.1052	.04343	.90484	0.1002	.00072	1.0050	.00217	.09967
0.11	1.1163	.04777	.89583	0.1102	.04227	1.0061	.00262	.10956
0.12	1.1275	.05212	.88692	0.1203	.08022	1.0072	.00312	.11943
0.13	1.1388	.05646	.87809	0.1304	.11517	1.0085	.00366	.12927
0.14	1.1503	.06080	.86936	0.1405	.14755	1.0098	.00424	.13909
0.15	1.1618	.06514	.86071	0.1506	.17772	1.0113	.00487	.14889
0.16	1.1735	.06949	.85214	0.1607	.20597	1.0128	.00554	.15865
0.17	1.1853	.07383	.84366	0.1708	.23254	1.0145	.00625	.16838
0.18	1.1972	.07817	.83527	0.1810	.25762	1.0162	.00700	.17808
0.19	1.2092	.08252	.82696	0.1911	.28136	1.0181	.00779	.18775
0.20	1.2214	.08686	.81873	0.2013	.30392	1.0201	.00863	.19738
0.21	1.2337	.09120	.81058	0.2115	.32541	1.0221	.00951	.20697
0.22	1.2461	.09554	.80252	0.2218	.34592	1.0243	.01043	.21652
0.23	1.2586	.09989	.79453	0.2320	.36555	1.0266	.01139	.22603
0.24	1.2712	.10423	.78663	0.2423	.38437	1.0289	.01239	.23550
0.25	1.2840	.10857	.77880	0.2526	.40245	1.0314	.01343	.24492
0.26	1.2969	.11292	.77105	0.2629	.41986	1.0340	.01452	.25430
0.27	1.3100	.11726	.76338	0.2733	.43663	1.0367	.01564	.26362
0.28	1.3231	.12160	.75578	0.2837	.45282	1.0395	.01681	.27291
0.29	1.3364	.12595	.74826	0.2941	.46847	1.0423	.01801	.28213
0.30	1.3499	.13029	.74082	0.3045	.48362	1.0453	.01926	.29131
0.31	1.3634	.13463	.73345	0.3150	.49830	1.0484	.02054	.30044
0.32	1.3771	.13897	.72615	0.3255	.51254	1.0516	.02187	.30951
0.33	1.3910	.14332	.71892	0.3360	.52637	1.0549	.02323	.31852
0.34	1.4049	.14766	.71177	0.3466	.53981	1.0584	.02463	.32748
0.35	1.4191	.15200	.70469	0.3572	.55290	1.0619	.02607	.33638
0.36	1.4333	.15635	.69768	0.3678	.56564	1.0655	.02755	.34521
0.37	1.4477	.16069	.69073	0.3785	.57807	1.0692	.02907	.35399
0.38	1.4623	.16503	.68386	0.3892	.59019	1.0731	.03063	.36271
0.39	1.4770	.16937	.67706	0.4000	.60202	1.0770	.03222	.37136
0.40	1.4918	.17372	.67032	0.4108	.61358	1.0811	.03385	.37995
0.41	1.5068	.17806	.66365	0.4216	.62488	1.0852	.03552	.38847
0.42	1.5220	.18240	.65705	0.4325	.63594	1.0895	.03723	.39693
0.43	1.5373	.18675	.65051	0.4434	.64677	1.0939	.03897	.40532
0.44	1.5527	.19109	.64404	0.4543	.65738	1.0984	.04075	.41364
0.45	1.5683	.19543	.63763	0.4653	.66777	1.1030	.04256	.42190
0.46	1.5841	.19978	.63128	0.4764	.67797	1.1077	.04441	.43008
0.47	1.6000	.20412	.62500	0.4875	.68797	1.1125	.04630	.43820
0.48	1.6161	.20846	.61878	0.4986	.69779	1.1174	.04822	.44624
0.49	1.6323	.21280	.61263	0.5098	.70744	1.1225	.05018	.45422
0.50	1.6487	.21715	.60653	0.5211	.71692	1.1276	.05217	.46212

Table XV

Page 221

VALUES AND LOGARITHMS OF EXPONENTIAL AND HYPERBOLIC FUNCTIONS

x	e^x Value	e^x Log$_{10}$	e^{-x} Value	Sinh x Value	Sinh x Log$_{10}$	Cosh x Value	Cosh x Log$_{10}$	Tanh x Value
0.50	1.6487	.21715	.60653	0.5211	.71692	1.1276	.05217	.46212
0.51	1.6653	.22149	.60050	0.5324	.72624	1.1329	.05419	.46995
0.52	1.6820	.22583	.59452	0.5438	.73540	1.1383	.05625	.47770
0.53	1.6989	.23018	.58860	0.5552	.74442	1.1438	.05834	.48538
0.54	1.7160	.23452	.58275	0.5666	.75330	1.1494	.06046	.49299
0.55	1.7333	.23886	.57695	0.5782	.76204	1.1551	.06262	.50052
0.56	1.7507	.24320	.57121	0.5897	.77065	1.1609	.06481	.50798
0.57	1.7683	.24755	.56553	0.6014	.77914	1.1669	.06703	.51536
0.58	1.7860	.25189	.55990	0.6131	.78751	1.1730	.06929	.52267
0.59	1.8040	.25623	.55433	0.6248	.79576	1.1792	.07157	.52990
0.60	1.8221	.26058	.54881	0.6367	.80390	1.1855	.07389	.53705
0.61	1.8404	.26492	.54335	0.6485	.81194	1.1919	.07624	.54413
0.62	1.8589	.26926	.53794	0.6605	.81987	1.1984	.07861	.55113
0.63	1.8776	.27361	.53259	0.6725	.82770	1.2051	.08102	.55805
0.64	1.8965	.27795	.52729	0.6846	.83543	1.2119	.08346	.56490
0.65	1.9155	.28229	.52205	0.6967	.84308	1.2188	.08593	.57167
0.66	1.9348	.28664	.51685	0.7090	.85063	1.2258	.08843	.57836
0.67	1.9542	.29098	.51171	0.7213	.85809	1.2330	.09095	.58498
0.68	1.9739	.29532	.50662	0.7336	.86548	1.2402	.09351	.59152
0.69	1.9937	.29966	.50158	0.7461	.87278	1.2476	.09609	.59798
0.70	2.0138	.30401	.49659	0.7586	.88000	1.2552	.09870	.60437
0.71	2.0340	.30835	.49164	0.7712	.88715	1.2628	.10134	.61068
0.72	2.0544	.31269	.48675	0.7838	.89423	1.2706	.10401	.61691
0.73	2.0751	.31703	.48191	0.7966	.90123	1.2785	.10670	.62307
0.74	2.0959	.32138	.47711	0.8094	.90817	1.2865	.10942	.62915
0.75	2.1170	.32572	.47237	0.8223	.91504	1.2947	.11216	.63515
0.76	2.1383	.33006	.46767	0.8353	.92185	1.3030	.11493	.64108
0.77	2.1598	.33441	.46301	0.8484	.92859	1.3114	.11773	.64693
0.78	2.1815	.33875	.45841	0.8615	.93527	1.3199	.12055	.65271
0.79	2.2034	.34309	.45384	0.8748	.94190	1.3286	.12340	.65841
0.80	2.2255	.34744	.44933	0.8881	.94846	1.3374	.12627	.66404
0.81	2.2479	.35178	.44486	0.9015	.95498	1.3464	.12917	.66959
0.82	2.2705	.35612	.44043	0.9150	.96144	1.3555	.13209	.67507
0.83	2.2933	.36046	.43605	0.9286	.96784	1.3647	.13503	.68048
0.84	2.3164	.36481	.43171	0.9423	.97420	1.3740	.13800	.68581
0.85	2.3396	.36915	.42741	0.9561	.98051	1.3835	.14099	.69107
0.86	2.3632	.37349	.42316	0.9700	.98677	1.3932	.14400	.69626
0.87	2.3869	.37784	.41895	0.9840	.99299	1.4029	.14704	.70137
0.88	2.4109	.38218	.41478	0.9981	.99916	1.4128	.15009	.70642
0.89	2.4351	.38652	.41066	1.0122	.00528	1.4229	.15317	.71139
0.90	2.4596	.39087	.40657	1.0265	.01137	1.4331	.15627	.71630
0.91	2.4843	.39521	.40252	1.0409	.01741	1.4434	.15939	.72113
0.92	2.5093	.39955	.39852	1.0554	.02341	1.4539	.16254	.72590
0.93	2.5345	.40389	.39455	1.0700	.02937	1.4645	.16570	.73059
0.94	2.5600	.40824	.39063	1.0847	.03530	1.4753	.16888	.73522
0.95	2.5857	.41258	.38674	1.0995	.04119	1.4862	.17208	.73978
0.96	2.6117	.41692	.38289	1.1144	.04704	1.4973	.17531	.74428
0.97	2.6379	.42127	.37908	1.1294	.05286	1.5085	.17855	.74870
0.98	2.6645	.42561	.37531	1.1446	.05864	1.5199	.18181	.75307
0.99	2.6912	.42995	.37158	1.1598	.06439	1.5314	.18509	.75736
1.00	2.7183	.43429	.36788	1.1752	.07011	1.5431	.18839	.76159

VALUES AND LOGARITHMS OF EXPONENTIAL
AND HYPERBOLIC FUNCTIONS

x	e^x		e^{-x}	Sinh x		Cosh x		Tanh x
	Value	Log_{10}	Value	Value	Log_{10}	Value	Log_{10}	Value
1.00	2.7183	.43429	.36788	1.1752	.07011	1.5431	.18839	.76159
1.01	2.7456	.43864	.36422	1.1907	.07580	1.5549	.19171	.76576
1.02	2.7732	.44298	.36060	1.2063	.08146	1.5669	.19504	.76987
1.03	2.8011	.44732	.35701	1.2220	.08708	1.5790	.19839	.77391
1.04	2.8292	.45167	.35345	1.2379	.09268	1.5913	.20176	.77789
1.05	2.8577	.45601	.34994	1.2539	.09825	1.6038	.20515	.78181
1.06	2.8864	.46035	.34646	1.2700	.10379	1.6164	.20855	.78566
1.07	2.9154	.46470	.34301	1.2862	.10930	1.6292	.21197	.78946
1.08	2.9447	.46904	.33960	1.3025	.11479	1.6421	.21541	.79320
1.09	2.9743	.47338	.33622	1.3190	.12025	1.6552	.21886	.79688
1.10	3.0042	.47772	.33287	1.3356	.12569	1.6685	.22233	.80050
1.11	3.0344	.48207	.32956	1.3524	.13111	1.6820	.22582	.80406
1.12	3.0649	.48641	.32628	1.3693	.13649	1.6956	.22931	.80757
1.13	3.0957	.49075	.32303	1.3863	.14186	1.7093	.23283	.81102
1.14	3.1268	.49510	.31982	1.4035	.14720	1.7233	.23636	.81441
1.15	3.1582	.49944	.31664	1.4208	.15253	1.7374	.23990	.81775
1.16	3.1899	.50378	.31349	1.4382	.15783	1.7517	.24346	.82104
1.17	3.2220	.50812	.31037	1.4558	.16311	1.7662	.24703	.82427
1.18	3.2544	.51247	.30728	1.4735	.16836	1.7808	.25062	.82745
1.19	3.2871	.51681	.30422	1.4914	.17360	1.7957	.25422	.83058
1.20	3.3201	.52115	.30119	1.5095	.17882	1.8107	.25784	.83365
1.21	3.3535	.52550	.29820	1.5276	.18402	1.8258	.26146	.83668
1.22	3.3872	.52984	.29523	1.5460	.18920	1.8412	.26510	.83965
1.23	3.4212	.53418	.29229	1.5645	.19437	1.8568	.26876	.84258
1.24	3.4556	.53853	.28938	1.5831	.19951	1.8725	.27242	.84546
1.25	3.4903	.54287	.28650	1.6019	.20464	1.8884	.27610	.84828
1.26	3.5254	.54721	.28365	1.6209	.20975	1.9045	.27979	.85106
1.27	3.5609	.55155	.28083	1.6400	.21485	1.9208	.28349	.85380
1.28	3.5966	.55590	.27804	1.6593	.21993	1.9373	.28721	.85648
1.29	3.6328	.56024	.27527	1.6788	.22499	1.9540	.29093	.85913
1.30	3.6693	.56458	.27253	1.6984	.23004	1.9709	.29467	.86172
1.31	3.7062	.56893	.26982	1.7182	.23507	1.9880	.29842	.86428
1.32	3.7434	.57327	.26714	1.7381	.24009	2.0053	.30217	.86678
1.33	3.7810	.57761	.26448	1.7583	.24509	2.0228	.30594	.86925
1.34	3.8190	.58195	.26185	1.7786	.25008	2.0404	.30972	.87167
1.35	3.8574	.58630	.25924	1.7991	.25505	2.0583	.31352	.87405
1.36	3.8962	.59064	.25666	1.8198	.26002	2.0764	.31732	.87639
1.37	3.9354	.59498	.25411	1.8406	.26496	2.0947	.32113	.87869
1.38	3.9749	.59933	.25158	1.8617	.26990	2.1132	.32495	.88095
1.39	4.0149	.60367	.24908	1.8829	.27482	2.1320	.32878	.88317
1.40	4.0552	.60801	.24660	1.9043	.27974	2.1509	.33262	.88535
1.41	4.0960	.61236	.24414	1.9259	.28464	2.1700	.33647	.88749
1.42	4.1371	.61670	.24171	1.9477	.28952	2.1894	.34033	.88960
1.43	4.1787	.62104	.23931	1.9697	.29440	2.2090	.34420	.89167
1.44	4.2207	.62538	.23693	1.9919	.29926	2.2288	.34807	.89370
1.45	4.2631	.62973	.23457	2.0143	.30412	2.2488	.35196	.89569
1.46	4.3060	.63407	.23224	2.0369	.30896	2.2691	.35585	.89765
1.47	4.3492	.63841	.22993	2.0597	.31379	2.2896	.35976	.89958
1.48	4.3929	.64276	.22764	2.0827	.31862	2.3103	.36367	.90147
1.49	4.4371	.64710	.22537	2.1059	.32343	2.3312	.36759	.90332
1.50	4.4817	.65144	.22313	2.1293	.32823	2.3524	.37151	.90515

Table XV   *Page 223*

VALUES AND LOGARITHMS OF EXPONENTIAL AND HYPERBOLIC FUNCTIONS

x	e^x		e^{-x}	Sinh x		Cosh x		Tanh x
	Value	Log_{10}	Value	Value	Log_{10}	Value	Log_{10}	Value
1.50	4.4817	.65144	.22313	2.1293	.32823	2.3524	.37151	.90515
1.51	4.5267	.65578	.22091	2.1529	.33303	2.3738	.37545	.90694
1.52	4.5722	.66013	.21871	2.1768	.33781	2.3955	.37939	.90870
1.53	4.6182	.66447	.21654	2.2008	.34258	2.4174	.38334	.91042
1.54	4.6646	.66881	.21438	2.2251	.34735	2.4395	.38730	.91212
1.55	4.7115	.67316	.21225	2.2496	.35211	2.4619	.39126	.91379
1.56	4.7588	.67750	.21014	2.2743	.35686	2.4845	.39524	.91542
1.57	4.8066	.68184	.20805	2.2993	.36160	2.5073	.39921	.91703
1.58	4.8550	.68619	.20598	2.3245	.36633	2.5305	.40320	.91860
1.59	4.9037	.69053	.20393	2.3499	.37105	2.5538	.40719	.92015
1.60	4.9530	.69487	.20190	2.3756	.37577	2.5775	.41119	.92167
1.61	5.0028	.69921	.19989	2.4015	.38048	2.6013	.41520	.92316
1.62	5.0531	.70356	.19790	2.4276	.38518	2.6255	.41921	.92462
1.63	5.1039	.70790	.19593	2.4540	.38987	2.6499	.42323	.92606
1.64	5.1552	.71224	.19398	2.4806	.39456	2.6746	.42725	.92747
1.65	5.2070	.71659	.19205	2.5075	.39923	2.6995	.43129	.92886
1.66	5.2593	.72093	.19014	2.5346	.40391	2.7247	.43532	.93022
1.67	5.3122	.72527	.18825	2.5620	.40857	2.7502	.43937	.93155
1.68	5.3656	.72961	.18637	2.5896	.41323	2.7760	.44341	.93286
1.69	5.4195	.73396	.18452	2.6175	.41788	2.8020	.44747	.93415
1.70	5.4739	.73830	.18268	2.6456	.42253	2.8283	.45153	.93541
1.71	5.5290	.74264	.18087	2.6740	.42717	2.8549	.45559	.93665
1.72	5.5845	.74699	.17907	2.7027	.43180	2.8818	.45966	.93786
1.73	5.6407	.75133	.17728	2.7317	.43643	2.9090	.46374	.93906
1.74	5.6973	.75567	.17552	2.7609	.44105	2.9364	.46782	.94023
1.75	5.7546	.76002	.17377	2.7904	.44567	2.9642	.47191	.94138
1.76	5.8124	.76436	.17204	2.8202	.45028	2.9922	.47600	.94250
1.77	5.8709	.76870	.17033	2.8503	.45488	3.0206	.48009	.94361
1.78	5.9299	.77304	.16864	2.8806	.45948	3.0492	.48419	.94470
1.79	5.9895	.77739	.16696	2.9112	.46408	3.0782	.48830	.94576
1.80	6.0496	.78173	.16530	2.9422	.46867	3.1075	.49241	.94681
1.81	6.1104	.78607	.16365	2.9734	.47325	3.1371	.49652	.94783
1.82	6.1719	.79042	.16203	3.0049	.47783	3.1669	.50064	.94884
1.83	6.2339	.79476	.16041	3.0367	.48241	3.1972	.50476	.94983
1.84	6.2965	.79910	.15882	3.0689	.48698	3.2277	.50889	.95080
1.85	6.3598	.80344	.15724	3.1013	.49154	3.2585	.51302	.95175
1.86	6.4237	.80779	.15567	3.1340	.49610	3.2897	.51716	.95268
1.87	6.4883	.81213	.15412	3.1671	.50066	3.3212	.52130	.95359
1.88	6.5535	.81647	.15259	3.2005	.50521	3.3530	.52544	.95449
1.89	6.6194	.82082	.15107	3.2341	.50976	3.3852	.52959	.95537
1.90	6.6859	.82516	.14957	3.2682	.51430	3.4177	.53374	.95624
1.91	6.7531	.82950	.14808	3.3025	.51884	3.4506	.53789	.95709
1.92	6.8210	.83385	.14661	3.3372	.52338	3.4838	.54205	.95792
1.93	6.8895	.83819	.14515	3.3722	.52791	3.5173	.54621	.95873
1.94	6.9588	.84253	.14370	3.4075	.53244	3.5512	.55038	.95953
1.95	7.0287	.84687	.14227	3.4432	.53696	3.5855	.55455	.96032
1.96	7.0993	.85122	.14086	3.4792	.54148	3.6201	.55872	.96109
1.97	7.1707	.85556	.13946	3.5156	.54600	3.6551	.56290	.96185
1.98	7.2427	.85990	.13807	3.5523	.55051	3.6904	.56707	.96259
1.99	7.3155	.86425	.13670	3.5894	.55502	3.7261	.57126	.96331
2.00	7.3891	.86859	.13534	3.6269	.55953	3.7622	.57544	.96403

VALUES AND LOGARITHMS OF EXPONENTIAL
AND HYPERBOLIC FUNCTIONS

x	e^x Value	e^x Log$_{10}$	e^{-x} Value	Sinh x Value	Sinh x Log$_{10}$	Cosh x Value	Cosh x Log$_{10}$	Tanh x Value
2.00	7.3891	.86859	.13534	3.6269	.55953	3.7622	.57544	.96403
2.01	7.4633	.87293	.13399	3.6647	.56403	3.7987	.57963	.96473
2.02	7.5383	.87727	.13266	3.7028	.56853	3.8355	.58382	.96541
2.03	7.6141	.88162	.13134	3.7414	.57303	3.8727	.58802	.96609
2.04	7.6906	.88596	.13003	3.7803	.57753	3.9103	.59221	.96675
2.05	7.7679	.89030	.12873	3.8196	.58202	3.9483	.59641	.96740
2.06	7.8460	.89465	.12745	3.8593	.58650	3.9867	.60061	.96803
2.07	7.9248	.89899	.12619	3.8993	.59099	4.0255	.60482	.96865
2.08	8.0045	.90333	.12493	3.9398	.59547	4.0647	.60903	.96926
2.09	8.0849	.90768	.12369	3.9806	.59995	4.1043	.61324	.96986
2.10	8.1662	.91202	.12246	4.0219	.60443	4.1443	.61745	.97045
2.11	8.2482	.91636	.12124	4.0635	.60890	4.1847	.62167	.97103
2.12	8.3311	.92070	.12003	4.1056	.61337	4.2256	.62589	.97159
2.13	8.4149	.92505	.11884	4.1480	.61784	4.2669	.63011	.97215
2.14	8.4994	.92939	.11765	4.1909	.62231	4.3085	.63433	.97269
2.15	8.5849	.93373	.11648	4.2342	.62677	4.3507	.63856	.97323
2.16	8.6711	.93808	.11533	4.2779	.63123	4.3932	.64278	.97375
2.17	8.7583	.94242	.11418	4.3221	.63569	4.4362	.64701	.97426
2.18	8.8463	.94676	.11304	4.3666	.64015	4.4797	.65125	.97477
2.19	8.9352	.95110	.11192	4.4116	.64460	4.5236	.65548	.97526
2.20	9.0250	.95545	.11080	4.4571	.64905	4.5679	.65972	.97574
2.21	9.1157	.95979	.10970	4.5030	.65350	4.6127	.66396	.97622
2.22	9.2073	.96413	.10861	4.5494	.65795	4.6580	.66820	.97668
2.23	9.2999	.96848	.10753	4.5962	.66240	4.7037	.67244	.97714
2.24	9.3933	.97282	.10646	4.6434	.66684	4.7499	.67668	.97759
2.25	9.4877	.97716	.10540	4.6912	.67128	4.7966	.68093	.97803
2.26	9.5831	.98151	.10435	4.7394	.67572	4.8437	.68518	.97846
2.27	9.6794	.98585	.10331	4.7880	.68016	4.8914	.68943	.97888
2.28	9.7767	.99019	.10228	4.8372	.68459	4.9395	.69368	.97929
2.29	9.8749	.99453	.10127	4.8668	.68903	4.9881	.69794	.97970
2.30	9.9742	.99888	.10026	4.9370	.69346	5.0372	.70219	.98010
2.31	10.074	1.00322	.09926	4.9876	.69789	5.0868	.70645	.98049
2.32	10.176	1.00756	.09827	5.0387	.70232	5.1370	.71071	.98087
2.33	10.278	1.01191	.09730	5.0903	.70675	5.1876	.71497	.98124
2.34	10.381	1.01625	.09633	5.1425	.71117	5.2388	.71923	.98161
2.35	10.486	1.02059	.09537	5.1951	.71559	5.2905	.72349	.98197
2.36	10.591	1.02493	.09442	5.2483	.72002	5.3427	.72776	.98233
2.37	10.697	1.02928	.09348	5.3020	.72444	5.3954	.73203	.98267
2.38	10.805	1.03362	.09255	5.3562	.72885	5.4487	.73630	.98301
2.39	10.913	1.03796	.09163	5.4109	.73327	5.5026	.74056	.98335
2.40	11.023	1.04231	.09072	5.4662	.73769	5.5569	.74484	.98367
2.41	11.134	1.04665	.08982	5.5221	.74210	5.6119	.74911	.98400
2.42	11.246	1.05099	.08892	5.5785	.74652	5.6674	.75338	.98431
2.43	11.359	1.05534	.08804	5.6354	.75093	5.7235	.75766	.98462
2.44	11.473	1.05968	.08716	5.6929	.75534	5.7801	.76194	.98492
2.45	11.588	1.06402	.08629	5.7510	.75975	5.8373	.76621	.98522
2.46	11.705	1.06836	.08543	5.8097	.76415	5.8951	.77049	.98551
2.47	11.822	1.07271	.08458	5.8689	.76856	5.9535	.77477	.98579
2.48	11.941	1.07705	.08374	5.9288	.77296	6.0125	.77906	.98607
2.49	12.061	1.08139	.08291	5.9892	.77737	6.0721	.78334	.98635
2.50	12.182	1.08574	.08208	6.0502	.78177	6.1323	.78762	.98661

Table XV

Page 225

VALUES AND LOGARITHMS OF EXPONENTIAL
AND HYPERBOLIC FUNCTIONS

x	e^x Value	e^x Log_{10}	e^{-x} Value	Sinh x Value	Sinh x Log_{10}	Cosh x Value	Cosh x Log_{10}	Tanh x Value
2.50	12.182	1.08574	.08208	6.0502	.78177	6.1323	.78762	.98661
2.51	12.305	1.09008	.08127	6.1118	.78617	6.1931	.79191	.98688
2.52	12.429	1.09442	.08046	6.1741	.79057	6.2545	.79619	.98714
2.53	12.554	1.09877	.07966	6.2369	.79497	6.3166	.80048	.98739
2.54	12.680	1.10311	.07887	6.3004	.79937	6.3793	.80477	.98764
2.55	12.807	1.10745	.07808	6.3645	.80377	6.4426	.80906	.98788
2.56	12.936	1.11179	.07730	6.4293	.80816	6.5066	.81335	.98812
2.57	13.066	1.11614	.07654	6.4946	.81256	6.5712	.81764	.98835
2.58	13.197	1.12048	.07577	6.5607	.81695	6.6365	.82194	.98858
2.59	13.330	1.12482	.07502	6.6274	.82134	6.7024	.82623	.98881
2.60	13.464	1.12917	.07427	6.6947	.82573	6.7690	.83052	.98903
2.61	13.599	1.13351	.07353	6.7628	.83012	6.8363	.83482	.98924
2.62	13.736	1.13785	.07280	6.8315	.83451	6.9043	.83912	.98946
2.63	13.874	1.14219	.07208	6.9008	.83890	6.9729	.84341	.98966
2.64	14.013	1.14654	.07136	6.9709	.84329	7.0423	.84771	.98987
2.65	14.154	1.15088	.07065	7.0417	.84768	7.1123	.85201	.99007
2.66	14.296	1.15522	.06995	7.1132	.85206	7.1831	.85631	.99026
2.67	14.440	1.15957	.06925	7.1854	.85645	7.2546	.86061	.99045
2.68	14.585	1.16391	.06856	7.2583	.86083	7.3268	.86492	.99064
2.69	14.732	1.16825	.06788	7.3319	.86522	7.3998	.86922	.99083
2.70	14.880	1.17260	.96721	7.4063	.86960	7.4735	.87352	.99101
2.71	15.029	1.17694	.06654	7.4814	.87398	7.5479	.87783	.99118
2.72	15.180	1.18128	.06587	7.5572	.87836	7.6231	.88213	.99136
2.73	15.333	1.18562	.06522	7.6338	.88274	7.6991	.88644	.99153
2.74	15.487	1.18997	.06457	7.7112	.88712	7.7758	.89074	.99170
2.75	15.643	1.19431	.06393	7.7894	.89150	7.8533	.89505	.99186
2.76	15.800	1.19865	.06329	7.8683	.89588	7.9316	.89936	.99202
2.77	15.959	1.20300	.06266	7.9480	.90026	8.0106	.90367	.99218
2.78	16.119	1.20734	.06204	8.0285	.90463	8.0905	.90798	.99233
2.79	16.281	1.21168	.06142	8.1098	.90901	8.1712	.91229	.99248
2.80	16.445	1.21602	.06081	8.1919	.91339	8.2527	.91660	.99263
2.81	16.610	1.22037	.06020	8.2749	.91776	8.3351	.92091	.99278
2.82	16.777	1.22471	.05961	8.3586	.92213	8.4182	.92522	.99292
2.83	16.945	1.22905	.05901	8.4432	.92651	8.5022	.92953	.99306
2.84	17.116	1.23340	.05843	8.5287	.93088	8.5871	.93385	.99320
2.85	17.288	1.23774	.05784	8.6150	.93525	8.6728	.93816	.99333
2.86	17.462	1.24208	.05727	8.7021	.93963	8.7594	.94247	.99346
2.87	17.637	1.24643	.05670	8.7902	.94400	8.8469	.94679	.99359
2.88	17.814	1.25077	.05613	8.8791	.94837	8.9352	.95110	.99372
2.89	17.993	1.25511	.05558	8.9689	.95274	9.0244	.95542	.99384
2.90	18.174	1.25945	.05502	9.0596	.95711	9.1146	.95974	.99396
2.91	18.357	1.26380	.05448	9.1512	.96148	9.2056	.96405	.99408
2.92	18.541	1.26814	.05393	9.2437	.96584	9.2976	.96837	.99420
2.93	18.728	1.27248	.05340	9.3371	.97021	9.3905	.97269	.99431
2.94	18.916	1.27683	.05287	9.4315	.97458	9.4844	.97701	.99443
2.95	19.106	1.28117	.05234	9.5268	.97895	9.5791	.98133	.99454
2.96	19.298	1.28551	.05182	9.6231	.98331	9.6749	.98565	.99464
2.97	19.492	1.28985	.05130	9.7203	.98768	9.7716	.98997	.99475
2.98	19.688	1.29420	.05079	9.8185	.99205	9.8693	.99429	.99485
2.99	19.886	1.29854	.05029	9.9177	.99641	9.9680	.99861	.99496
3.00	20.086	1.30288	.04979	10.018	1.00078	10.068	1.00293	.99505

VALUES AND LOGARITHMS OF EXPONENTIAL
AND HYPERBOLIC FUNCTIONS

x	e^x		e^{-x}	Sinh x		Cosh x		Tanh x
	Value	Log^{10}	Value	Value	Log$_{10}$	Value	Log$_{10}$	Value
3.00	20.086	1.30288	.04979	10.018	1.00078	10.068	1.00293	.99505
3.05	21.115	1.32460	.04736	10.534	1.02259	10.581	1.02454	.99552
3.10	22.198	1.34631	.04505	11.076	1.04440	11.122	1.04616	.99595
3.15	23.336	1.36803	.04285	11.647	1.06620	11.690	1.06779	.99633
3.20	24.533	1.38974	.04076	12.246	1.08799	12.287	1.08943	.99668
3.25	25.790	1.41146	.03877	12.876	1.10977	12.915	1.11108	.99700
3.30	27.113	1.43317	.03688	13.538	1.13155	13.575	1.13273	.99728
3.35	28.503	1.45489	.03508	14.234	1.15332	14.269	1.15439	.99754
3.40	29.964	1.47660	.03337	14.965	1.17509	14.999	1.17605	.99777
3.45	31.500	1.49832	.03175	15.734	1.19685	15.766	1.19772	.99799
3.50	33.115	1.52003	.03020	16.543	1.21860	16.573	1.21940	.99818
3.55	34.813	1.54175	.02872	17.392	1.24036	17.421	1.24107	.99835
3.60	36.598	1.56346	.02732	18.286	1.26211	18.313	1.26275	.99851
3.65	38.475	1.58517	.02599	19.224	1.28385	19.250	1.28444	.99865
3.70	40.447	1.60689	.02472	20.211	1.30559	20.236	1.30612	.99878
3.75	42.521	1.62860	.02352	21.249	1.32733	21.272	1.32781	.99889
3.80	44.701	1.65032	.02237	22.339	1.34907	22.362	1.34951	.99900
3.85	46.993	1.67203	.02128	23.486	1.37081	23.507	1.37120	.99909
3.90	49.402	1.69375	.02024	24.691	1.39254	24.711	1.39290	.99918
3.95	51.935	1.71546	.01925	25.958	1.41427	25.977	1.41459	.99926
4.00	54.598	1.73718	.01832	27.290	1.43600	27.308	1.43629	.99933
4.10	60.340	1.78061	.01657	30.162	1.47946	30.178	1.47970	.99945
4.20	66.686	1.82404	.01500	33.336	1.52291	33.351	1.52310	.99955
4.30	73.700	1.86747	.01357	36.843	1.56636	36.857	1.56652	.99963
4.40	81.451	1.91090	.01227	40.719	1.60980	40.732	1.60993	.99970
4.50	90.017	1.95433	.01111	45.003	1.65324	45.014	1.65335	.99975
4.60	99.484	1.99775	.01005	49.737	1.69668	49.747	1.69677	.99980
4.70	109.95	2.04118	.00910	54.969	1.74012	54.978	1.74019	.99983
4.80	121.51	2.08461	.00823	60.751	1.78355	60.759	1.78361	.99986
4.90	134.29	2.12804	.00745	67.141	1.82699	67.149	1.82704	.99989
5.00	148.41	2.17147	.00674	74.203	1.87042	74.210	1.87046	.99991
5.10	164.02	2.21490	.00610	82.008	1.91389	82.014	1.91389	.99993
5.20	181.27	2.25833	.00552	90.633	1.95729	90.639	1.95731	.99994
5.30	200.34	2.30176	.00499	100.17	2.00074	100.17	2.00074	.99995
5.40	221.41	2.34519	.00452	110.70	2.04415	110.71	2.04417	.99996
5.50	244.69	2.38862	.00409	122.34	2.08758	122.35	2.08760	.99997
5.60	270.43	2.43205	.00370	135.21	2.13101	135.22	2.13103	.99997
5.70	298.87	2.47548	.00335	149.43	2.17444	149.44	2.17445	.99998
5.80	330.30	2.51891	.00303	165.15	2.21787	165.15	2.21788	.99998
5.90	365.04	2.56234	.00274	182.52	2.26130	182.52	2.26131	.99998
6.00	403.43	2.60577	.00248	201.71	2.30473	201.72	2.30474	.99999
6.25	518.01	2.71434	.00193	259.01	2.41331	259.01	2.41331	.99999
6.50	665.14	2.82291	.00150	332.57	2.52188	332.57	2.52189	1.0000
6.75	854.06	2.93149	.00117	427.03	2.63046	427.03	2.63046	1.0000
7.00	1096.6	3.04006	.00091	548.32	2.73903	548.32	2.73903	1.0000
7.50	1808.0	3.25721	.00055	904.02	2.95618	904.02	2.95618	1.0000
8.00	2981.0	3.47436	.00034	1490.5	3.17333	1490.5	3.17333	1.0000
8.50	4914.8	3.69150	.00020	2457.4	3.39047	2457.4	3.39047	1.0000
9.00	8103.1	3.90865	.00012	4051.5	3.60762	4051.5	3.60762	1.0000
9.50	13360.	4.12580	.00007	6679.9	3.82477	6679.9	3.82477	1.0000
10.00	22026.	4.34294	.00005	11013.	4.04191	11013.	4.04191	1.0000

Table XVI

MULTIPLES OF M AND OF 1/M

N	N·M	N	N·M
0	0.00000 000	50	21.71472 410
1	0.43429 448	51	22.14901 858
2	0.86858 896	52	22.58331 306
3	1.30288 345	53	23.01760 754
4	1.73717 793	54	23.45190 202
5	2.17147 241	55	23.88619 650
6	2.60576 689	56	24.32049 099
7	3.04006 137	57	24.75478 547
8	3.47435 586	58	25.18907 995
9	3.90865 034	59	25.62337 443
10	4.34294 482	60	26.05766 891
11	4.77723 930	61	26.49196 340
12	5.21153 378	62	26.92625 788
13	5.64582 826	63	27.36055 236
14	6.08012 275	64	27.79484 684
15	6.51441 723	65	28.22914 132
16	6.94871 171	66	28.66343 581
17	7.38300 619	67	29.09773 029
18	7.81730 067	68	29.53202 477
19	8.25159 516	69	29.96631 925
20	8.68588 964	70	30.40061 373
21	9.12018 412	71	30.83490 822
22	9.55447 860	72	31.26920 270
23	9.98877 308	73	31.70349 718
24	10.42306 757	74	32.13779 166
25	10.85736 205	75	32.57208 614
26	11.29165 653	76	33.00638 062
27	11.72595 101	77	33.44067 511
28	12.16024 549	78	33.87496 959
29	12.59453 998	79	34.30926 407
30	13.02883 446	80	34.74355 855
31	13.46312 894	81	35.17785 303
32	13.89742 342	82	35.61214 752
33	14.33171 790	83	36.04644 200
34	14.76601 238	84	36.48073 648
35	15.20030 687	85	36.91503 096
36	15.63460 135	86	37.34932 544
37	16.06889 583	87	37.78361 993
38	16.50319 031	88	38.21791 441
39	16.93748 479	89	38.65220 889
40	17.37177 928	90	39.08650 337
41	17.80607 376	91	39.52079 785
42	18.24036 824	92	39.95509 234
43	18.67466 272	93	40.38938 682
44	19.10895 720	94	40.82368 130
45	19.54325 169	95	41.25797 578
46	19.97754 617	96	41.69227 026
47	20.41184 065	97	42.12656 474
48	20.84613 513	98	42.56085 923
49	21.28042 961	99	42.99515 371
50	21.71472 410	100	43.42944 819

N	N÷M	N	N÷M
0	0.00000 000	50	115.12925 465
1	2.30258 509	51	117.43183 974
2	4.60517 019	52	119.73442 484
3	6.90775 528	53	122.03700 993
4	9.21034 037	54	124.33959 502
5	11.51292 546	55	126.64218 011
6	13.81551 056	56	128.94476 521
7	16.11809 565	57	131.24735 030
8	18.42068 074	58	133.54993 539
9	20.72326 584	59	135.85252 049
10	23.02585 093	60	138.15510 558
11	25.32843 602	61	140.45769 067
12	27.63102 112	62	142.76027 577
13	29.93360 621	63	145.06286 086
14	32.23619 130	64	147.36544 595
15	34.53877 639	65	149.66803 104
16	36.84136 149	66	151.97061 614
17	39.14394 658	67	154.27320 123
18	41.44653 167	68	156.57578 632
19	43.74911 677	69	158.87837 142
20	46.05170 186	70	161.18095 651
21	48.35428 695	71	163.48354 160
22	50.65687 205	72	165.78612 670
23	52.95945 714	73	168.08871 179
24	55.26204 223	74	170.39129 688
25	57.56462 732	75	172.69388 197
26	59.86721 242	76	174.99646 707
27	62.16979 751	77	177.29905 216
28	64.47238 260	78	179.60163 725
29	66.77496 770	79	181.90422 235
30	69.07755 279	80	184.20680 744
31	71.38013 788	81	186.50939 253
32	73.68272 298	82	188.81197 763
33	75.98530 807	83	191.11456 272
34	78.28789 316	84	193.41714 781
35	80.59047 825	85	195.71973 290
36	82.89306 335	86	198.02231 800
37	85.19564 844	87	200.32490 309
38	87.49823 353	88	202.62748 818
39	89.80081 863	89	204.93007 328
40	92.10340 372	90	207.23265 837
41	94.40598 881	91	209.53524 346
42	96.70857 391	92	211.83782 856
43	99.01115 900	93	214.14041 365
44	101.31374 409	94	216.44299 874
45	103.61632 918	95	218.74558 383
46	105.91891 428	96	221.04816 893
47	108.22149 937	97	223.35075 402
48	110.52408 446	98	225.65333 911
49	112.82666 956	99	227.95592 421
50	115.12925 465	100	230.25850 930

$$M = \log_{10}e = .43429\ 44819\ 03251\ 82765$$

$$\frac{1}{M} = \log_e10 = 2.30258\ 50929\ 94045\ 68402$$

$$\log_{10}n = \log_e n \cdot \log_{10}e = M \log_e n$$

$$\log_e n = \log_{10}n \cdot \log_e10 = \frac{1}{M}\log_{10}n.$$

$$\log_{10}e^x = x \cdot \log_{10}e = x \cdot M.$$

$$\log_e(10^n \cdot x) = \log_e x + n\frac{1}{M}\ .$$

Table XVII

LOGARITHMS OF PRIMES—2 to 997

N	Log N			N	Log N			N	Log N		
2	0.301	029	9957	269	2.429	752	2800	617	2.790	285	1640
3	.477	121	2547	271	.432	969	2909	619	.791	690	6490
5	.698	970	0043	277	.442	479	7691	631	.800	029	3592
7	.845	098	0400	281	.448	706	3199	641	.806	858	0295
11	1.041	392	6852	283	.451	786	4355	643	.808	210	9729
13	1.113	943	3523	293	2.466	867	6204	647	2.810	904	2807
17	.230	448	9214	307	.487	138	3755	653	.814	913	1813
19	.278	753	6010	311	.492	760	3890	659	.818	885	4146
23	.361	727	8360	313	.495	544	3375	661	.820	201	4595
29	.462	397	9979	317	.501	059	2622	673	.828	015	0642
31	1.491	361	6938	331	2.519	827	9938	677	2.830	588	6687
37	.568	201	7241	337	.527	629	9009	683	.834	420	7037
41	.612	783	8567	347	.540	329	4748	691	.839	478	0474
43	.633	468	4556	349	.542	825	4270	701	.845	718	0180
47	.672	097	8579	353	.547	774	7054	709	.850	646	2352
53	1.724	275	8696	359	2.555	094	4486	719	2.856	728	8904
59	.770	852	0116	367	.564	666	0643	727	.861	534	4109
61	.785	329	8350	373	.571	708	8318	733	.865	103	9746
67	.826	074	8027	379	.578	639	2100	739	.868	644	4384
71	.851	258	3487	383	.583	198	7740	743	.870	988	8138
73	1.863	322	8601	389	2.589	949	6013	751	2.875	639	9370
79	.897	627	0913	397	.598	790	5068	757	.879	095	8795
83	.919	078	0924	401	.603	144	3726	761	.881	384	6568
89	.949	390	0066	409	.611	723	3080	769	.885	926	3398
97	.986	771	7343	419	.622	214	0230	773	.888	179	4939
101	2.004	321	3738	421	2.624	282	0958	787	2.895	974	7324
103	.012	837	2247	431	.634	477	2702	797	.901	458	3214
107	.029	383	7777	433	.636	487	8964	809	.907	948	5216
109	.037	426	4979	439	.642	464	5202	811	.909	020	8542
113	.053	078	4435	443	.646	403	7262	821	.914	343	1571
127	2.103	803	7210	449	2.652	246	3410	823	2.915	399	8352
131	.117	271	2957	457	.659	916	2001	827	.917	505	5096
137	.136	720	5672	461	.663	700	9254	829	.918	554	5306
139	.143	014	8003	463	.665	580	9910	839	.923	761	9608
149	.173	186	2684	467	.669	316	8806	853	.930	949	0312
151	2.178	976	9473	479	2.680	335	5134	857	2.932	980	8219
157	.195	899	6524	487	.687	528	9612	859	.933	993	1638
163	.212	187	6044	491	.691	081	4921	863	.936	010	7957
167	.222	716	4711	499	.698	100	5456	877	.942	999	5934
173	.238	046	1031	503	.701	567	9851	881	.944	975	9084
179	2.252	853	0310	509	2.706	717	7823	883	2.945	960	7036
181	.257	678	5749	521	.716	837	7233	887	.947	923	6198
191	.281	033	3672	523	.718	501	6889	907	.957	607	2871
193	.285	557	3090	541	.733	197	2651	911	.959	518	3770
197	.294	466	2262	547	.737	987	3263	919	.963	315	5114
199	2.298	853	0764	557	2.745	855	1952	929	2.968	015	7140
211	.324	282	4553	563	.750	508	3949	937	.971	739	5909
223	.348	304	8630	569	.755	112	2664	941	.973	589	6234
227	.356	025	8572	571	.756	636	1082	947	.976	349	9790
229	.359	835	4823	577	.761	175	8132	953	.979	092	9006
233	2.367	355	9210	587	2.768	638	1012	967	2.985	426	4741
239	.378	397	9009	593	.773	054	6934	971	.987	219	2299
241	.382	017	0426	599	.777	426	8224	977	.989	894	5637
251	.399	673	7215	601	.778	874	4720	983	.992	553	5178
257	.409	933	1233	607	.783	188	6911	991	.996	073	6545
263	2.419	955	7485	613	2.787	460	4745	997	2.998	695	1583

Table XVIII*

COMMON LOGARITHMS OF $\Gamma(n)$

$$\Gamma(n) = \int_0^\infty x^{n-1} \cdot e^{-x}\, dx = \int_0^1 \left[\log \frac{1}{x}\right]^{n-1} dx .$$

N	$\log_{10}\Gamma(n)+10$	N	$\log_{10}\Gamma(n)+10$	N	$\log_{10}\Gamma(n)+10$	N	$\log_{10}\Gamma(n)+10$	N	$\log_{10}\Gamma(n)+10$
1.01	9.9975	1.21	9.9617	1.41	9.9478	1.61	9.9517	1.81	9.9704
1.02	9.9951	1.22	9.9605	1.42	9.9476	1.62	9.9523	1.82	9.9717
1.03	9.9928	1.23	9.9594	1.43	9.9475	1.63	9.9529	1.83	9.9730
1.04	9.9905	1.24	9.9583	1.44	9.9473	1.64	9.9536	1.84	9.9743
1.05	9.9883	1.25	9.9573	1.45	9.9473	1.65	9.9543	1.85	9.9757
1.06	9.9862	1.26	9.9564	1.46	9.9472	1.66	9.9550	1.86	9.9771
1.07	9.9841	1.27	9.9554	1.47	9.9473	1.67	9.9558	1.87	9.9786
1.08	9.9821	1.28	9.9546	1.48	9.9473	1.68	9.9566	1.88	9.9800
1.09	9.9802	1.29	9.9538	1.49	9.9474	1.69	9.9575	1.89	9.9815
1.10	9.9783	1.30	9.9530	1.50	9.9475	1.70	9.9584	1.90	9.9831
1.11	9.9765	1.31	9.9523	1.51	9.9477	1.71	9.9593	1.91	9.9846
1.12	9.9748	1.32	9.9516	1.52	9.9479	1.72	9.9603	1.92	9.9862
1.13	9.9731	1.33	9.9510	1.53	9.9482	1.73	9.9613	1.93	9.9878
1.14	9.9715	1.34	9.9505	1.54	9.9485	1.74	9.9623	1.94	9.9895
1.15	9.9699	1.35	9.9500	1.55	9.9488	1.75	9.9633	1.95	9.9912
1.16	9.9684	1.36	9.9495	1.56	9.9492	1.76	9.9644	1.96	9.9929
1.17	9.9669	1.37	9.9491	1.57	9.9496	1.77	9.9656	1.97	9.9946
1.18	9.9655	1.38	9.9487	1.58	9.9501	1.78	9.9667	1.98	9.9964
1.19	9.9642	1.39	9.9483	1.59	9.9506	1.79	9.9679	1.99	9.9982
1.20	9.9629	1.40	9.9481	1.60	9.9511	1.80	9.9691	2.00	0.0000

$$\Gamma(x+1) = x \cdot \Gamma(x), \; x > 0. \quad \Gamma(2) = \Gamma(1) = 1.$$

* See Page 80.

Interpolation

Let $f(x)$ be an analytic function of x. If the values of $f(x)$ are given in a table for a set of values of x separated from one another consecutively by the constant small interval h, the differences between the successive values of the function as tabulated are called *first tabular differences*, the differences of these first differences, *second tabular differences*, etc. The first, second and third tabular differences corresponding to $x = a$ and the tabulated value of $f(a)$ are:

$$\Delta_1 \equiv f(a+h) - f(a),$$
$$\Delta_2 \equiv f(a+2h) - 2 \cdot f(a+h) + f(a),$$
$$\Delta_3 \equiv f(a+3h) - 3 \cdot f(a+2h) + 3 \cdot f(a+h) - f(a).$$

The value of $f(x)$ for $x = a+\delta$, where $\delta = kh$, $0 < k < 1$, is:

$$f(a+\delta) = f(a) + k \cdot \Delta_1 + \frac{k(k-1)}{2!} \cdot \Delta_2 + \frac{k(k-1)(k-2)}{3!} \cdot \Delta_3 + \cdots.$$

Table XIX

COMPOUND INTEREST*: $(1+r)^n$

Amount of One Dollar Principal at Compound Interest After n Years

n	2%	2½%	3%	3½%	4%	4½%	5%	6%	7%
1	1.0200	1.0250	1.0300	1.0350	1.0400	1.0450	1.0500	1.0600	1.0700
2	1.0404	1.0506	1.0609	1.0712	1.0816	1.0920	1.1025	1.1236	1.1449
3	1.0612	1.0769	1.0927	1.1087	1.1249	1.1412	1.1576	1.1910	1.2250
4	1.0824	1.1038	1.1255	1.1475	1.1699	1.1925	1.2155	1.2625	1.3108
5	1.1041	1.1314	1.1593	1.1877	1.2167	1.2462	1.2763	1.3382	1.4026
6	1.1262	1.1597	1.1941	1.2293	1.2653	1.3023	1.3401	1.4185	1.5007
7	1.1487	1.1887	1.2299	1.2723	1.3159	1.3609	1.4071	1.5036	1.6058
8	1.1717	1.2184	1.2668	1.3168	1.3686	1.4221	1.4775	1.5938	1.7182
9	1.1951	1.2489	1.3048	1.3629	1.4233	1.4861	1.5513	1.6895	1.8385
10	1.2190	1.2801	1.3439	1.4106	1.4802	1.5530	1.6289	1.7908	1.9672
11	1.2434	1.3121	1.3842	1.4600	1.5395	1.6229	1.7103	1.8983	2.1049
12	1.2682	1.3449	1.4258	1.5111	1.6010	1.6959	1.7959	2.0122	2.2522
13	1.2936	1.3785	1.4685	1.5640	1.6651	1.7722	1.8856	2.1329	2.4098
14	1.3195	1.4130	1.5126	1.6187	1.7317	1.8519	1.9799	2.2609	2.5785
15	1.3459	1.4483	1.5580	1.6753	1.8009	1.9353	2.0789	2.3966	2.7590
16	1.3728	1.4845	1.6047	1.7340	1.8730	2.0224	2.1829	2.5404	2.9522
17	1.4002	1.5216	1.6528	1.7947	1.9479	2.1134	2.2920	2.6928	3.1588
18	1.4282	1.5597	1.7024	1.8575	2.0258	2.2085	2.4066	2.8543	3.3799
19	1.4568	1.5987	1.7535	1.9225	2.1068	2.3079	2.5270	3.0256	3.6165
20	1.4859	1.6386	1.8061	1.9898	2.1911	2.4117	2.6533	3.2071	3.8697
21	1.5157	1.6796	1.8603	2.0594	2.2788	2.5202	2.7860	3.3996	4.1406
22	1.5460	1.7216	1.9161	2.1315	2.3699	2.6337	2.9253	3.6035	4.4304
23	1.5769	1.7646	1.9736	2.2061	2.4647	2.7522	3.0715	3.8197	4.7405
24	1.6084	1.8087	2.0328	2.2833	2.5633	2.8760	3.2251	4.0489	5.0724
25	1.6406	1.8539	2.0938	2.3632	2.6658	3.0054	3.3864	4.2919	5.4274
26	1.6734	1.9003	2.1566	2.4460	2.7725	3.1407	3.5557	4.5494	5.8074
27	1.7069	1.9478	2.2213	2.5316	2.8834	3.2820	3.7335	4.8223	6.2139
28	1.7410	1.9965	2.2879	2.6202	2.9987	3.4297	3.9201	5.1117	6.6488
29	1.7758	2.0464	2.3566	2.7119	3.1187	3.5840	4.1161	5.4184	7.1143
30	1.8114	2.0976	2.4273	2.8068	3.2434	3.7453	4.3219	5.7435	7.6123
31	1.8476	2.1500	2.5001	2.9050	3.3731	3.9139	4.5380	6.0881	8.1451
32	1.8845	2.2038	2.5751	3.0067	3.5081	4.0900	4.7649	6.4534	8.7153
33	1.9222	2.2589	2.6523	3.1119	3.6484	4.2740	5.0032	6.8406	9.3253
34	1.9607	2.3153	2.7319	3.2209	3.7943	4.4664	5.2533	7.2510	9.9781
35	1.9999	2.3732	2.8139	3.3336	3.9461	4.6673	5.5160	7.6861	10.6766
36	2.0399	2.4325	2.8983	3.4503	4.1039	4.8774	5.7918	8.1473	11.4239
37	2.0807	2.4933	2.9852	3.5710	4.2681	5.0969	6.0814	8.6361	12.2236
38	2.1223	2.5557	3.0748	3.6960	4.4388	5.3262	6.3855	9.1543	13.0793
39	2.1647	2.6196	3.1670	3.8254	4.6164	5.5659	6.7048	9.7035	13.9948
40	2.2080	2.6851	3.2620	3.9593	4.8010	5.8164	7.0400	10.2857	14.9745
41	2.2522	2.7522	3.3599	4.0978	4.9931	6.0781	7.3920	10.9029	16.0227
42	2.2972	2.8210	3.4607	4.2413	5.1928	6.3516	7.7616	11.5570	17.1443
43	2.3432	2.8915	3.5645	4.3897	5.4005	6.6374	8.1497	12.2505	18.3444
44	2.3901	2.9638	3.6715	4.5433	5.6165	6.9361	8.5572	12.9855	19.6285
45	2.4379	3.0379	3.7816	4.7024	5.8412	7.2482	8.9850	13.7646	21.0025
46	2.4866	3.1139	3.8950	4.8669	6.0748	7.5744	9.4343	14.5905	22.4726
47	2.5363	3.1917	4.0119	5.0373	6.3178	7.9153	9.9060	15.4659	24.0457
48	2.5871	3.2715	4.1323	5.2136	6.5705	8.2715	10.4013	16.3939	25.7289
49	2.6388	3.3533	4.2562	5.3961	6.8333	8.6437	10.9213	17.3775	27.5299
50	2.6916	3.4371	4.3839	5.5849	7.1067	9.0326	11.4674	18.4202	29.4570

*See §18.

Table XX

COMPOUND DISCOUNT *: 1 / $(1+r)^n$

Present Value of One Dollar Due at the End of n Years

n	2%	$2\frac{1}{2}\%$	3%	$3\frac{1}{2}\%$	4%	$4\frac{1}{2}\%$	5%	6%	7%
1	.98039	.97561	.97087	.96618	.96154	.95694	.95238	.94340	.93458
2	.96117	.95181	.94260	.93351	.92456	.91573	.90703	.89000	.87344
3	.94232	.92860	.91514	.90194	.88900	.87630	.86384	.83962	.81630
4	.92385	.90595	.88849	.87144	.85480	.83856	.82270	.79209	.76290
5	.90573	.88385	.86261	.84197	.82193	.80245	.78353	.74726	.71299
6	.88797	.86230	.83748	.81350	.79031	.76790	.74622	.70496	.66634
7	.87056	.84127	.81309	.78599	.75992	.73483	.71068	.66506	.62275
8	.85349	.82075	.78941	.75941	.73069	.70319	.67684	.62741	.58201
9	.83676	.80073	.76642	.73373	.70259	.67290	.64461	.59190	.54393
10	.82035	.78120	.74409	.70892	.67556	.64393	.61391	.55839	.50835
11	.80426	.76214	.72242	.68495	.64958	.61620	.58468	.52679	.47509
12	.78849	.74356	.70138	.66178	.62460	.58966	.55684	.49697	.44401
13	.77303	.72542	.68095	.63940	.60057	.56427	.53032	.46884	.41496
14	.75788	.70773	.66112	.61778	.57748	.53997	.50507	.44230	.38782
15	.74301	.69047	.64186	.59689	.55526	.51672	.48102	.41727	.36245
16	.72845	.67362	.62317	.57671	.53391	.49447	.45811	.39365	.33873
17	.71416	.65720	.60502	.55720	.51337	.47318	.43630	.37136	.31657
18	.70016	.64117	.58739	.53836	.49363	.45280	.41552	.35034	.29586
19	.68643	.62553	.57029	.52016	.47464	.43330	.39573	.33051	.27651
20	.67297	.61027	.55368	.50257	.45639	.41464	.37689	.31180	.25842
21	.65978	.59539	.53755	.48557	.43883	.39679	.35894	.29416	.24151
22	.64684	.58086	.52189	.46915	.42196	.37970	.34185	.27751	.22571
23	.63416	.56670	.50669	.45329	.40573	.36335	.32557	.26180	.21095
24	.62172	.55288	.49193	.43796	.39012	.34770	.31007	.24698	.19715
25	.60953	.53939	.47761	.42315	.37512	.33273	.29530	.23300	.18425
26	.59758	.52623	.46369	.40884	.36069	.31840	.28124	.21981	.17220
27	.58586	.51340	.45019	.39501	.34682	.30469	.26785	.20737	.16093
28	.57437	.50088	.43708	.38165	.33348	.29157	.25509	.19563	.15040
29	.56311	.48866	.42435	.36875	.32065	.27902	.24295	.18456	.14056
30	.55207	.47674	.41199	.35628	.30832	.26700	.23138	.17411	.13137
31	.54125	.46511	.39999	.34423	.29646	.25550	.22036	.16425	.12277
32	.53063	.45377	.38834	.33259	.28506	.24450	.20987	.15496	.11474
33	.52023	.44270	.37703	.32134	.27409	.23397	.19987	.14619	.10723
34	.51003	.43191	.36604	.31048	.26355	.22390	.19035	.13791	.10022
35	.50003	.42137	.35538	.29998	.25342	.21425	.18129	.13011	.09366
36	.49022	.41109	.34503	.28983	.24367	.20503	.17266	.12274	.08754
37	.48061	.40107	.33498	.28003	.23430	.19620	.16444	.11580	.08181
38	.47119	.39128	.32523	.27056	.22529	.18775	.15661	.10924	.07646
39	.46195	.38174	.31575	.26141	.21662	.17967	.14915	.10306	.07146
40	.45289	.37243	.30656	.25257	.20829	.17193	.14205	.09722	.06678
41	.44401	.36335	.29763	.24403	.20028	.16453	.13528	.09172	.06241
42	.43530	.35448	.28896	.23578	.19257	.15744	.12884	.08653	.05833
43	.42677	.34584	.28054	.22781	.18517	.15066	.12270	.08163	.05451
44	.41840	.33740	.27237	.22010	.17805	.14417	.11686	.07701	.05095
45	.41020	.32917	.26444	.21266	.17120	.13796	.11130	.07265	.04761
46	.40215	.32115	.25674	.20547	.16461	.13202	.10600	.06854	.04450
47	.39427	.31331	.24926	.19852	.15828	.12634	.10095	.06466	.04159
48	.38654	.30567	.24200	.19181	.15219	.12090	.09614	.06100	.03887
49	.37896	.29822	.23495	.18532	.14634	.11569	.09156	.05755	.03632
50	.37153	.29094	.22811	.17905	.14071	.11071	.08720	.05429	.03395

* See §20.

Table XXI

AMOUNT OF AN ANNUITY*

Amount of an Annuity of One Dollar per Year after n Years

n	2%	2½%	3%	3½%	4%	4½%	5%	6%	7%
1	1.0000	1.0000	1.0000	1.0000	1.0000	1.0000	1.0000	1.0000	1.0000
2	2.0200	2.0250	2.0300	2.0350	2.0400	2.0450	2.0500	2.0600	2.0700
3	3.0604	3.0756	3.0909	3.1062	3.1216	3.1370	3.1525	3.1836	3.2149
4	4.1216	4.1525	4.1836	4.2149	4.2465	4.2782	4.3101	4.3746	4.4399
5	5.2040	5.2563	5.3091	5.3625	5.4163	5.4707	5.5256	5.6371	5.7507
6	6.3081	6.3877	6.4684	6.5502	6.6330	6.7169	6.8019	6.9753	7.1533
7	7.4343	7.5474	7.6625	7.7794	7.8983	8.0192	8.1420	8.3938	8.6540
8	8.5830	8.7361	8.8923	9.0517	9.2142	9.3800	9.5491	9.8975	10.2598
9	9.7546	9.9545	10.1591	10.3685	10.5828	10.8021	11.0266	11.4913	11.9780
10	10.9497	11.2034	11.4639	11.7314	12.0061	12.2882	12.5779	13.1808	13.8164
11	12.1687	12.4835	12.8078	13.1420	13.4864	13.8412	14.2068	14.9716	15.7836
12	13.4121	13.7956	14.1920	14.6020	15.0258	15.4640	15.9171	16.8699	17.8885
13	14.6803	15.1404	15.6178	16.1130	16.6268	17.1599	17.7130	18.8821	20.1406
14	15.9739	16.5190	17.0863	17.6770	18.2919	18.9321	19.5986	21.0151	22.5505
15	17.2934	17.9319	18.5989	19.2957	20.0236	20.7841	21.5786	23.2760	25.1290
16	18.6393	19.3802	20.1569	20.9710	21.8245	22.7193	23.6575	25.6725	27.8881
17	20.0121	20.8647	21.7616	22.7050	23.6975	24.7417	25.8404	28.2129	30.8402
18	21.4123	22.3863	23.4144	24.4997	25.6454	26.8551	28.1324	30.9057	33.9990
19	22.8406	23.9460	25.1169	26.3572	27.6712	29.0636	30.5390	33.7600	37.3790
20	24.2974	25.5447	26.8704	28.2797	29.7781	31.3714	33.0660	36.7856	40.9955
21	25.7833	27.1833	28.6765	30.2695	31.9692	33.7831	35.7193	39.9927	44.8652
22	27.2990	28.8629	30.5368	32.3289	34.2480	36.3034	38.5052	43.3923	49.0057
23	28.8450	30.5844	32.4529	34.4604	36.6179	38.9370	41.4305	46.9958	53.4361
24	30.4219	32.3490	34.4265	36.6665	39.0826	41.6892	44.5020	50.8156	58.1767
25	32.0303	34.1578	36.4593	38.9499	41.6459	44.5652	47.7271	54.8645	63.2490
26	33.6709	36.0117	38.5530	41.3131	44.3117	47.5706	51.1135	59.1564	68.6765
27	35.3443	37.9120	40.7096	43.7591	47.0842	50.7113	54.6691	63.7058	74.4838
28	37.0512	39.8598	42.9309	46.2906	49.9676	53.9933	58.4026	68.5281	80.6977
29	38.7922	41.8563	45.2189	48.9108	52.9663	57.4230	62.3227	73.6398	87.3465
30	40.5681	43.9027	47.5754	51.6227	56.0849	61.0071	66.4388	79.0582	94.4608
31	42.3794	46.0003	50.0027	54.4295	59.3283	64.7524	70.7608	84.8017	102.0730
32	44.2270	48.1503	52.5028	57.3345	62.7015	68.6662	75.2988	90.8898	110.2182
33	46.1116	50.3540	55.0778	60.3412	66.2095	72.7562	80.0638	97.3432	118.9334
34	48.0338	52.6129	57.7302	63.4532	69.8579	77.0303	85.0670	104.1838	128.2588
35	49.9945	54.9282	60.4621	66.6740	73.6522	81.4966	90.3203	111.4348	138.2369
36	51.9944	57.3014	63.2759	70.0076	77.5983	86.1640	95.8363	119.1209	148.9135
37	54.0343	59.7339	66.1742	73.4579	81.7022	91.0413	101.6281	127.2681	160.3374
38	56.1149	62.2273	69.1594	77.0289	85.9703	96.1382	107.7095	135.9042	172.5610
39	58.2372	64.7830	72.2342	80.7249	90.4091	101.4644	114.0950	145.0585	185.6403
40	60.4020	67.4026	75.4013	84.5503	95.0255	107.0303	120.7998	154.7620	199.6351
41	62.6100	70.0876	78.6633	88.5095	99.8265	112.8467	127.8398	165.0477	214.6096
42	64.8622	72.8398	82.0232	92.6074	104.8196	118.9248	135.2318	175.9505	230.6322
43	67.1595	75.6608	85.4839	96.8486	110.0124	125.2764	142.9933	187.5076	247.7765
44	69.5027	78.5523	89.0484	101.2383	115.4129	131.9138	151.1430	199.7580	266.1209
45	71.8927	81.5161	92.7199	105.7817	121.0294	138.8500	159.7002	212.7435	285.7493
46	74.3306	84.5540	96.5015	110.4840	126.8706	146.0982	168.6852	226.5081	306.7518
47	76.8172	87.6679	100.3965	115.3510	132.9454	153.6726	178.1194	241.0986	329.2244
48	79.3535	90.8596	104.4084	120.3883	139.2632	161.5879	188.0254	256.5645	353.2701
49	81.9406	94.1311	108.5406	125.6018	145.8337	169.8594	198.4267	272.9584	378.9990
50	84.5794	97.4843	112.7969	130.9979	152.6671	178.5030	209.3480	290.3359	406.5289

*See §23.

Table XXII

PRESENT VALUE OF AN ANNUITY*

Present Value of One Dollar per Year for *n* Years

n	2%	2½%	3%	3½%	4%	4½%	5%	6%	7%
1	.9804	.9756	.9709	.9662	.9615	.9569	.9524	.9434	.9346
2	1.9416	1.9274	1.9135	1.8997	1.8861	1.8727	1.8594	1.8334	1.8080
3	2.8839	2.8560	2.8286	2.8016	2.7751	2.7490	2.7232	2.6730	2.6243
4	3.8077	3.7620	3.7171	3.6731	3.6299	3.5875	3.5460	3.4651	3.3872
5	4.7135	4.6458	4.5797	4.5151	4.4518	4.3900	4.3295	4.2124	4.1002
6	5.6014	5.5081	5.4172	5.3286	5.2421	5.1579	5.0757	4.9173	4.7665
7	6.4720	6.3494	6.2303	6.1145	6.0021	5.8927	5.7864	5.5824	5.3893
8	7.3255	7.1701	7.0197	6.8740	6.7327	6.5959	6.4632	6.2098	5.9713
9	8.1622	7.9709	7.7861	7.6077	7.4353	7.2688	7.1078	6.8017	6.5152
10	8.9826	8.7521	8.5302	8.3166	8.1109	7.9127	7.7217	7.3601	7.0236
11	9.7868	9.5142	9.2526	9.0016	8.7605	8.5289	8.3064	7.8869	7.4987
12	10.5753	10.2578	9.9540	9.6633	9.3851	9.1186	8.8633	8.3838	7.9427
13	11.3484	10.9832	10.6350	10.3027	9.9856	9.6829	9.3936	8.8527	8.3577
14	12.1062	11.6909	11.2961	10.9205	10.5631	10.2228	9.8986	9.2950	8.7455
15	12.8493	12.3814	11.9379	11.5174	11.1184	10.7395	10.3797	9.7122	9.1079
16	13.5777	13.0550	12.5611	12.0941	11.6523	11.2340	10.8378	10.1059	9.4466
17	14.2919	13.7122	13.1661	12.6513	12.1657	11.7072	11.2741	10.4773	9.7632
18	14.9920	14.3534	13.7535	13.1897	12.6593	12.1600	11.6896	10.8276	10.0591
19	15.6785	14.9789	14.3238	13.7098	13.1339	12.5933	12.0853	11.1581	10.3356
20	16.3514	15.5892	14.8775	14.2124	13.5903	13.0079	12.4622	11.4699	10.5940
21	17.0112	16.1845	15.4150	14.6980	14.0292	13.4047	12.8212	11.7641	10.8355
22	17.6580	16.7654	15.9369	15.1671	14.4511	13.7844	13.1630	12.0416	11.0612
23	18.2922	17.3321	16.4436	15.6204	14.8568	14.1478	13.4886	12.3034	11.2722
24	18.9139	17.8850	16.9355	16.0584	15.2470	14.4955	13.7986	12.5504	11.4693
25	19.5235	18.4244	17.4131	16.4815	15.6221	14.8282	14.0939	12.7834	11.6536
26	20.1210	18.9506	17.8768	16.8904	15.9828	15.1466	14.3752	13.0032	11.8258
27	20.7069	19.4640	18.3270	17.2854	16.3296	15.4513	14.6430	13.2105	11.9867
28	21.2813	19.9649	18.7641	17.6670	16.6631	15.7429	14.8981	13.4062	12.1371
29	21.8444	20.4535	19.1885	18.0358	16.9837	16.0219	15.1411	13.5907	12.2777
30	22.3965	20.9303	19.6004	18.3920	17.2920	16.2889	15.3725	13.7648	12.4090
31	22.9377	21.3954	20.0004	18.7363	17.5885	16.5444	15.5928	13.9291	12.5318
32	23.4683	21.8492	20.3888	19.0689	17.8736	16.7889	15.8027	14.0840	12.6466
33	23.9886	22.2919	20.7658	19.3902	18.1476	17.0229	16.0025	14.2302	12.7538
34	24.4986	22.7238	21.1318	19.7007	18.4112	17.2468	16.1929	14.3681	12.8540
35	24.9986	23.1452	21.4872	20.0007	18.6646	17.4610	16.3742	14.4982	12.9477
36	25.4888	23.5563	21.8323	20.2905	18.9083	17.6660	16.5469	14.6210	13.0352
37	25.9695	23.9573	22.1672	20.5705	19.1426	17.8622	16.7113	14.7368	13.1170
38	26.4406	24.3486	22.4925	20.8411	19.3679	18.0500	16.8679	14.8460	13.1935
39	26.9026	24.7303	22.8082	21.1025	19.5845	18.2297	17.0170	14.9491	13.2649
40	27.3555	25.1028	23.1148	21.3551	19.7928	18.4016	17.1591	15.0463	13.3317
41	27.7995	25.4661	23.4124	21.5991	19.9931	18.5661	17.2944	15.1380	13.3941
42	28.2348	25.8206	23.7014	21.8349	20.1856	18.7236	17.4232	15.2245	13.4524
43	28.6616	26.1664	23.9819	22.0627	20.3708	18.8742	17.5459	15.3062	13.5070
44	29.0800	26.5038	24.2543	22.2828	20.5488	19.0184	17.6628	15.3832	13.5579
45	29.4902	26.8330	24.5187	22.4955	20.7200	19.1563	17.7741	15.4558	13.6055
46	29.8923	27.1542	24.7754	22.7009	20.8847	19.2884	17.8801	15.5244	13.6500
47	30.2866	27.4675	25.0247	22.8994	21.0429	19.4147	17.9810	15.5890	13.6910
48	30.6731	27.7732	25.2667	23.0912	21.1951	19.5356	18.0772	15.6500	13.7305
49	31.0521	28.0714	25.5017	23.2766	21.3415	19.6513	18.1687	15.7076	13.7668
50	31.4236	28.3623	25.7298	23.4556	21.4822	19.7620	18.2559	15.7619	13.8007

* See §24.

Table XXIII LOGARITHMS FOR INTEREST COMPUTATIONS

r	1 + r	log (1 + r)	r	1 + r	log (1 + r)
½ %	1.005	00216 60617 56508	5½ %	1.055	02325 24596 33711
1 %	1.010	00432 13737 82643	6 %	1.060	02530 58652 64770
1½ %	1.015	00646 60422 49232	6½ %	1.065	02734 96077 74757
2 %	1.020	00860 01717 61918	7 %	1.070	02938 37776 85210
2½ %	1.025	01072 38653 91773	7½ %	1.075	03140 84642 51624
3 %	1.030	01283 72247 05172	8 %	1.080	03342 37554 86950
3½ %	1.035	01494 03497 92937	8½ %	1.085	03542 97381 84548
4 %	1.040	01703 33392 98780	9 %	1.090	03742 64979 40624
4½ %	1.045	01911 62904 47073	9½ %	1.095	03941 41191 76137
5 %	1.050	02118 92990 69938	10 %	1.100	04139 26851 58225

The amount A of principal P at compound interest after n years is: $A = P(1 + r)^n$.
The present value P of an amount A due at end of n years is: $P = A/(1 + r)^n$.

Table XXIV AMERICAN EXPERIENCE MORTALITY TABLE

x	l_x	d_x	q_x	p_x	x	l_x	d_x	q_x	p_x
10	100 000	749	0.007 490	0.992 510	53	66 797	1 091	0.016 333	0.983 667
11	99 251	746	0.007 516	0.992 484	54	65 706	1 143	0.017 396	0.982 604
12	98 505	743	0.007 543	0.992 457	55	64 563	1 199	0.018 571	0.981 429
13	97 762	740	0.007 569	0.992 431	56	63 364	1 260	0.019 885	0.980 115
14	97 022	737	0.007 596	0.992 404	57	62 104	1 325	0.021 335	0.978 665
15	96 285	735	0.007 634	0.992 366	58	60 779	1 394	0.022 936	0.977 064
16	95 550	732	0.007 661	0.992 339	59	59 385	1 468	0.024 720	0.975 280
17	94 818	729	0.007 688	0.992 312	60	57 917	1 546	0.026 693	0.973 307
18	94 089	727	0.007 727	0.992 273	61	56 371	1 628	0.028 880	0.971 120
19	93 362	725	0.007 765	0.992 235	62	54 743	1 713	0.031 292	0.968 708
20	92 637	723	0.007 805	0.992 195	63	53 030	1 800	0.033 943	0.966 057
21	91 914	722	0.007 855	0.992 145	64	51 230	1 889	0.036 873	0.963 127
22	91 192	721	0.007 906	0.992 094	65	49 341	1 980	0.040 129	0.959 871
23	90 471	720	0.007 958	0.992 042	66	47 361	2 070	0.043 707	0.956 293
24	89 751	719	0.008 011	0.991 989	67	45 291	2 158	0.047 647	0.952 353
25	89 032	718	0.008 065	0.991 935	68	43 133	2 243	0.052 002	0.947 998
26	88 314	718	0.008 130	0.991 870	69	40 890	2 321	0.056 762	0.943 238
27	87 596	718	0.008 197	0.991 803	70	38 569	2 391	0.061 993	0.938 007
28	86 878	718	0.008 264	0.991 736	71	36 178	2 448	0.067 665	0.932 335
29	86 160	719	0.008 345	0.991 655	72	33 730	2 487	0.073 733	0.926 267
30	85 441	720	0.008 427	0.991 573	73	31 243	2 505	0.080 178	0.919 822
31	84 721	721	0.008 510	0.991 490	74	28 738	2 501	0.087 028	0.912 972
32	84 000	723	0.008 607	0.991 393	75	26 237	2 476	0.094 371	0.905 629
33	83 277	726	0.008 718	0.991 282	76	23 761	2 431	0.102 311	0.897 689
34	82 551	729	0.008 831	0.991 169	77	21 330	2 369	0.111 064	0.888 936
35	81 822	732	0.008 946	0.991 054	78	18 961	2 291	0.120 827	0.879 173
36	81 090	737	0.009 089	0.990 911	79	16 670	2 196	0.131 734	0.868 266
37	80 353	742	0.009 234	0.990 766	80	14 474	2 091	0.144 466	0.855 534
38	79 611	749	0.009 408	0.990 592	81	12 383	1 964	0.158 605	0.841 395
39	78 862	756	0.009 586	0.990 414	82	10 419	1 816	0.174 297	0.825 703
40	78 106	765	0.009 794	0.990 206	83	8 603	1 648	0.191 561	0.808 439
41	77 341	774	0.010 008	0.989 992	84	6 955	1 470	0.211 359	0.788 641
42	76 567	785	0.010 252	0.989 748	85	5 485	1 292	0.235 552	0.764 448
43	75 782	797	0.010 517	0.989 483	86	4 193	1 114	0.265 681	0.734 319
44	74 985	812	0.010 829	0.989 171	87	3 079	933	0.303 020	0.696 980
45	74 173	828	0.011 163	0.988 837	88	2 146	744	0.346 692	0.653 308
46	73 345	848	0.011 562	0.988 438	89	1 402	555	0.395 863	0.604 137
47	72 497	870	0.012 000	0.988 000	90	847	385	0.454 545	0.545 455
48	71 627	896	0.012 509	0.987 491	91	462	246	0.532 468	0.467 532
49	70 731	927	0.013 106	0.986 894	92	216	137	0.634 259	0.365 741
50	69 804	962	0.013 781	0.986 219	93	79	58	0.734 177	0.265 823
51	68 842	1 001	0.014 541	0.985 459	94	21	18	0.857 143	0.142 857
52	67 841	1 044	0.015 389	0.984 611	95	3	3	1.000 000	0.000 000

Based on 100,000 living at age 10.

x = age, l_x = number living, d_x = number of deaths,
q_x = yearly probability of dying, p_x = yearly probability of living.

Table XXV

PROBABILITY FUNCTIONS

$$\tfrac{1}{2}(1+\alpha) = \int_{-\infty}^{x} \Phi(x)\,dx = \text{Area under } \Phi(x) \text{ from } -\infty \text{ to } x,$$

$$\alpha = \int_{-x}^{x} \Phi(x)dx, \qquad \Phi(x) = \frac{1}{\sqrt{2\pi}}\,e^{\frac{-x^2}{2}} = \text{Normal function.}$$

$\Phi^{(2)}(x) = (x^2-1)\,\Phi(x)$ = Second derivative of $\Phi(x)$.

$\Phi^{(3)}(x) = (3x-x^3)\,\Phi(x)$ = Third derivative of $\Phi(x)$.

$\Phi^{(4)}(x) = (x^4-6x^2+3)\,\Phi(x)$ = Fourth derivative of $\Phi(x)$.

x	$\tfrac{1}{2}(1+\alpha)$	$\Phi(x)$	$\Phi^{(2)}(x)$	$\Phi^{(3)}(x)$	$\Phi^{(4)}(x)$	x	$\tfrac{1}{2}(1+\alpha)$	$\Phi(x)$	$\Phi^{(2)}(x)$	$\Phi^{(3)}(x)$	$\Phi^{(4)}(x)$
0.00	.5000	.3989	−.3989	.0000	1.1968	0.50	.6915	.3521	−.2641	.4841	.5501
0.01	.5040	.3989	−.3989	.0120	1.1965	0.51	.6950	.3503	−.2592	.4895	.5279
0.02	.5080	.3989	−.3987	.0239	1.1956	0.52	.6985	.3485	−.2543	.4947	.5056
0.03	.5120	.3988	−.3984	.0359	1.1941	0.53	.7019	.3467	−.2493	.4996	.4831
0.04	.5160	.3986	−.3980	.0478	1.1920	0.54	.7054	.3448	−.2443	.5043	.4605
0.05	.5199	.3984	−.3975	.0597	1.1894	0.55	.7088	.3429	−.2392	.5088	.4378
0.06	.5239	.3982	−.3968	.0716	1.1861	0.56	.7123	.3410	−.2341	.5131	.4150
0.07	.5279	.3980	−.3960	.0834	1.1822	0.57	.7157	.3391	−.2289	.5171	.3921
0.08	.5319	.3977	−.3951	.0952	1.1778	0.58	.7190	.3372	−.2238	.5209	.3691
0.09	.5359	.3973	−.3941	.1070	1.1727	0.59	.7224	.3352	−.2185	.5245	.3461
0.10	.5398	.3970	−.3930	.1187	1.1671	0.60	.7257	.3332	−.2133	.5278	.3231
0.11	.5438	.3965	−.3917	.1303	1.1609	0.61	.7291	.3312	−.2080	.5309	.3000
0.12	.5478	.3961	−.3904	.1419	1.1541	0.62	.7324	.3292	−.2027	.5338	.2770
0.13	.5517	.3956	−.3889	.1534	1.1468	0.63	.7357	.3271	−.1973	.5365	.2539
0.14	.5557	.3951	−.3873	.1648	1.1389	0.64	.7389	.3251	−.1919	.5389	.2309
0.15	.5596	.3945	−.3856	.1762	1.1304	0.65	.7422	.3230	−.1865	.5411	.2078
0.16	.5636	.3939	−.3838	.1874	1.1214	0.66	.7454	.3209	−.1811	.5431	.1849
0.17	.5675	.3932	−.3819	.1986	1.1118	0.67	.7486	.3187	−.1757	.5448	.1620
0.18	.5714	.3925	−.3798	.2097	1.1017	0.68	.7517	.3166	−.1702	.5463	.1391
0.19	.5753	.3918	−.3777	.2206	1.0911	0.69	.7549	.3144	−.1647	.5476	.1164
0.20	.5793	.3910	−.3754	.2315	1.0799	0.70	.7580	.3123	−.1593	.5486	.0937
0.21	.5832	.3902	−.3730	.2422	1.0682	0.71	.7611	.3101	−.1538	.5495	.0712
0.22	.5871	.3894	−.3706	.2529	1.0560	0.72	.7642	.3079	−.1483	.5501	.0487
0.23	.5910	.3885	−.3680	.2634	1.0434	0.73	.7673	.3056	−.1428	.5504	.0265
0.24	.5948	.3876	−.3653	.2737	1.0302	0.74	.7704	.3034	−.1373	.5506	.0043
0.25	.5987	.3867	−.3625	.2840	1.0165	0.75	.7734	.3011	−.1318	.5505	−.0176
0.26	.6026	.3857	−.3596	.2941	1.0024	0.76	.7764	.2989	−.1262	.5502	−.0394
0.27	.6064	.3847	−.3566	.3040	0.9878	0.77	.7794	.2966	−.1207	.5497	−.0611
0.28	.6103	.3836	−.3535	.3138	0.9727	0.78	.7823	.2943	−.1153	.5490	−.0825
0.29	.6141	.3825	−.3504	.3235	0.9572	0.79	.7852	.2920	−.1098	.5481	−.1037
0.30	.6179	.3814	−.3471	.3330	0.9413	0.80	.7881	.2897	−.1043	.5469	−.1247
0.31	.6217	.3802	−.3437	.3423	0.9250	0.81	.7910	.2874	−.0988	.5456	−.1455
0.32	.6255	.3790	−.3402	.3515	0.9082	0.82	.7939	.2850	−.0934	.5440	−.1660
0.33	.6293	.3778	−.3367	.3605	0.8910	0.83	.7967	.2827	−.0880	.5423	−.1862
0.34	.6331	.3765	−.3330	.3693	0.8735	0.84	.7995	.2803	−.0825	.5403	−.2063
0.35	.6368	.3752	−.3293	.3779	0.8556	0.85	.8023	.2780	−.0771	.5381	−.2260
0.36	.6406	.3739	−.3255	.3864	0.8373	0.86	.8051	.2756	−.0718	.5358	−.2455
0.37	.6443	.3726	−.3216	.3947	0.8186	0.87	.8078	.2732	−.0664	.5332	−.2646
0.38	.6480	.3712	−.3176	.4028	0.7996	0.88	.8106	.2709	−.0611	.5305	−.2835
0.39	.6517	.3697	−.3135	.4107	0.7803	0.89	.8133	.2685	−.0558	.5276	−.3021
0.40	.6554	.3683	−.3094	.4184	0.7607	0.90	.8159	.2661	−.0506	.5245	−.3203
0.41	.6591	.3668	−.3059	.4259	0.7408	0.91	.8186	.2637	−.0453	.5212	−.3383
0.42	.6628	.3653	−.3008	.4332	0.7206	0.92	.8212	.2613	−.0401	.5177	−.3559
0.43	.6664	.3637	−.2965	.4403	0.7001	0.93	.8238	.2589	−.0350	.5140	−.3731
0.44	.6700	.3621	−.2920	.4472	0.6793	0.94	.8264	.2565	−.0299	.5102	−.3901
0.45	.6736	.3605	−.2875	.4539	0.6583	0.95	.8289	.2541	−.0248	.5062	−.4066
0.46	.6772	.3589	−.2830	.4603	0.6371	0.96	.8315	.2516	−.0197	.5021	−.4228
0.47	.6808	.3572	−.2783	.4666	0.6156	0.97	.8340	.2492	−.0147	.4978	−.4387
0.48	.6844	.3555	−.2736	.4727	0.5940	0.98	.8365	.2468	−.0098	.4933	−.4541
0.49	.6879	.3538	−.2689	.4785	0.5721	0.99	.8389	.2444	−.0049	.4887	−.4692

PROBABILITY FUNCTIONS

x	$\frac{1}{2}(1+\alpha)$	$\Phi(x)$	$\Phi^{(2)}(x)$	$\Phi^{(3)}(x)$	$\Phi^{(4)}(x)$	x	$\frac{1}{2}(1+\alpha)$	$\Phi(x)$	$\Phi^{(2)}(x)$	$\Phi^{(3)}(x)$	$\Phi^{(4)}(x)$
1.00	.8413	.2420	.0000	.4839	$-.4839$	1.50	.9332	.1295	.1619	.1457	$-.7043$
1.01	.8438	.2396	.0048	.4790	$-.4983$	1.51	.9345	.1276	.1633	.1387	$-.6994$
1.02	.8461	.2371	.0096	.4740	$-.5122$	1.52	.9357	.1257	.1647	.1317	$-.6942$
1.03	.8485	.2347	.0143	.4688	$-.5257$	1.53	.9370	.1238	.1660	.1248	$-.6888$
1.04	.8508	.2323	.0190	.4635	$-.5389$	1.54	.9382	.1219	.1672	.1180	$-.6831$
1.05	.8531	.2299	.0236	.4580	$-.5516$	1.55	.9394	.1200	.1683	.1111	$-.6772$
1.06	.8554	.2275	.0281	.4524	$-.5639$	1.56	.9406	.1182	.1694	.1044	$-.6710$
1.07	.8577	.2251	.0326	.4467	$-.5758$	1.57	.9418	.1163	.1704	.0977	$-.6646$
1.08	.8599	.2227	.0371	.4409	$-.5873$	1.58	.9429	.1145	.1714	.0911	$-.6580$
1.09	.8621	.2203	.0414	.4350	$-.5984$	1.59	.9441	.1127	.1722	.0846	$-.6511$
1.10	.8643	.2179	.0458	.4290	$-.6091$	1.60	.9452	.1109	.1730	.0781	$-.6441$
1.11	.8665	.2155	.0500	.4228	$-.6193$	1.61	.9463	.1092	.1738	.0717	$-.6368$
1.12	.8686	.2131	.0542	.4166	$-.6292$	1.62	.9474	.1074	.1745	.0654	$-.6293$
1.13	.8708	.2107	.0583	.4102	$-.6386$	1.63	.9484	.1057	.1751	.0591	$-.6216$
1.14	.8729	.2083	.0624	.4038	$-.6476$	1.64	.9495	.1040	.1757	.0529	$-.6138$
1.15	.8749	.2059	.0664	.3973	$-.6561$	1.65	.9505	.1023	.1762	.0468	$-.6057$
1.16	.8770	.2036	.0704	.3907	$-.6643$	1.66	.9515	.1006	.1766	.0408	$-.5975$
1.17	.8790	.2012	.0742	.3840	$-.6720$	1.67	.9525	.0989	.1770	.0349	$-.5891$
1.18	.8810	.1989	.0780	.3772	$-.6792$	1.68	.9535	.0973	.1773	.0290	$-.5806$
1.19	.8830	.1965	.0818	.3704	$-.6861$	1.69	.9545	.0957	.1776	.0233	$-.5720$
1.20	.8849	.1942	.0854	.3635	$-.6926$	1.70	.9554	.0940	.1778	.0176	$-.5632$
1.21	.8869	.1919	.0890	.3566	$-.6986$	1.71	.9564	.0925	.1779	.0120	$-.5542$
1.22	.8888	.1895	.0926	.3496	$-.7042$	1.72	.9573	.0909	.1780	.0065	$-.5452$
1.23	.8907	.1872	.0960	.3425	$-.7094$	1.73	.9582	.0893	.1780	.0011	$-.5360$
1.24	.8925	.1849	.0994	.3354	$-.7141$	1.74	.9591	.0878	.1780	$-.0042$	$-.5267$
1.25	.8944	.1826	.1027	.3282	$-.7185$	1.75	.9599	.0863	.1780	$-.0094$	$-.5173$
1.26	.8962	.1804	.1060	.3210	$-.7224$	1.76	.9608	.0848	.1778	$-.0146$	$-.5079$
1.27	.8980	.1781	.1092	.3138	$-.7259$	1.77	.9616	.0833	.1777	$-.0196$	$-.4983$
1.28	.8997	.1758	.1123	.3065	$-.7291$	1.78	.9625	.0818	.1774	$-.0245$	$-.4887$
1.29	.9015	.1736	.1153	.2992	$-.7318$	1.79	.9633	.0804	.1772	$-.0294$	$-.4789$
1.30	.9032	.1714	.1182	.2918	$-.7341$	1.80	.9641	.0790	.1769	$-.0341$	$-.4692$
1.31	.9049	.1691	.1211	.2845	$-.7361$	1.81	.9649	.0775	.1765	$-.0388$	$-.4593$
1.32	.9066	.1669	.1239	.2771	$-.7376$	1.82	.9656	.0761	.1761	$-.0433$	$-.4494$
1.33	.9082	.1647	.1267	.2697	$-.7388$	1.83	.9664	.0748	.1756	$-.0477$	$-.4395$
1.34	.9099	.1626	.1293	.2624	$-.7395$	1.84	.9671	.0734	.1751	$-.0521$	$-.4295$
1.35	.9115	.1604	.1319	.2550	$-.7399$	1.85	.9678	.0721	.1746	$-.0563$	$-.4195$
1.36	.9131	.1582	.1344	.2476	$-.7400$	1.86	.9686	.0707	.1740	$-.0605$	$-.4095$
1.37	.9147	.1561	.1369	.2402	$-.7396$	1.87	.9693	.0694	.1734	$-.0645$	$-.3995$
1.38	.9162	.1539	.1392	.2328	$-.7389$	1.88	.9699	.0681	.1727	$-.0685$	$-.3894$
1.39	.9177	.1518	.1415	.2254	$-.7378$	1.89	.9706	.0669	.1720	$-.0723$	$-.3793$
1.40	.9192	.1497	.1437	.2180	$-.7364$	1.90	.9713	.0656	.1713	$-.0761$	$-.3693$
1.41	.9207	.1476	.1459	.2107	$-.7347$	1.91	.9719	.0644	.1705	$-.0797$	$-.3592$
1.42	.9222	.1456	.1480	.2033	$-.7326$	1.92	.9726	.0632	.1697	$-.0832$	$-.3492$
1.43	.9236	.1435	.1500	.1960	$-.7301$	1.93	.9732	.0620	.1688	$-.0867$	$-.3392$
1.44	.9251	.1415	.1519	.1887	$-.7274$	1.94	.9738	.0608	.1679	$-.0900$	$-.3292$
1.45	.9265	.1394	.1537	.1815	$-.7243$	1.95	.9744	.0596	.1670	$-.0933$	$-.3192$
1.46	.9279	.1374	.1555	.1742	$-.7209$	1.96	.9750	.0584	.1661	$-.0964$	$-.3093$
1.47	.9292	.1354	.1572	.1670	$-.7172$	1.97	.9756	.0573	.1651	$-.0994$	$-.2994$
1.48	.9306	.1334	.1588	.1599	$-.7132$	1.98	.9761	.0562	.1641	$-.1024$	$-.2895$
1.49	.9319	.1315	.1604	.1528	$-.7089$	1.99	.9767	.0551	.1630	$-.1052$	$-.2797$

PROBABILITY FUNCTIONS

x	$\frac{1}{2}(1+\alpha)$	$\Phi(x)$	$\Phi^{(2)}(x)$	$\Phi^{(3)}(x)$	$\Phi^{(4)}(x)$	x	$\frac{1}{2}(1+\alpha)$	$\Phi(x)$	$\Phi^{(2)}(x)$	$\Phi^{(3)}(x)$	$\Phi^{(4)}(x)$
2.00	.9772	.0540	.1620	$-.1080$	$-.2700$	2.50	.9938	.0175	.0920	$-.1424$	.0800
2.01	.9778	.0529	.1609	$-.1106$	$-.2603$	2.51	.9940	.0171	.0906	$-.1416$	.0836
2.02	.9783	.0519	.1598	$-.1132$	$-.2506$	2.52	.9941	.0167	.0892	$-.1408$	.0871
2.03	.9788	.0508	.1586	$-.1157$	$-.2411$	2.53	.9943	.0163	.0878	$-.1399$	.0905
2.04	.9793	.0498	.1575	$-.1180$	$-.2316$	2.54	.9945	.0158	.0864	$-.1389$	.0937
2.05	.9798	.0488	.1563	$-.1203$	$-.2222$	2.55	.9946	.0154	.0850	$-.1380$	.0968
2.06	.9803	.0478	.1550	$-.1225$	$-.2129$	2.56	.9948	.0151	.0836	$-.1370$	.0998
2.07	.9808	.0468	.1538	$-.1245$	$-.2036$	2.57	.9949	.0147	.0823	$-.1360$	.1027
2.08	.9812	.0459	.1526	$-.1265$	$-.1945$	2.58	.9951	.0143	.0809	$-.1350$	.1054
2.09	.9817	.0449	.1513	$-.1284$	$-.1854$	2.59	.9952	.0139	.0796	$-.1339$	.1080
2.10	.9821	.0440	.1500	$-.1302$	$-.1765$	2.60	.9953	.0136	.0782	$-.1328$	.1105
2.11	.9826	.0431	.1487	$-.1320$	$-.1676$	2.61	.9955	.0132	.0769	$-.1317$	.1129
2.12	.9830	.0422	.1474	$-.1336$	$-.1588$	2.62	.9956	.0129	.0756	$-.1305$	.1152
2.13	.9834	.0413	.1460	$-.1351$	$-.1502$	2.63	.9957	.0126	.0743	$-.1294$	.1173
2.14	.9838	.0404	.1446	$-.1366$	$-.1416$	2.64	.9959	.0122	.0730	$-.1282$	.1194
2.15	.9842	.0395	.1433	$-.1380$	$-.1332$	2.65	.9960	.0119	.0717	$-.1270$	.1213
2.16	.9846	.0387	.1419	$-.1393$	$-.1249$	2.66	.9961	.0116	.0705	$-.1258$	.1231
2.17	.9850	.0379	.1405	$-.1405$	$-.1167$	2.67	.9962	.0113	.0692	$-.1245$	.1248
2.18	.9854	.0371	.1391	$-.1416$	$-.1086$	2.68	.9963	.0110	.0680	$-.1233$	.1264
2.19	.9857	.0363	.1377	$-.1426$	$-.1006$	2.69	.9964	.0107	.0668	$-.1220$	.1279
2.20	.9861	.0355	.1362	$-.1436$	$-.0927$	2.70	.9965	.0104	.0656	$-.1207$	.1293
2.21	.9864	.0347	.1348	$-.1445$	$-.0850$	2.71	.9966	.0101	.0644	$-.1194$	.1306
2.22	.9868	.0339	.1333	$-.1453$	$-.0774$	2.72	.9967	.0099	.0632	$-.1181$	.1317
2.23	.9871	.0332	.1319	$-.1460$	$-.0700$	2.73	.9968	.0096	.0620	$-.1168$	.1328
2.24	.9875	.0325	.1304	$-.1467$	$-.0626$	2.74	.9969	.0093	.0608	$-.1154$	.1338
2.25	.9878	.0317	.1289	$-.1473$	$-.0554$	2.75	.9970	.0091	.0597	$-.1141$	.1347
2.26	.9881	.0310	.1275	$-.1478$	$-.0484$	2.76	.9971	.0088	.0585	$-.1127$	.1356
2.27	.9884	.0303	.1260	$-.1483$	$-.0414$	2.77	.9972	.0086	.0574	$-.1114$	.1363
2.28	.9887	.0297	.1245	$-.1486$	$-.0346$	2.78	.9973	.0084	.0563	$-.1100$	.1369
2.29	.9890	.0290	.1230	$-.1490$	$-.0279$	2.79	.9974	.0081	.0552	$-.1087$	.1375
2.30	.9893	.0283	.1215	$-.1492$	$-.0214$	2.80	.9974	.0079	.0541	$-.1073$	.1379
2.31	.9896	.0277	.1200	$-.1494$	$-.0150$	2.81	.9975	.0077	.0531	$-.1059$	.1383
2.32	.9898	.0270	.1185	$-.1495$	$-.0088$	2.82	.9976	.0075	.0520	$-.1045$	.1386
2.33	.9901	.0264	.1170	$-.1496$	$-.0027$	2.83	.9977	.0073	.0510	$-.1031$	.1389
2.34	.9904	.0258	.1155	$-.1496$	.0033	2.84	.9977	.0071	.0500	$-.1017$	.1390
2.35	.9906	.0252	.1141	$-.1495$	.0092	2.85	.9978	.0069	.0490	$-.1003$	.1391
2.36	.9909	.0246	.1126	$-.1494$	.0149	2.86	.9979	.0067	.0480	$-.0990$	.1391
2.37	.9911	.0241	.1111	$-.1492$	.0204	2.87	.9979	.0065	.0470	$-.0976$	.1391
2.38	.9913	.0235	.1096	$-.1490$	.0258	2.88	.9980	.0063	.0460	$-.0962$	.1389
2.39	.9916	.0229	.1081	$-.1487$	.0311	2.89	.9981	.0061	.0451	$-.0948$	.1388
2.40	.9918	.0224	.1066	$-.1483$	.0362	2.90	.9981	.0060	.0441	$-.0934$	.1385
2.41	.9920	.0219	.1051	$-.1480$	.0412	2.91	.9982	.0058	.0432	$-.0920$	.1382
2.42	.9922	.0213	.1036	$-.1475$	.0461	2.92	.9982	.0056	.0423	$-.0906$	.1378
2.43	.9925	.0208	.1022	$-.1470$	.0508	2.93	.9983	.0055	.0414	$-.0893$	.1374
2.44	.9927	.0203	.1007	$-.1465$	.0554	2.94	.9984	.0053	.0405	$-.0879$	.1369
2.45	.9929	.0198	.0992	$-.1459$	.0598	2.95	.9984	.0051	.0396	$-.0865$	.1364
2.46	.9931	.0194	.0978	$-.1453$	.0641	2.96	.9985	.0050	.0388	$-.0852$	.1358
2.47	.9932	.0189	.0963	$-.1446$	.0683	2.97	.9985	.0048	.0379	$-.0838$	.1352
2.48	.9934	.0184	.0949	$-.1439$	.0723	2.98	.9986	.0047	.0371	$-.0825$	.1345
2.49	.9936	.0180	.0935	$-.1432$	.0762	2.99	.9986	.0046	.0363	$-.0811$	.1337

PROBABILITY FUNCTIONS

x	$\frac{1}{2}(1+\alpha)$	$\Phi(x)$	$\Phi^{(2)}(x)$	$\Phi^{(3)}(x)$	$\Phi^{(4)}(x)$	x	$\frac{1}{2}(1+\alpha)$	$\Phi(x)$	$\Phi^{(2)}(x)$	$\Phi^{(3)}(x)$	$\Phi^{(4)}(x)$
3.00	.9987	.0044	.0355	−.0798	.1330	3.50	.9998	.0009	.0098	−.0283	.0694
3.01	.9987	.0043	.0347	−.0785	.1321	3.51	.9998	.0008	.0095	−.0276	.0681
3.02	.9987	.0042	.0339	−.0771	.1313	3.52	.9998	.0008	.0093	−.0269	.0669
3.03	.9988	.0040	.0331	−.0758	.1304	3.53	.9998	.0008	.0090	−.0262	.0656
3.04	.9988	.0039	.0324	−.0745	.1294	3.54	.9998	.0008	.0087	−.0256	.0643
3.05	.9989	.0038	.0316	−.0732	.1285	3.55	.9998	.0007	.0085	−.0249	.0631
3.06	.9989	.0037	.0309	−.0720	.1275	3.56	.9998	.0007	.0082	−.0243	.0618
3.07	.9989	.0036	.0302	−.0707	.1264	3.57	.9998	.0007	.0080	−.0237	.0606
3.08	.9990	.0035	.0295	−.0694	.1254	3.58	.9998	.0007	.0078	−.0231	.0594
3.09	.9990	.0034	.0288	−.0682	.1243	3.59	.9998	.0006	.0075	−.0225	.0582
3.10	.9990	.0033	.0281	−.0669	.1231	3.60	.9998	.0006	.0073	−.0219	.0570
3.11	.9991	.0032	.0275	−.0657	.1220	3.61	.9999	.0006	.0071	−.0214	.0559
3.12	.9991	.0031	.0268	−.0645	.1208	3.62	.9999	.0006	.0069	−.0208	.0547
3.13	.9991	.0030	.0262	−.0633	.1196	3.63	.9999	.0006	.0067	−.0203	.0536
3.14	.9992	.0029	.0256	−.0621	.1184	3.64	.9999	.0005	.0065	−.0198	.0524
3.15	.9992	.0028	.0249	−.0609	.1171	3.65	.9999	.0005	.0063	−.0192	.0513
3.16	.9992	.0027	.0243	−.0598	.1159	3.66	.9999	.0005	.0061	−.0187	.0502
3.17	.9992	.0026	.0237	−.0586	.1146	3.67	.9999	.0005	.0059	−.0182	.0492
3.18	.9993	.0025	.0232	−.0575	.1133	3.68	.9999	.0005	.0057	−.0177	.0481
3.19	.9993	.0025	.0226	−.0564	.1120	3.69	.9999	.0004	.0056	−.0173	.0470
3.20	.9993	.0024	.0220	−.0552	.1107	3.70	.9999	.0004	.0054	−.0168	.0460
3.21	.9993	.0023	.0215	−.0541	.1093	3.71	.9999	.0004	.0052	−.0164	.0450
3.22	.9994	.0022	.0210	−.0531	.1080	3.72	.9999	.0004	.0051	−.0159	.0440
3.23	.9994	.0022	.0204	−.0520	.1066	3.73	.9999	.0004	.0049	−.0155	.0430
3.24	.9994	.0021	.0199	−.0509	.1053	3.74	.9999	.0004	.0048	−.0150	.0420
3.25	.9994	.0020	.0194	−.0499	.1039	3.75	.9999	.0004	.0046	−.0146	.0410
3.26	.9994	.0020	.0189	−.0488	.1025	3.76	.9999	.0003	.0045	−.0142	.0401
3.27	.9995	.0019	.0184	−.0478	.1011	3.77	.9999	.0003	.0043	−.0138	.0392
3.28	.9995	.0018	.0180	−.0468	.0997	3.78	.9999	.0003	.0042	−.0134	.0382
3.29	.9995	.0018	.0175	−.0458	.0983	3.79	.9999	.0003	.0041	−.0131	.0373
3.30	.9995	.0017	.0170	−.0449	.0969	3.80	.9999	.0003	.0039	−.0127	.0365
3.31	.9995	.0017	.0166	−.0439	.0955	3.81	.9999	.0003	.0038	−.0123	.0356
3.32	.9996	.0016	.0162	−.0429	.0941	3.82	.9999	.0003	.0037	−.0120	.0347
3.33	.9996	.0016	.0157	−.0420	.0927	3.83	.9999	.0003	.0036	−.0116	.0339
3.34	.9996	.0015	.0153	−.0411	.0913	3.84	.9999	.0003	.0034	−.0113	.0331
3.35	.9996	.0015	.0149	−.0402	.0899	3.85	.9999	.0002	.0033	−.0110	.0323
3.36	.9996	.0014	.0145	−.0393	.0885	3.86	.9999	.0002	.0032	−.0107	.0315
3.37	.9996	.0014	.0141	−.0384	.0871	3.87	1.0000	.0002	.0031	−.0104	.0307
3.38	.9996	.0013	.0138	−.0376	.0857	3.88	1.0000	.0002	.0030	−.0100	.0299
3.39	.9997	.0013	.0134	−.0367	.0843	3.89	1.0000	.0002	.0029	−.0098	.0292
3.40	.9997	.0012	.0130	−.0359	.0829	3.90	1.0000	.0002	.0028	−.0095	.0284
3.41	.9997	.0012	.0127	−.0350	.0815	3.91	1.0000	.0002	.0027	−.0092	.0277
3.42	.9997	.0012	.0123	−.0342	.0801	3.92	1.0000	.0002	.0026	−.0089	.0270
3.43	.9997	.0011	.0120	−.0334	.0788	3.93	1.0000	.0002	.0026	−.0086	.0263
3.44	.9997	.0011	.0116	−.0327	.0774	3.94	1.0000	.0002	.0025	−.0084	.0256
3.45	.9997	.0010	.0113	−.0319	.0761	3.95	1.0000	.0002	.0024	−.0081	.0250
3.46	.9997	.0010	.0110	−.0311	.0747	3.96	1.0000	.0002	.0023	−.0079	.0243
3.47	.9997	.0010	.0107	−.0304	.0734	3.97	1.0000	.0002	.0022	−.0076	.0237
3.48	.9998	.0009	.0104	−.0297	.0721	3.98	1.0000	.0001	.0022	−.0074	.0230
3.49	.9998	.0009	.0101	−.0290	.0707	3.99	1.0000	.0001	.0021	−.0072	.0224

x	$\frac{1}{2}(1+\alpha)$	$\Phi(x)$	$\Phi^{(2)}(x)$	$\Phi^{(3)}(x)$	$\Phi^{(4)}(x)$	x	$\frac{1}{2}(1+\alpha)$	$\Phi(x)$	$\Phi^{(2)}(x)$	$\Phi^{(3)}(x)$	$\Phi^{(4)}(x)$
4.00	1.0000	.0001	.0020	−.0070	.0218	4.50	1.0000	.0000	.0003	−.0012	.0047
4.05	1.0000	.0001	.0017	−.0059	.0190	4.55	1.0000	.0000	.0003	−.0010	.0039
4.10	1.0000	.0001	.0014	−.0051	.0165	4.60	1.0000	.0000	.0002	−.0009	.0033
4.15	1.0000	.0001	.0012	−.0043	.0143	4.65	1.0000	.0000	.0002	−.0007	.0027
4.20	1.0000	.0001	.0010	−.0036	.0123	4.70	1.0000	.0000	.0001	−.0006	.0023
4.25	1.0000	.0001	.0008	−.0031	.0105	4.75	1.0000	.0000	.0001	−.0005	.0019
4.30	1.0000	.0000	.0007	−.0026	.0090	4.80	1.0000	.0000	.0001	−.0004	.0016
4.35	1.0000	.0000	.0006	−.0022	.0077	4.85	1.0000	.0000	.0001	−.0003	.0013
4.40	1.0000	.0000	.0005	−.0018	.0065	4.90	1.0000	.0000	.0001	−.0003	.0011
4.45	1.0000	.0000	.0004	−.0015	.0055	4.95	1.0000	.0000	.0000	−.0002	.0009

Table XXV b

FACTORS FOR COMPUTING PROBABLE ERRORS

n	$\dfrac{1}{\sqrt{n}}$	$\dfrac{1}{\sqrt{n(n-1)}}$	$\dfrac{.6745}{\sqrt{n-1}}$	$\dfrac{.6745}{\sqrt{n(n-1)}}$	$\dfrac{.8453}{n\sqrt{n-1}}$	$\dfrac{.8453}{\sqrt{n(n-1)}}$
2	.707 107	.707 107	.6745	.4769	.4227	.5978
3	.577 350	.408 248	.4769	.2754	.1993	.3451
4	.500 000	.288 675	.3894	.1947	.1220	.2440
5	.447 214	.223 607	.3372	.1508	.0845	.1890
6	.408 248	.182 574	.3016	.1231	.0630	.1543
7	.377 964	.154 303	.2754	.1041	.0493	.1304
8	.353 553	.133 631	.2549	.0901	.0399	.1130
9	.333 333	.117 851	.2385	.0795	.0332	.0996
10	.316 228	.105 409	.2248	.0711	.0282	.0891
11	.301 511	.095 346	.2133	.0643	.0243	.0806
12	.288 675	.087 039	.2034	.0587	.0212	.0736
13	.277 350	.080 064	.1947	.0540	.0188	.0677
14	.267 261	.074 125	.1871	.0500	.0167	.0627
15	.258 199	.069 007	.1803	.0465	.0151	.0583
16	.250 000	.064 550	.1742	.0435	.0136	.0546
17	.242 536	.060 634	.1686	.0409	.0124	.0513
18	.235 702	.057 166	.1636	.0386	.0114	.0483
19	.229 416	.054 074	.1590	.0365	.0105	.0457
20	.223 607	.051 299	.1547	.0346	.0097	.0434
21	.218 218	.048 795	.1508	.0329	.0090	.0412
22	.213 201	.046 524	.1472	.0314	.0084	.0393
23	.208 514	.044 455	.1438	.0300	.0078	.0376
24	.204 124	.042 563	.1406	.0287	.0073	.0360
25	.200 000	.040 825	.1377	.0275	.0069	.0345
26	.196 116	.039 223	.1349	.0265	.0065	.0332
27	.192 450	.037 743	.1323	.0255	.0061	.0319
28	.188 982	.036 370	.1298	.0245	.0058	.0307
29	.185 695	.035 093	.1275	.0237	.0055	.0297
30	.182 574	.033 903	.1252	.0229	.0052	.0287
31	.179 605	.032 791	.1231	.0221	.0050	.0277
32	.176 777	.031 750	.1211	.0214	.0047	.0268
33	.174 078	.030 773	.1192	.0208	.0045	.0260
34	.171 499	.029 854	.1174	.0201	.0043	.0252
35	.169 031	.028 989	.1157	.0196	.0041	.0245
36	.166 667	.028 172	.1140	.0190	.0040	.0238
37	.164 399	.027 400	.1124	.0185	.0038	.0232
38	.162 221	.026 669	.1109	.0180	.0037	.0225
39	.160 128	.025 976	.1094	.0175	.0035	.0220
40	.158 114	.025 318	.1080	.0171	.0034	.0214
41	.156 174	.024 693	.1066	.0167	.0033	.0209
42	.154 303	.024 098	.1053	.0163	.0031	.0204
43	.152 499	.023 531	.1041	.0159	.0030	.0199
44	.150 756	.022 990	.1029	.0155	.0029	.0194
45	.149 071	.022 473	.1017	.0152	.0028	.0190
46	.147 442	.021 979	.1005	.0148	.0027	.0186
47	.145 865	.021 507	.0994	.0145	.0027	.0182
48	.144 338	.021 054	.0984	.0142	.0026	.0178
49	.142 857	.020 620	.0974	.0139	.0025	.0174

FACTORS FOR COMPUTING PROBABLE ERRORS

n	$\dfrac{1}{\sqrt{n}}$	$\dfrac{1}{\sqrt{n(n-1)}}$	$\dfrac{.6745}{\sqrt{n-1}}$	$\dfrac{.6745}{\sqrt{n(n-1)}}$	$\dfrac{.8453}{n\sqrt{n-1}}$	$\dfrac{.8453}{\sqrt{n(n-1)}}$
50	.141 421	.020 203	.0964	.0136	.0024	.0171
51	.140 028	.019 803	.0954	.0134	.0023	.0167
52	.138 675	.019 418	.0945	.0131	.0023	.0164
53	.137 361	.019 048	.0935	.0129	.0022	.0161
54	.136 083	.018 692	.0927	.0126	.0022	.0158
55	.134 840	.018 349	.0918	.0124	.0021	.0155
56	.133 631	.018 019	.0910	.0122	.0020	.0152
57	.132 453	.017 700	.0901	.0119	.0020	.0150
58	.131 306	.017 392	.0893	.0117	.0019	.0147
59	.130 189	.017 095	.0886	.0115	.0019	.0145
60	.129 099	.016 807	.0878	.0113	.0018	.0142
61	.128 037	.016 529	.0871	.0112	.0018	.0140
62	.127 000	.016 261	.0864	.0110	.0018	.0138
63	.125 988	.016 001	.0857	.0108	.0017	.0135
64	.125 000	.015 749	.0850	.0106	.0017	.0133
65	.124 035	.015 504	.0843	.0105	.0016	.0131
66	.123 091	.015 268	.0837	.0103	.0016	.0129
67	.122 169	.015 038	.0830	.0101	.0016	.0127
68	.121 268	.014 815	.0824	.0100	.0015	.0125
69	.120 386	.014 599	.0818	.0099	.0015	.0123
70	.119 523	.014 389	.0812	.0097	.0015	.0122
71	.118 678	.014 185	.0806	.0096	.0014	.0120
72	.117 851	.013 986	.0801	.0094	.0014	.0118
73	.117 041	.013 793	.0795	.0093	.0014	.0117
74	.116 248	.013 606	.0789	.0092	.0013	.0115
75	.115 470	.013 423	.0784	.0091	.0013	.0113
76	.114 708	.013 245	.0779	.0089	.0013	.0112
77	.113 961	.013 072	.0773	.0088	.0013	.0111
78	.113 228	.012 904	.0769	.0087	.0012	.0109
79	.112 509	.012 739	.0764	.0086	.0012	.0108
80	.111 803	.012 579	.0759	.0085	.0012	.0106
81	.111 111	.012 423	.0754	.0084	.0012	.0105
82	.110 432	.012 270	.0749	.0083	.0012	.0104
83	.109 764	.012 121	.0745	.0082	.0011	.0103
84	.109 109	.011 976	.0740	.0081	.0011	.0101
85	.108 465	.011 835	.0736	.0080	.0011	.0100
86	.107 833	.011 696	.0732	.0079	.0011	.0099
87	.107 211	.011 561	.0727	.0078	.0011	.0098
88	.106 600	.011 429	.0723	.0077	.0010	.0097
89	.106 000	.011 300	.0719	.0076	.0010	.0096
90	.105 409	.011 173	.0715	.0075	.0010	.0094
91	.104 828	.011 050	.0711	.0075	.0010	.0093
92	.104 257	.010 929	.0707	.0074	.0010	.0092
93	.103 695	.010 811	.0703	.0073	.0010	.0091
94	.103 142	.010 695	.0699	.0072	.0009	.0090
95	.102 598	.010 582	.0696	.0071	.0009	.0089
96	.102 062	.010 471	.0692	.0071	.0009	.0089
97	.101 535	.010 363	.0688	.0070	.0009	.0088
98	.101 015	.010 257	.0685	.0069	.0009	.0087
99	.100 504	.010 152	.0681	.0069	.0009	.0086
100	1.000 000	.010 050	.0678	.0068	.0008	.0085

Table XXVI

COMPLETE ELLIPTIC INTEGRALS, *K* AND *E*, FOR DIFFERENT VALUES OF THE MODULUS, *k*

$$K = \int_0^{\frac{\pi}{2}} \frac{dx}{\sqrt{1 - k^2 \sin^2 x}}; \quad E = \int_0^{\frac{\pi}{2}} \sqrt{1 - k^2 \sin^2 x} \cdot dx$$

$\sin^{-1}k$	K	E	$\sin^{-1}k$	K	E	$\sin^{-1}k$	K	E
0°	1.5708	1.5708	50°	1.9356	1.3055	81°.0	3.2553	1.0338
1	1.5709	1.5707	51	1.9539	1.2963	81.2	3.2771	1.0326
2	1.5713	1.5703	52	1.9729	1.2870	81.4	3.2995	1.0313
3	1.5719	1.5697	53	1.9927	1.2776	81.6	3.3223	1.0302
4	1.5727	1.5689	54	2.0133	1.2681	81.8	3.3458	1.0290
5	1.5738	1.5678	55	2.0347	1.2587	82.0	3.3699	1.0278
6	1.5751	1.5665	56	2.0571	1.2492	82.2	3.3946	1.0267
7	1.5767	1.5649	57	2.0804	1.2397	82.4	3.4199	1.0256
8	1.5785	1.5632	58	2.1047	1.2301	82.6	3.4460	1.0245
9	1.5805	1.5611	59	2.1300	1.2206	82.8	3.4728	1.0234
10	1.5828	1.5589	60	2.1565	1.2111	83.0	3.5004	1.0223
11	1.5854	1.5564	61	2.1842	1.2015	83.2	3.5288	1.0213
12	1.5882	1.5537	62	2.2132	1.1921	83.4	3.5581	1.0202
13	1.5913	1.5507	63	2.2435	1.1826	83.6	3.5884	1.0192
14	1.5946	1.5476	64	2.2754	1.1732	83.8	3.6196	1.0182
15	1.5981	1.5442	65	2.3088	1.1638	84.0	3.6519	1.0172
16	1.6020	1.5405	65.5	2.3261	1.1592	84.2	3.6853	1.0163
17	1.6061	1.5367	66.0	2.3439	1.1546	84.4	3.7198	1.0153
18	1.6105	1.5326	66.5	2.3622	1.1499	84.6	3.7557	1.0144
19	1.6151	1.5283	67.0	2.3809	1.1454	84.8	3.7930	1.0135
20	1.6200	1.5238	67.5	2.4001	1.1408	85.0	3.8317	1.0127
21	1.6252	1.5191	68.0	2.4198	1.1362	85.2	3.8721	1.0118
22	1.6307	1.5141	68.5	2.4401	1.1317	85.4	3.9142	1.0110
23	1.6365	1.5090	69.0	2.4610	1.1273	85.6	3.9583	1.0102
24	1.6426	1.5037	69.5	2.4825	1.1228	85.8	4.0044	1.0094
25	1.6490	1.4981	70.0	2.5046	1.1184	86.0	4.0528	1.0087
26	1.6557	1.4924	70.5	2.5273	1.1140	86.2	4.1037	1.0079
27	1.6627	1.4864	71.0	2.5507	1.1096	86.4	4.1574	1.0072
28	1.6701	1.4803	71.5	2.5749	1.1053	86.6	4.2142	1.0065
29	1.6777	1.4740	72.0	2.5998	1.1011	86.8	4.2744	1.0059
30	1.6858	1.4675	72.5	2.6256	1.0968	87.0	4.3387	1.0053
31	1.6941	1.4608	73.0	2.6521	1.0927	87.2	4.4073	1.0047
32	1.7028	1.4539	73.5	2.6796	1.0885	87.4	4.4812	1.0041
33	1.7119	1.4469	74.0	2.7081	1.0844	87.6	4.5619	1.0036
34	1.7214	1.4397	74.5	2.7375	1.0804	87.8	4.6477	1.0031
35	1.7312	1.4323	75.0	2.7681	1.0764	88.0	4.7427	1.0026
36	1.7415	1.4248	75.5	2.7998	1.0725	88.2	4.8479	1.0022
37	1.7522	1.4171	76.0	2.8327	1.0686	88.4	4.9654	1.0017
38	1.7633	1.4092	76.5	2.8669	1.0648	88.6	5.0988	1.0014
39	1.7748	1.4013	77.0	2.9026	1.0611	88.8	5.2527	1.0010
40	1.7868	1.3931	77.5	2.9397	1.0574	89.0	5.4349	1.0008
41	1.7992	1.3849	78.0	2.9786	1.0538	89.1	5.5402	1.0006
42	1.8122	1.3765	78.5	3.0192	1.0502	89.2	5.6579	1.0005
43	1.8256	1.3680	79.0	3.0617	1.0468	89.3	5.7914	1.0005
44	1.8396	1.3594	79.5	3.1064	1.0434	89.4	5.9455	1.0003
45	1.8541	1.3506	80.0	3.1534	1.0401	89.5	6.1278	1.0002
46	1.8691	1.3418	80.2	3.1729	1.0388	89.6	6.3504	1.0001
47	1.8848	1.3329	80.4	3.1928	1.0375	89.7	6.6385	1.0001
48	1.9011	1.3238	80.6	3.2132	1.0363	89.8	7.0440	1.0000
49	1.9180	1.3147	80.8	3.2340	1.0350	89.9	7.7371	1.0000

Table XXVII

LOGARITHMS OF TRIGONOMETRIC FUNCTIONS

Deg.	Log Rad	Log Sin	Log Cos	Log Tan	Log Ctn	Log Sec	Log Csc		
0	. . . . .	. . . . .	10.0000	. . . . .	. . . . .	0.0000	. . . . .	0.1961	90
1	8.2419	8.2419	9.9999	8.2419	1.7581	0.0001	1.7581	0.1913	89
2	8.5429	8.5428	9.9997	8.5431	1.4569	0.0003	1.4572	0.1864	88
3	8.7190	8.7188	9.9994	8.7194	1.2806	0.0006	1.2812	0.1814	87
4	8.8439	8.8436	9.9989	8.8446	1.1554	0.0011	1.1564	0.1764	86
5	8.9408	8.9403	9.9983	8.9420	1.0580	0.0017	1.0597	0.1713	85
6	9.0200	9.0192	9.9976	9.0216	0.9784	0.0024	0.9808	0.1662	84
7	9.0870	9.0859	9.9968	9.0891	0.9109	0.0032	0.9141	0.1610	83
8	9.1450	9.1436	9.9958	9.1478	0.8522	0.0042	0.8564	0.1557	82
9	9.1961	9.1943	9.9946	9.1997	0.8003	0.0054	0.8057	0.1504	81
10	9.2419	9.2397	9.9934	9.2463	0.7537	0.0066	0.7603	0.1450	80
11	9.2833	9.2806	9.9919	9.2887	0.7113	0.0081	0.7194	0.1395	79
12	9.3211	9.3179	9.9904	9.3275	0.6725	0.0096	0.6821	0.1340	78
13	9.3558	9.3521	9.9887	9.3634	0.6366	0.0113	0.6479	0.1284	77
14	9.3880	9.3837	9.9869	9.3968	0.6032	0.0131	0.6163	0.1227	76
15	9.4180	9.4130	9.9849	9.4281	0.5719	0.0151	0.5870	0.1169	75
16	9.4460	9.4403	9.9828	9.4575	0.5425	0.0172	0.5597	0.1111	74
17	9.4723	9.4659	9.9806	9.4853	0.5147	0.0194	0.5341	0.1052	73
18	9.4971	9.4900	9.9782	9.5118	0.4882	0.0218	0.5100	0.0992	72
19	9.5206	9.5126	9.9757	9.5370	0.4630	0.0243	0.4874	0.0931	71
20	9.5429	9.5341	9.9730	9.5611	0.4389	0.0270	0.4659	0.0870	70
21	9.5641	9.5543	9.9702	9.5842	0.4158	0.0298	0.4457	0.0807	69
22	9.5843	9.5736	9.9672	9.6064	0.3936	0.0328	0.4264	0.0744	68
23	9.6036	9.5919	9.9640	9.6279	0.3721	0.0360	0.4081	0.0680	67
24	9.6221	9.6093	9.9607	9.6486	0.3514	0.0393	0.3907	0.0614	66
25	9.6398	9.6259	9.9573	9.6687	0.3313	0.0427	0.3741	0.0548	65
26	9.6569	9.6418	9.9537	9.6882	0.3118	0.0463	0.3582	0.0481	64
27	9.6732	9.6570	9.9499	9.7072	0.2928	0.0501	0.3430	0.0412	63
28	9.6890	9.6716	9.9459	9.7257	0.2743	0.0541	0.3284	0.0343	62
29	9.7042	9.6856	9.9418	9.7438	0.2562	0.0582	0.3144	0.0272	61
30	9.7190	9.6990	9.9375	9.7614	0.2386	0.0625	0.3010	0.0200	60
31	9.7332	9.7118	9.9331	9.7788	0.2212	0.0669	0.2882	0.0127	59
32	9.7470	9.7242	9.9284	9.7958	0.2042	0.0716	0.2758	0.0053	58
33	9.7604	9.7361	9.9236	9.8125	0.1875	0.0764	0.2639	9.9978	57
34	9.7734	9.7476	9.9186	9.8290	0.1710	0.0814	0.2524	9.9901	56
35	9.7859	9.7586	9.9134	9.8452	0.1548	0.0866	0.2414	9.9822	55
36	9.7982	9.7692	9.9080	9.8613	0.1387	0.0920	0.2308	9.9743	54
37	9.8101	9.7795	9.9023	9.8771	0.1229	0.0977	0.2205	9.9662	53
38	9.8217	9.7893	9.8965	9.8928	0.1072	0.1035	0.2107	9.9579	52
39	9.8329	9.7989	9.8905	9.9084	0.0916	0.1095	0.2011	9.9494	51
40	9.8439	9.8081	9.8843	9.9238	0.0762	0.1157	0.1919	9.9408	50
41	9.8547	9.8169	9.8778	9.9392	0.0608	0.1222	0.1831	9.9321	49
42	9.8651	9.8255	9.8711	9.9544	0.0456	0.1289	0.1745	9.9231	48
43	9.8753	9.8338	9.8641	9.9697	0.0303	0.1359	0.1662	9.9140	47
44	9.8853	9.8418	9.8569	9.9848	0.0152	0.1431	0.1582	9.9046	46
45	9.8951	9.8495	9.8495	0.0000	0.0000	0.1505	0.1505	9.8951	45
		Log Cos	Log Sin	Log Ctn	Log Tan	Log Csc	Log Sec	Log Rad	Deg.

Table XXVIII

NATURAL TRIGONOMETRIC FUNCTIONS

Deg.	Rad	Sin	Cos	Tan	Ctn	Sec	Csc		
0	0.0000	0.0000	1.0000	0.0000	......	1.0000	......	1.5708	90
1	0.0175	0.0175	0.9998	0.0175	57.290	1.0002	57.299	1.5533	89
2	0.0349	0.0349	0.9994	0.0349	28.636	1.0006	28.654	1.5359	88
3	0.0524	0.0523	0.9986	0.0524	19.081	1.0014	19.107	1.5184	87
4	0.0698	0.0698	0.9976	0.0699	14.301	1.0024	14.336	1.5010	86
5	0.0873	0.0872	0.9962	0.0875	11.430	1.0038	11.474	1.4835	85
6	0.1047	0.1045	0.9945	0.1051	9.5144	1.0055	9.5668	1.4661	84
7	0.1222	0.1219	0.9925	0.1228	8.1443	1.0075	8.2055	1.4486	83
8	0.1396	0.1392	0.9903	0.1405	7.1154	1.0098	7.1853	1.4312	82
9	0.1571	0.1564	0.9877	0.1584	6.3138	1.0125	6.3925	1.4137	81
10	0.1745	0.1736	0.9848	0.1763	5.6713	1.0154	5.7588	1.3963	80
11	0.1920	0.1908	0.9816	0.1944	5.1446	1.0187	5.2408	1.3788	79
12	0.2094	0.2079	0.9781	0.2126	4.7046	1.0223	4.8097	1.3614	78
13	0.2269	0.2250	0.9744	0.2309	4.3315	1.0263	4.4454	1.3439	77
14	0.2443	0.2419	0.9703	0.2493	4.0108	1.0306	4.1336	1.3265	76
15	0.2618	0.2588	0.9659	0.2679	3.7321	1.0353	3.8637	1.3090	75
16	0.2793	0.2756	0.9613	0.2867	3.4874	1.0403	3.6280	1.2915	74
17	0.2967	0.2924	0.9563	0.3057	3.2709	1.0457	3.4203	1.2741	73
18	0.3142	0.3090	0.9511	0.3249	3.0777	1.0515	3.2361	1.2566	72
19	0.3316	0.3256	0.9455	0.3443	2.9042	1.0576	3.0716	1.2392	71
20	0.3491	0.3420	0.9397	0.3640	2.7475	1.0642	2.9238	1.2217	70
21	0.3665	0.3584	0.9336	0.3839	2.6051	1.0711	2.7904	1.2043	69
22	0.3840	0.3746	0.9272	0.4040	2.4751	1.0785	2.6695	1.1868	68
23	0.4014	0.3907	0.9205	0.4245	2.3559	1.0864	2.5593	1.1694	67
24	0.4189	0.4067	0.9135	0.4452	2.2460	1.0946	2.4586	1.1519	66
25	0.4363	0.4226	0.9063	0.4663	2.1445	1.1034	2.3662	1.1345	65
26	0.4538	0.4384	0.8988	0.4877	2.0503	1.1126	2.2812	1.1170	64
27	0.4712	0.4540	0.8910	0.5095	1.9626	1.1223	2.2027	1.0996	63
28	0.4887	0.4695	0.8829	0.5317	1.8807	1.1326	2.1301	1.0821	62
29	0.5061	0.4848	0.8746	0.5543	1.8040	1.1434	2.0627	1.0647	61
30	0.5236	0.5000	0.8660	0.5774	1.7321	1.1547	2.0000	1.0472	60
31	0.5411	0.5150	0.8572	0.6009	1.6643	1.1666	1.9416	1.0297	59
32	0.5585	0.5299	0.8480	0.6249	1.6003	1.1792	1.8871	1.0123	58
33	0.5760	0.5446	0.8387	0.6494	1.5399	1.1924	1.8361	0.9948	57
34	0.5934	0.5592	0.8290	0.6745	1.4826	1.2062	1.7883	0.9774	56
35	0.6109	0.5736	0.8192	0.7002	1.4281	1.2208	1.7434	0.9599	55
36	0.6283	0.5878	0.8090	0.7265	1.3764	1.2361	1.7013	0.9425	54
37	0.6458	0.6018	0.7986	0.7536	1.3270	1.2521	1.6616	0.9250	53
38	0.6632	0.6157	0.7880	0.7813	1.2799	1.2690	1.6243	0.9076	52
39	0.6807	0.6293	0.7771	0.8098	1.2349	1.2868	1.5890	0.8901	51
40	0.6981	0.6428	0.7660	0.8391	1.1918	1.3054	1.5557	0.8727	50
41	0.7156	0.6561	0.7547	0.8693	1.1504	1.3250	1.5243	0.8552	49
42	0.7330	0.6691	0.7431	0.9004	1.1106	1.3456	1.4945	0.8378	48
43	0.7505	0.6820	0.7314	0.9325	1.0724	1.3673	1.4663	0.8203	47
44	0.7679	0.6947	0.7193	0.9657	1.0355	1.3902	1.4396	0.8029	46
45	0.7854	0.7071	0.7071	1.0000	1.0000	1.4142	1.4142	0.7854	45
		Cos	Sin	Ctn	Tan	Csc	Sec	Rad	Deg.

Table XXIX

FOUR-PLACE LOGARITHMS

N	L. 0	1	2	3	4	5	6	7	8	9	Proportional Parts 1 2 3 4 5
10	0000	0043	0086	0128	0170	0212	0253	0294	0334	0374	4 8 12 17 21
11	0414	0453	0492	0531	0569	0607	0645	0682	0719	0755	4 8 11 15 19
12	0792	0828	0864	0899	0934	0969	1004	1038	1072	1106	3 7 10 14 17
13	1139	1173	1206	1239	1271	1303	1335	1367	1399	1430	3 6 10 13 16
14	1461	1492	1523	1553	1584	1614	1644	1673	1703	1732	3 6 9 12 15
15	1761	1790	1818	1847	1875	1903	1931	1959	1987	2014	3 6 8 11 14
16	2041	2068	2095	2122	2148	2175	2201	2227	2253	2279	3 5 8 11 13
17	2304	2330	2355	2380	2405	2430	2455	2480	2504	2529	2 5 7 10 12
18	2553	2577	2601	2625	2648	2672	2695	2718	2742	2765	2 5 7 9 12
19	2788	2810	2833	2856	2878	2900	2923	2945	2967	2989	2 4 7 9 11
20	3010	3032	3054	3075	3096	3118	3139	3160	3181	3201	2 4 6 8 11
21	3222	3243	3263	3284	3304	3324	3345	3365	3385	3404	2 4 6 8 10
22	3424	3444	3464	3483	3502	3522	3541	3560	3579	3598	2 4 6 8 10
23	3617	3636	3655	3674	3692	3711	3729	3747	3766	3784	2 4 6 7 9
24	3802	3820	3838	3856	3874	3892	3909	3927	3945	3962	2 4 5 7 9
25	3979	3997	4014	4031	4048	4065	4082	4099	4116	4133	2 4 5 7 9
26	4150	4166	4183	4200	4216	4232	4249	4265	4281	4298	2 3 5 7 8
27	4314	4330	4346	4362	4378	4393	4409	4425	4440	4456	2 3 5 6 8
28	4472	4487	4502	4518	4533	4548	4564	4579	4594	4609	2 3 5 6 8
29	4624	4639	4654	4669	4683	4698	4713	4728	4742	4757	1 3 4 6 7
30	4771	4786	4800	4814	4829	4843	4857	4871	4886	4900	1 3 4 6 7
31	4914	4928	4942	4955	4969	4983	4997	5011	5024	5038	1 3 4 5 7
32	5051	5065	5079	5092	5105	5119	5132	5145	5159	5172	1 3 4 5 7
33	5185	5198	5211	5224	5237	5250	5263	5276	5289	5302	1 3 4 5 7
34	5315	5328	5340	5353	5366	5378	5391	5403	5416	5428	1 2 4 5 6
35	5441	5453	5465	5478	5490	5502	5514	5527	5539	5551	1 2 4 5 6
36	5563	5575	5587	5599	5611	5623	5635	5647	5658	5670	1 2 4 5 6
37	5682	5694	5705	5717	5729	5740	5752	5763	5775	5786	1 2 4 5 6
38	5798	5809	5821	5832	5843	5855	5866	5877	5888	5899	1 2 3 5 6
39	5911	5922	5933	5944	5955	5966	5977	5988	5999	6010	1 2 3 4 5
40	6021	6031	6042	6053	6064	6075	6085	6096	6107	6117	1 2 3 4 5
41	6128	6138	6149	6160	6170	6180	6191	6201	6212	6222	1 2 3 4 5
42	6232	6243	6253	6263	6274	6284	6294	6304	6314	6325	1 2 3 4 5
43	6335	6345	6355	6365	6375	6385	6395	6405	6415	6425	1 2 3 4 5
44	6435	6444	6454	6464	6474	6484	6493	6503	6513	6522	1 2 3 4 5
45	6532	6542	6551	6561	6571	6580	6590	6599	6609	6618	1 2 3 4 5
46	6628	6637	6646	6656	6665	6675	6684	6693	6702	6712	1 2 3 4 5
47	6721	6730	6739	6749	6758	6767	6776	6785	6794	6803	1 2 3 4 5
48	6812	6821	6830	6839	6848	6857	6866	6875	6884	6893	1 2 3 4 5
49	6902	6911	6920	6928	6937	6946	6955	6964	6972	6981	1 2 3 4 4
50	6990	6998	7007	7016	7024	7033	7042	7050	7059	7067	1 2 3 3 4
51	7076	7084	7093	7101	7110	7118	7126	7135	7143	7152	1 2 3 3 4
52	7160	7168	7177	7185	7193	7202	7210	7218	7226	7235	1 2 3 3 4
53	7243	7251	7259	7267	7275	7284	7292	7300	7308	7316	1 2 2 3 4
54	7324	7332	7340	7348	7356	7364	7372	7380	7388	7396	1 2 2 3 4
N	L. 0	1	2	3	4	5	6	7	8	9	1 2 3 4 5

FOUR-PLACE LOGARITHMS

N	L. 0	1	2	3	4	5	6	7	8	9	Proportional parts 1	2	3	4	5
55	7404	7412	7419	7427	7435	7443	7451	7459	7466	7474	1	2	2	3	4
56	7482	7490	7497	7505	7513	7520	7528	7536	7543	7551	1	2	2	3	4
57	7559	7566	7574	7582	7589	7597	7604	7612	7619	7627	1	1	2	3	4
58	7634	7642	7649	7657	7664	7672	7679	7686	7694	7701	1	1	2	3	4
59	7709	7716	7723	7731	7738	7745	7752	7760	7767	7774	1	1	2	3	4
60	7782	7789	7796	7803	7810	7818	7825	7832	7839	7846	1	1	2	3	4
61	7853	7860	7868	7875	7882	7889	7896	7903	7910	7917	1	1	2	3	3
62	7924	7931	7938	7945	7952	7959	7966	7973	7980	7987	1	1	2	3	3
63	7993	8000	8007	8014	8021	8028	8035	8041	8048	8055	1	1	2	3	3
64	8062	8069	8075	8082	8089	8096	8102	8109	8116	8122	1	1	2	3	3
65	8129	8136	8142	8149	8156	8162	8169	8176	8182	8189	1	1	2	3	3
66	8195	8202	8209	8215	8222	8228	8235	8241	8248	8254	1	1	2	3	3
67	8261	8267	8274	8280	8287	8293	8299	8306	8312	8319	1	1	2	3	3
68	8325	8331	8338	8344	8351	8357	8363	8370	8376	8382	1	1	2	3	3
69	8388	8395	8401	8407	8414	8420	8426	8432	8439	8445	1	1	2	3	3
70	8451	8457	8463	8470	8476	8482	8488	8494	8500	8506	1	1	2	3	3
71	8513	8519	8525	8531	8537	8543	8549	8555	8561	8567	1	1	2	3	3
72	8573	8579	8585	8591	8597	8603	8609	8615	8621	8627	1	1	2	3	3
73	8633	8639	8645	8651	8657	8663	8669	8675	8681	8686	1	1	2	2	3
74	8692	8698	8704	8710	8716	8722	8727	8733	8739	8745	1	1	2	2	3
75	8751	8756	8762	8768	8774	8779	8785	8791	8797	8802	1	1	2	2	3
76	8808	8814	8820	8825	8831	8837	8842	8848	8854	8859	1	1	2	2	3
77	8865	8871	8876	8882	8887	8893	8899	8904	8910	8915	1	1	2	2	3
78	8921	8927	8932	8938	8943	8949	8954	8960	8965	8971	1	1	2	2	3
79	8976	8982	8987	8993	8998	9004	9009	9015	9020	9025	1	1	2	2	3
80	9031	9036	9042	9047	9053	9058	9063	9069	9074	9079	1	1	2	2	3
81	9085	9090	9096	9101	9106	9112	9117	9122	9128	9133	1	1	2	2	3
82	9138	9143	9149	9154	9159	9165	9170	9175	9180	9186	1	1	2	2	3
83	9191	9196	9201	9206	9212	9217	9222	9227	9232	9238	1	1	2	2	3
84	9243	9248	9253	9258	9263	9269	9274	9279	9284	9289	1	1	2	2	3
85	9294	9299	9304	9309	9315	9320	9325	9330	9335	9340	1	1	2	2	3
86	9345	9350	9355	9360	9365	9370	9375	9380	9385	9390	1	1	2	2	3
87	9395	9400	9405	9410	9415	9420	9425	9430	9435	9440	1	1	2	2	3
88	9445	9450	9455	9460	9465	9469	9474	9479	9484	9489	0	1	1	2	2
89	9494	9499	9504	9509	9513	9518	9523	9528	9533	9538	0	1	1	2	2
90	9542	9547	9552	9557	9562	9566	9571	9576	9581	9586	0	1	1	2	2
91	9590	9595	9600	9605	9609	9614	9619	9624	9628	9633	0	1	1	2	2
92	9638	9643	9647	9652	9657	9661	9666	9671	9675	9680	0	1	1	2	2
93	9685	9689	9694	9699	9703	9708	9713	9717	9722	9727	0	1	1	2	2
94	9731	9736	9741	9745	9750	9754	9759	9763	9768	9773	0	1	1	2	2
95	9777	9782	9786	9791	9795	9800	9805	9809	9814	9818	0	1	1	2	2
96	9823	9827	9832	9836	9841	9845	9850	9854	9859	9863	0	1	1	2	2
97	9868	9872	9877	9881	9886	9890	9894	9899	9903	9908	0	1	1	2	2
98	9912	9917	9921	9926	9930	9934	9939	9943	9948	9952	0	1	1	2	2
99	9956	9961	9965	9969	9974	9978	9983	9987	9991	9996	0	1	1	2	2
N	L. 0	1	2	3	4	5	6	7	8	9	1	2	3	4	5

Table XXX

FOUR-PLACE ANTILOGARITHMS

N	A. 0	1	2	3	4	5	6	7	8	9	Proportional parts 1	2	3	4	5
.00	1000	1002	1005	1007	1009	1012	1014	1016	1019	1021	0	0	1	1	1
.01	1023	1026	1028	1030	1033	1035	1038	1040	1042	1045	0	0	1	1	1
.02	1047	1050	1052	1054	1057	1059	1062	1064	1067	1069	0	0	1	1	1
.03	1072	1074	1076	1079	1081	1084	1086	1089	1091	1094	0	0	1	1	1
.04	1096	1099	1102	1104	1107	1109	1112	1114	1117	1119	0	1	1	1	1
.05	1122	1125	1127	1130	1132	1135	1138	1140	1143	1146	0	1	1	1	1
.06	1148	1151	1153	1156	1159	1161	1164	1167	1169	1172	0	1	1	1	1
.07	1175	1178	1180	1183	1186	1189	1191	1194	1197	1199	0	1	1	1	1
.08	1202	1205	1208	1211	1213	1216	1219	1222	1225	1227	0	1	1	1	1
.09	1230	1233	1236	1239	1242	1245	1247	1250	1253	1256	0	1	1	1	1
.10	1259	1262	1265	1268	1271	1274	1276	1279	1282	1285	0	1	1	1	1
.11	1288	1291	1294	1297	1300	1303	1306	1309	1312	1315	0	1	1	1	2
.12	1318	1321	1324	1327	1330	1334	1337	1340	1343	1346	0	1	1	1	2
.13	1349	1352	1355	1358	1361	1365	1368	1371	1374	1377	0	1	1	1	2
.14	1380	1384	1387	1390	1393	1396	1400	1403	1406	1409	0	1	1	1	2
.15	1413	1416	1419	1422	1426	1429	1432	1435	1439	1442	0	1	1	1	2
.16	1445	1449	1452	1455	1459	1462	1466	1469	1472	1476	0	1	1	1	2
.17	1479	1483	1486	1489	1493	1496	1500	1503	1507	1510	0	1	1	1	2
.18	1514	1517	1521	1524	1528	1531	1535	1538	1542	1545	0	1	1	1	2
.19	1549	1552	1556	1560	1563	1567	1570	1574	1578	1581	0	1	1	1	2
.20	1585	1589	1592	1596	1600	1603	1607	1611	1614	1618	0	1	1	1	2
.21	1622	1626	1629	1633	1637	1641	1644	1648	1652	1656	0	1	1	1	2
.22	1660	1663	1667	1671	1675	1679	1683	1687	1690	1694	0	1	1	2	2
.23	1698	1702	1706	1710	1714	1718	1722	1726	1730	1734	0	1	1	2	2
.24	1738	1742	1746	1750	1754	1758	1762	1766	1770	1774	0	1	1	2	2
.25	1778	1782	1786	1791	1795	1799	1803	1807	1811	1816	0	1	1	2	2
.26	1820	1824	1828	1832	1837	1841	1845	1849	1854	1858	0	1	1	2	2
.27	1862	1866	1871	1875	1879	1884	1888	1892	1897	1901	0	1	1	2	2
.28	1905	1910	1914	1919	1923	1928	1932	1936	1941	1945	0	1	1	2	2
.29	1950	1954	1959	1963	1968	1972	1977	1982	1986	1991	0	1	1	2	2
.30	1995	2000	2004	2009	2014	2018	2023	2028	2032	2037	0	1	1	2	2
.31	2042	2046	2051	2056	2061	2065	2070	2075	2080	2084	0	1	1	2	2
.32	2089	2094	2099	2104	2109	2113	2118	2123	2128	2133	0	1	1	2	2
.33	2138	2143	2148	2153	2158	2163	2168	2173	2178	2183	0	1	1	2	2
.34	2188	2193	2198	2203	2208	2213	2218	2223	2228	2234	1	1	2	2	3
.35	2239	2244	2249	2254	2259	2265	2270	2275	2280	2286	1	1	2	2	3
.36	2291	2296	2301	2307	2312	2317	2323	2328	2333	2339	1	1	2	2	3
.37	2344	2350	2355	2360	2366	2371	2377	2382	2388	2393	1	1	2	2	3
.38	2399	2404	2410	2415	2421	2427	2432	2438	2443	2449	1	1	2	2	3
.39	2455	2460	2466	2472	2477	2483	2489	2495	2500	2506	1	1	2	2	3
.40	2512	2518	2523	2529	2535	2541	2547	2553	2559	2564	1	1	2	2	3
.41	2570	2576	2582	2588	2594	2600	2606	2612	2618	2624	1	1	2	2	3
.42	2630	2636	2642	2649	2655	2661	2667	2673	2679	2685	1	1	2	2	3
.43	2692	2698	2704	2710	2716	2723	2729	2735	2742	2748	1	1	2	2	3
.44	2754	2761	2767	2773	2780	2786	2793	2799	2805	2812	1	1	2	3	3
.45	2818	2825	2831	2838	2844	2851	2858	2864	2871	2877	1	1	2	3	3
.46	2884	2891	2897	2904	2911	2917	2924	2931	2938	2944	1	1	2	3	3
.47	2951	2958	2965	2972	2979	2985	2992	2999	3006	3013	1	1	2	3	3
.48	3020	3027	3034	3041	3048	3055	3062	3069	3076	3083	1	1	2	3	3
.49	3090	3097	3105	3112	3119	3126	3133	3141	3148	3155	1	1	2	3	4
N	A. 0	1	2	3	4	5	6	7	8	9	1	2	3	4	5

FOUR-PLACE ANTILOGARITHMS

N	A. 0	1	2	3	4	5	6	7	8	9	Proportional Parts 1 2 3 4 5				
.50	3162	3170	3177	3184	3192	3199	3206	3214	3221	3228	1	1	2	3	4
.51	3236	3243	3251	3258	3266	3273	3281	3289	3296	3304	1	1	2	3	4
.52	3311	3319	3327	3334	3342	3350	3357	3365	3373	3381	1	1	2	3	4
.53	3388	3396	3404	3412	3420	3428	3436	3443	3451	3459	1	2	2	3	4
.54	3467	3475	3483	3491	3499	3508	3516	3524	3532	3540	1	2	2	3	4
.55	3548	3556	3565	3573	3581	3589	3597	3606	3614	3622	1	2	2	3	4
.56	3631	3639	3648	3656	3664	3673	3681	3690	3698	3707	1	2	2	3	4
.57	3715	3724	3733	3741	3750	3758	3767	3776	3784	3793	1	2	3	3	4
.58	3802	3811	3819	3828	3837	3846	3855	3864	3873	3882	1	2	3	3	4
.59	3890	3899	3908	3917	3926	3936	3945	3954	3963	3972	1	2	3	4	5
.60	3981	3990	3999	4009	4018	4027	4036	4046	4055	4064	1	2	3	4	5
.61	4074	4083	4093	4102	4111	4121	4130	4140	4150	4159	1	2	3	4	5
.62	4169	4178	4188	4198	4207	4217	4227	4236	4246	4256	1	2	3	4	5
.63	4266	4276	4285	4295	4305	4315	4325	4335	4345	4355	1	2	3	4	5
.64	4365	4375	4385	4395	4406	4416	4426	4436	4446	4457	1	2	3	4	5
.65	4467	4477	4487	4498	4508	4519	4529	4539	4550	4560	1	2	3	4	5
.66	4571	4581	4592	4603	4613	4624	4634	4645	4656	4667	1	2	3	4	5
.67	4677	4688	4699	4710	4721	4732	4742	4753	4764	4775	1	2	3	4	5
.68	4786	4797	4808	4819	4831	4842	4853	4864	4875	4887	1	2	3	5	6
.69	4898	4909	4920	4932	4943	4955	4966	4977	4989	5000	1	2	3	5	6
.70	5012	5023	5035	5047	5058	5070	5082	5093	5105	5117	1	2	3	5	6
.71	5129	5140	5152	5164	5176	5188	5200	5212	5224	5236	1	2	4	5	6
.72	5248	5260	5272	5284	5297	5309	5321	5333	5346	5358	1	2	4	5	6
.73	5370	5383	5395	5408	5420	5433	5445	5458	5470	5483	1	3	4	5	6
.74	5495	5508	5521	5534	5546	5559	5572	5585	5598	5610	1	3	4	5	6
.75	5623	5636	5649	5662	5675	5689	5702	5715	5728	5741	1	3	4	5	7
.76	5754	5768	5781	5794	5808	5821	5834	5848	5861	5875	1	3	4	5	7
.77	5888	5902	5916	5929	5943	5957	5970	5984	5998	6012	1	3	4	5	7
.78	6026	6039	6053	6067	6081	6095	6109	6124	6138	6152	1	3	4	6	7
.79	6166	6180	6194	6209	6223	6237	6252	6266	6281	6295	1	3	4	6	7
.80	6310	6324	6339	6353	6368	6383	6397	6412	6427	6442	1	3	4	6	7
.81	6457	6471	6486	6501	6516	6531	6546	6561	6577	6592	2	3	5	6	8
.82	6607	6622	6637	6653	6668	6683	6699	6714	6730	6745	2	3	5	6	8
.83	6761	6776	6792	6808	6823	6839	6855	6871	6887	6902	2	3	5	6	8
.84	6918	6934	6950	6966	6982	6998	7015	7031	7047	7063	2	3	5	7	8
.85	7079	7096	7112	7129	7145	7161	7178	7194	7211	7228	2	3	5	7	8
.86	7244	7261	7278	7295	7311	7328	7345	7362	7379	7396	2	3	5	7	8
.87	7413	7430	7447	7464	7482	7499	7516	7534	7551	7568	2	4	5	7	9
.88	7586	7603	7621	7638	7656	7674	7691	7709	7727	7745	2	4	5	7	9
.89	7762	7780	7798	7816	7834	7852	7870	7889	7907	7925	2	4	6	7	9
.90	7943	7962	7980	7998	8017	8035	8054	8072	8091	8110	2	4	6	7	9
.91	8128	8147	8166	8185	8204	8222	8241	8260	8279	8299	2	4	6	8	9
.92	8318	8337	8356	8375	8395	8414	8433	8453	8472	8492	2	4	6	8	10
.93	8511	8531	8551	8570	8590	8610	8630	8650	8670	8690	2	4	6	8	10
.94	8710	8730	8750	8770	8790	8810	8831	8851	8872	8892	2	4	6	8	10
.95	8913	8933	8954	8974	8995	9016	9036	9057	9078	9099	2	4	6	8	10
.96	9120	9141	9162	9183	9204	9226	9247	9268	9290	9311	2	4	6	9	11
.97	9333	9354	9376	9397	9419	9441	9462	9484	9506	9528	2	4	6	9	11
.98	9550	9572	9594	9616	9638	9661	9683	9705	9727	9750	2	4	7	9	11
.99	9772	9795	9817	9840	9863	9886	9908	9931	9954	9977	2	5	7	9	11
N	A. 0	1	2	3	4	5	6	7	8	9	1	2	3	4	5

INDEX